ELEMENTARY STATISTICS
AND APPLICATIONS

The quality of the materials used in the manufacture of this book is governed by continued postwar shortages.

FUNDAMENTALS OF THE THEORY OF STATISTICS

by JAMES G. SMITH
and ACHESON J. DUNCAN

★ELEMENTARY STATISTICS AND APPLICATIONS
★★SAMPLING STATISTICS AND APPLICATIONS

Elementary Statistics and Applications

FUNDAMENTALS OF THE THEORY OF STATISTICS

BY

JAMES G. SMITH

Department of Economics and Social Institutions
Princeton University

AND

ACHESON J. DUNCAN

Department of Political Economy
Johns Hopkins University

FIRST EDITION
FOURTH IMPRESSION

McGRAW-HILL BOOK COMPANY, INC.
NEW YORK AND LONDON
1944

PREFACE

Elementary Statistics and Applications is designed for a beginning course. Principles of gathering and presenting statistics, frequency-distribution analysis, probability theory and the normal curve, correlation, time-series analysis, and forecasting are included. Elementary sampling procedure, only so far as it is founded upon the assumption of normal sampling distributions, is also included.

No attempt has been made to include any of the less conventional methods of time-series analysis. Some are too mathematical for treatment in an elementary text. Others are so highly specialized or so subjective as to be unsuited for textbook material. Many of these are new methods that need to be further systematized, coordinated, and tested in the crucible of time and experience.

The approach in this book is that of the teacher. The authors have been associated in teaching statistics for more than ten years. The manuscript of the present text evolved during those years in mimeographed form, modified from year to year as new theories developed and as teaching use required. The suggestions of students, whether consciously or unconsciously made, have helped formulate this book. Experience has shown that students gain a sense of the close association of statistics to reality from the brief discussions of the historical origin of important steps in the development of statistical theory that are included.

The descriptions of frequency-distribution, correlation, and time-series analysis are first completed in their simplest aspects, with elementary illustrations. This enables the student to visualize basic method unmixed with the more advanced phases. More complex illustrations of practical application are then given in separate chapters or separate sections. This practice eliminates the apparent digression that seems to hamper the student when exposition of method and complicated illustrations are

v

intermixed, as in the conventional text. In separating the two, moreover, the fact is recognized that the best order of presentation for teaching is not the best order of procedure for working an actual problem. For example, the handiest method for making a frequency-distribution analysis is to set up a work sheet with a Charlier check and first calculate the moments or the k statistics; but the theories of the moments and of the k statistics are among the most difficult parts of the analysis to explain and are not therefore good introductory topics for the teaching of frequency-distribution analysis. In addition, the practical analysis of the frequency distribution introduces short cuts, cross checks, or other timesaving devices. The authors believe that this new arrangement will also prove to be a boon to research workers who may use the text as a reference book.

The more advanced points of statistical theory pertaining to frequency curves and sampling analysis have been placed in a separate book entitled *Sampling Statistics and Applications.* The two books together constitute a set on the subject of *Fundamentals of the Theory of Statistics.*

In both volumes, the authors have drawn freely upon the many monographs and the periodical literature that have appeared during recent years. Care has been exercised to make acknowledgment in footnotes to the sources of new ideas that have been incorporated into the authors' own development of the subject. To all these vigorous workers in the field, too numerous to be listed by name, the authors as well as other statisticians are greatly indebted.

More particularly the authors here acknowledge a debt of gratitude to several generous professional colleagues who have read parts of the manuscript with critical and judicious eye. Sidney W. Wilcox, Chief Statistician of the Bureau of Labor Statistics in the United States Department of Labor, made especially helpful suggestions for Chap. XIX, Index Numbers, for the chapters on probability theory, and for Parts I and II of *Elementary Statistics and Applications.* John H. Smith of the Bureau of Labor Statistics, contributed many stimulating criticisms and suggestions that the authors believe inspired important improvements. Lester S. Kellogg, Bureau of Labor Statistics, read Chap. III, Sources of Statistics, and made suggestions that led to a constructive reworking of that material.

The authors are profoundly grateful for such generous assistance and wish to make full acknowledgment of their professional indebtedness to these men.

The authors are grateful to the International Finance Section of Princeton University for the financial assistance given Acheson J. Duncan some years ago to enable him to study statistics and mathematical economics with the late Henry Schultz of the University of Chicago and with Harold Hotelling of Columbia University. The authors are indebted to those men, and to colleagues in the Mathematics Department at Princeton University. The authors are also indebted to Professor R. A. Fisher, also to Messrs. Oliver & Boyd, Ltd., of Edinburgh, for permission to reprint an abridged edition of Table III, Table of χ^2, from their book *Statistical Methods for Research Workers*.

Naturally, it is not to be supposed that the whole or any part of the manuscript carries the endorsement of the authors' former teachers or those who have helped with criticisms of the manuscript. The authors assume full responsibility for errors of theory or calculation that may be present in the volumes.

JAMES G. SMITH.

ACHESON J. DUNCAN.

PRINCETON, N. J.,
  August, 1944.

CONTENTS

PART I

INTRODUCTION

PART II

ANALYSIS OF FREQUENCY DISTRIBUTIONS

PART III

THE NORMAL FREQUENCY CURVE

PART IV

STUDY OF BIVARIATES AND MULTIVARIATES

PART V
STUDY OF DYNAMIC VARIABILITY

PART VI
FORECASTING

APPENDIX

PART I

Introduction

CHAPTER I

STATISTICS IN THE ARTS AND SCIENCES

From the sixteenth century to the present day, modern sciences have stressed empirical method—the gathering of data by laboratory experiment or by statistical observation. Laboratory experimentation has been more spectacularly employed in the natural sciences (biology, chemistry, physics, botany, and the like), and statistical observation has been more widely used in the social sciences (such as politics, economics, and psychology). Yet laboratory technique is used for some types of investigation in the social sciences, especially in psychology, education, and agriculture; and statistical technique is frequently employed in the natural sciences; for example, the modern kinetic theory of gases is a statistical argument.

Economy and Flexibility of Statistics. *Meaning of Statistics.* Statistics and scientific method are of value wherever a mass of complicated facts exists and wherever those facts are amenable to quantitative expression. Qualitative knowledge must be converted into quantitative units of enumeration or of measurement before it becomes statistics. The quantitative units are either enumerative or measurement units. An enumerative unit depends upon proper definition of the objects to be counted; thus statistics may be compiled on the number of blue-eyed as compared with brown-eyed people, the number of yellow as compared with green beans, etc. A measurement unit depends upon contrivance of some unit of measurement for the purpose of converting qualitative knowledge into quantitative expression; thus properly devised tests make it possible to measure intellectual aptitude on a scale so that certain quantity figures can

1

be depended upon to measure relative amounts of intellectual aptitude.

Such quantitative description of facts makes it possible to give in a brief space a great amount of information. In order to accomplish this economy of time and space, however, it is of the greatest importance that the units of measurement or of enumeration be uniformly applied and that the nature of these units of measurement for observation or of enumeration be constantly kept in mind when the data are used. Furthermore, having always in mind the nature of the statistical units chosen as criteria of measurement, it is possible to arrange statistical data in such a manner as greatly to facilitate their interpretation.

A large degree of flexibility is thus available when facts are expressed quantitatively; and, so long as the original units of measurement are not obscured, it is possible for specific purposes to arrange and rearrange a given set of data. A part of this flexibility is due to the fact that otherwise long, time-consuming methods of analysis can be resolved into relatively simple mathematical operations. These short cuts and the savings of human effort they make possible in the search for truth are only possible where knowledge can be expressed quantitatively, which is to say, by statistics. In using these short-cut methods, however, it is necessary to be ever watchful for hidden inconsistencies with the original units of measurement, for it is in this realm that many of the misuses of statistics are found.

Economy and a high degree of flexibility are characteristics of statistics that well fit them to serve a dynamic society's needs for analysis and formulation of policy. It is a lesson learned from sad but profitable experience that statistics are something more than the mere will to collect facts in quantitative form. Careful study by many scholars has given rise to rules of procedure that must be followed if the economy and flexibility of which statistics are capable are to be realized. These rules of procedure constitute the science of statistics, to several aspects of which attention should be directed for differentiation. "Statistics" is used broadly to refer to the whole field of the quantitative approach to knowledge, including the gathering of data, problems of statistical measurement, statistical analysis, statistical theory, and scientific method in general. The word "statistics" is also used to refer to any one of these parts of the whole subject.

Accordingly, while "statistics" is used in the broad sense indicated, it applies also more particularly and more accurately to compiled *data* that are systematic and quantitative expressions of facts or events.

The *theory of statistics* is also called "statistics." The theory of statistics is the body of principles that has been developed, partly a priori by the mathematical approach and partly by empirical methods, to serve as a guide for sound statistics and sound statistical method. Understanding of the theory of statistics is required also for compiling statistics. Statistical theory is required because nearly all compilations of quantitative facts are samples and not complete enumerations and because the fundamental rules regarding units of measurement must be obeyed in statistical enumeration if the resulting data are to be homogeneous, that is, comparable one with another.

"Statistics" also refers to *statistical method*, a term used to describe the process of interpreting facts by the use of statistics and statistical theory. Careful study of the assembled statistical data, obtained in a manner to secure internal comparability and arranged in well-planned tables, may be used as a basis for judgments or action. Further quantitative treatment, however, may frequently give greater significance to the statistics. Selected summaries may bring out many relationships that would be difficult to visualize if they were in tables of figures that had been compiled for general purposes. This additional quantitative treatment is of the nature of classification and summarization. It is called "statistical analysis" and includes the methods of tabulation, graphs, averages, measures of variability, correlation, index numbers, and similar quantitative analyses that have been developed. Judgments based on statistical analysis are called "statistical inferences." Statistical method, then, consists of two parts, (1) statistical analysis and (2) statistical inferences.

In recent years the word "statistics" has also been used to describe figures that have been obtained by statistical analysis; for example, arithmetic means, average deviations, measures of correlation, and the like, are all called "statistics," and any one of them alone is called a "statistic."

The word "statistics" is thus used to mean all these various things together and any one of them separately. This may make for confusion, and in the above discussion such usage makes it appear as if terms were defined by use of the term defined; but such is established conventional, albeit confused, use of this all-inclusive word "statistics."

THREE TYPES OF DATA

Empirical vs. Experimental Data. Answering the accusation that their conclusions are so vague and unpredictable as to preclude scientific sanction, the social scientists have often pleaded that social studies cannot, like the theories of the natural sciences, be tested in the laboratory. The social sciences must rely only on statistics and empirical or historical methods. Social theories can be interpreted with respect to true life only if viewed in the light of a *ceteris paribus* assumption. The assumption that other things are equal, or unchanged, or in balance serves the social scientist in the same manner as controls over experimental conditions serve the natural scientists.

With the development, on the one hand, of statistical methods in the natural sciences and the development, on the other hand, of experimental methods in the social sciences, this contrast is becoming less real. While it is still true that social science predominantly uses empirical or historical data, some important work has been done, and more important work appears in the offing, with experimental data in the fields of psychology, sociology, education, medicine, population studies, agricultural economics, and statistical control of quality of manufactured products. Such outstanding progress in the technical development of this experimental work has been made as to constitute almost a special field called "design of experiments."[1]

Design of Experiments. The arrangements for making the experiment and for recording the data therefrom constitute the design of the experiment. In designing an experiment, methods of so controlling the experiment as to prevent biased results must be devised. If, for example, the experiment is to test the effects upon cotton culture of a certain kind of fertilizer, several areas in various localities may be chosen in order to test the effect of the selected fertilizer under a number of climatic conditions. The design for the experiment must then plan also some means of measuring these various other influences, namely, temperature

[1] FISHER, R. A., *The Design of Experiments* (1935).

and rainfall. Some method must also be devised for discovering, in the resulting data, not only how much of the productivity of cotton is due to the fertilizer, but also how much is due to the differing qualities of the soil, to varying amounts of rainfall, and to varying levels of temperature. The design for the experiment must plan and organize the procedure so that from the resulting data it will in truth be possible to measure the net influence of the new fertilizer.

Where cost is a consideration, and it seldom is not, an important part of the design of experiment is to decide to what extent to experiment, in other words, how small an experiment will give trustworthy results. Before doing this it must be decided how much precision in the results, for practical purposes, is required.

The solution of some of the problems relating to design of experiment may be found by applying the theory of statistics. The solution to others is a matter of common sense, which sometimes is more difficult to apply than might be supposed.

Not only in such a case as testing the use of fertilizer, but in many problems, the researcher finds that a number of factors influence a given result. In agricultural phenomena, weather, climate, and other natural and human factors are present; in medicine, age, sex, and other conditions affect the application of treatment; in biochemical and in psychological experimentation, many human and natural variables enter. When it is necessary for a given purpose of analysis to isolate one of several influences, the data can be so selected or the treatments so applied as to hold other influences constant. For example, if age and sex as well as inoculation affect the outcome of pneumonia cases, the inoculation can be tested by comparing inoculated and noninoculated for those of the same sex or age group. It has become the practice to call the noninoculated group the "control" in the experiment.[1]

Hypothetico-observational Data. In addition to empirical and experimental data scientists make extensive use of a third type, namely, hypothetico-observational data.[2] For example, in the physical sciences, that the moon is about 240,000 miles from the earth is a hypothetico-observational datum—no one has carried

---

[1] *Cf.* HILL, A. BRADFORD, *Principles of Medical Statistics* (1939), pp. 4–8 and 170–178.

[2] EDDINGTON, SIR ARTHUR, *The Philosophy of Physical Science* (1939), pp. 12–14.

out the experiment of measuring the distance from the earth to the moon; yet on the basis of certain hypotheses it is measured to a comparatively high degree of precision. In the social sciences, index numbers purporting to measure such items as the general level of prices are hypothetico-observational data. In both illustrations, upon the basis of certain hypotheses or theories, practical methods are devised for estimating the measurement in question. In appraising the resulting estimate, the precision of the underlying theory or hypothesis is of primary importance.

SERVING THE ARTS AND SCIENCES

Statistics and the Social Sciences and Arts. *Politics.* Public opinion, the opinion of the masses, can be ascertained at any time on a wide variety of social and political issues by means of statistical data collected by random questionnaires from a comparatively small number of people. The employment of statistical technique for this purpose has stirred the imagination and stimulated the ingenuity of students of the social and governmental processes. The widespread demand for such information and the relatively low cost of obtaining it by the sampling method have also gratified the acquisitiveness and lined the purses of a number of enterprising polling agents. Increasingly, political strategists appear to pay attention to these systematic statistical studies of public opinion. Both the major political parties in the United States have had expert statisticians engaged during the quadrennial presidential campaigns to keep their fingers on the pulse of public opinion.

It has been claimed that "sampling referenda make the mass articulate, define the mandate of our leaders, reveal the true popular strength of pressure groups, and show social taboos quantitatively for what they are worth, . . . " that they are, in the language of journalism, "the fourth dimension for the Fourth Estate."[1]

Governmental Administration. Statistics are extensively used as guides to various kinds of governmental administration, such as sanitation, hospitalization, highway supervision, and public industrial accident and compensation insurance laws. For example, on the assumption that industrial accidents are due to unsafe

[1] GALLUP, GEORGE, "Government and Sampling Referendum," *Journal of the American Statistical Association*, Vol. 33 (1938), pp. 131–142.

conditions and unsafe practices that, if eliminated, would prevent repetition of the same or similar types of accident, statistical data on causes of accident have been assembled. Study of these data enables the statistician to identify and select the unsafe elements in transportation conditions and then to present the data to safety engineers for guidance in accident prevention.[1]

From its beginning in 1790 to the present day, the Federal government has considered statistics on foreign trade so important that an organization has been maintained for the express purpose of assembling such statistics. In the early years of the republic they were gathered by the Treasury Department, but now they are collected and published regularly by the Department of Commerce. With the rapid development of large-scale business organization in the latter half of the nineteenth century, public policy with respect to social and economic conditions has required the Federal government to maintain a Bureau of Labor Statistics which has been engaged principally in the task of collecting and publishing statistics on prices, cost of living, and wages and, in more recent years, on employment and pay rolls in manufacturing industries of the United States.

It is a matter of common knowledge to all who read newspapers that important laws are passed by city, state, and Federal governments on the basis of statistical facts assembled regularly or collected by special legislative committees. For example, the Federal Reserve System of banks in the United States was created in 1913 after a thorough study, involving extensive use of statistics, of the banking situation in this and other countries; legislation in the decade of the 1930's on public works, relief work, and social security was largely based on studies of a statistical nature.

Business Administration. Statistics are valuable in business administration, enabling the manufacturer executive to obtain more or less satisfactory answers to such a perplexing question as: Making allowance for seasonal changes and expected prices of substitute goods, what will be consumer demand for the coming year? Some manufacturers must make estimates for a year in advance; others can proceed successfully with monthly estimates.

[1] Kossoris, M. D., "A Statistical Approach to Accident Prevention," *Journal of the American Statistical Association*, Vol. 34 (1939), p. 526.

Retail-store executives frequently require weekly or even daily estimates on some articles, while sellers of perishable vegetables or other foods may even have to make hourly estimates.

When the manufacturing executive has a satisfactory answer to the above type of question, he can schedule production to maintain as nearly level a rate as is feasible and to keep as constant a labor force as possible. In some large business enterprises statistics are assembled daily on working capital position, factory expense, output, and consumer credit extended. Control by the executive is kept flexible and timely by a continuous stream of statistics both on the internal state of the business and on external economic conditions. As one rather erudite businessman says, "There has been an insistence from the very top of the organization on getting the facts, so that we might, to apply Descartes's picturesque phrase, 'be clear about our actions and walk surefootedly in this life.'"[1]

In his determination of policies regarding prices, production, and employment in his own business, the enterpriser must make judgments based upon knowledge of the world of prices in which he lives. Prices he must pay for raw materials, for labor, for equipment and its upkeep are his guide for determining his own production activity and the price he can eventually obtain for his product. Since all or at least part of the system of prices, that is, the prices he pays and the prices consumers pay for competitive or substitute articles, is beyond his control, the individual producer adapts his plans to any uncontrollable conditions he finds in the market. It is by the use of statistics that the modern businessman comes to understand conditions to which, if he is to profit, he must succeed in adapting his own business.

During recent years polling agencies have been hired by business executives to obtain certain types of information with respect to potential markets and changes in consumer tastes or habits. Student groups and student publications on the campuses of colleges and universities are employed by businessmen to make widespread use of polling techniques. It has also been found that a carefully conducted student poll can do more to make college administrators and trustees cognizant of student attitudes toward vital campus issues than the older and less

---

[1] HAYFORD, F. L., "Some Uses of Statistics in Executive Control," *Journal of the American Statistical Association*, Vol. 31 (1936), pp. 31–37.

effective means of circulating petitions. In the large university the student poll performs many of the functions of the open forum in a small university or college. Similarly, merchants and classes in advertising can determine the efficacy of advertising by the extent to which students express a preference for branded and highly advertised cigarettes, toilet articles, school supplies, and items of clothing to the little or nonadvertised varieties. The radio programs to which students listen, the magazines to which they subscribe, the amounts they spend for various budgetary items, the type of motion picture they most enjoy, the mileage they travel, and the means of transportation they prefer are typical items of information eagerly sought by advertising organizations and business firms in college and other kinds of markets as well.[1]

In a wide variety of practical ways the statistical principle of sampling is used in business. For example, by the use of a small spectroscope, an entire trainload of pig iron can be tested. The spectroscopist opens the car door, fastens a wire to a sample pig, strikes an electric arc between this and a bar of pure iron he carries, and observes the light in the spectroscope. The bands of color in the spectroscope reveal to him whether or not the amount of impurity in the pig is below a previously determined standard. By properly selecting sample pigs at random the trainload of metal can be tested before it is unloaded.[2] In a similar manner, though perhaps with less sensational instruments than the spectroscope, other types of more or less homogeneous or standardized goods, such as shipments of ores, grains, oranges, potatoes, or lettuce, can be tested by sampling.

Education. The grading and selection of teachers have in some instances been based upon intelligence tests, which have been perfected by the use of statistical technique correlating test grades with empirical results.[3] The scientific use of intelligence

[1] For further illustrations see, for example, W. B. Dygert, *Radio as an Advertising Medium;* H. E. Agnew and W. B. Dygert, *Advertising Media;* E. R. Walter, *Effective Marketing;* E. H. Schell and F. F. Gilmore, *Manual for Executives and Foremen;* and H. B. Maynard and G. J. Stegemerten, *Operation Analysis.*

[2] HARRISON, G. R., *Atoms in Action* (1939), p. 165. *Cf.*, on sampling for grading cars of iron ore, Stewart H. Holbrook, *Iron Brew* (1939), pp. 164–165.

[3] WEST, MICHAEL, "The Psychology of the Teacher," *Journal of Education,* March, 1939, p. 158.

tests has developed since the First World War. In 1917 a test called the American Army Intelligence Test was given to the drafted soldiers. The set of questions included on the Army Intelligence Test were based upon the cumulative experience, comparatively limited in extent with such tests up to that time. The war experience with the tests proved to be a landmark in their development in that it constituted a major experiment in their use and stimulated rapid development in the principles of their use.[1] Subsequently, the art of constructing questions for testing intelligence, now called "aptitude" in order to contrast the testing of natural ability with the mere testing of acquired ability, has greatly progressed. In addition to the college-entrance tests, which in part measure opportunity, scholastic-aptitude tests are used by the leading universities as a basis for selecting students. As a consequence, statistical data that measure not only acquired intelligence but also native ability, or aptitude, are being accumulated. The aptitude-test rating is often called the "intelligence quotient," or simply I.Q.

Mental tests have most frequently been employed with the feeble-minded in connection with problems of detection and placement and for determining the type of training best suited to individual persons. Studies of criminals by the use of intelligence tests disclose relationships between intelligence and the type of crime committed, but apparently a high I.Q. neither prevents nor stimulates crime in general. Delinquent children have been found to exhibit more neurotic traits than do unselected school children. Tests of emotional control, dishonesty, and lack of self-control have been found useful in forecasting incorrigibility among delinquent children.

Recently a study was made in which the I.Q.'s of 214 foster children, all of whom were adopted before the age of twelve months, and of 105 control children living with their own parents were compared with the I.Q.'s of the foster and real parents. The I.Q. of the parents was supplemented by information on occupational status and other pertinent data. Information regarding the true parents of adopted children were secured from placement records. There was far greater correspondence between the

---

[1] BRIGHAM, CARL C., "Two Studies in Mental Tests," *Psychological Review*, Psychological Monographs, Vol. 24 (1917); *A Study of American Intelligence* (1923); *A Study of Error* (1932).

I.Q.'s of foster children and their true parents than between the I.Q.'s of foster children and their foster parents. It was estimated by statistical techniques that the contribution of heredity to individual differences in I.Q. is probably not far from 70 to 80 per cent and that the very best environment might, however, raise I.Q. as much as 20 points, while the poorest environment might lower it as much as 20 points.[1]

Sociology. Modern sociology employs statistical method almost to the exclusion of other methods. This may be a mistaken emphasis that will be corrected by future sociologists, but in that discipline the twentieth-century reaction to nineteenth-century abstraction was particularly great. Moreover, this extreme emphasis upon fact by American sociologists[2] can be traced to the picturesque Lester Frank Ward, who, despite the abstract qualities of his writing, emphasized the statistical approach. A farmer, a Civil War soldier, a Federal government official, a lawyer, a botanist, a chief of the Division of Navigation and Immigration, and, finally, toward the end of his life, a professor of sociology at Brown University, Ward came to the study of sociology with a richly varied experience. Among the voices raised against nineteenth-century emphasis on nature and the neglect of humanity his was the most vigorous. So eager was the reading world for this new approach that some of Ward's books were translated into every Continental tongue.[3]

Economic Theory. From Adam Smith to the present time economic theory has been, at least in part, an inductive science. In Adam Smith's day there were few statistics, but he made extensive use of trade, price, and wage data in his analyses. In modern times, especially since the turn of the century, more

---

[1] Study by Miss Burks, described in H. E. Garrett and M. R. Schneck, *Psychological Tests, Methods, and Results* (1933), pp. 189–190.

[2] LYND, R. S., and H. M. LYND, *Middletown: A Study in Contemporary American Culture* (1929); *Middletown in Transition: A Study in Cultural Conflicts* (1937). These remarkable books are modern classics in sociology and are based almost entirely upon observational method largely statistical in character.

[3] CHUGERMAN, SAMUEL, *Lester F. Ward, The American Aristotle* (1939). Because of Ward's optimistic views it has been suggested lately that he should be widely read both for information and encouragement. *Cf.* a review of Chugerman's book by Prof. Rudolph Binder in *The New York Times Book Review*, Oct. 15, 1939, p. 10.

complete statistical data are available, and an increasingly important volume of statistical writings that have significance in economic theory has been forthcoming.   The theory of allocation of income to the owners of capital, to the laborers, and to the enterprisers, as well as other comprehensive economic hypotheses such as business-cycle theories and theories of money and prices are today being tested by careful statistical studies.[1]   In addition, theoretical questions concerning the factors determining particular prices are being studied by the use of statistical methods.

Mathematical Economics.   In recent years the subject of statistics has become closely related to the mathematical approach to economic theory.   Starting with the nineteenth-century work of Cournot a group of mathematical economists have attempted to work out a purely abstract theory of economics by using the shorter and more precise methods of mathematical reasoning. The origin of this school of economists, often called the "mathematical school of economists," was independent of the development of statistics.   As statistical methods became more refined and economic data more plentiful and more accurate, the mathematical school of economists turned to statistics to derive demand curves and supply curves from the actual statistical events of the market place.   This development during the 1930's was one of the most sensational and also one of the most controversial contributions to economics, and it continues to be energetically discussed in scientific meetings and journal articles by proponents and opponents of the methods used.   Meanwhile, without waiting for the issue to be settled by the theoreticians, business enterprise and government, and notably the United States Department of Agriculture, are making extensive practical use of statistical demand and cost curves.[2]

Statistics and the Natural Sciences and Arts.   *Astronomy.* One of the foundations of statistical theory, the method of least

[1] *Cf.* National Bureau of Economic Research, *Studies in Income and Wealth*, Vols. 1–3.   National Resources Committee, *The Structure of the American Economy* (1939), Part I, Basic Characteristics.   TINBERGEN, J., *A Method and Its Application to Investment Activity* (1939); *Business Cycles in the United States of America*, 1919–1932 (League of Nations Economic Intelligence Service, 1939).

[2] EZEKIEL, M., and L. H. BEAN, *Economic Bases for Agricultural Adjustment Act* (1933); SCHULTZ, HENRY, *Theory and Measurement of Demand* (1938).

squares, was first discovered and applied in astronomy early in the nineteenth century. The method continues to be employed in astronomy to trace the paths of stars, comets, planets, and other heavenly bodies. Modern astronomy deals with large numbers of observations, which become the statistical raw material for the science. For example, the Harvard College Observatory receives monthly, from nearly one hundred different observers distributed the world over, and on report blanks containing seven to seven hundred observations each, an average of forty-five hundred observations. It has been found best not to attempt to analyze each observer's work separately, but instead to depend on multiplicity and frequency of observations well distributed throughout, to obtain the best possible light curves. Over fifty thousand observations come to the Harvard College Observatory each year, and from 1911 to 1939 it collected three-quarters of a million observations.[1]

For years the Smithsonian Institution has been using methods essentially statistical in nature to record measurements of the amount of heat received from the sun by the earth. Smithsonian stations in three of the most arid regions of the earth are daily recording the sun's radiation. Observers in Chile, in South Africa, and in Western United States have been taking records. According to these observations, which have been made at widely separated stations, correlations exist between changes in solar radiation and temperatures on the earth. Study of these records, study of records of the earth's weather as recorded in the growth rings of trees, and study of similar phenomena have revealed recurrent cycles in the weather that may be of great value in foretelling long-range trends in the future succession of fat and lean years.[2]

Zoology. A considerable amount of the experimental work in the life sciences involves such quantitative considerations as weights, measurements, enumerations, pointer readings of various kinds, comparisons, and classifications. If the results arrived at by experimentation are to give rise to general principles rather

---

[1] *Cf.* CAMPBELL, LEON, "The Light Curve of SS Cygni, 213843," *Annals of Harvard College Observatory*, Vol. 90, No. 3, pp. 93–162; STERNE, T. E., and LEON CAMPBELL, "Properties of the Light Curve of SS Cygni," *ibid.*, Vol. 90, No. 6, pp. 189–206.

[2] So says G. R. Harrison, *op. cit.*, pp. 290–291.

than just to meaningless and incoherent single observations, the zoological data must be consistently assembled, uniformity of units must be observed, and the data classified. In other words statistical method must be used to bring order from isolated chaotic measurements.

In addition to routine problems of analysis in zoology, statistical and mathematical devices have had interesting applications in certain special problems. For example, in 1934 Zeuner used a statistical study of a system of cranial angles as a basis for biological inferences regarding rhinoceroses; in 1930 Soergel emphasized the importance of statistical methods for certain paleontological problems, employing numerical and mathematical procedures to study footprints and from these drawing inferences regarding the animals that made them; and in 1912 Ridgway attempted to put the study of faunal coloration on a statistical basis.[1] Paleontologists use various mathematical and graphic means to restore missing parts in fossil animals and to reconstruct hypothetical intermediate stages between less and more specialized animals. They also use statistical methods to study averages and variation in characteristics of different age groups, rate of growth, and the like, of various animals.[2]

Biology. Considering the modern emphasis on statistics in the social sciences it is interesting to note, not only that the method of least squares was first applied in a natural science, but also that a second highly important statistical method was first developed in the natural science of biology. This is the statistical measurement of correlation, which in the 1870's was used by Sir Francis Galton to measure the effect that characteristics of midparents— that is, the average of their two parents—had on their children.[3]

Biological experimentation in the nineteenth and twentieth centuries involving as it does rats, guinea pigs, and the like, makes use of procedures that combine the laboratory test with the assembling of statistical data and their subsequent analysis. In this way, the effects and incidence of various diseases and

---

[1] SOERGEL, W., *Die Bedeutung variationsstatistischer Untersuchungen für die Säugetier—paläontologie*, Bund 63, pp. 349–450; RIDGWAY, R., *Color Standards and Color Nomenclature* (1912). Also see SIMPSON, G. G., and ANNE ROE, *Quantitative Zoology*, (1939), pp. 24, 404–406.

[2] SIMPSON and ROE, *op. cit.*, p. 335.

[3] See Chap. XIII.

of various cures for those diseases are measured; thus also are tested the various theories regarding the relative importance of hereditary factors as compared with environmental factors in animal life. Much of this experimental work later becomes the basis for theories regarding human life and for theories in respect to the effects of human diseases and their cure.

Some problems in biology have interesting applications to the homely arts of living. A recent illustration of the use of statistics in biology is the standardizing of liquid household insecticides, a matter of considerable importance to certain private enterprisers engaged in the business.[1] By a series of experiments that established the sex ratio of houseflies statistically, hitherto unknown sources of variability in the effects of insecticides were thrown into bold relief. It was found, for example, that flies at ages of less than three days vary considerably in their reaction to the spray, while flies four to six days old exhibit a fairly constant susceptibility. It was known that male houseflies are markedly more susceptible to certain sprays than female houseflies.

A recent book on heredity[2] illustrates the extent to which biology depends upon statistical technique. Widespread interest in the Dionnes led biologists to calculate the probability of quintuplets as compared with the probability of twins. The probability of quintuplets is $1/41,600,000$, while that of twins is $\frac{1}{85}$. In addition, the statistical method was used in an interesting way to answer the question of heredity vs. environment, epitomized in the highly talented musical family of Johann Sebastian Bach, a talent that ran through five generations. Were the Bachs musical because of inborn talent or because of the musical environment in the home? To answer this question the author of the above-mentioned book resorted to statistical technique. He obtained information from 36 outstanding instrumental musicians, from 36 principals of the Metropolitan Opera Company, and from 50 students of the Juilliard Graduate School of Music. From facts obtained by

[1] CAMPBELL, F. L., G. W. SNEDECOR, and W. A. SIMONTON, "Biostatistical Problems Involved in the Standardization of Liquid Household Insecticides," *Journal of the American Statistical Association*, Vol. 34 (1939), pp. 62–80.

[2] SCHEINFELD, A., *You and Heredity* (1939).

questioning these persons, the author concludes that their talent is largely inherited. Many will welcome this trend toward basing studies of man upon statistics of human beings rather than upon statistics of vegetables or fruit flies.

Medicine. Much of the statistical work in biology has application in the field of medicine, and interest in statistics on the part of the medical profession has increased. In addition, the medical profession has become interested in statistics on economic and social welfare, factors of importance in the control of epidemics, and of certain types of disease in the modern community.[1] The practical advantages to the physician and to the sanitarian of the development of medical statistics are very great. Matters that were fiercely debated two generations ago and concerning which only few physicians of a hundred years ago could form an opinion are now a regular part of the knowledge of a junior medical student through the study of mortality statistics and vital statistics.[2] Indeed, the medical profession in England has recently contributed a textbook on medical statistics designed to acquaint medical students with the fundamentals of statistical theory.[3]

Engineering. Since the success of their work depends not only on the machines but on the human beings who operate them, mechanical engineers have become increasingly interested in the use of statistical method for making time studies in machine operations. It is now realized that such studies cannot be safely based upon some a priori scale of the machine's capacity or upon the record of only one or two operatives. Rather, time-study data must be collected from an entire group of operatives so that adjustments can be made according to the effects upon operation of the human traits found by statistical study to prevail in the machine or in the manner of operation.[4]

Two simple examples of the application of statistics to electrical engineering are the study of elevator capacity for buildings and

[1] *Cf.* DAVIS, MICHAEL M., "Wanted: Research in the Economic and Social Aspects of Medicine," *The Milbank Memorial Fund Quarterly*, October, 1935, pp. 339–346.

[2] *Cf.* PEARL, RAYMOND, *Introduction to Medical Biometry and Statistics* (1923), pp. 2, 38.

[3] HILL, A. B., *Principles of Medical Statistics* (1939).

[4] BERGEN, H. B., "Scientific Management in Unionized Plants," *Mechanical Engineering*, March, 1938, pp. 235–240.

telephone calls to be handled by an exchange. Statistics regarding the number of passengers taken on at the first floor are used to determine the time required for passengers to leave the elevator, the round-trip time, and the number of passengers carried by a given elevator. The most desirable type of elevator equipment to install is determined from such data.[1]

Since engineers are dealing with natural phenomena that cannot be affected by human bias, many of their problems can be solved approximately by the application of the principles of probability. For example, during a long period of gaugings of a stream the frequency of floods is often the best indication of probable future floods. Such important engineering data as forecasts of future floods, low annual rainfall, and consequent depletion of storage reservoir can be estimated by applying the theory of probabilities to statistics on the past history of such events. From such data, the use of statistical technique makes it possible to estimate the proper size of a hydroelectric power plant and to predict its output and earnings.[2]

One of the most striking illustrations of the use of statistics in engineering is the control of the quality of manufactured products.[3] In ordinary manufacture, with the exception of the making of optical or other precision instruments of infinite refinement, all units of a product are not identical, in spite of the vaunted standardization of products in industry. The cost of so refining the machines or of so regulating their operation as to make all units of product identical would be prohibitive and in most cases unwarranted because of the low market value of the product. Variations in quality are thus considered to be justified, and it is the purpose of quality control to develop

---

[1] COOK, H. B., "Selecting Elevators for an Office Building," *Power*, Mar. 8, 1932, pp. 404–408.

[2] CREAGER, W. P., and J. D. JUSTIN, *Hydro-electric Handbook* (1927), pp. 43 and 171. For other illustrations of the use of statistics in engineering science and art, see C. W. Hubbard, "Investigation of Errors of Pitot Tubes," *Transactions of the American Society of Mechanical Engineers*, August, 1939, pp. 477–506; H. K. Barrows, *Water Power Engineering* (1927), pp. 54–57.

[3] SHEWHART, W. A., *Economic Control of Quality of Manufactured Product* (1931). Since Shewhart's pioneer efforts on this important subject, much progress has been made, so much that one might say a new craft has been created.

statistical means of showing the actual statistics of variations in quality, the economically permissible variations in quality, and the statistical measurement of ways of locating and correcting causes of quality variation beyond set limits. Such control is designed to reduce the number of products that must be discarded as below standard; consequently, if successful, quality control reduces waste and lowers manufacturing costs per unit of output. In addition, selling costs are reduced and good will improved, because quality control decreases the number of customers who become dissatisfied as the result of the inconvenient necessity of returning inferior products.

Although used in the American Telephone and Telegraph Company under the leadership of Dr. Shewhart, application of statistical quality control has been negligible in the United States.[1] In Great Britain, however, the idea of statistical quality control was accorded an enthusiastic reception following Shewhart's visit to London in 1932. A committee headed by Dr. E. S. Pearson was organized by interested British industrialists to consolidate previous progress and facilitate adoption of the technique.[2] By 1937 in England the methods had been applied to coal, coke, cotton yarns, cotton textiles, woolen textiles, spectacles glass, lamps, building materials, and manufactured chemicals.[3]

Physics and Chemistry. There is no dispute among modern physicists and chemists as to the importance of statistical methods in their sciences. Even the highly metaphysical Sir Arthur Stanley Eddington in his *Nature of the Physical World* (1928) attaches great importance to statistics in the natural

---

[1] Two reasons have been given for this failure of statistical quality control to be applied in the United States: "[first,] a deep-seated conviction of American production engineers that their principal function is so to improve technical methods that no important quality variations remain, and that in any case the laws of chance have no proper place among modern 'scientific' production methods; second, . . . the difficulty of obtaining industrial statisticians who are adequately trained in this fairly complicated field." FREEMAN, H. A., "Statistical Methods for Quality Control," *Mechanical Engineering*, Vol. 59 (1937), pp. 261–262.

[2] PEARSON, E. S., *The Application of Statistical Methods to Industrial Standardization and Quality Control* (British Standards Institution, London, 1935).

[3] FREEMAN, *op. cit.*, pp. 261–262.

sciences. In fact, he says that the laws of nature divide themselves into three classes, (1) identical laws, such as the law of conservation and the law of gravitation; (2) statistical laws, such as Boyle's law, the second law of thermodynamics, and quantum laws; and (3) transcendental laws, which are "genuine laws of control in the physical world."[1]

In physics, statistical technique is employed in the study of molecules. This modern statistical approach has a philosophical background that goes back at least as far as Boltzmann, who in 1866 expressed the second law of thermodynamics in terms of probabilities. His contribution was regarded as a form of mysticism until it was demonstrated by research during the first two decades of the twentieth century.[2] At the turn of the twentieth century Max Planck was trying to explain why pieces of matter heated to high temperatures emit more light of one wave length than of any other and less light at both larger and shorter wave lengths. He could not explain this phenomenon except by supposing that light is emitted by atoms not as continuous trains of electromagnetic waves but in discrete bundles of energy that he called "quanta." Similar experimental work accompanied by new theoretical contributions, notably those of Heisenberg, led to the formulation of the modern statistical approach to the natural sciences. Within three decades this new theory has come into widespread practical use also, having found application in explanation of the behavior of photographic plates, the conduction of electricity through wires, the conduction of heat through walls, the behavior of photoelectric cells, the manner of emission and absorption of light by atoms and molecules, and in the theory of metals.[3]

As explained by a recent popularizer of the natural sciences,[4] Newtonian mechanics succeeds in accurately predicting motion

[1] STEBBING, L. S., *Philosophy and the Physicists* (1937), p. 70.

[2] HAAS, ARTHUR, *The New Physics* (1923), pp. 38–44.

[3] *Cf.* ELDRIDGE, J. A., *The Physical Basis of Things* (1934), pp. 357–358.

[4] DE BROGLIE, LOUIS, *Matter and Light. The New Physics*, translated by W. H. Johnson (1939). For a popularized description of the experimental development based upon Boltzmann and later Heisenberg's theories, see also Eddington, *op. cit.* *Cf.* William M. Malisoff, review of De Broglie's *Matter and Light*, in *The New York Times Book Review*, Oct. 1, 1939. Also see H. Lifschutz and O. S. Duffendack, "The Counting Losses in Geiger-Müller Counter Circuits and Recorders," *Physical Review*, Vol. 54 (Nov. 1,

occurring on the human scale and also on the scale of celestial bodies. In other words, Newtonian mechanics does well for macroscopic measurements. But in the investigations of the motion of the microscopic particles inside the atom, Newtonian mechanics ceases to have value, while quantum mechanics makes it possible to grasp the meaning of new principles that must necessarily be introduced in these more minute analyses. The principles referred to are statistical in nature and are based in large part on the theory of probability. "It is impossible to measure several physical quantities (as energy, position, momentum) accurately at the same time. It is this necessary inexactness that has forced us to find our ultimate laws in probabilities."[1]

It must not be supposed that the new statistical approach, which is said to have been derived from Heisenberg's uncertainty principle, necessarily has thrown into chaos concepts of physical measurement. The admission that laws in quantum mechanics are statistical may destroy the idea that the universe is a huge machine; but in a given case, with the initial conditions determined as precisely as the principle of uncertainty permits, the probability of all subsequent states is determined by exact mathematical probabilities. There is nothing lawless in quantum phenomena.[2] Analysis shows, moreover, that the theoretical uncertainty, which prohibits a simultaneous accurate measurement of position and of velocity, is noticeable only in dealing with the very minute masses of the subatomic world. With ordinary masses, the theoretical uncertainty, though still existing, falls below the practical uncertainties, which are due to the imperfection of human observations, and is completely submerged by the latter. This gradual obliteration of the quantum uncertainties, as the scientific observer passes to the commonplace level of average masses, is the reason why Newtonian mechanics is still used. For the small velocities and relatively large masses with

---

1938), pp. 714–725; A. Ruark, "The Time Distribution of So-called Random Events," *Physical Review*, vol. 56 (Dec. 1, 1939), pp. 1165–1167; E. R. Rutherford, *Radiations from Radioactive Substances* (1930), Chap. VII, pp. 171–172.

[1] ELDRIDGE, *op. cit.*, p. 376.   *Cf.* TOLMAN, R. C., *The Principles of Statistical Mechanics* (1938), p. 65.

[2] STEBBING, *op. cit.*, p. 183.

which the scientist is usually concerned, the two mechanics yield results so nearly alike that in practice no experiment would be sufficiently refined to detect the difference. Since the Newtonian mechanics is mathematically the simpler, there is every advantage in retaining it.[1]

Except for Einstein's theory of relativity there has been nothing so to stir the imagination of the natural scientists in the twentieth century as this new statistical approach. In fact, one writer has said that the entire structure of modern physics and chemistry, and therefore of all the natural sciences to which they are fundamental, rests upon quantum mechanics.[2]

From the above discussion it is readily apparent that statistical techniques are helpful, not only to theories in the natural and social sciences, but to the arts dependent on those sciences. Yet for many students the most important reason for knowing something about the fundamentals of statistical method is the need for intelligent discrimination between the proper and improper use of statistics. Unfortunately, a large portion of the extensive modern employment of statistics in all fields falls under the latter heading. This is especially true in popular presentations of modern scientific and political matters. Too close attention to the mechanics of a method and the neglect of common sense are responsible for a large number of these horrible examples. All too often, preoccupation with the technique dims common sense.

Statistics and Philosophy. Nineteenth-century cocksureness of the scientific approach, pretending to such a degree of precision and to such broad scope as to annihilate the foundations for ethical, moral, and religious faiths, has largely disappeared. Under the aegis of the assertive and materialistic science of the nineteenth century, belief in free will was dwindling to a mere superstition; but the element of indeterminacy brought into science as a result of the application of the theory of probabilities again permits freedom. This decline of mechanistic assurance in science has not been ignored by philosophic thought, which has emphasized as never before a lesson that has often recurred in the history of philosophy: objective reality is not always identical with subjective concepts.[3] Eddington expresses these doubts

---

[1] D'ABRO, A., *The Decline of Mechanism* (1939), pp. 37–57.

[2] HARRISON, *op. cit.*, pp. 341–342.

[3] ELDRIDGE, *op. cit.*, pp. 379–380.

in the following words:[1] "Does the spectroscope *find* the colors, or does it *make* them? When the late Lord Rutherford showed us the atomic nucleus, did he find it or did he make it? How much do we discover and how much do we manufacture by our experiments?"

Just as surely as the railroad destroyed the supremacy of the stagecoach or the radio eclipsed the popularity of the phonograph, so have the discoveries of modern science eclipsed faith in many ideals and beliefs that served to give reason to the lives of the masses of the people. In the realm of ethical and moral values, buttressed by the dogma of a bygone age, nineteenth-century scientific method was almost wholly destructive and hardly at all constructive. Modern philosophy criticized scientific method, both the laboratory and statistical branches, for failing to provide new moral values to replace outmoded prescientific ones. Despite this gloomy aspect, philosophy's greatest spokesmen look to scientific method itself to obtain the necessary enlargement of the conception of human nature and the formulation of the required new moral values. John Dewey envisages the use of scientific method to create a comprehensive democratic culture as a guarantor of genuine freedom.[2]

SUMMARY

Statistical method—the quantitative expression of knowledge, the marshaling of facts and their arrangement in a form suitable for scrutiny—has been the means employed by businessmen, natural scientists, and social scientists to establish bases for judgments regarding factual data so complex or so numerous as to be, in the unmarshaled state, intellectually incomprehensible. Commercial statistics and their interpretation may, indeed, be said to constitute the scientific background of business today. Men cannot conduct their business intelligently without them. Quite as important as statistics of commerce and trade are the more recently developed industrial and social statistics, data on employment and pay rolls in industry, trade, and finance and on the distribution of income.

In the science of government and its practical art the statistical approach has proved itself essential as facts have accumu-

[1] *Op. cit.*, pp. 108–109.
[2] *Freedom and Culture* (1939), *passim.*

lated and, to an increasing extent, as means have been developed for making the quantitative units of measurement required. The importance of statistical techniques in the natural sciences is attested to by the definition of "science" so familiar to every schoolboy: Science is systematized knowledge. Statistical mechanics is essential to an understanding of modern physics and chemistry. Whatever the individual's station or calling, he is to a greater or lesser extent using statistical techniques.

CHAPTER II

GATHERING STATISTICS

Before the commercial revolution of the sixteenth century, social and economic life was relatively simple. The small villages and towns were self-sufficing economic and social units. Little or no statistical enumeration of facts was required to comprehend the extent of the population, the number of buildings, the number of cattle, and the quantity of other constituent units in the community. Within the limited range of space and time usually contemplated, events having to do with the welfare or distress of the community were not complex. Judged by modern standards, government was simple and inexpensive because social and economic relationships were not complicated. Even the great cities of the time were not large compared with modern metropolitan districts. In population, wealth, and trade, the extent of a sixteenth-century nation was inconsiderable and, furthermore, was growing almost imperceptibly. In other words, conditions were relatively simple and static.

Genesis of Fact Marshaling. Under such conditions, little was done in the way of the systematic gathering and analysis of statistical data. The situation did not demand the continuous assembling of up-to-the-minute facts. Indeed, it was not profitable to do so. The motive did not exist in sufficient force to direct attention to the problem of expressing quantitatively the events of contemporary social and economic life; and the facts of the natural sciences were obscured in medieval mysticism or cherished from a forgotten age by a few scattered and scholarly churchmen. Nevertheless, it was found useful on occasions to make great surveys that could subsequently serve as the basis of governmental decision in regard to taxation and other social activities, and that might also be a guide to private enterprise. Pepin the Short in 758 and Charlemagne in 762 demanded detailed descriptions of church lands, while several works written in France during the first half of the ninth century gave a partial enumeration of the serfs attached to the land.[1] Likewise, when William the Conqueror undertook the reorganization of the national government of England in the eleventh century, he found it desirable to make his famous survey, which resulted in Domesday Book, completed about 1086.[2] Also, as early as the fourteenth century, the medieval guilds gathered statistics in connection with their regulation of markets.[3] Later, in the fifteenth century, as the breakup of the medieval system gathered momentum and as the rise of trading groups accelerated, there was a great increase in the amount of statistical work done by guilds as well as by central governments—the latter not infrequently through guild organizations or through the Church. Economic statistics were collected when the occasion demanded, for example, when the upsetting of a customary price by a flood or drought required explanation and the determination of a new customary price. Although there is evidence that in these several ways statistics were assembled, they were neither methodically made nor preserved. There are isolated instances of the registration of deaths or baptisms in the fourteenth and fifteenth centuries, but it was not until the sixteenth century that any considerable movement toward statistical enumeration of facts occurred.

Development of a Dynamic Social Order. During the Renaissance, from thirteenth-century Italy to fifteenth-century Spain and England, the quantity of data in the physical sciences steadily accumulated from experimental efforts of astronomers and other scientists. The most dramatic of all human experiments was made by the voyagers seeking to prove that the world is round. The discovery of America and the voyages of exploration of the sixteenth century gave great impetus to the development of trade and the growth of nations.[4] Motivated by the economic ideals of mercantilism, a period of trade development followed, the domestic system of manufacture rapidly expanded,

[1] WALKER, HELEN M., *Studies in the History of Statistical Method* (1929), pp. 32–33. *The History of Statistics* (compiled and edited by John Koren, 1918).

[2] CHEYNEY, EDWARD P., *An Introduction to the Industrial and Social History of England* (1925), pp. 17–18.

[3] FAURE, FERNAND, "The Development and Progress of Statistics in France," in Koren, *History of Statistics*, pp. 229–233.

[4] FAULKNER, H. U., *American Economic History* (1931), pp. 34–57.

and the colonial empires of Portugal, Spain, France, Holland, and then England, emerged. The change was from haphazard and occasional trade of the merchant adventurers of the sixteenth century to the more or less systematic and regular international and intercolonial trade of the seventeenth and eighteenth centuries. Along with this trade development came the necessity for obtaining more regular information concerning markets, population, wealth, prices, and the movements of merchandise and gold. Furthermore, with this growth of trade both in volume and in complexity, governmental and social organization became more complex.

As the fact of change was revealed by the events of the commercial revolution, national governments began to feel the need of more regular fact finding in order to visualize and to interpret changing conditions. Yet it must not be supposed that well-organized or any considerable amount of statistical data for the sixteenth or even the seventeenth century can now be found. It was more a case of an awakening of the will to do rather than a case of actual accomplishment. For it was really the Industrial Revolution and the vigorous growth that took place in the eighteenth and nineteenth centuries that gave the actual impetus to systematic marshaling of quantitative facts. It was not until the early part of the nineteenth century, indeed, that most of the essential principles of statistical method, even for purely descriptive purposes, had been evolved. Also, the compilation and current use of statistics as practiced today have been made possible only by the growth in transportation and communication facilities, a nineteenth-century phenomenon. It was also from the eighteenth century onward that the achievements of scientists in accumulating experimental data for the natural sciences fired the imagination of scholars to solve the problem of data accumulation for the sciences of life and social behavior.

Quantitative Expression of Facts. Where there are large populations, great nations of tens of millions of people, all problems of social, economic, and political organization are increased many times in complexity and, furthermore, new problems arise. The problem of feeding such large populations, the problem of housing them, the problem of keeping them employed and preventing them from harming each other, to

mention but a few of the considerations confronting the governmental administrator—all these are vastly complex owing to the
great expanse of geographical space covered and the varying
conditions at different places and times. In simple economies
many of these problems can be solved by permitting individual
freedom of choice and free economic enterprise; but as the
community becomes more and more closely knit in economic
and social relations and as various forms of economic power
emerge, individual freedom of choice and free economic enterprise become goals that must be consciously sought by organization rather than natural tendencies that develop unaided.[1]

In the intricate social and economic organizations of the
modern era, it is inconceivable that any individual or group of
individuals can obtain the knowledge necessary to form judgments concerning the issues that arise. An individual can
comprehend only those conditions within a reasonable geographical area about him; the more complicated society is, the
smaller the area about him that he can understand without the
use of statistics. "We are overwhelmed, not only by the diversity of knowledge, but also by the diversity of possible deeds, of
possible values, and of possible judgments," and, further, "this
human mind, whose needs Plato so perfectly understood, still
insists upon constructing for itself a fixed world in the midst
of a fluid one. It persists in thinking in terms of aims and
ends and perfections; of ideals, of purposes, and final goods;
and, at the very last, it insists upon assuming some direction in change, something toward which the chain of events is
moving."[2]

In this effort it is impossible for the individual to survey the
conditions qualitatively—it would take him many human life-
times to inspect the whole population, and the capacity of the
human brain is not adequate to the task of absorbing so complex
an impression. If he attempts a microscopic survey, he is
quickly smothered by overwhelming detail. If he attempts a
macroscopic survey without the use of statistics, he is compelled

[1] For the complexity of modern society, as it is reflected in statistics, see
publications of the United States Bureau of the Census. For suggestive
special studies, see Corrington Gill, *Wasted Manpower* (1939); Henry Pratt
Fairchild, *People* (1939).

[2] KRUTCH, J. W., *Art and Experience* (1932), pp. 121, 211.

to resort to guesswork and commonly originates "cloud-push-ing" fantasies. Furthermore, the individual's personality tends to bias him not only in his observations but also in his judgments. If he is temperamentally inclined to be impressed by sordid things, he is likely to notice them more than the good things in his surroundings, and his judgment is correspondingly pessi-mistic. On the other hand, if he is temperamentally optimistic, he tends to consider as the rule the good things and to regard as unusual the sordid things of life. Where it is necessary to gain knowledge concerning large populations of people and things, where social and economic life is complex, there is need to use statistics.

Rational Basis for Gathering Data. Quixotically, accumulating data is not to be confused with scientific fact gathering. The progressive accumulation of useful quantitative facts has been stimulated and furthered by a definite, conscious purpose. To look at the process historically, it was the rise of nationalism and the mercantilistic ideal that supplied definite purpose for the fact-finding inquiries of the eighteenth-century political arithmeticians. Modern survivals of the same nationalistic and mercantilistic ideals impel governments to spend vast sums for the collection of statistics designed to measure the wealth and material position of the nation and to furnish business enterprise with facts about markets. Underlying much of this effort abides also a sincere interest, stimulated by scientific research, in real human welfare. As a consequence, the modern census attempts to collect quantitative facts directly or indirectly concerning the health and morals of the nation's people. The subsequent usefulness of such statistical data depends upon how well the simple rules of common sense have been followed in assembling and in presenting the data.

Units of Description and Measurement. The units of descrip-tion or measurement by means of which quantitative facts are to be assembled must be carefully defined. When defined, such units must be strictly applied during the assembling of the data and in all subsequent analysis. It is accordingly of the utmost importance clearly and fully to describe units of descrip-tion and measurement in all subsequent use of the data. Such rules are so clear and so easily resolved into matters of simple common sense that it seems almost a waste of time to direct attention to them; yet to follow them is not always so simple a matter as might be supposed.

For example, in 1940 thousands of enumerators undertook the task of counting the population of the United States, of counting the number of farms, farm animals, and all other types of wealth, and of obtaining specified information concerning every person living in the United States. One may ask: Why should mere counting be a complicated task? This question would be quickly answered by the farmer's boy who has just finished trying to count the number of chickens in his pens. Everything would be easy if they would only stand still. People, as well as chickens, do not stand still while they are being counted, and simple matters mount up into a veritable host of intricate difficulties. Suppose you were an enumerator and in the first house approached you found that the mother is in the maternity hospital, a baby was born at 10 A.M. of the census day, one son is away at college in another state, a daughter is boarding and rooming in a neighboring town, where she teaches school, and the father is in jail for evading income taxes. On several points you would feel the need for very specific instructions. To avoid double counting or the failure to count many individuals, instructions to the enumerators must be given with great care; every possible complication must be foreseen.

In recording facts about manufacturing and trading, or merchandising, enterprises in separate categories, when is an enterprise a manufacturing concern and when is it a trading, or merchandising, concern? In recording statistics about farms, when is a farm not a farm but a truck garden? These few examples are probably sufficient to emphasize the point that the unit must be carefully defined and that the defined unit must be strictly followed and freely or even religiously disclosed to all who in the future use the statistics.

Carefully planned schedules of questions, often called "questionnaires," are the principal means of gathering statistics. These vary from schedules simple enough for oral presentation, as frequently utilized in polls, to the elaborate forms used by the government or research organizations. In the first phase of statistical investigation, the gathering of facts, care in following all the rules of common sense and logical definition is epitomized in the formulation of the questionnaire, or schedule.

QUESTIONNAIRES OR SCHEDULES

Official Example of Care in Description of Units.   In taking the United States census, for example, the assurance of accuracy in regard to these important but detailed matters is guarded by a skillfully organized system.   Forms are supplied, with column arrangement for writing in all the required information.   A question appears at the head of each column, and the columns, and therefore the questions, are grouped into subjects; thus in the schedule for the 1940 population census there are 34 columns grouped under the subjects location, household data, name, relation, personal description, education, place of birth, citizenship, residence, and employment status.   In addition, columns 35 to 50 contain supplementary questions to be asked only a sample of all the persons enumerated.   Figures 1 to 3 show in three sections the 34 questions asked of all persons.   Figure 4 is included to show the questions on employment status in the 1930 census, revealing thereby the great elaboration of this type of question in the 1940 census.

Sample forms that had been filled in with illustrative answers were supplied to enumerators, and a complete, simple description of the manner in which the form was to be filled out was printed on the sample schedule.   Pamphlets were issued for the use of enumerators, giving detailed instructions.   For the 1940 census there were issued to enumerators taking the census of population and agriculture a printed and indexed pamphlet 173 pages long. This gave detailed definitions and described procedure for enumerators to follow under the various circumstances that might arise in their house-to-house canvasses.

Moreover, the enumerators worked directly under experienced district supervisors, who, in turn, were under area managers responsible to the Bureau of the Census in Washington.   To train the 529 district supervisors in the 1940 census taking and census procedures, a picked group of more than one hundred men from all parts of the country were given a special course of instructions in Washington.   Those who passed the examination were sent out as area managers to the 104 census areas, each to direct the training of five to seven district supervisors and to act as regional manager between them and the Bureau of Census in Washington.

The 529 districts were broken into enumeration districts of which there were about 147,000.   Generally speaking, there was

Form P-2

ILLUSTRATIVE EXAMPLE of Completed Pop...

State ...... Iowa ...... Incorporated place ...... Orange city ...... Ward of city ......

County ...... Stanton ...... Township or other division of county ...... Royce ...... Block Nos. 370...

U.S. GOVERNMENT PRINTING OFFICE: 1940—O-201407

	LOCATION		HOUSEHOLD DATA				NAME	RELATION		PERSONAL DESCRIPTION			
Line No.	Street, avenue, road, etc.	House number (in cities and towns)	Number of household in order of visitation	Home owned (O) or rented (R)	Value of home, if owned, or monthly rental, if rented	Does this household live on a farm? (Yes or No)	Name of each person whose *usual place of residence* on April 1, 1940, was in this household. BE SURE TO INCLUDE: 1. Persons temporarily absent from household. Write "Ab" after names of such persons. 2. Children under 1 year of age. Write "Infant" if child has not been given a first name. Enter ⊗ after name of person furnishing information.	Relationship of this person to the head of the household, as wife, daughter, father, mother-in-law, grandson, lodger, lodger's wife, servant, hired hand, etc.	CODE (Leave blank)	Sex—Male (M), Female (F)	Color or race	Age at last birthday	Marital status—Single (S), Married (M), Widowed (Wd), Divorced (D)
	1	2	3	4	5	6	7	8	A	9	10	11	12
1		317	195	O	4500	No	Owens, Robert S. ⊗	Head		M	W	56	M
2							——, Ethel	Wife		F	W	52	M
3							Lancaster, John J.	Nephew		M	W	14	S
4						No	Moore, Roberta B. ⊗	Lodger		F	W	27	S

FIG. 1.—The first 12 questions on the 1940 census schedule grouped under topics location, household data, name, relation, and personal description. Notice the sample entries.

ed Population Schedule

DEPARTMENT OF CO

SIXTEENTH CENSUS

POPULA

Your report is required by Act of Congress. This Act makes it unlawful for the Bureau to disclose collected will be used solely for preparing statistical information concerning the Nation's population

ity .... 2 .... Unincorporated place ....
(Name of unincorporated place having 100 or more inhabitants)

os. .....370-371..... Institution ....
(Name of institution and lines on which entries are made)

AL TION		EDUCATION			PLACE OF BIRTH		CITIZENSHIP	RESIDENCE, APRIL 1, 1935						
Marital status—Single (S), Married (M), Widowed (Wd), Divorced (D)	Attended school or college any time since March 1, 1939? (Yes or No)	Highest grade of school completed	CODE (Leave blank)		If born in the United States, give State, Territory, or possession. If foreign born, give country in which birthplace was situated on January 1, 1937. Distinguish Canada-French from Canada-English and Irish Free State (Eire) from Northern Ireland.	CODE (Leave blank)	Citizenship of the foreign born	IN WHAT PLACE DID THIS PERSON LIVE ON APRIL 1, 1935? City, town, or village having 2,500 or more inhabitants. Enter "R" for all other places.	COUNTY	STATE (or Territory or foreign country)	On a farm? (Yes or No)	CODE (Leave blank)	Was this person AT WORK for pay or profit in private or nonemergency Govt. work during week of March 24-30? (Yes or No)	If not, was he at work on, or assigned to, public EMERGENCY WORK (WPA, NYA, CCC, etc.) during week
12	13	14	B		15	C	16	17	18	19	20	D	21	22
6	M	No	C-5		England		Na	Same house					Yes	-
	M	No	C-4		Northern Ireland		Na	Same house					Yes	
	S	Yes	H-1		Indiana			R	Denton	Indiana	Yes		No	No
7	S	No	C-4		Canada-English		Al	Detroit		Michigan	No		No	No

Fig. 2.—Questions 13 to 20 on the 1940 census schedule grouped under topics education, place of birth, citizenship, and residence.

16—385

Sheet No.

9 ..A

...that to disclose any facts, including names or identity, from your census reports. Only sworn census employees will see your statements. Data
...n's population, resources, and business activities. Your Census Reports Cannot Be Used for Purposes of Taxation, Regulation, or Investigation.

T OF COMMERCE—BUREAU OF THE CENSUS

S. D. No. ......9......   E D. No. ..71–16......

ENSUS OF THE UNITED STATES: 1940

Enumerated by me on ......April 5......, 1940.

ULATION SCHEDULE

Harold W. Thompson......, Enumerator.

PERSONS 14 YEARS OLD AND OVER—EMPLOYMENT STATUS

21	22	23	24	25	26	27	28	29	30	F	31	32	33	34
Yes	–	–	–	–	45		Medical doctor	Private practice	OA		52	0	Yes	1
Yes	No	Yes	–	–	35		Receptionist	Doctor's office	NP		52	0	No	2
No	No	No	–	–		2	Delivery boy	Retail grocery store	PW		13	130	No	3
No	No	No	Yes	Yes			Art teacher	Private high school	PW		42	1200	No	4

FIG. 3.—Questions 21 to 34 on the 1940 census schedule grouped under topic employment status of person fourteen years old and over, with subgrouping indicated in captions of columns. Notice the sample entries.

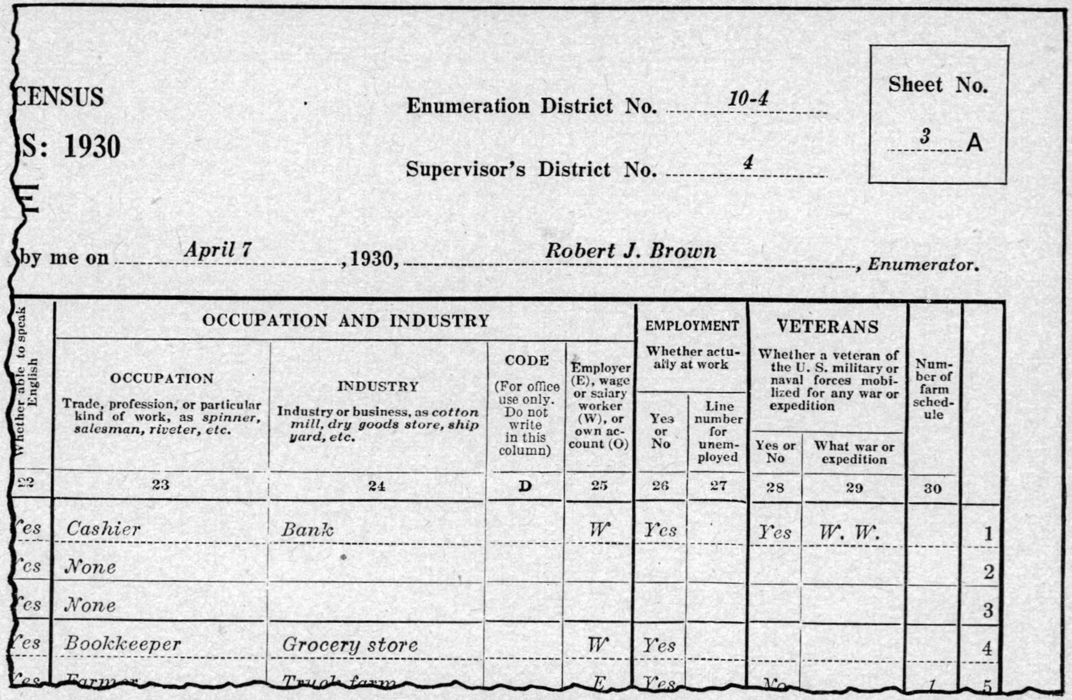

CENSUS
S: 1930

Enumeration District No. 10-4

Supervisor's District No. 4

Sheet No. 3 A

by me on April 7, 1930, Robert J. Brown, Enumerator.

Whether able to speak English	OCCUPATION AND INDUSTRY				EMPLOYMENT		VETERANS			
	OCCUPATION: Trade, profession, or particular kind of work, as *spinner, salesman, riveter, etc.*	INDUSTRY: Industry or business, as *cotton mill, dry goods store, ship yard, etc.*	CODE (For office use only. Do not write in this column)	Employer (E), wage or salary worker (W), or own account (O)	Whether actually at work: Yes or No	Line number for unemployed	Whether a veteran of the U. S. military or naval forces mobilized for any war or expedition: Yes or No	What war or expedition	Number of farm schedule	
22	23	24	D	25	26	27	28	29	30	
Yes	*Cashier*	*Bank*		*W*	*Yes*		*Yes*	*W. W.*		1
Yes	*None*									2
Yes	*None*									3
Yes	*Bookkeeper*	*Grocery store*		*W*	*Yes*					4
Yes	*Farmer*	*Truck farm*		*E*	*Yes*		*No*		*1*	5

Fig. 4.—Questions in the 1930 census schedule on employment status under topics occupation, industry, and employment. In the 1940 census schedule these questions were placed among the supplementary ones.

one enumerator in each of these districts, but in certain regions one enumerator covered more than one district. Therefore, about 123,000 enumerators were used. Wide publicity for such careful preparation in the case of the 1940 census resulted from Congressional protests about some of the new questions.[1]

To illustrate the necessity for careful definition of units and description of procedure and to solve the census problem of the amazing family described above, the following is quoted from the *Instructions to Enumerators:*[2]

Who Is to Be Enumerated in Your District

300. The problem of who is to be enumerated in your district is extremely important. Therefore, study very carefully the following rules and instructions.

301. *The Census Day.* There should be a return on the population schedule for each person alive at the beginning of the census day, *i.e.*, 12:01 A.M. on Apr. 1, 1940. Thus, persons who died after 12:01 A.M. should be enumerated; and infants born after 12:01 A.M. on Apr. 1, 1940, should not be enumerated

302. *Usual Place of Residence.* Enumerate every person at his "usual place of residence." This means, usually, the place that he would name in reply to the question "Where do you live?" or the place that he regards as his home. As a rule, it will be the place where the person usually sleeps.

. . . .

Persons to Be Enumerated in Your District

304. Enumerate all men, women, and children (including infants) *whose usual place of residence* is in your district or who, if temporarily in your district, have no usual place of residence elsewhere. Persons who move into your district after Apr. 1, 1940, for permanent residence should be enumerated by you, unless you find that they have already been enumerated in the district from which they came.

305. *Residents Absent at Time of Enumeration.* Some persons having their usual place of residence in your district may be temporarily absent from the household at the time of the enumeration. These you must enumerate with the other members of the household, obtaining the information regarding them from their families, relatives, acquaintances, or other persons able to give it. However, do not include with

---

[1] *The New York Times,* Feb. 27–29, Mar. 1–3, 1940.

[2] Bureau of the Census, *Instructions to Enumerators, Population and Agriculture,* pp. 14–18, 80–81.

the household a son or daughter permanently located elsewhere or regularly employed elsewhere and not sleeping at home.

306. Persons to be counted as members of the household include the following:

a. Members of the household temporarily absent at the time of the enumeration, either in foreign countries or elsewhere in the United States, on business or visiting.

b. Members of the household attending schools or colleges located in other districts, except student nurses away from home and students in the Naval Academy at Annapolis or in the Military Academy at West Point or in any other training school or institution operated by the War or the Navy Departments or the United States Coast Guard.

c. Members of the household who are in a hospital or a sanitarium but who are expected to return in a short period of time.

d. Servants or other employees who live with the household or sleep in the same dwelling.

e. Boarders or lodgers who sleep in the house.

f. Members of the household enrolled in the Civilian Conservation Corps.

307. In the great majority of cases the names of absent members will not be given to you by the persons furnishing the information, unless particular attention is called to them. Before finishing the enumeration of a household, therefore, you should ask the question: Are there any members of the household who are absent?

.   .   .   .   .

Persons Not to Be Enumerated in Your District

313. There will be a certain number of persons present, and perhaps lodging and sleeping in your district at the time of the enumeration, who do not have their usual place of residence there. As a rule, do not enumerate as residents of your district any of the following classes, except as provided in paragraph 314:

a. Persons temporarily visiting with the household. If, however, they do not have any usual place of residence from which they will be reported, they should be enumerated with the household.

b. Households temporarily in your district which have a usual place of residence elsewhere from which they will be reported.

c. Transient boarders or lodgers who have some other usual or permanent place of residence, that is, who have a house or apartment elsewhere in which they usually reside and where they will be enumerated.

d. Persons from abroad temporarily visiting or traveling in the United States and foreign persons employed in the diplomatic or consular service of your country (see paragraph 331). (Enumerate other persons from abroad who are *students in this country* or who are *employed here*, however, even though they do not expect to remain here permanently.)

e. Students or children living or boarding with this household in order to attend some school, college, or other educational institution in the locality but who have a usual place of residence elsewhere from which they will be reported.

f. Persons who take their meals with the household but usually lodge or sleep elsewhere.

g. Servants or other persons employed by the household but *not sleeping in the same dwelling.*

h. Persons who were formerly members of this household but have since become inmates of a jail; or a mental institution, home for the aged, infirm, or needy, reformatory, prison, or any other institution in which the inmates may remain for long periods of time.

i. Transient patients of hospitals or sanitariums. Such patients are to be enumerated as residents in the households of which they are members and not as residents in the institution, unless they have no other place of residence at which they will be reported.

314. *When to Make Exceptions.* In deciding when to make exceptions to the rules indicated above, consider whether the household or persons temporarily residing in your district will be reported at another place of residence by some person in a position to supply the information required. If the persons or household will not be so reported, enumerate them as residents of your district.

Enumeration of Special Classes of Persons

315. You may experience some difficulty in determining whether to enumerate certain special classes of persons indicated below. In any instance in which you are not sure whether to include persons as residents of your district, ask your squad leader or supervisor for further instructions.

316. *Servants.* Enumerate with the household any servants, laborers, or other employees who live with the household and sleep in the same house or dwelling unit. However, enumerate servants who sleep in separate and completely detached dwellings as separate households, even though the dwelling is on land owned by members of the household by which the servants are employed.

. . . .

318. *Students at School or College.* If there is a school, college, or other educational institution in your district that has students from outside your district, enumerate as residents of the school only those students who have no usual places of residence elsewhere. Especially

in a university or professional school there will be a considerable number of the older students who are not members of any household located elsewhere. Find and enumerate all such persons.

319. *Schoolteachers.* Enumerate teachers in a school or college at the place where they live while engaged in teaching, even though they may spend the summer vacation at their parents' home or elsewhere.

320. *Student Nurses.* Enumerate student nurses as residents of the hospital, nurses' home, or other place in which they live while they are receiving their training.

321. *Patients in Hospitals, Sanitariums, and Convalescent Homes.* Most patients in hospitals, sanitariums, and convalescent homes are there temporarily and have some other usual place of residence. Enumerate patients as residents of such an institution only if they have no other place of residence from which they will be reported. A list of persons having no permanent homes can usually be obtained from the institution records.

322. *Inmates of Prisons, Asylums, and Institutions Other than Hospitals.* Your district may include a prison, reformatory, or jail, a home for orphans, for aged, infirm, or needy persons, for blind, deaf, or incurable persons, a soldiers' home, an asylum or hospital for the insane or the feeble-minded, or a similar institution in which the inmates usually remain for long periods of time. Enumerate *all* the inmates of such institutions at the institutions. Note that in the case of jails you must enumerate the prisoners there, however short the sentence.

·   ·   ·   ·

Census of Agriculture

General Information

Purpose of the Census of Agriculture. An act of Congress provides that a census of agriculture be taken every 5 years, for the purpose of obtaining basic information on farm acreage, land values, crops, livestock, and other general items relating to agriculture. The Sixteenth Census, which will be taken as of Apr. 1, 1940, will include comprehensive information on agriculture, including irrigation and drainage of farm land.

Every enumerator must fill out a farm and ranch schedule for each tract of land in his enumeration district that might classify as a "farm" under the census classification, giving *all* the requested information. The information should be obtained by a personal visit of the enumerator. It is absolutely necessary that the census be complete and accurate. Census data are widely used by both private and public agencies and often form the basis for legislative and administrative programs.

The farmer should be made to feel that his contribution to the census is of real value to himself and to his community.

Census Schedules Are Confidential. The Federal law providing for the census prescribes heavy penalties for revealing information to unauthorized persons. The enumerator should make it clear, in dealing with persons who seem unwilling to give the information requested, that he is not allowed to give any information to their neighbors or other persons; that only sworn census employees will have access to the farm schedules; and that those records for individual farms cannot be used for purposes of taxation, regulation, or investigation.

Definition of a Farm. The definition of a farm found on the face of the schedule must be carefully studied by the enumerator. Note that for tracts of land of 3 acres or more the $250 limitation for value of agricultural products does not apply. Such tracts, however, must have had some agricultural operations performed in 1939 or contemplated in 1940. A schedule must be prepared for each farm, ranch, or other establishment that meets the requirements set up in the definition. A schedule must be filled out for all tracts of land on which some agricultural operations were performed in 1939 or are contemplated in 1940 and which might possibly meet the minimum requirement of a "farm." When in doubt, always make out a schedule.

You now have instructions that will help enumerate the interesting family first encountered above—the mother will be enumerated (paragraph 321), the baby will not be enumerated (paragraph 301), the son will be enumerated (paragraph 318), the daughter will not be enumerated (paragraph 319), and the father will not be enumerated at the household, although if the jail is in town he will there be enumerated (paragraph 322).

Figures 5 and 6 are photographic reproductions of parts of the Farm and Ranch Schedule used for the census of agriculture. On Fig. 6 appears the definition of a farm to which reference is made in the general information quoted above from the manual of instructions. Altogether the farm and ranch schedule contains 232 questions on 16 subjects. The subjects include information about the operator, farm acreage, values, farm mortgage and taxes, irrigation, cooperative selling and purchasing, farm labor, farm expenditures in 1939, farm machinery and facilities, live-

CONFIDENTIAL CENSUS REPORT.—Your report is required by Act of Congress. This Act also makes it unlawful for the Bureau to disclose any facts, including population, resources, and business activities. Your

16–240–1

SAMPLE

DEPARTMENT OF COMMERCE—BUREAU OF THE CENSUS
WASHINGTON
SIXTEENTH CENSUS OF THE UNITED STATES: 1940
FARM AND RANCH SCHEDULE
(Including Special Agricultural Operations)

Inventory Items, April 1, 1940   Production Items, Calendar Year 1939

I.—FARM OPERATOR, APRIL 1. 1940

SAMPLE COPY   Code

1. Name of person
2. Address _____ (Street or Route No.) _____ (Post office) _____ (State)
3. Age _____ NOTE.—Report age and color or race as shown on Population Schedule.
4. Color or race: [Place a check (√) in proper block]

22. White, including Mexican	23. Negro	24. Indian	25. Chinese	26. Japanese	Other (specify)

Code A — 1

5. Do you reside on this farm? _____ (Yes or No)   2

II.—FARM TENURE, APRIL 1, 1940

6. If you rent any farm land from others or manage any farm land for others, give names and addresses of the owners of the land and indicate for each owner whether a corporation:

Name _____ Incorporated? _____ (Yes or No)

Address _____ (Street or Route No.) _____ (Post office) _____ (State)   3

IV.—VALUES, APRIL 1, 1940

Code A

19. Total value of this farm (land and buildings), including farm land and buildings rented from others.
Give the amount for which this farm (Question 12) would sell. Include the land actually operated by you as owner, renter, or manager, and all the buildings and improvements. Omit implements and machinery, livestock, and land rented by you to tenants or croppers.
$ _____ (Omit cents)   12

If you own a part, but not all, of this farm—
(a) How much of the total amount under Question 19 represents the value of the land and buildings owned by you?
$ _____ (Omit cents)   13

20. Value of all buildings on this farm. Included in answer to Question 19.
$ _____ (Omit cents)   14

21. Value of farm implements and machinery used in operating this farm, including automobiles, tractors, motortrucks, and trailers (present market value).
$ _____ (Omit cents)   15

Include all farm implements; tools; wagons; harnesses; dairy equipment; cotton gins; threshing machines; combines; apparatus for making cider, grape juice, and sirup and for drying fruits; and all other farm machinery. Omit commercial mills and factories; also permanently installed irrigation and drainage equipment.

V.—FARM MORTGAGE DEBT AND FARM TAXES

B

If you own all or part of this farm—

22. Was there any mortgage debt on the land and buildings so owned on April 1, 1940? _____ (Yes or No)   2

23. Total amount of outstanding mortgage debt on such land and buildings.
$ _____ (Omit cents)   3

24. What was the annual rate (contract rate) of interest on the first mortgage debt? (Report fractions) _____ (Percent)   4

SAMPLE

Fig. 5.—A portion of the Farm and Ranch Schedule to illustrate the type of questions included.

names or identity, from your census reports. Only sworn census employees will see your statements. Data collected will be used solely for preparing statistical information concerning the Nation's
Census Reports Cannot Be Used for Purposes of Taxation, Regulation, or Investigation

16—11333

SCHEDULE No.

	Code

DEFINITION OF A FARM

A farm, for Census purposes, is all the land on which some agricultural operations are performed by one person, either by his own labor alone or with the assistance of members of his household, or hired employees. The land operated by a partnership is likewise considered a farm. A "farm" may consist of a single tract of land, or a number of separate tracts, and the several tracts may be held under different tenures, as when one tract is owned by the farmer and another tract is rented by him. When a landowner has one or more tenants, renters, croppers, or managers, the land operated by each is considered a farm. Thus, on a plantation the land operated by each cropper, renter, or tenant should be reported as a separate farm, and the land operated by the owner or manager by means of wage hands should likewise be reported as a separate farm.

Include dry-lot or barn dairies, nurseries, greenhouses, hatcheries, fur farms, mushroom cellars, apiaries, cranberry bogs, etc.

Exclude "fish farms," fish hatcheries, "oyster farms," and "frog farms."
Do not report as a farm any tract of land of less than 3 acres, unless its agricultural products in 1939 were valued at $250 or more.

ENUMERATOR'S RECORD AND CERTIFICATE

E. D.
State .... County .... No. ....

Number of farm in order of visitation. ....

From Population Schedule:
Farm operator's name appears on Sheet No. .... ; Line No. ....

Visitation number of farm operator's household ....

Visitation numbers of other households on this farm. ....
If no dwelling, or if no occupied dwelling, on this farm, give the identification used to designate the place on your map, as: F–1; V–3, F–2; etc. ....

Minor Civil Division ....
Give name, also class, as township, town, ward, precinct, district, beat, etc.

If any part of this farm is in another Minor Civil Division, give location and acreage.

M. C. D.	COUNTY	ACRES

If this farm is located—
In surveyed area, give Sec. No. .... ; Township .... ; Range ....
Sec. No. .... ; Township .... ; Range ....

In incorporated place; give name ....
Enumeration completed by me at .... {a. m.} {p. m.} on the .... day of ...., 1940.

(Signed) .... Enumerator.

XIII.—SUPPLEMENTAL INFORMATION

Give any changes in the area of this farm or in your tenure since September 1, 1939 (if none, write "None")

	Code	D	20
		Q	
			2, 3, 4, 5,

IX.—COOPERATIVE SELLING AND PURCHASING, 1939

	Code
Did you, in 1939, transact any business with or through—	C
	6
34. A cooperative SELLING organization? .... (Yes or No)	7
35. A cooperative BUYING organization? .... (Yes or No)	
36. A cooperative SERVICE organization? .... (Yes or No)	8

X.—FARM LABOR

37. Number of workers 14 years old and over and wages paid for farm work on this farm (do not include housework or contract construction work):

CLASS OF LABOR	Number of persons 14 years old and over working the equivalent of 2 or more days the week of—		Total cash wages paid for all hired labor in 1939
	Mar. 24–30, this year	Sept. 24–30, last year	

THIS COLUMN FOR OFFICE USE ONLY

CODE

TENURE

1. Full owner.
2. Part owner.
3. Manager.
4. Cash tenant.

Fig. 6.—Another portion of the Farm and Ranch Schedule to illustrate the type of question included and the definition of a farm.

stock and livestock products, crops harvested on the farm in 1939, and value of products used and of forest products sold in 1939.

Only trained enumerators can successfully use such elaborate questionnaires as those illustrated; only when properly instructed can enumerators know how to get the information requested in each question of these complex schedules. In some cases, the questionnaires, or schedules of questions, are tried out by a person-to-person call at the sources of information in advance of collecting the data for the final enumeration. There was during the summer of 1939 a trial census, covering a sample area in Indiana, taken by the United States Bureau of the Census while formulating the new and more complicated 1940 census schedule.

Statistics Obtained from Samples. Every twentieth person enumerated on the 1940 census was asked supplementary questions. The results constitute a 5 per cent sample. For the sample of population, the following subjects were covered: the usual occupation, industry, and worker class as a supplement to information obtained concerning present occupation, in order to determine the availability of and shifts to various kinds of labor; whether the respondent has a Federal social-security account number and whether wage deductions have been made for Federal old-age insurance during the 12 months ending Dec. 31, 1939; data showing the number of children born to women who are or have been married (women married, widowed, or divorced), to make studies of differential fertility; mother tongue, or native language, obtained by a question asking what language was spoken in the home in earliest childhood; the status of veterans of foreign wars and their wives, widows, and children; and information concerning the place of birth of the father and the mother of the respondents.

This is the first decennial census in which the sampling process has been applied, and the results of the experiment are eagerly awaited by statisticians everywhere. While the decennial census has always been presumably a complete enumeration, other governmental statistics have frequently been drawn from samples. Indeed, because of limited funds, it is necessary for the Bureau of Labor Statistics to resort to the sampling method to obtain data on wages and hours in industry. Preliminary to the collection of such data the census data for the industry are studied to determine in which states the industry is of material importance.

UNION SCALE OF WAGES
AND HOURS

June 1, 1939.

U. S. DEPARTMENT OF LABOR
BUREAU OF LABOR STATISTICS
WASHINGTON

1. ....
(Name and title of union official)

....
(Address)

....
(City)   (State)

Union ....

2. Industry ....

3. Affiliation ....

4. Does union have an effective agreement? Yes ☐ No ☐

5. Kind of agreement? Written ☐ Oral ☐

6. Is copy of agreement or scale attached? Yes ☐ No ☐

7. Date agreement went into effect or was renewed ....

8. Expiration date ....

Yr.	City	Size	Reg.	Ag.	Ind.

9.

TRADE, CRAFT, OR OCCUPATION (a)	LEAVE BLANK		RATE OF WAGES			HOURS			Days first rate (h)	Sun- day rate (i)	Number members at each rate (k)	1938			LEAVE BLANK			
	Tr. (b)	H. R. (c)	Amount (d)	Unit (e)		Per day (f)	Per week (g)					Rate (l)	Hours (m)	Number members (n)	R. C. (o)	H. C. (p)	Amount R. C. (q)	Amount H. C. (r)

10. If any changes in rates or hours between June 1, 1938, and June 1, 1939, give changes and dates of changes ....

11. Specify any variations from above, especially as to rules for rotating or sharing work ....

....

....
(Agent)

....
(Date)

....
(Signature and official position of person furnishing information)

....
(Address)

[OVER]

FIG. 7.—First portion of questionnaire used by the Bureau of Labor Statistics to obtain data on union wages and hours.

Manufacturers' directories are examined and books and periodicals relating to the industry are read, thus obtaining the essential a priori background of knowledge to form the basis for sound proportional sampling.[1]

To obtain the data on wages and hours of labor, the Bureau of Labor Statistics uses carefully prepared and elaborate questionnaires, one of which is illustrated in Figs. 7 and 8. Trained agents obtain the information from a responsible official of each local union. Each scale of wages and hours is verified by the union official interviewed and is further checked by comparison with the written agreements when copies are available. For example, in the building-trades survey for June 1, 1939, interviews were obtained with 1,551 union representatives, and 2,729 quotations of scales were received. The union membership covered by these contractual scales of wages and hours was approximately 444,000. Great care is exercised to see that the agents are adequately trained to collect the data; written instructions are supplied them by the Bureau of Labor Statistics, in which they are cautioned as follows:[2]

In the final analysis the accuracy and value of the entire survey must rest upon the agents who collect the data. These data must be absolutely correct and so presented on the schedule as not to be confusing or ambiguous. Each agent is, therefore, requested to study thoroughly the instructions, not once but repeatedly, and to question any point therein which may not be perfectly clear. It is extremely important that the agent check every schedule carefully before mailing to the office to be sure that each item is correctly entered and explained. When agreements accompany the schedules, the agent must compare each quotation with the provisions in the agreement and must explain any differences.

In order to ensure the collection of comparable data from all agents, the instructions give painstaking definitions of "union scale," "collective agreement," "apprentices" and "foremen,"

---

[1] For further details of the methods employed by the Bureau of Labor Statistics, see "Methods of Procuring and Computing Statistical Information of the Bureau of Labor Statistics (1923)," *Bulletin* 326; also "Union Scale of Wages and Hours in the Building Trades, June 1, 1939," *Serial* R1034, from *Monthly Labor Review*, November, 1939.

[2] Bureau of Labor Statistics, "Instructions for Survey of Union Scales of Wages and Hours, 1939" (No. 7468), p. 1.

12. Remarks or amplification of data reported on front of schedule ....

....

....

....

....

13. Have there been any changes in rates since June 1, 1939, or have any changes been agreed upon to become effective in the near future?

Date effective	Occupation	Rate
....	....	....
....	....	....
....	....	....
....	....	....

14. Agreements are negotiated with:

(a) Individual employers .... (b) Employers' association(s) ....

If (b), what proportion of union firms participate or are represented in the association(s)? ....

....

For Building Trades Only

15. Does union cooperate with employer in establishing or enforcing standards of fair competition?

Yes ☐   No ☐   If there is a written code of fair competition please attach a copy.   If oral or customary

arrangements, please explain ....

....

....

16. What proportion of the 1- and 2-family dwellings in this community are being built under union conditions

so far as this trade is concerned? ....

Does the union have a special rate for this type of work?   Yes ☐   No ☐

Explain ....

....

....

....

....

....

FIG. 8.—Second portion of questionnaire used by the Bureau of Labor Statistics to obtain data on union wages and hours.

B. L. S. 937

U. S. DEPARTMENT OF LABOR
BUREAU OF LABOR STATISTICS
IN COOPERATION WITH
NATIONAL RESOURCES COMMITTEE
WORKS PROGRESS ADMINISTRATION
DEPARTMENT OF AGRICULTURE
WASHINGTON

STUDY OF CONSUMER PURCHASES
A FEDERAL WORKS PROJECT
FAMILY SCHEDULE—URBAN

CONFIDENTIAL.—The information requested in this schedule is strictly confidential. Giving it is voluntary. It will not be seen by any except sworn agents of the cooperating agencies and will not be available for taxation purposes.

I. YEAR COVERED BY SCHEDULE.

Twelve months beginning ...., 1935, and ending ...., 193...

II. FAMILY COMPOSITION (during schedule year)

A	B	C	D	E
		Age at last birth-day	Number of weeks during living year	
Members of economic family (all persons sharing family income, including those temporarily away from home)	Sex		In home	Away from home
1. Husband	M			
2. Wife	F			
Other Members of Family (give relationship)				
3.				
4.				
5.				
6.				
7.				
8.				
9.				
10.				

If any member of family died during year, circle number in front of name.

11—2280

III. OTHER MEMBERS OF HOUSEHOLD (during schedule year)

Status	Per-sons	No. weeks
1. Sons and daughters boarding and rooming -at home: Age ...., sex		
2. Other roomers with board		
3. Roomers without board		
4. Boarders without room		
5. Tourists or transients		
6. Guests		
7. Paid help living in		

IV. HOME OWNERSHIP

1. Number of months during schedule year living:
   a. As renter ...... *b.* As owner: 1st home ......
   2d home ......

	1st home	2d home
IF AN OWNER:		
2. Monthly rental value	$............	$............
3. Was home mortgaged (or being purchased on land contract)?	{*a.* □ Yes. *b.* □ No.}	{*a.* □ Yes. *b.* □ No.}
4. If mortgaged, interest on mort-gage (or land contract) for months occupied	$............	$............

Code No. ....

Schedule No. ....

City .... Dist. ....

Agent ....

Date of interview ...., 1936.

V. RESIDENCE IN THIS CITY

For how many months of schedule year did the family live in this city? ....

VI. LIVING QUARTERS OCCUPIED (at date of interview)

1. Did family occupy these living quarters at end of schedule year? *a.* □ Yes. *b.* □ No.
2. Does family □ own or □ rent these living quarters?

3. Monthly rent $..........., if renter.
4. Type of living quarters:
   One-family house:
     a. □ Detached.
     b. □ Attached.
   Two-family house:
     c. □ Side by side.
     d. □ Two decker.
   Apartment in building for:
     e. □ Three families.
     f. □ Four families.
     g. □ Five or more families.
   Dwelling unit in business bldg.:
     h. □
   Room or rooms:
     i. □ With another family.
     j. □ In rooming house.
   Other:
     k. □

VII. COLOR

a. □ White.   *b.* □ Negro.

VIII. MONEY EARNINGS OF FAMILY FROM EMPLOYMENT OR BUSINESS OUTSIDE OF HOME OR AT HOME
(during schedule year)

A	B	C	D	E	F	G	H	J
Members of family gainfully employed			OCCUPATION during year					
Relationship	Line No. II A	Age	Kind of work (such as machinist, bookkeeper, merchant, author)	Nature of industry (such as cotton mill, bank, shoe store, independent)	Status of worker (s, x, o)	Rate of earnings per unit of time	Time employed (use same time unit as in col. G)	Total money earnings from employment or business
1.						$......per......		$......
2.						......per......		
3.						......per......		
4.						......per......		
5.						......per......		
6.						......per......		
7.						......per......		
8.						......per......		
9.						......per......		
10.						......per......		

IX. OTHER MONEY INCOME

	Total for year
1. Income from roomers and boarders (gross)	$......
2. Income from work in home not entered in VIII above (specify)	
3. Interest and dividends from stocks, bonds, bank accounts, trust funds, etc.	
4. Profits not included in VIII above, less expenses	
5. Rents from property, less expenses	
6. Pensions, annuities, benefits	

IX. OTHER MONEY INCOME (continued)

	Total for year
7. Gifts in cash for current use from persons not members of economic family	$......
8. Losses in business (subtract). $......	x x x x
9. TOTAL money income	$......

10. Has family received direct relief (in cash or kind) during schedule year? *a.* ☐Yes. *b.* ☐No.
11. Has any member of family had work relief during schedule year? *a.* ☐Cash. *b.* ☐Kind. *c.* ☐None.

FIG. 9.—Questionnaire used for consumers' purchases study.

"union rates" and "actual rates," "union rates" and "prevailing rates," and "averages."

Study of Family Income and Expenditures. In 1929 the Social Science Research Council suggested the advantages of conducting a study of consumption in such a way that the sample would cover a wide range of incomes, all types of natural families, and all occupations within representative communities of different sizes. Income data and certain other facts would be collected from all families visited, through the use of a short schedule. These data would provide the basis for selection of an adequate number of families in each income class to furnish more careful estimates of income and the details of expenditures. Following these suggestions, the National Resources Committee and the Bureau of Home Economics of the United States Department of Agriculture completed in 1939 a study of family income and expenditures. Figure 9 shows the questionnaire used.[1] Tables of data based upon this questionnaire are shown in Chap. IV. It may be noticed that the type of question and indeed the whole schedule are much less complex, involving much simpler units, than any thus far illustrated. It was necessary for this schedule to be simpler than those discussed above because for the consumer-income study the agents were not so well trained as are, for example, the regularly employed field agents of the Bureau of Labor Statistics.

Mailed Questionnaires. In some cases, especially where the schedule of questions is comparatively simple, questionnaires are sent through the mail to the sources of information. Such a method may be used either where the units involved are very simple or where those who are filling out the questionnaires are known to be qualified to do so. The United States Bureau of the Census and the Bureau of Labor Statistics have been able to use this method to obtain certain types of information from manufacturing concerns regarding employment, pay rolls, manufacturing output, labor turnover, and the like. The method appears to be most used where fairly simple facts are collected at regular intervals. Data on pay rolls and employment are

[1] Bureau of Home Economics, U.S. Department of Agriculture, "Consumer Purchases Study," Part I, Family Income, *Miscellaneous Publication* 339, pp. 338–339; *cf.* National Resources Committee, *Consumers' Incomes in the United States* (1938), p. 49.

obtained by mailed questionnaires monthly by the Bureau of Labor Statistics from representative manufacturing establishments in 90 manufacturing industries.[1] Figure 10 is an illustration of the type of letter used by such agencies to secure the good will and cooperation of businessmen.[2]

Where the questionnaire-by-mail method is used, the returns must be carefully edited and subsequent correspondence is frequently required to correct mistakes made on the returns. Manufacturing and merchandising concerns in this country have become trained in the matter of filling out questionnaires for the government through years of practice so that there has been built up a cooperative enterprise between the government and business in the gathering of business statistics. Although sometimes feeling the heavy burden of filling out numerous forms of this type, business is nevertheless glad to cooperate because it is eager to see each month the compilation of business data that emanates from government sources.

Income-tax returns are of the nature of questionnaires and are a source of many important statistics. Everyone is familiar with the care necessary in the examination of the units involved; everyone who has had to handle a return or listen to the head of the family talk about it knows how detailed and specific are the printed instructions accompanying each form on which the return is made. In the case of the income-tax return, which frequently becomes so complicated as to require legal advice and expert accountants, the penalty for failure to file a return is sufficient to supply any incentive needed to overcome all obstacles. For failure to supply information for the other types of questionnaire that have been discussed, with the exception of the census, there is no similar penalty—the business concerns fill out such questionnaires in a spirit of public service and to obtain the resulting compilations of data.

Rules for Constructing Questionnaires. Any investigator who is tempted to seek information by the questionnaire method will be well advised to spend considerable effort first, to make certain that the facts are not already available, and then to

[1] Bureau of Labor Statistics, "Employment and Pay Rolls," *Serial* R1052, November, 1939, pp. 7, 11, and 16.

[2] This letter was used in January, 1940, with a new questionnaire revised to obtain better monthly data on labor turnover.

U.S. DEPARTMENT OF LABOR
BUREAU OF LABOR STATISTICS
WASHINGTON

Dear Sir:

In response to numerous requests for more detailed information regarding labor turn-over in manufacturing industries, and in order that the monthly reports published may become of greater value to you and others who cooperate with us, the Bureau of Labor Statistics has revised the form used in collecting turn-over data.

I am sure you will agree that one of the most important revisions of this form is the separation of accessions into two groups: the first, to show the number of workers rehired after a separation of three months or less; the second, to include all other workers hired. The purpose of this breakdown, of course, is to determine whether or not accessions occur in connection with new job opportunities or whether they are the result of temporary suspensions.

We have also provided space to report separately changes in clerical, sales and supervisory personnel, so as to permit tabulations for the turn-over of these employees. If it is difficult or impossible for you to report this information separately, we shall appreciate the data either for the total of all employees or, if this too is not feasible, for plant employees only.

We are enclosing copies of the revised forms for January. I want to assure you that the data which you furnish will be kept strictly confidential and will be used in such a way as not to reveal the identity of any individual firm.

We sincerely hope that our labor turn-over reports based on this new procedure will be more useful and valuable to you, and we shall greatly appreciate your continued cooperation.

Very truly yours,

Isador Lubin,
Commissioner of Labor Statistics

Enclosures

(8678)

FIG. 10.—A typical letter from the Bureau of Labor Statistics seeking to secure the good will and cooperation of businessmen in the reporting of statistics.

investigate well the pitfalls of questionnaire making, which is a highly specialized art. There are six fundamental but simple rules to be followed:

1. The interest of the recipients of the questionnaires must be aroused or their cooperation obtained through some means. This may be done by engaging the support of some organization with which the individual informants are associated. For example, if the questionnaire is to go to bankers, the support or endorsement of the American Bankers Association should be enlisted. Interest in the questionnaire may also be aroused by the promise to furnish free copies of the summarized information when compiled. In this manner and by the promise of secrecy regarding individual returns, various governmental units obtain great quantities of statistical information.

2. The questionnaire should be as short as possible, consistent with the scope of information sought; and the individual questions should be so formulated as to be free of all ambiguity. They should be simple. Avoid presenting "problems" that will puzzle the recipients of questionnaires.

3. Where possible, arrange the individual questions so that replies can be brief and unequivocal. "Yes" or "no" or perhaps merely a check mark is the ideal answer.

4. The letter transmitting the questionnaire should be brief and dignified and yet should "sell" the idea to the informants.

5. After all is prepared, try out the questionnaire along with the transmittal letter on a dozen or so of the potential questionnaire recipients in order to make final revisions before printing the questionnaires, or schedules.

6. Always include a self-addressed stamped return envelope.

The first five rules apply whether the questionnaire is to be used by trained enumerators or to be sent by mail, but special care must be exercised if sent by mail. Study of Fig. 9 will reveal that answers to all questions are quite simple, in some cases merely a check mark (see questions VI, 1, 2, 4, and VII), in other cases the entry of a familiar numerical item. Less highly trained enumerators are required for handling such a questionnaire than are required for handling the United States census schedules.

EDITING

When the questionnaire is received from the agent or from the respondent by mail, it must be examined. If any statement on the schedule conflicts with other statements or if the schedule is incomplete or lacks clearness, it may have to be returned to the agent or respondent for explanation or revision. This is called "editing" the returns or the schedules. In any case, a certain amount of editing must always be done before tabulation of the data is begun. When trained visiting enumerators have been used in the survey, there will, of course, be a minimum of mistakes. When the questionnaires have been filled out by the informant directly, it may be necessary to write for further information or for corrections because of inadvertent mistakes in replies. If the respondents have been interested sufficiently to return the questionnaire with answers filled in, they will probably be willing to answer further simple questions to elucidate their former replies. If it is believed that the information has been deliberately falsified or withheld, it may be necessary to discard the entire schedule or at least the replies in it that seem to be of doubtful truth.

Editing the schedules is the process of preparing the original statements in the schedule for classification, coding, and tabulation. Careful editing is necessary in order to obtain compilations of data that will truly reflect the conditions being investigated. One task of editing is to see that all figures entered on the return are clear. If not, the editor rewrites the figures. If so poorly written that even the editor cannot read them, the schedule must be abandoned or the information obtained by further correspondence. If the editing is done locally, many of these difficulties may be eliminated by telephoning.

The principal task in editing is to locate all incomplete, inconsistent, or improbable and impossible answers. When such answers are found, it is necessary either to discard the defective schedules or to obtain correct replies through further inquiry. This does not, of course, imply the elimination of "unexpected" replies. An incomplete answer, for example, would be if pneumonia is given as the cause of death; it is necessary to know whether it is bronchial or lobar pneumonia. An inconsistent answer, for example, would be if a return shows a person widowed when from his age it is clear that he never could have been married. If a person who is a male is reported having died of a disease that is known to occur only in females, this is an impossible answer. There is somewhat less distinct a line between improbable and simple unexpected replies.

Only after incomplete, inconsistent, or improbable and impossible replies have been completed or corrected and all unclear figures carefully clarified are the schedules ready for coding, classification, and tabulation. For elaborate undertakings like the census, instructions are printed not only for the guidance of the enumerators but also for the editing and coding of the returns. For example, it is pointed out that the examination for completeness and consistency should be made family by family and not line by line. It will be easier to follow the entries belonging to the family if a strip of cardboard is placed across the schedule just under the line containing the entries for the last member of the family.[1] The coding and editing instructions say that all corrections and code figures entered on the schedule by the coding clerks should be made with red ink and a medium-point pen (neither a stub nor an extremely fine pen). Such a detailed instruction as this is necessary in order to secure uniformity and when tabulation is undertaken will enormously facilitate the work of the card-punching operators.

CODING

Whether or not machine tabulation is used, the coding of the schedules is a measure for economizing time. When large amounts of data are involved, consistent classification is enormously simplified by the use of code numbers. In arranging data it is then necessary only to observe a code number conspicuously and uniformly placed on the return instead of reading a title and remembering to what class that title belongs. On a Works Progress Administration project to construct indexes of manufacturing employment and pay rolls in the state of New Jersey, 1923–1940, it was not possible to obtain the use of tabulating machines. It was found necessary, nevertheless, to use a carefully worked out coding procedure to avoid hopeless confusion in the handling of the data, which came monthly from

[1] *Cf.* United States Bureau of the Census, *Instruction Manuals on Coding, passim.*

several hundred reporting firms. When machine tabulation is used, the coding procedure is a necessary step; it will be noticed that on the schedules (see Figs. 1 to 8) columns are inserted for the code numbers or letters to represent the various types of information on the schedule.

An Illustration of Coding. In the 1939 census of manufactures, the manufacturing industries in the United States were grouped into 20 groups, each with a number. Food and kindred products constitute group 1; its code number is 100. Lumber and timber basic products form group 5; its code number is 500. Chemicals and allied products are group 9; its code number is 900. All subgroups of industries in the food and kindred products classification have code numbers in the 100's; for example, beverages are numbered in the 180's—nonalcoholic beverages is 181; malt liquors 182, wines 184, and so on. Grain-mill products are numbered in the 140's—flour and other grain-mill products is 141, cereal preparations 143, rice cleaning and polishing 144, and so on. Confectionery and related products are numbered in the 170's—chocolate and cocoa products is 172, chewing gum 173, and so on. Similarly, subgroups of industries in the chemicals and allied products classification have code numbers in the 900's; for example, industrial-chemical industries are numbered in the 980's—plastic materials is 982, explosives 983, coal-tar products, crude and intermediate, 981, and so on.[1]

The classifications adopted by the United States Bureau of the Census for the 1939 census of manufactures follow closely the suggestions made by the Technical Subcommittee on Industrial Classification composed of representatives of various government agencies.[2] The suggested classification of this subcommittee, designated the Standard Industrial Classification Code, was made according to the following principles:[3]

1. The classification should conform to the existing structure of American industry.

[1] United States Bureau of the Census, "Industry Classifications for the Census of Manufactures, 1939," *Form* 75.

[2] Members of the subcommittee included representatives of the Department of Labor and Industry of New York State, the Federal Social Security Board, the Bureau of Internal Revenue, the Bureau of Labor Statistics, the Bureau of the Census, the United States Employment Service, and the Central Statistical Board.

[3] Central Statistical Board, May 10, 1938

2. The reporting units to be classified are establishments. (An establishment is defined as a place of business. All persons working at the same location or place of business are classified in the same industry.)

3. Each establishment is to be classified according to its major activity.

4. Each industry group established must have significance from the standpoint of the number of establishments and employees involved, volume of business, employment and pay-roll fluctuations, and other important economic features.

TABULATION

When the schedules have been edited and coded they are ready for the operations of the card-punch machines, and the final machine tabulations are made from these punched cards. The information on each schedule is transferred in code to the punch cards. With a machine resembling a toy typewriter, operators punch holes or combinations of holes in the cards so that the electrically operated machinery for sorting and tabulating can automatically transfer the information to totals by any classification desired. The punch card somewhat resembles the music roll of an old-time player piano, and most of the operations through which it goes are mechanical and electrical.

The 1930 census required the punching of 326,635,219 cards, which required an additional handling for verification. These cards represented 2,000,000 pounds of paper and would make a belt reaching nearly twice around the world at the equator. Punching, tabulating, and related work were equivalent to the handling of 4,701,671,697 cards once.

The Bureau of the Census has its own unit tabulating equipment. Some of these machines can digest 400 cards a minute. The unit machines were invented and developed within the Bureau by Herman Hollerith, who was employed in the Bureau and invented the first machine to tabulate the 1890 census. He is now known as the "father of machine tabulation," used throughout the world by governments and business to handle large statistical jobs.

CHAPTER III

SOURCES OF STATISTICS

Primary and Secondary Sources. The original collector of data is their primary source. Generally speaking, data obtained from a primary source inspire greater confidence than the same data taken from a secondary source. The primary source is presumably the one sure place to find the exact definition of the units of observation involved. Subsequent reproductions of the data may fail to reproduce this essential information and lead to a misunderstanding of the true meaning of the data.

The United States Bureau of the Census is the primary source of population data, of census data in general, and of all the statistical data published by the United States Department of Commerce, for the Bureau of the Census is the data-gathering agency of the Department. The Bureau of Foreign and Domestic Commerce, on the other hand, is a large retailer of statistical data gathered not only from the records of the Bureau of the Census but also from numerous other governmental and non-governmental sources. While governmental publications are thus not uniformly primary sources, they are usually very careful to give exact reference to the primary sources and to define units adequately.

In some cases, secondary sources may be better than the primary. Such is the case when experts presumably better qualified than the general run of statistical researchers have selected the good statistics from the poor ones in some primary source that may be either obscure and difficult to obtain or of a highly technical nature. Occasionally a secondary source performs the valuable function of selecting data impartially from primary sources that are biased in one way or another. Sometimes it is necessary also to be on guard against bias in government sources.[1]

[1] HINRICKS, A. F., "Statistical Bias in Primary Data and Public Policy," *Journal of the American Statistical Association*, Vol. 33 (1938), pp. 143–152.

Natural Sciences. After the development of the statistical theories of gases (Charles's law, Boyle's law, Avogadro's law, the work of Gay-Lussac, and the like) the physical sciences and arts accumulated source materials of a statistical character. Beginning with the last quarter of the nineteenth century, biology and zoology also accumulated source materials of a statistical character when a group of English biologists concluded that mass observation was necessary for the successful solution of their problems.[1]

Nongovernmental Sources. Statistical data of the natural sciences consist to a large extent of hypothetico-observational or experimental data. The principal sources of these data are handbooks of the special fields of study and monographs written by scholars at the great centers of research. For example, sources of astronomical data are the observatories located in various places throughout the world. The sources of currently discovered data in biology, physics, and chemistry are the laboratories maintained by universities, by private business enterprisers, or by such institutions as the Smithsonian Institution at Washington, D.C.

Additional primary sources of statistics in the natural sciences are the several hundred technical journals, publications of the learned societies, trade journals, publications of commercial research organizations, college bulletins, and the publications of endowed research enterprises. Fortunately for those who desire to make use of them, the data currently accumulated in such sources are summarized or abstracted in publications that maintain sections of their respective issues for the purpose.[2]

Statistical data for the natural sciences are also found in handbooks for the numerous special fields of study. For example, there are handbooks in medical entomology, physical therapy, geology, botany, experimental physics, and geophysics.[3]

---

[1] ANDERSON, O. N., "Statistical Method," *Encyclopaedia of the Social Sciences.*

[2] A partial list of such abstracting agencies is as follows: *Science Abstracts, Abstracts of Geology, Abstracts of Bacteriology, Abstracts of Chemical Papers, Zentralblatt für Mathematik, Jahrbuch über die Fortschritte der Mathematik, Physikalische Berichte,* and *Biometrika.*

[3] *Handbook of Physical Therapy* (1939); *Handbuch der allgemeinen Chemie, unter Mitwirkung vieler Fachlente* (1918–1937); *Handbuch der Experimentalphysik* (1926–1935), 43 vols.; *Handbook for Chemistry and Physics.*

Governmental Sources.   Sources of data in the natural sciences are enormously supplemented by governmental agencies. The government weather bureau supplies current and historical data important to many kinds of research in such natural sciences as botany, zoology, and geology. The *Minerals Yearbook*, published by the United States Department of the Interior, is a source of data for natural scientists. The Geological Survey is a source not only of geological data but of data on electrical power production and other information useful to engineers. Engineers also find that government agencies are sources of statistics on railroads, flood control, roads, and other similar subjects having to do with construction.

Biologists find the chief source of modern vitality statistics of all sorts among the publications of governmental agencies. An important source of statistical data for medical men results from medical research recorded in the files of hospitals, some of which are governmentally operated.

The quantity of statistical data relating directly to the natural sciences is thus large, but the natural sciences in addition make extensive use of the highly organized mass of statistical data collected largely by social scientists. Scholars in the natural sciences frequently make use of statistics concerning social and economic events. It is not at all uncommon for data concerning the behavior of human beings to enter into the calculations of engineers, physicists, and chemists engaged in practical business enterprise or pure research. Some illustrations were given in Chap. I.

Social Sciences. *Genesis of Statistical Sources.*   The increasing complexity of economic and social life has furnished the motive for the systematic marshaling of statistical data about human society; and, in addition, the dynamic quality of modern life makes it necessary to repeat statistical enumeration frequently in order to have knowledge of current facts and, what may be more important, knowledge of change. In the static conditions of earlier times one public fact-gathering enterprise could serve for years as a basis for judgments and for political and social action. Under modern dynamic conditions, this is not the case.

In a democracy the timing of governmental action is dependent on the consent of the people, and that requires widespread knowledge of many economic and social facts and their interpretation. If democracy is to preserve its high standards of achievement, its powers of expression in the face of tremendous forces that appeal to sentiment rather than to reasoned judgment, adequate factual information must be in the hands of the voters and of their governmental administrators and representatives in time for necessary action. Modern business enterprisers, too, faced with rapidly changing conditions, must lean more and more heavily on statistics to point the way to the solution of their problems.

During a great national crisis, such as a severe depression or a war, the value of statistical data is enormously enhanced. In depression periods, published statistical data from governmental sources, which in retrospect appear to have been but a trickle in prosperity, swell to flood proportions. Modern war, moreover, as well as being a "war of supply," "a war of machines," or a "war of production," is a "war of statistics." The fact that much of the increasing wartime volume of statistical data is confidential explains the apparent and deceptive appearance of fewer statistics in wartime than in peacetime. During the Second World War the statistics published by the United States Bureau of the Census, for example, sharply decreased because its organization and equipment were almost fully employed doing wartime statistical work, especially for such agencies as the War Production Board and the Office of Price Administration.

So diligent have been the efforts to obtain current knowledge by means of statistics during the past fifty years that a vast source of raw material now exists, covering many fields of knowledge. Elementary acquaintance with these sources is essential to all those who hope to work in either the natural or the social sciences. Complete familiarity with sources of statistics can come only with long practice in their use. It would be futile to attempt to impart to the student this desirable familiarity by giving a complete description of all sources.

The Pattern of Statistical Sources. The student cannot hope to memorize the names of all sources of statistics; indeed, the attempt would not be useful, for the names change and new ones are added as time goes by. Comprehension of the pattern of development of statistical sources, however, will enable the student to become a scholar who, when confronted by a statistical problem, will have acquired a "statistical sense" that will guide

him to the appropriate sources.   This presumption explains why
the present chapter on sources is given an historical or a genetic
setting.   Let the names of all the statistical agencies be changed
by the Second World War, and the study of the historical and
genetic explanation of statistical sources will still help the student
acquire that scholarly ability required to locate sources; he will
have historical perspective to facilitate his prompt understanding
of the postwar world of statistical sources.   In any case, the
period between the First and the Second World War will long
continue to be one intensively studied by statisticians of coming
generations.

In the ensuing description of sources of statistics, which is
presented in its historical or genetic aspects, governmental
sources are given more space than nongovernmental sources,
because the general statistician deals mostly with the former.
While the specialized statistician must acquire detailed knowledge
of sources in his special field, he also needs to be familiar with
governmental sources in his field.   Governmental sources, moreover, are themselves one of the best guides to the successful use of
nongovernmental sources, because many governmental agencies
are secondary sources that give complete and very useful descriptions of the primary sources used.

The motive underlying the gathering and publication of
statistics by private enterprise has usually been the profit
available through the sale of such statistical information to
commercial, banking, and manufacturing or distributing enterprises.   In many instances these services emerged as incidental
features of existing publications; an example is the increasing
amount of statistics of all kinds published in newspapers and
periodicals.   In other instances the statistical feature was the
original purpose of the publication; many trade journals are
cases in point.

The state and privately endowed universities of the nation are
important sources of statistical research, especially of a pioneering
character, in all branches of knowledge—some being famous for
certain fields of statistical work.

During recent years one of the most striking aspects of "big
business" development has been the maintenance of research
organizations contributing to statistical knowledge, a fact that the
public was not permitted to forget as it visited the 1939 World's

Fair in New York and read newspaper and magazine wartime advertisements in the early 1940's. Some corporation-financed research organizations, primarily intended for profit making, have incidentally contributed in important ways to the advancement of scientific statistics in engineering, business, and the use of agricultural products. Most of the pioneering statistical research in agriculture, however, as well as in labor organization, wages, and the like, is done by governmental units or by the governmentally sponsored agricultural experiment stations connected with various state colleges or universities.

The motive underlying governmental activity in the collection and publication of statistics has been to increase knowledge of facts so that administrators may adjust government action to the changing needs of a dynamic society, so that democratic representatives of the people may legislate more expeditiously and wisely, and so that the voters in a democracy may have the opportunity to know the facts. In recent years, a great expansion in the governmental activity of collecting and publishing statistics to aid business enterprise has occurred. In short, governmental statistical agencies assist both public and private economic planning. The large quantities of statistical information released by the Department of Labor and Department of Commerce are eagerly awaited by business enterprisers seeking to keep up to date in their methods, labor policies, coverage of potential markets, and knowledge of desirable sources of raw materials. True, their zeal in filling out the questionnaires that constitute the sources of the desired statistics sometimes falters, but on the whole businessmen recognize the truly cooperative character of the system of collecting and disseminating business statistics and stoically endure the barrage.

As a consequence of the manner of their historical and genetic origin, therefore, modern statistical sources in the United States fit into a pattern that is more or less uniform among the various fields of knowledge. This pattern is roughly as follows:

Research of private enterprisers:
  Individual enterprisers. Special monographs, articles, and other contributions are made by individuals and published under the sponsorship of universities, professional publications, and the like.
  Research associations. Quantities of statistical data are collected by research organizations, some of which are hired by corporate or

noncorporate "private enterprise" in the business world, some connected with universities, and some independently endowed.
Commercial sources, *i.e.*, privately financed publications:
These sources are in the business of collecting and publishing statistics as a profit-making enterprise; they include
Trade journals.
Commercial and financial periodicals and services.
Official publications of the government:
Federal or national governmental agencies.
Local, *i.e.*, state or municipal, governmental agencies.

Guides to Sources of Statistics.

If a trained professional librarian is available for consultation, he is the best informant on the subject of guides or handbooks to all general fields of research. However extensive may be the experience and training of the research scholar, he finds himself continually relying upon the local librarian, who makes a specialty of keeping posted on new developments with respect to handbooks and literary guides of all kinds.

Guides to Nongovernmental Statistics. Practically every conceivable occurrence in the world of man or beast, in the heavens, on the ground, under the ground, on the sea, under the sea, or in astronomical space holds an interest for some individual or group of individuals; either as a hobby or as a means of livelihood some individual or group of individuals is now and has for many years been collecting statistical facts about all these world events. The existing sources of statistics necessarily therefore appear at first glance to be an unwieldy mass; but, fortunately both for beginners and for practiced scholars, this mass has been for some time culled over and classified, indexed and cross-indexed by various types of handbooks, yearbooks, or guides of one sort or another.

The general magazine indexes constitute one class of such guides; the principal ones are as follows:

Agricultural Index.
Education Index.
Engineering Index.
Industrial Arts Index.
Public Affairs Information Service.
Readers' Guide to Periodical Literature.

Such indexes or guides are compiled monthly and cumulated into annual volumes, and articles of a statistical character appearing in a comprehensive variety of journals and trade magazines can be discovered by the intelligent use of these alphabetically arranged indexes. The above-listed indexes are not specifically organized as guides to statistical sources; their collective purpose is as broad in scope as all modern knowledge, but one of their varied uses is to serve as guides to sources of statistics.

Indexes or handbooks specifically dedicated to serve as guides to sources of statistics do, however, exist in considerable number. In 1937 the United States Department of Commerce published "Sources of Current Trade Statistics" (*Market Research Series* 13), which lists practically all current trade statistics by governmental and nongovernmental agencies; this handbook was designed for the use of manufacturers, distributors, financial institutions, advertising agencies, trade associations, bureaus of business research, and individuals engaged in research work. In 1942 the United States Department of Commerce published a handbook entitled *Trade and Professional Associations of the United States*, which lists the sources of practically every conceivable type of trade statistics compiled by nongovernmental agencies.

In 1934 a scholarly attempt was made by Gerlof Verwey and D. C. Renooy to construct a manual of statistical sources under the title *The Economist's Handbook;* this book was published in Amsterdam, Holland, and a supplement appeared in 1937. It is a guide to statistical sources on economic subjects, covering Belgium, France, Germany, the Netherlands, Switzerland, the United Kingdom, and the United States. In the United States, D. H. Davenport and F. V. Scott were authors in 1937 of *An Index to Business Indexes*, a book containing information about the many indexes used in business, including the name of the compiler, description of the index, frequency of publication, period covered, and the name of the publication in which current data appear. In 1937 the Special Libraries Association published a handbook *Guides to Business Facts and Figures* in which Part III is an index of statistical sources of information.

A multiple assortment of handbooks in various special fields serve as guides to statistics in each special field of knowledge, along with other purposes for which the handbooks are issued. For example, *Management Handbook, Flitcraft*, and *Handbook of Accountants* serve, in their respective fields, as guides to statistical sources.

Often the purpose of a handbook or index of sources of statistics is served by one of the numerous abstracts of statistical data. *The Statistical Abstract of the United States,* published annually by the United States Department of Commerce, is itself a source of statistics, but it is also an index to sources because at the head of or in a footnote to each table of data it records the primary source from which the data are obtained. Similarly, the *World Almanac,* which for 58 years has been published by the *New York World* or the *New York World-Telegram,* is itself a source of statistics and also a guide to sources for the same reason.

Guides to Governmental Statistics. Many of the handbooks serving as guides to statistical sources compiled by nongovernmental agencies, include also in their alphabetical indexes a large range of governmental statistical sources as well; but there are a number of important handbooks specifically intended to serve as guides to the maze of governmental sources of statistics. The best-known and most comprehensive guide is the *United States Government Manual,* published by the government. In 1938 the Central Statistical Board (later the Division of Statistical Standards of the Bureau of the Budget) published a *Directory of Federal Statistical Agencies.* The Central Statistical Board was organized in 1933 in order to find some means of coordinating the various types of Federal statistics.[1] The business of the Central Statistical Board was to serve as an agency for the reorganization in collection, tabulation, and use of Federal statistics. It was hoped such an agency could help solve the problem of overlapping in statistical function, which caused unnecessary burdens upon respondents to questionnaires and which also resulted in inefficiency in the utilization of statistical information.

In response to a request by the President in a letter of May 16, 1938, the Central Statistical Board made a report on the question as to whether or not it is possible to reduce the amount of duplication in statistical reports. The board concluded that much could be done in the way of coordinating the gathering, tabula-

---

[1] In the task of perfecting Federal statistics the government has received the advice of scientific professional associations. See American Statistical Association and the Social Science Research Council, *Government Statistics: A Report of the Committee on Government Statistics and Information Services* (1937).

tion, and presentation of Federal statistics; by such coordination, comparability in definition would bring about a great improvement in the efficiency of data collected. With reference to the reduction in the amount of duplication, however, the board concluded that a majority of the financial and other statistical reports and returns made by the public to the Federal government are incidental to the administration of governmental functions; the statistics are a by-product of either administrative or control functions of the government. Consequently, the board recommended that the Federal statistical and reporting services should remain largely decentralized so that they may be associated with the respective governmental functions to which most of them specifically relate; but that there is a continuing need for a statistical coordinating agency, with a specially trained staff and with broad powers.[1] One important result of the coordinating functions of the Central Statistical Board was the publication of a directory of federal statistical agencies, which has already been mentioned.

A general guide to government publications, Anne Morris Boyd's *United States Government Publications* (1941), serves incidentally as a guide to governmental sources of statistics. This book also gives an analytical picture of the character and scope of government publications. The same may be said regarding Laurence F. Schmeckebier's *Government Publications and Their Use* (1939).

RESEARCH OF PRIVATE ENTERPRISERS

Individual Enterprise. *Pioneers.* In spite of the fact that Domesday Book was an eleventh-century product and that even earlier examples of governmental collection of statistics can be cited, it remains true both historically and currently that the pioneer work of converting public records into statistics is nongovernmental. The pioneers have been and are individuals. The father of modern vital statistics is John Graunt, who in the seventeenth century made statistical investigations that served as the basis for founding life insurance. Another seventeenth-century scholar, Sir William Petty, was the outstanding pioneer in developing statistics for the social sciences. Both these

[1] Report of the Central Statistical Board, 76th Congress, 1st Session, *House Document* 27, Jan. 10, 1939.

men were associated with the early development of the *Royal Society of London*, which was incorporated in 1662 and is the oldest of modern learned societies.

Pioneering in the art as well as the science of statistics continues in modern times to be highly individualistic. This is exemplified by the work of Karl Pearson in England[1] and in the United States by such men as Wesley C. Mitchell and his works on index numbers and the business cycle, Warren Persons and his work on the statistical analysis of business statistics, and many others.[2] Individual contributions are commonly presented in the publications of learned societies, such as the *Journal of the Royal Statistical Society*, the *Journal of the Statistical Society of London* (founded in 1834), and the *Journal of the American Statistical Association* (founded in 1839). These and the publications of other learned societies are indexed in the guides mentioned earlier in this chapter.

Research Associations. During the 1920's and 1930's a number of important research organizations in the field of economics and social institutions were organized. The Brookings Institution in Washington, D.C., the Harvard Committee on Economic Research, the National Industrial Conference Board, the National Bureau of Economic Research, and the Cowles Commission were among the most prominent.

The Harvard Committee on Economic Research was organized in 1919 to study business trends and cycles and to publish a scientific business forecaster; its work was launched under the leadership of Warren Persons. In addition to the forecasting service, this research organization publishes the *Review of Economic Statistics* (quarterly) and once or twice a year a summary of statistics called the *Statistical Record*.

The National Industrial Conference Board was organized by a group of comparatively public-spirited manufacturers to study the various problems of employer-employee relationships, leading them into special studies of real wages, income distribution, and general economic conditions. It publishes its studies in the form of books appearing as they are written. In addition to the subjects mentioned above there have been National Industrial Conference Board books on cost of living, statistics of income

[1] See Chaps. XIII and XIV.
[2] See Chaps. XIX and XX.

by states, and availability of bank credit. The National Industrial Conference Board has also published since 1940 *The Economic Almanac*, which is a widely used annual.

The National Bureau of Economic Research was founded in 1920, sponsored by a group who believed that a purely disinterested approach is desirable and that no group should control the findings of this new statistical organization. It is so constituted as to produce this desirable result. A number of special studies of economic and social conditions have been made and published under its auspices and some in cooperation with the government. For several years it has occasionally issued bulletins containing data resulting from studies that usually appear later in more detail in book form.

The nature and accomplishments of the National Bureau of Economic Research are indicated by the following quotation from the twentieth annual report of the director of research:[1]

The National Bureau was established by men who believed that it is becoming possible to apply quantitative methods to the study of economic behavior. They realized that this field is far more difficult than the fields in which science has won its major triumphs and demonstrated its practical usefulness most conclusively. Also they recognized that investigators cannot experiment at will upon society; though society can and does experiment loosely upon itself. . . . Economics was not likely to grow faster at this turning point in its career than its elder sisters [the natural sciences]. But at the close of the First World War the materials for observing actual behavior were multiplying so rapidly and analytic methods of extracting significant conclusions were becoming so versatile and powerful that our founders thought their staff had good prospects of rendering valuable service at once. Also they hoped that one modest success would lead to others, fostering cumulative growth of the kind that has characterized systematic research in other fields. . . .

Twenty years of effort along the lines laid down in 1920 have confirmed our faith in the social value of what the National Bureau set out to do. Our accomplishments have not been spectacular, but they have been substantial, and they afford a secure foundation on which to build in future. We have more reason than ever to believe that in trying to establish a few economic fundamentals firmly we are aiding thoughtful men of all persuasions to plan wisely. If tested knowledge is the safest and surest guide in practical affairs, our work has social meaning, how-

[1] MITCHELL, WESLEY C., "The National Bureau's Social Function," March, 1940, pp. 13–15, 19.

ever technical its character. . . . We hold that advance will be rapid and continuous in proportion as the workings of our economic system are understood. In trying to replace speculative opinions about economic relations by conclusions resting upon evidence we are expediting progress in the most effective manner we know.

. . . Another device, peculiar to the National Bureau, is to select directors who have divergent views on public policy and give each an opportunity to criticize every manuscript. That device has been of inestimable help to us in keeping our reports nonpartisan and therefore worthy of credence by the public. Having such a board we cannot expect unanimous consent from its members to many policies that individuals among us favor. But the mere fact that the National Bureau never takes sides upon controversial issues adds its bit of protection against bias in our publications and helps toward meriting and winning public confidence.

. . . . .

The more thoughtful sections of the public we are now reaching in various ways. Physical scientists are coming to recognize the contributions of research in economics; for example, in *I Believe* Robert A. Millikan says

"In economics and the social sciences long and elaborate statistical studies must be made in order to eliminate the disturbing factors and thus obtain the controlled conditions. We are just beginning to have available, through the National Bureau of Economic Research and other similar agencies, a large amount of such definite, dependable, statistical knowledge in economics."

The Twentieth Century Fund is another research association organized to function in a manner similar to that of the National Bureau of Economic Research. It publishes occasional pamphlets or books.

THE COMMERCIAL SOURCES

In addition to the numerous sources of statistics resulting from individual or group research such as those described above, a great quantity of statistical sources has come into existence as the result of the activities of those who go into the business for the profit of collecting and selling statistical data. Such are the trade journals and the commercial and financial periodicals.

Trade Journals. A large number of trade journals are actively engaged in collecting statistical data for various types of enterprise. The *Iron Age*, for example, founded in 1855, is the trade journal for the iron and steel industry, publishing statistics on iron and steel production in all states and the prices of iron, steel, copper, zinc, etc. Another example is *Wileman's Brazilian Review*, which is the trade journal for coffee. The trade journals are frequently used by governmental statistical organizations, such as the Bureau of Labor Statistics, the Department of Commerce, and the Board of Governors of the Federal Reserve System, as the primary sources of particular data assembled by them. Occasionally the trade journals will publish in special pamphlet form or in books assembled data of the trade.

During the 1920's, a large expansion in the collection and publication of statistics in various lines of economic activity on physical commodity production and distribution took place. In a few instances this work was done by private companies. Thus Seidman and Seidman compiled data on furniture for the Grand Rapids district, and R. L. Polk and Company compiled data on new cars registered; the function of the latter was subsequently taken over by *Ward's Automotive Reports*. Many such series were compiled by the trade journals from public records. The *Iron Age* compiled data on physical quantities of production of pig iron, and the *Statistical Sugar Trade Journal* published quantitative sugar statistics.

Trade Associations. Most of the production and distribution series are compiled by the various trade associations, such as the American Face Brick Association (merged with the Structural Clay Products Institute), the American Paper and Pulp Association, and the United States Cane Sugar Refiners' Association.

The production and distribution statistical series are of various types. Some measure the flow of commodities through the process of production and distribution, for example, data on raw material received or consumed, like the figures on cotton consumption by textile mills or on cattle receipts at stockyards. Others give a measurement of quantity or stock of a commodity on hand. Still others are figures on the amount of orders or sales of the product, such as the unfilled orders of the United States Steel Corporation. As noted elsewhere, many of these series are collected from their original sources and published by the United States Department of Commerce in the *Survey of Current Business*. Consequently, the appendix of the *Survey* contains a description of about every important commercial source of statistics. In fact, the Department of Commerce publishes a description of such statistical sources.[1] Frequently a trade association will publish a sort of handbook or abstract of statistics for the trade, covering historical as well as current statistics.[2]

Commercial and Financial Publications. The commercial and financial journals and services are also too numerous to mention in detail, but a few may be described as typical. Among these are the *Commercial and Financial Chronicle* (weekly), the *New York Journal of Commerce* (daily), the *Wall Street Journal*[3] (daily), *Bradstreet's* (merged in 1933 with *Dun's*), *Babson's Reports*, *Moody's Investors' Service*, *Standard & Poor's Corporation*, *Brookmire Economic Service*, and the *Dodge Statistical Service*.

While there is much overlapping of published commercial and financial statistics through these various publications and services, nevertheless each has become noted for especially good statistical service in a particular line. For example, the user of business-failure statistics thinks first of Bradstreet's, because for many years the data that it has published on business failures have been widely used. Bradstreet's was also famous for its index of wholesale prices for the United States, being a pioneer in the development and publication of such an index. Babson's and Brookmire's services are noted for business forecasting and for investment services and forecasting the stock market. The *New York Journal of Commerce* is noted for its current data on new securities issued and on the produce markets. The *New York Times* is noted for its index of business activity, which was published in the *Annalist* (weekly) until that periodical was discontinued. The *Commercial and Financial Chronicle* is particularly useful for its detailed array of current data on bank clearings, business failures, interest rates, stock and bond prices, corporations, capital stock and bond issues, and the money markets of the world. This remarkable publication can be

---

[1] "Sources of Current Trade Statistics," *Market Research Series* 13 (1937).

[2] United States Cane Sugar Refiners' Association, *Sugar Economics, Statistics, and Documents* (1938).

[3] Often referred to in footnotes as *Dow, Jones and Company*, which sometimes mystifies beginners.

traced in its lineage back to 1820, when it started as *Niles'
Weekly Register*, famous as an early preacher of the doctrines of
high tariffs and the "American system." From 1839 to 1865 it
was called *Hunt's Merchant's Magazine*. Since 1865 it has
gone under its present name. The financial statements of all
kinds of corporations, together with other statistics and corporate
histories, are to be found in Moody's *Manual of Corporations*.

The *Commodity Yearbook* is published by the Commodity
Research Bureau, New York, N.Y. This is a private organization devoted to the dissemination of accurate information on
commodities and other related subjects, including production,
consumption, prices, stocks, imports, exports, etc. Some are
annual, some are monthly data.

All the above-described sources are extensively used by
American and foreign business enterprisers, whose subscriptions
to them and advertising in them make possible the vast statistical
undertakings on a profitable basis. The fact that they are so
supported would seem to prove the value of statistics to modern
business enterprise.

OFFICIAL PUBLICATIONS OF THE GOVERNMENT

Federal Statistical Agencies. *Department of Commerce.* The
Department of Commerce is one of the greatest fact-gathering
organizations of the Federal government, if not the greatest.
It contains a number of bureaus chiefly engaged in the dissemination of facts concerning not only commerce but economic and
social life in general. The Bureau of the Census is the fact-
gathering agency of the Department.

The Articles of Confederation provided for the taking of a
triennial census, but the Constitution of the United States
provides for the taking of a population census every 10 years,
to serve as the basis for Congressional apportionment. The
first one was taken in 1790. The broad practical and scientific
purposes that the census today serves were not in the minds of
the American founders, and the earlier census publications were
meager affairs compared with the modern census.[1] The census
of 1790, for example, returned the number of free white males
over, and the number under, sixteen years of age, the number of

[1] CUMMINGS, JOHN, "Statistical Work of the Federal Government of the
United States," in Koren, *History of Statistics*, pp. 670–672.

free white females without distinction by age, all other free persons, and slaves—without, in the case of the last two classes, distinction by either sex or age. The published census of 1790 consisted of a volume of 52 pages. At the census of 1800 and of 1810, five age classes were distinguished and the age classification was extended to white females. In addition, at the census of 1810, some facts were compiled relating to manufacturing establishments, their number, nature, extent, situation, and value. A digest of the results of these data was prepared by Tench Coxe and published in 233 pages. The census of 1820 introduced the idea of collecting occupational statistics, calling for enumerations of persons engaged in agriculture, commerce, and manufactures. The census of 1830 returned to the original idea of obtaining merely a population enumeration; but in 1838 President Van Buren suggested to Congress in his annual message that the census should be extended so as to include "authentic statistical returns of the great interests specially entrusted to or necessarily effected by the legislation of Congress."[1] As a result, Congress provided in the act for the Sixth Census (1840) that the marshals should "return in statistical tables . . . all such information in relation to mines, agriculture, commerce, manufactures, and schools, as will exhibit a full view of the pursuits, industry, education, and resources of the country."[2] Congress overreached the capacity of those entrusted with the task of census taking, for the census of 1840 is famous for its inaccuracies. At the census of 1850, improvements in the organization of collecting and compiling the statistics were made; and, according to Cummings, with the census of 1850 the decennial enumeration began to assume modern proportions and character.

One of the outstanding American economists of the nineteenth century, Francis A. Walker, was a pioneer in developing the census to what we understand it to be now. He did particularly notable work in perfecting the organization and presentation of statistical data in the Tenth Census (1880), of which he had charge.

At the Eleventh Census (1890), machine tabulation was introduced (the Hollerith tabulating machines), at a great

[1] *Ibid.*, p. 672.
[2] *Ibid.*, pp. 672–675.

saving of time and expense. The printed reports of the census of 1890 aggregated 21,410 pages, in 25 quarto volumes, the final report being issued in 1897. The Bureau of the Census was established as a permanent one in 1902 and since that time has been in continuous operation as a great fact-gathering organization for the national government. The tendency since that time has been to confine the decennial census to the major subjects of population, manufacturing, agriculture, mines, and quarries, and in intervening years to take censuses of business. In intercensus years the Bureau also has charge of the annual collection of mortality data, statistics on religious bodies, the collection and compilation of statistics of cotton and tobacco, and the annual compilation of statistics of cities of 30,000 population and over, and financial statistics of states.[1]

After 1902 the census of manufactures has been taken every 5 years until 1919 and since 1919 every 2 years until 1939. The census of agriculture has been taken every 5 years since 1910. The *Statistical Atlas* (containing graphic illustrations of much of the census data) was first issued in 1874 [based on the Ninth Census (1870)] and has appeared irregularly since that date.

In 1929 a census of distribution as well as of manufactures was taken; but when the National Recovery Administration began operations, many of the data assembled in the census year 1930 were out of date owing to the sharp business recession and the increase of unemployment following that year. Along with the regular biennial census of manufactures for 1933 the Bureau of the Census undertook an extensive census of business of types other than manufacturing, such as amusements, service businesses, barbershops, beauty parlors, repair shops, and tourist camps, covering more than 2,400,000 individual establishments.

[1] By order of the Secretary of Commerce, the collecting of financial statistics of states was discontinued temporarily after the 1931 report. With no comparative basis provided by the statistics for smaller cities and no individual reports for states, the remaining reports were of greatly reduced value. A detailed analysis was therefore made of the needs for data in this field and of the Bureau's past and present inquiries. Closely related reports were prepared for the director by the Central Statistical Board, the Advisory Committee to the Director of the Census, and the Municipal Finance Officers' Association of the United States and Canada. Accordingly, the Division of Financial Statistics of States and Cities was reorganized in 1936. Annual Report of the United States Bureau of the Census, 1937, pp. 23–24; 1938, pp. 28–29.

For subsequent biennial dates the census of business was further developed. The census of business covering the calendar year 1935, for example, was much broader in scope than either the census of distribution of 1929 or the census of American business for 1933. The 1935 census of business attempted to obtain a reasonably complete picture of essential and comparable items of business information concerning practically all lines of business activity in the United States. It comprised a complete census of retail and wholesale trade, service businesses, amusement enterprises, hotels, broadcasting stations, advertising agencies, banking, insurance, real estate, bus transportation, trucking, warehousing, construction, and distribution of manufacturer's sales through primary channels.

Elaborate care was exercised in preparing the 17 schedules; before final use they were submitted for criticism to representatives of the business groups and governmental agencies principally concerned. Special efforts were made by the Bureau to integrate the census of business and the biennial census of manufactures by the adoption of common definitions, instructions, area designations, and field procedures. In order to perfect procedure, conferences were held to discuss schedules, procedures, and other problems inherent in such an expanded business census. These conferences were attended by representatives of trade associations, professional groups, chain-store organizations, etc., and by official representatives of a number of governmental agencies—the Central Statistical Board, Interstate Commerce Commission, Bureau of Foreign and Domestic Commerce, Tariff Commission, Federal Reserve Board, and Bureau of Labor Statistics.[1]

The population schedule for the census of 1940 is notable for a number of new questions concerning employment status, migration, income status, housing, and education. It is also notable for the innovation of the sampling technique applied to one group of questions in order to widen the scope of the inquiries. It dropped the question on literacy.

Employment and unemployment queries have been made in previous censuses, but the 1940 census made a new approach. The new data permit classification of the nation's labor force

[1] Annual Report of the United States Bureau of the Census, 1936, pp. 19–21.

into the employed, the unemployed who have had previous work experience, and the unemployed without previous work experience—new workers. They provide some measure of the volume of employment both during the whole year and during the week prior to the census day, Apr. 1, 1940.

The schedule included questions that distinguish people at work, people unemployed who are seeking work, and people who have a job but are not at work because of temporary illness, industrial disputes, or vacations. Persons at work were asked to indicate the number of hours they worked during the week preceding the census, and the unemployed were asked to state the number of weeks they had been seeking work. Workers were classified as to whether they were in private industries or were employed by the government and whether they were own-account workers or unpaid family workers.

The new inquiry on wages and salaries is important as a measure of national purchasing power and its distribution, and the resulting data have been helpful to business in indicating potential market areas.

The net effects of internal population migration during the preceding 5 years were obtained by requesting the place of residence for each person as of Apr. 1, 1935. It is expected that compilation of the statistics comparing such residence with that of Apr. 1, 1940, which is also recorded on the schedule, will measure the effects of industry shifts, droughts, depressions, floods, the backflow west to east, and the shift from the city to the country, or vice versa.

In 1940, for the first time, the decennial census included a separate housing schedule designed to give detailed information for each dwelling unit in the United States, whether occupied or vacant, rural or urban. Data were obtained as to the number of rooms, water supply, bath and toilet facilities, and light equipment. For each occupied unit or household, information was obtained concerning the principal means of refrigeration used, the presence or absence of a radio, the character of the heating equipment, and the principal heating and cooking fuels used. Each residential structure was described in respect to single, double, or multiple family occupancy, whether or not it contained a business unit, for what purpose and in what year it was originally built, the principal exterior material of the structure, and

whether it was in need of major repairs.   The schedule included
a question on whether the family leases or owns, whether there
is mortgage indebtedness, and methods of home finance.

It is expected that the compilation of these data will provide
valuable information on the latent purchasing power of a community.   There is no more important index of the social and
economic status of a population than the standard of its housing.
Housing experts believe that the information gathered will be of
inestimable value in determining future housing policies.   It
will be of especial interest to manufacturers, builders, distributors,
and bankers in their study of trends in home ownership and
building in the United States.   Cities will be able to determine
the distribution of the various types of housing within their
limits, together with the possible need of expansion of transportation and communication systems, police and fire protection,
schools, and similar facilities.   Data showing the equipment in
houses, together with the state of repair of the homes, will be of
value to manufacturers and distributors of housing products
in the planning of their sales campaigns.[1]

The agricultural schedules for the census of 1940 likewise had
a number of new features.   Nine regional schedules, each used
in a separate group of states, were especially designed to fit
national variations in cropping practices.   Questions designed
to obtain subtotals for the value of various major categories of
farm products sold or traded in 1939 made possible a much
closer estimate of total farm income and of farm income by
principal sources.   The 1940 census also introduced a supplementary plantation schedule for use in the cotton belt that made
possible a refined distinction between farms and plots cultivated
by croppers and defined the exact status of each cropper and
certain other tenants in relation to the plantation owner.   Questions to measure the effects of current agricultural policies were
also asked, relating to soil-improvement crops, summer fallow,
crop failure, and succession or interplanted double cropping.

The Bureau of Foreign and Domestic Commerce is the great
Federal fact analyzer and fact publisher in the Department of
Commerce.   It has a curious and rather complicated history.
From the beginning of the national period, the statistics of

---

[1] *Cf. The New York Times*, Jan. 24, 1940.

foreign commerce were linked up with our tariff policy and maintained by the Treasury Department. In 1856, growing out of an investigation of the tariff policies of other countries by the State Department, there was created a Bureau of Foreign Commerce as a permanent bureau for the purpose of collecting statistics on foreign trade. In 1866, the Bureau of Statistics of the Treasury Department was created to take special charge of this work, and at the same time Congress gave it power to collect statistics on domestic trade as well as on foreign trade. In 1905, a Bureau of Manufactures in the Department of Commerce was organized to foster, promote, and develop the various manufacturing industries of the United States, and markets for the same at home and abroad, by gathering and publishing all available and useful information concerning industries and markets.

As a consequence, there were bureaus in three separate departments (Treasury, State, and Commerce) concerned with the gathering of foreign-trade statistics. In 1912, however, these functions were centralized in the Bureau of Foreign and Domestic Commerce of the Department of Commerce.

The most important statistical publications of this bureau are the monthly *Survey of Current Business* (with a weekly supplement) and the annual *Statistical Abstract of the United States*. Special publications, designed to aid business are also prepared, for example, historical studies of industries, studies of the national income produced, and studies of market data.[1]

Other bureaus of the Department of Commerce are the Bureaus of Fisheries, of Patents, and of Navigation and Steamboat Inspection, each of which publishes specialized statistics. The two great statistical organizations in the Department of Commerce, however, are the Bureau of the Census and the Bureau of Foreign and Domestic Commerce.

Department of Labor. The United States Department of Labor also contains bureaus that publish statistics, the most important

---

[1] Illustrations are P. W. Barker, *Rubber Industry of the United States*, 1839–1939 (1939); Division of Economic Research, *National Income in the United States*, 1929–35 (1936); B. P. Haynes and G. R. Smith, *Consumer Market Data Handbook* (1939). For other statistical publications of the Bureau of Foreign and Domestic Commerce, see the *United States Government Manual*.

from the point of view of quantity of data compiled and published being the Bureau of Labor Statistics. This was created in 1884 as the Bureau of Labor, although the Treasury Bureau of Statistics created in 1866 had been enjoined to collect wage statistics. In 1888 the Bureau of Labor was made an independent Department of Labor. The duties of the Department of Labor were to acquire and diffuse among the people of the United States useful information on subjects connected with labor, in the most general and comprehensive sense, and especially on its relation to capital, the hours of labor, the earnings of laboring men and women, and the means of promoting their material, social, intellectual, and moral prosperity. The commissioner of labor in charge of the Department was specially charged to investigate the causes of and facts relating to all controversies and disputes between employers and employees, and he was also empowered to make special studies of articles controlled by trusts and their effect on production and prices and other special subjects. Owing to the excellent work of the Department under the wise guidance of Carroll D. Wright, the first commissioner of labor, there is available a large mass of statistics in the field of labor for this country, including studies of strikes, the effect of the introduction of machinery on employment and wages, the conditions of living and work of the laboring population, etc. Upon the basis of the wage and price data collected, index figures showing the trends of wages and prices, wholesale and retail, have been constructed and published by this bureau.

In 1903, the old Department of Labor was transferred to the newly created Department of Commerce and Labor; but in 1913 there was created a new Department of Labor, and in that department the Bureau of Labor Statistics. At the present time, the principal publications of the Bureau of Labor Statistics are the *Monthly Labor Review* (published since 1915), bulletins on special topics such as wholesale prices, retail prices, cost of living, wages, and labor turnover, and monthly serials to supplement the bulletins and give current information on those topics. Beginning in August, 1939, the Bureau of Labor Statistics published a daily index of 28 basic commodity prices at wholesale; but following the inauguration of wartime price controls this index was published only once a week since control in the raw-

material field was widely effective. During wartime the index
was of little importance.[1]

Treasury Department. For the period before the Civil War
the chief source of financial and price statistics in the United
States, as well as data on governmental finance, consists in the
finance reports of the Secretary of the Treasury.

Before the development of statistical bureaus in the Department of Commerce and the Department of Labor, the Treasury
Department was the most important source of Federal statistics;
and it is still important in the fields of banking and monetary
statistics, owing to the work of the comptroller of the currency,
and in the field of income and Federal taxation and indebtedness,
owing to the work of the commissioner of internal revenue and
the Secretary of the Treasury.

From the United States Treasury Department comes the
monthly Statement of the Public Debt of the United States.
The commissioner of internal revenue of the Treasury publishes
an annual report of income-tax returns, constituting the most
important source of data regarding income statistics in the
United States. The annual reports of the comptroller of the
currency give financial and banking statistics and monetary
data going back as far as the Civil War, when the national banking system began. The comptroller publishes these data in
an annual report and also several times a year in the *Abstract of
Condition of the National Banks.*[2] The annual reports of the
director of the mint contain statistics on the production of the
precious metals, including gold and silver. The Life Saving
Service of the United States Treasury Department publishes
data on marine accidents.

Interior Department. The Department of the Interior has
important statistical aspects, too. The Bureau of Mines publishes data on fatalities in coal mines. The Geological Survey
publishes data on metal statistics and minerals. In the census
years it has authority to collect statistics from primary sources.
Since 1880 it has collected statistics carefully as to the crude

[1] For other statistics published by the Department of Labor see the *United
States Government Manual* and see also Bureau of Labor Statistics, *Selected
List of Publications of the Bureau of Labor Statistics* (1939), which can be
purchased from the Government Printing Office.

[2] See page 82 on the Federal Reserve System.

oil lifted from the ground, iron ore, etc., watching the physical consumption of our natural wealth. It also collects and publishes statistics on electrical power production which are now considered useful in the study of the general trend of business, so important to business is the use of electricity. Other bureaus in the Department of the Interior are the Bureau of Education, Bureau of Pensions, and the Bureau of Indian Affairs, each publishing certain specialized statistics indicated by their titles.

Department of Agriculture. The Department of Agriculture was not founded until 1862, but statistical work relating to agriculture of a more or less systematic nature dates back to 1839, when Congress appropriated $1,000 out of the patent fund, to be expended under direction of the commissioner of patents, "in the collection of agricultural statistics, and for other agricultural purposes." At the present time the great bulk of Federal statistics on agricultural matters is collected and published by the Bureau of Agricultural Economics, which originally was the Bureau of Statistics in the Department of Agriculture and later was known as the Bureau of Markets and Crop Estimates. In addition to a host of bulletins on special subjects related to agriculture, this bureau publishes a monthly report on weather conditions, *Crops and Markets,* and gives out estimates of annual crop yields. In recent years it has become the source of pioneer statistical work in the measurement of the factors influencing the demand for agricultural products and other similar statistical studies in connection with the conduct of the Agricultural Adjustment Administration. The agricultural yearbook, published by this Department, is a valuable record of agricultural progress in the United States and contains also extensive summaries of agricultural statistics. Since 1936 these summaries have been published separately under the title *Agricultural Statistics.* Current agricultural data are disseminated by the Department of Agriculture in its monthly publication, the *Agricultural Situation.* The Bureau of Agricultural Economics, which has direct charge of the above publications, also furnishes part of the program for the Farm and Home Hour on the radio, designed to distribute timely agricultural information to the farming population of the nation.

The administrative departments of the government thus constitute sources of statistics on a large scale, and statisticians continually make use of these Federal sources of statistics. These publications of the government are available to everyone at very low cost and can be found for free use in most large libraries of the country or at offices maintained for the purpose by the government.

The Independent Establishments. In addition to the administrative departments of the national government there are many national commissions or boards or agencies, collectively described as the "independent establishments" of the government. Some of these have become well-known sources of statistical data in special fields. The principal ones are the Interstate Commerce Commission, the Federal Trade Commission, the Federal Security Agency, the Federal Power Commission, the Federal Deposit Insurance Corporation, the Securities and Exchange Commission, the Tariff Commission, the Maritime Commission, and the Board of Governors of the Federal Reserve System.

The Interstate Commerce Commission was created in 1887 as the Federal government's solution of the railroad problem, following detailed Congressional reports of the situation, known as the Windom Report (1873–1874) and the Cullom Report (1886). These reports may be said to be the beginning of Federal railroad transportation and communication statistics. Since 1887, such statistics have been gathered and published by the Interstate Commerce Commission, its powers having been gradually extended to include other types of transportation, oil pipe lines, and express companies. In 1934 Congress created the Federal Communications Commission, which is devoted primarily to telephone, telegraph, cable, and radio.

The Federal Trade Commission is the Federal source of data on the monopoly problem. In 1890 the Sherman Antitrust Act was passed; and in 1903 Congress realized that there was need to collect facts to be used as a basis for the enforcement of the Sherman Act. At the urgent request of President Roosevelt, Congress created the Bureau of Corporations for the purpose of gathering data that would aid in the proper enforcement. Following the passage of the Federal Trade Commission Act of 1914, the Bureau of Corporations was merged with the Commission. This Commission publishes reports on its investigations of various trusts, such as the investigation of coal, cotton, cereals, meat packing, and a number of others. During the 1920's and 1930's it was a collector and publisher of statistics concerning trade associations and trade practices.

The Board of Governors of the Federal Reserve System, which has operated since 1913, has become the greatest national source of statistics on banking and financial subjects. It publishes an annual report containing statistics on banking and related subjects, the *Member Bank Call Report* several times a year, and the *Federal Reserve Bulletin,* a monthly publication invaluable to bankers and statisticians working in banking subjects. In addition, it publishes weekly mimeographed press releases on the condition of Federal reserve banks and of reporting member banks in order to make available more current data than is possible with the monthly or annual publications. In addition to financial and banking statistics the Board also has constructed through its Division of Research and Statistics an index of production calculated upon a comprehensive basis; this index and other special studies are also published in the annual reports and in the *Federal Reserve Bulletin.*

The United States Tariff Commission, created in 1916, gathers statistics purporting to aid in the administration of the tariff laws and to help determine when duties should be raised or lowered. Owing to the strong influence of politics upon the question of the tariff, the studies of the Tariff Commission, with certain notable exceptions, constitute a great source of misuse of statistics. This was particularly true for the period from 1920 to 1932 when most of its studies were for the purpose of proving the need to raise tariffs. After the passage of the Reciprocal Trade Agreements Act in 1934 extensive improvements were inaugurated, and additional data were made available with the numerous studies that were conducted in cooperation with the State and other governmental departments.

Finally, in connection with Federal statistics, it should be mentioned that frequently Congressional investigations result in the assembly and publication of valuable statistical material often constituting original sources or at least original compilations of such material. Mention has already been made of the Windom Report in 1873–1874 and the Cullom Report in 1886, both on transportation, which led to the creation of the Interstate Commerce Commission in 1887. Other examples are the Pujo Money Trust Report of 1913 and the various reports of the Senate and House Committees on Banking and Currency during the 1930's on brokers' loans, branch banks, the operation of the national and Federal reserve banking systems, foreign loans, and stock-exchange practices. Important Federal legislation of that decade was based on these investigations.

Several noteworthy special commissions, created by Congress from time to time, have produced published documents that have become famous as great sources of primary statistical information. The Aldrich Reports from the Senate Committee on Finance, on Retail Prices and Wages (1892) and Wholesale Prices, Wages, and Transportation (1893) constitute extensive compilations of price data covering a period of over fifty years. These reports have been extensively used as source material for statistical studies of prices and wages for the period 1850 to 1900.

The Industrial Commission created by act of Congress of June 18, 1898, submitted a report to Congress in 1902, consisting of 19 volumes and presenting a substantially complete epitome of the industrial life of the nation and of the important changes in business methods that occurred in the latter part of the nineteenth century. These volumes are largely statistical in their methods of description. The Immigration Commission, created in 1907, presented to Congress in 42 volumes a full inquiry into the subject of immigration, reviewing statistically immigration to the United States during the period 1820 to 1910 and the component elements in our population as determined by immigration from 1850 to 1900. The National Monetary Commission, created in 1908, studied the banking and currency systems of the United States as compared with those of other countries. This Commission collected more complete statistical information with regard to the banks of foreign countries such as Great Britain, France, and Germany than had ever been collected before and for the first time in this country obtained comparable statistics for all banks in the United States. The full report of the Commission, consisting of 24 volumes, was completed in 1912 and served as the basis of the bank-reform legislation known as the Federal Reserve Act.

Other similar statistical studies in various fields of economic and social life have been made by commissions, such as those of the Select Committee on Wages and Prices established in 1910, the Commission on Industrial Relations created by an act of

1912, and the Commission on National Grants to Vocational Education. The Hoover Committees on Social Trends (1933) published extensive studies, partly statistical in character, of the economic and social life of the nation.

One of the most notable of such temporary organizations was the National Resources Planning Board, established in the executive office of the President of the United States under authority of the Reorganization Act of 1939. This Board succeeded the National Resources Committee, which had been established in 1935. Earlier names of the same organization were National Resources Board and Advisory Committee and National Resources Board, which was created in 1934 to succeed the planning organization of the Federal Emergency Administration of Public Works. When the United States Congress discovered what it felt was an attempt by the executive to usurp Congressional powers by having an economic planning board, it became hostile to the National Resources Planning Board. This hostility was not diminished when in 1943 the Board presented to the executive a plan for the postwar expansion of the Federal security program. President Roosevelt handed the report over to Congress for action, but the Board was abolished in that year when Congress refused to vote funds for its continued existence. During the course of its checkered career, however, the Board became the author of several noteworthy statistical publications: *Energy Resources and National Policy* (1939), *The Problems of a Changing Population* (1938), *Consumer Incomes in the United States* (1938), *Consumer Expenditures in the United States* (1939), and *The Structure of the American Economy* (1939).

State and Municipal Sources. The activities of the various state governments result also in the compilation and publication of statistics. Most states maintain departments of institutions and agencies that, through supervision of reform schools, prisons, hospitals, and the like, become sources of statistics on mental and physical pathology, as well as delinquency. Data concerning the records of penal and charitable institutions, hospitals, and asylums for the insane and feeble-minded are primarily recorded by state or by municipal organizations.

Vital statistics, that is, data relating to births and deaths and the classification of deaths by causes, have become an important part of the demographic work of municipalities and states and have thus made the state and municipal governments important primary sources of data of this character. In addition, statistics on marriage and divorce are recorded through state and municipal licensing administration.

Data are recorded by states and regularly reported, based on their tax-collecting, licensing, and registration responsibilities. For example, statistical data result from automobile registration by states.

State incorporation laws result in the accumulation of data. State incorporated banks and trust companies and building and loan associations, for example, are all regulated by the banking departments of the various states, and statistics regarding these institutions are regularly compiled and published by these departments. Similarly, life insurance, fire insurance, automobile and casualty insurance, and workmen's compensation laws and social-security laws have resulted in state-regulating bodies and the compilation and publication of statistical data on financial, commercial, and industrial subjects.

A number of the larger and older of the industrial states have highly efficient labor departments, which compile and publish statistics of industrial conditions. Of increasing importance and interest to social scientists is the development of the volume of statistics relating to industrial accidents and diseases, growing out of the need for such statistics in the administration of the workmen's compensation laws.

The regulation of public utilities and water companies and street-railway and bus companies by state and municipal authorities has made the public-utility commissions of the states the principal primary sources of statistical data on these important industries, although in the 1930's many of these data were gathered by the Federal Power Commission and the Security and Exchange Commission.

WORLD STATISTICS

Under the League of Nations progress has been made in the collection and publication of world statistics. These are published in the *Monthly Bulletin of Statistics* of the League of Nations and also in its *International Statistical Yearbook* and its annual *World Economic Survey*. Statistics on world commercial banking and finance were published in special League publications. Previous to the work of the League of Nations in this respect, the *World Almanac* had for many years been highly valued as a rough-and-ready source of a variety of world statistics and still constitutes a popular source.

The *Statesman's Yearbook*, published by Macmillan & Company, Ltd., London, is a statistical and historical annual of the states of the world, giving data on population, area, finance, commerce, and banking, as well as figures on the fleets of the world and the world's shipping. It has been issued annually since 1864. The United States government has always shown considerable interest in statistics of foreign countries and has published them along with the domestic data; but this practice has been far more systematic and thorough since the First World War. For example, the *Federal Reserve Bulletin* regularly publishes statistics of prices, banking, and currency conditions in the principal nations of the world; foreign price statistics are published by the Bureau of Labor Statistics in its special bulletins; and statistics on trade between other countries, that is, the trade of the world outside the United States and not with the United States, are published by the Department of Commerce in Vol. 2 of the *Commerce Yearbook* (as well as the statistics of our own foreign trade). In 1938 the Paris International Chamber of Commerce published a brochure on the economic statistics in 26 countries.

In addition to such collections of statistics for all or a majority of the countries of the world, mention should be made of the sources, in greater detail than the world volumes, for statistics concerning three of the important countries of Europe. For England and the Dominions, there is the *Statistical Abstract for the British Empire*, published by the Board of Trade. This combines what was previously published in the *Statistical Abstract for the United Kingdom* (first issued in 1864 for the years 1840–1853) and the *Statistical Abstract for the Several British Oversea Dominions and Protectorates* (first issued in 1864 for the years 1850–1863). The French government publishes *Annuaire statistique* (1878) and the *Bulletin de la statistique générale* (1911). In Germany the official source of statistics is the *Statistisches Jahrbuch für das deutsche Reich* (1880).

It has long been recognized that international statistics would be extremely important in obtaining true international, political, and economic understanding and cooperation. Consequently, for many decades, efforts have been made to arrive at some sort of international understanding on methods to make the compilation of international statistics feasible or at least to improve existing world statistics. The statistics of each country are gathered according to the needs of that country; and since the problems in respective countries differ, so do the statistics. Their compilation and classification, according to varying definitions of units and varying bases of classification, produce startling differences in the final results. Then, too, the economic organizations of the various countries are different. A country with a large amount of transit trade and heavy reexportation of goods imported needs a different sort of classification of foreign trade statistics than a country doing little reexport business. Furthermore, the statistics themselves are gathered and organized in diverse ways in the various countries; the methods of collecting the statistical raw materials, the periods for which these data are gathered, and the methods of classification are not the same in the various countries.

The endeavors made in the last eighty years for better international statistical information, therefore, were first concentrated on the problem of rendering national statistics more comparable, since national statistics must be comparable between the various nations before they can be added up or compared to obtain international or world statistics. Quételet, the Belgian who did so much to organize comparable international astronomical observations, was likewise the first to try to solve the problem of obtaining the fundamental basis for better world and international statistics. It is principally due to him that the First International Statistical Congress was organized in 1853 in Brussels. The main purpose of this Congress, the members of which attended in their private and not in their official capacity (although some were officials), was to bring about some degree of comparability in national statistics between the various nations.

Another attempt to obtain international cooperation in statistical work was made in 1887 when the International Statistical Institute was formed. This organization, still in existence, elects members who are active in statistical work as professors, government officials, or members of private statistical offices.

The Institute cannot bind its members or the national governments of its members but makes progress by suggesting improvements to different countries.

The first official or semiofficial attempts for better world
statistics were made in 1875 through the establishment of the
International Bureau of the Universal Postal Union and the
Bureau of the International Telecommunication Union (originally called the International Bureau of the Telegraph Union).
Both regularly gather statistics on postal and telegraphic developments. Similar efforts in another field were made for the first
time in 1882, by the International Congress for Hygiene and
Demography. In 1905, another significant official attempt was
made for greater comparability in world statistics. In that year,
at the suggestion of the United States government, a meeting
was held in Rome to formulate some plan for obtaining uniformity of agricultural statistics. This meeting led to the founding
of the International Agricultural Institute, which still is active
in the gathering of world statistics on agriculture, production,
consumption, prices, and trade. The statistical information
assembled by this body is published monthly and yearly and
special publications are also issued. Sixty-two different countries are members of the Institute. The Institute was very
successful in putting national agricultural statistics on an
internationally more comparable basis and in assembling regularly good and reliable world statistics on all fields of agriculture.

Since the First World War, the League of Nations has been
the natural organization to proceed with the work of interna-
tionalizing statistics. Shortly after its establishment, the League
started that work. At the International Economic Conference
of 1927 the problem of comparable national statistics in order to
secure good world statistics was studied. The League of Nations
subsequently brought about an official meeting on the subject
of international statistics and called an International Statistical
Conference to meet in Geneva in November, 1928. The keynote
of the Conference was that the general adoption of comparable
international statistics was desirable for good international
policies and in the interests of permanent world peace. The aim
of the Conference was to bring about the broadening of the scope
of national statistics in all countries where it seemed to be needed
and to attempt to make national statistics in different countries

comparable. The Conference emphasized once more that such attempts meet with many difficulties. Of the 42 countries represented (some nonmembers of the League, like the United States, were also represented), only 29 countries felt they could sign the Convention and Protocol of the Conference. To induce that number to sign, it was necessary to limit greatly the program of work.

Nevertheless, the Conference of 1928 did produce good results. A number of points were discussed, and important conclusions were reached. In addition, the Conference created a committee of technical experts to meet from time to time and make suggestions for further progress. This group met in March, 1931, and formulated a constitution for future work. It met again in December, 1933, to discuss problems of statistics on foreign trade. Up to the present time, its contribution to the solution of the problems involved has been inconsiderable, but it may make advances in this important work if the countries concerned will be willing to carry out the recommendations made by it, as they are apparently committed to do by the Convention and Protocol of the Conference of 1928.

In 1936 the twenty-third session of the International Institute of Statistics was held at Athens. At that session there were 75 members, of which 10 were from North America. Twenty-seven countries designated official delegates. Also, the Secretary of the League of Nations, the International Labor Office, the International Institute of Intellectual Cooperation, the International Institute of Agriculture, and the International Chamber of Commerce were represented.[1]

In May, 1940, one of the 11 sections of the Eighth American Scientific Congress convened by the government of the United States in connection with the observance of the fiftieth anniversary of the founding of the Pan American Union was devoted to statistics. The program of the section had the following broad objectives: (1) improvements in the comparability of official

---

[1] STUART, PROF. C. A. VERIJN, "La XXIIIème session de l'institut international de statistique, Athènes, 1936," *Revue de l'institut international de statistique*, vol. 4 (1936), pp. 367–403. The citation includes the summary of resolutions of the session (pp. 378–395) and communications from various delegations on methods, legislation, organization, and administration of statistics (pp. 396–403).

statistics among the American nations; (2) improvements in statistical methodology; (3) the furtherance of acquaintance among the statisticians of the American continent; (4) consideration by these statisticians of the possible development of a continuing professional medium for the interchange of statistical ideas and information. Correspondents in several of the American nations had pointed to the need for closer professional collaboration among the statisticians of this hemisphere, and it was proposed to explore at this meeting the possibilities of establishing some kind of an inter-American statistical organization of professional character. The result was the formation of the Inter-American Statistical Institute.

A new quarterly, the *Estadística*, published in Mexico, is the official organ of the Inter-American Statistical Institute, constituting one of its mediums for fostering statistical development in the Western Hemisphere. It endeavors to acquaint the persons in one country with statistical developments in other countries, to inform its readers concerning the availability of data, to present articles that will tend to encourage the adoption of improved methods, and hence to improve the quality of data. Articles may appear in any of the following four languages: Spanish, English, Portuguese, or French. An author's summary accompanies each article; the summary is reproduced in several languages. The Inter-American Statistical Institute also publishes a yearbook of statistics including statistical data for Latin-American countries and North America.

Prospects to secure comparable world statistics and for international statistics fluctuate with the rise and fall of isolationism and nationalism. Under the League of Nations and under the Pan American Union progress has been encouraged, only to be hampered by ever-persistent isolationism in one country or another. Nevertheless, the need for comparable data with respect to all nations of the world has become more and more evident, it has come to be more and more appreciated as the problems have been studied by these various institutes, conferences, and committees, and more and more is it coming to be realized that such statistics are a pressing necessity to businessmen with interests spread far and wide over the international field.

While it has been stressed in this section that there are as yet no truly comparable international statistics, the student of international affairs and the international businessman will be able to obtain what constitutes for the present the closest approximation to them from a number of sources, chief among them the following: (1) *International Statistical Yearbook* (published by the League of Nations); (2) Vol. 2 of the *Commerce Yearbook* (published by the United States Department of Commerce); (3) The International Appendix to the Statistics Yearbook of Germany (*Statistisches Jahrbuch für das deutsche Reich*); (4) the *Statesman's Yearbook*. The World Peace Foundation publishes also a subject index to the economic and financial documents of the League of Nations.

CHAPTER IV

PRESENTATION OF STATISTICS

TABLES

Principles of Tabulation. Tabulation is the mechanical part of classification. Its function is so to arrange the physical presentation of quantitative facts that there can be no misinterpretation of their significance. The attainment of this object depends upon the following principles:

1. Concise, clear, and complete titles attached to the table. Usually the title is placed at the top, above the table, but it is sometimes placed at the bottom. The function of the title is to give a general description of the contents of the table.

2. Careful, unambiguous description of the units of measurement or presentation used in the collection and recording of the data. This is ordinarily placed immediately under the title. Subheadings frequently require definition of units.

3. The arrangement of the data in columns and rows according to a clearly indicated basis for classification.

4. The exact description of columns and rows by the use of caption headings and stub headings.

5. Footnotes to clarify headings or subtitles or to specify limitations of particular figures.

The scheme shown on page 93 gives an abstraction of the mechanics of tabulation. It shows the position of the title and the description of units above the table and for illustration designates four columns, numbered (1), (2), (3), and (4), and three rows, lettered (x), (y), and (z).

The four columns are subcolumns—(1) and (2) are subcolumns of column (a), and (3) and (4) are subcolumns of column (b). The caption headings would appear in the spaces designated (a) and (b), respectively; and subcaption headings would appear in the spaces designated (1), (2), (3), and (4). Similarly, the three rows are described by stub headings appearing in (x), (y), and (z). The space (D) is for the general description of the stub

headings. It is possible also to have stub subheadings. In
order to illustrate further, there is reproduced in Table 1 on
page 94 data compiled from the replies to the questionnaire
shown on pages 46–47.

Title
(Description of units)

(D)	(a)		(b)	
	(1)	(2)	(3)	(4)
(x)				
(y)				
(z)				

General-purpose and Special-purpose Tables. A mere glance
at the specimen taken from the publication of the United States
Department of Agriculture is sufficient to lead to the conviction
that such tables are not meant for light reading. They are
essentially *reference tables,* or *general-purpose tables.* The principal guide in the construction of general-purpose tables is to
include as much as possible in as small a space as possible, consistent with presentation of the amount of information deemed
necessary. Thus the tables contained in such publications as
the United States Census reports or the *Federal Reserve Bulletin*
or the *Survey of Current Business* may not constitute popular
reading; but they are a great boon to all who seek ready access
to details, arranged in a manner so facilitating their discovery
by the careful observer that looking up a particular figure is
almost as easy as looking up a word in the dictionary.

When a table is to be read—is to tell a story—it is called a
special-purpose table. Such a table should have as its outstanding characteristic the quality of simplicity. It should not
try to tell too much at once; if necessary, more than one table
may be used for telling a more complex story. Special-purpose
tables should have a great deal of white space in and around
them to make lazy readers (and most people are lazy when it
comes to reading tables of figures) think them easy to read.
The type or print should be sufficiently large for easy reading.
The reader should be adequately prepared or oriented to the

TABLE 1.—Sources of Family Income: Number of Families Receiving Income from Specified Sources, Number Having Business Losses, Average Amount of Income Derived from Specified Sources, and Average Amount of Business Losses, by Income, Pacific Small Cities Combined, 1935–1936

(White nonrelief families that include a husband and wife, both native-born)

Family income class	Families	Money income from			Business losses	Nonmoney income from			Total family income (net)	Money income from				Nonmoney income from		
		Any source	Earnings	Other sources		Any source	Owned home (net)	Rent as pay		All sources	Earnings	Other sources	Business losses	All sources	Owned home (net)	Rent as pay
(1)	(2) Number	(3) Number	(4) Number	(5) Number	(6) Number	(7) Number	(8) Number	(9) Number	(10) Dollars	(11) Dollars	(12) Dollars	(13) Dollars	(14) Dollars	(15) Dollars	(16) Dollars	(17) Dollars
All incomes	2,711	2,705	2,654	721	58	1,238	1,199	41	1,876	1,784	1,699	88	3	92	89	3
0–249	20	14	12	4	1	8	7	1	158	120	112	18	10	38	38	3
250–499	48	48	40	21	1	24	21	3	391	328	266	63	1	63	54	9
500–749	128	128	114	42	3	54	49	5	625	569	482	89	2	56	51	5
750–999	225	225	214	56	2	72	70	2	878	830	766	65	1	48	47	1
1,000–1,249	374	374	371	71	9	114	103	12	1,135	1,091	1,061	34	4	44	37	7
1,250–1,499	324	324	320	74	3	137	133	4	1,363	1,300	1,253	47		63	60	3
1,500–1,749	350	350	347	89	8	151	148	3	1,612	1,539	1,486	55	2	73	71	2
1,750–1,999	307	307	306	83	8	133	128	6	1,855	1,776	1,721	57	2	79	75	4
2,000–2,249	248	248	248	56	5	120	117	3	2,114	2,013	1,962	53	2	101	99	2
2,250–2,499	181	181	180	54	0	98	98	0	2,372	2,251	2,160	91	0	121	121	0
2,500–2,999	190	190	188	53	5	118	118	0	2,703	2,553	2,463	93	3	150	150	0
3,000–3,499	129	129	129	49	3	77	76	1	3,198	3,040	2,882	162	4	158	155	3
3,500–3,999	71	71	71	26	1	46	45	0	3,716	3,540	3,389	153	2	176	175	1
4,000 and over	116	116	114	43	8	86	86	0	5,539	5,268	4,722	570	24	271	271	0

Source: Bureau of Home Economics, United States Department of Agriculture, "Consumers' Purchases Study," Family Income and Expenditure, Pacific Region, Part I, Family Income, Miscellaneous Publication 339, p. 22.

table by the text accompanying it and particularly by the title
of the table. Briefly, the story of the table should be told in
literary form in the text, reliance being placed on the table

TABLE 2.—AVERAGE DISBURSEMENTS OF CONSUMER UNITS[1] IN EACH THIRD
OF NATION, 1935–1936

Category of disbursement	Average disbursements of families and single individuals in			Percentage of income		
	Lower third, incomes under $780	Middle third, incomes of $780–$1,450	Upper third, incomes of $1,450 and over	Lower third	Middle third	Upper third
Current consumption:						
Food.....................	$236	$ 404	$ 642	50.2	37.5	21.7
Housing..................	115	199	408	24.4	18.5	13.8
Household operation.......	54	108	240	11.4	10.0	8.1
Clothing.................	47	102	251	10.0	9.5	8.5
Automobile...............	16	57	215	3.3	5.3	7.2
Medical care.............	20	41	106	4.3	3.9	3.6
Recreation...............	9	28	89	1.8	2.6	3.0
Furnishings..............	9	28	72	1.8	2.6	2.4
Personal care............	12	22	44	2.5	2.1	1.5
Tobacco..................	10	23	40	2.2	2.1	1.4
Transportation other than auto....................	11	19	37	2.4	1.7	1.3
Reading..................	6	12	23	1.3	1.2	0.8
Education................	2	7	30	0.5	0.6	1.0
Other items..............	3	6	15	0.6	0.5	0.5
All consumption items....	$550	$1,056	$2,212	116.7	98.1	74.8
Gifts and personal taxes[2]......	$ 13	$ 39	$ 181	2.8	3.7	6.1
Savings..................	−92	−19	566	−19.5	−1.8	19.1
All items................	$471	$1,076	$2,959	100.0	100.0	100.0

[1] Includes all families and single individuals, but excludes residents in institutional groups.
[2] Taxes shown here include only personal income taxes, poll taxes, and certain personal property taxes.
Source: National Resources Committee, *Consumer Expenditures in the United States, Estimates for* 1935–36 (1939), p. 40.

merely as a dramatic summary. Simple devices to aid interpretation and facilitate the mental vision of the table have a
useful place in special-purpose tables, such as accompanying
relative figures, methods of emphasis such as italics, or the
scheme of ruling the table.

The object of a special-purpose table may also be to compress into a small space a body of information "the narration of which in the text would be cumbersome and exhausting to the reader.

TABLE 3.—SHARE OF EACH THIRD OF NATION'S CONSUMER UNITS[1] IN AGGREGATE DISBURSEMENTS, 1935–1936

Category of disbursement	Aggregate disbursements, millions			Percentage of aggregate disbursement for each category made by		
	Lower third, incomes under $780	Middle third, incomes of $780–$1,450	Upper third, incomes of $1,450 and over	Lower third	Middle third	Upper third
Current consumption:						
Food.................	$3,108	$ 5,310	$ 8,447	18.4	31.5	50.1
Housing..............	1,515	2,621	5,370	15.9	27.6	56.5
Household operation....	703	1,422	3,160	13.3	26.9	59.8
Clothing..............	618	1,338	3,305	11.7	25.5	62.8
Automobile...........	203	755	2,823	5.4	20.0	74.6
Medical care..........	264	546	1,395	12.0	24.7	63.3
Recreation............	115	362	1,166	7.0	22.0	71.0
Furnishings...........	112	368	942	7.9	25.9	66.2
Personal care.........	155	292	585	15.1	28.2	56.7
Tobacco..............	134	301	531	13.8	31.2	55.0
Transportation other than auto............	150	247	487	17.0	27.9	55.1
Reading..............	84	165	302	15.3	29.9	54.8
Education.............	30	87	389	5.9	17.2	76.9
Other items...........	35	76	196	11.4	24.6	64.0
All consumption items.	$7,226	$13,890	$29,098	14.4	27.7	57.9
Gifts and personal taxes[2]...	$ 171	$ 516	$ 2,380	5.6	16.8	77.6
Savings...............	−1,207	−252	7,437	−20.2	−4.2	124.4
All items.............	$6,190	$14,154	$38,915	10.4	23.9	65.7

[1] Includes all families and single individuals, but excludes residents in institutional groups.
[2] Taxes shown here include only personal income taxes, poll taxes, and certain personal property taxes.

Source: National Resources Committee, *Consumer Expenditures in the United States, Estimates for* 1935–36 (1939), p. 51.

It is, in short, a method of condensation, and it is of the utmost importance that, as it tells so much in so small a compass, it tell it as clearly as practicable."[1]

[1] FALKNER, ROLAND P., "Statistical Tabulation and Practice," *Journal of the American Statistical Association,* vol. 11 (1916), pp. 192–200.

Tables 2 to 6 are examples of special-purpose tables. They tell stories that are more or less hidden in the detailed but well-

TABLE 4.—PERCENTAGE DISTRIBUTIONS OF NONRELIEF FAMILIES[1] IN SIX TYPES OF COMMUNITY, BY INCOME LEVEL, 1935–1936

| | | Families living in | | | | | |
| | | Urban communities | | | | Rural communities | |
Income level	All families	Metropolises,[2] 1,500,000 population and over	Large cities, 100,000–1,500,000 population	Middle-sized cities, 25,000–100,000 population	Small cities, 2,500–25,000 population	Non-farm[3]	Farm
Under $250....	2.8	1.7	2.0	2.4	3.1	3.0	3.8
$250–$500.....	7.8	2.8	4.4	5.5	6.3	8.9	13.9
$500–$750.....	11.3	5.2	7.6	9.4	10.3	11.8	18.0
$750–$1,000...	13.4	8.5	10.5	13.6	13.9	14.4	16.6
$1,000–$1,250..	13.2	10.9	12.4	13.9	14.6	14.0	12.8
$1,250–$1,500..	10.8	11.0	10.6	11.6	11.1	11.6	9.8
$1,500–$1,750..	9.1	10.8	10.0	9.7	9.4	9.1	7.0
$1,750–$2,000..	7.3	9.7	9.0	8.5	7.8	6.5	4.8
$2,000–$2,250..	5.5	7.9	6.9	6.1	5.8	5.1	3.1
$2,250–$2,500..	4.0	5.8	5.5	4.5	4.0	3.4	2.5
$2,500–$3,000..	5.2	8.5	7.1	5.4	5.3	4.4	2.9
$3,000–$3,500..	3.0	4.7	4.2	3.1	3.1	2.3	1.6
$3,500–$4,000..	1.8	2.9	2.7	1.7	1.7	1.3	1.0
$4,000–$4,500..	1.0	1.7	1.6	1.0	0.8	0.8	0.5
$4,500–$5,000..	0.6	0.9	0.9	0.7	0.5	0.6	0.3
$5,000–$7,500..	1.3	2.1	1.8	1.3	1.1	1.4	0.6
$7,500–$10,000	0.8	1.6	1.1	0.6	0.6	0.6	0.4
$10,000 and over......	1.1	3.3	1.7	1.0	0.6	0.8	0.4
All levels....	100.0	100.0	100.0	100.0	100.0	100.0	100.0

[1] Excludes all families receiving any direct or work relief (however little) at any time during year.

[2] Metropolises of this size are in North Central Region only (New York, Chicago, Philadelphia, and Detroit).

[3] Includes families living in communities with population under 2,500, and families living in the open country but not on farms.

Source: National Resources Committee, *Consumer Incomes in the United States, Their Distribution in 1935–36* (1938), pp. 24–25.

organized statistics collected by means of the questionnaire referred to above. In order to simplify the data for presentation,

TABLE 5.—AVERAGE OUTLAY OF AMERICAN FAMILIES FOR CONSUMPTION, GIFTS AND PERSONAL TAXES, AND SAVINGS, BY INCOME LEVEL, 1935–1936

Income level	Families		Average income per family, dollars	Average outlay per family, for			Percentage of income for		
	Number	Per cent		Current consumption	Gifts and personal taxes[1]	Savings	Current consumption	Gifts and personal taxes[1]	Savings
Under $500	4,178,284	14.2	$ 312	$ 466	$ 8	$ −162	149.3	2.6	−51.9
$500–$700	3,799,215	12.9	627	707	12	−92	112.7	1.9	−14.6
$750–$1,000	4,277,048	14.6	874	914	18	−58	104.6	2.0	−6.6
$1,000–$1,250	3,882,444	13.2	1,120	1,127	24	−31	100.6	2.2	−2.8
$1,250–$1,500	2,865,472	9.8	1,364	1,316	34	14	96.5	2.5	1.0
$1,500–$1,750	2,343,358	8.0	1,612	1,512	44	56	93.8	2.7	3.5
$1,750–$2,000	1,897,037	6.4	1,829	1,684	53	92	92.1	2.9	5.0
$2,000–$2,500	2,464,860	8.4	2,221	1,968	71	182	88.6	3.2	8.2
$2,500–$3,000	1,314,199	4.5	2,715	2,302	98	315	84.8	3.6	11.6
$3,000–$4,000	1,181,987	4.0	3,394	2,729	136	529	80.4	4.0	15.6
$4,000–$5,000	402,595	1.4	4,391	3,276	211	904	74.6	4.8	20.6
$5,000–$10,000	510,010	1.7	6,874	4,454	392	2,028	64.8	5.7	29.5
$10,000–$15,000	131,821	0.4	11,353	6,097	840	4,416	53.7	7.4	38.9
$15,000–$20,000	58,487	0.2	17,331	9,134	1,282	6,915	52.7	7.4	39.9
$20,000 and over	93,483	0.3	41,871	14,822	5,820	21,229	35.4	13.9	50.7
All levels	29,400,300	100.0	$1,622	$1,389	$ 69	$ 164	85.6	4.3	10.1

[1] Taxes shown here include only personal income taxes, poll taxes, and certain personal property taxes.
Source: National Resources Committee, Consumer Expenditures in the United States, Estimates for 1935–36 (1939), p. 20.

TABLE 6.—AVERAGE EXPENDITURES OF AMERICAN FAMILIES FOR MAIN CATEGORIES OF CONSUMPTION, BY INCOME LEVEL, 1935–1936

Income level	Average expenditure per family for														
	All items	Food	Housing	Household operation	Clothing	Automobile	Medical care	Recreation	Furnishings	Personal care	Tobacco	Transportation other than automobile	Reading	Education	Other items
Under $500	$466	$203	$90	$57	$35	$15	$22	$6	$9	$9	$9	$3	$4	$2	$2
$500–$750	707	310	125	85	56	28	29	11	16	14	14	5	6	3	5
$750–$1,000	914	380	161	106	78	44	38	17	27	18	19	9	9	4	4
$1,000–$1,250	1,127	433	203	130	100	70	47	25	38	24	22	11	11	7	6
$1,250–$1,500	1,316	487	230	149	123	93	57	31	48	27	27	14	14	9	7
$1,500–$1,750	1,512	527	267	166	147	123	71	42	56	32	29	16	15	11	10
$1,750–$2,000	1,684	558	302	186	164	154	79	49	68	35	33	18	16	15	7
$2,000–$2,500	1,968	617	349	213	207	200	91	62	76	42	38	22	20	20	11
$2,500–$3,000	2,302	690	404	260	255	242	109	81	84	49	41	24	22	30	11
$3,000–$4,000	2,729	770	485	319	316	289	132	105	102	54	48	31	27	37	14
$4,000–$5,000	3,276	852	571	400	408	382	158	136	110	66	53	35	31	57	17
$5,000–$10,000	4,454	1,038	784	584	557	522	248	206	158	89	62	48	41	83	34
$10,000–$15,000	6,097	1,214	1,204	761	829	681	227	340	227	114	79	114	57	227	23
$15,000–$20,000	9,134	1,785	1,490	1,179	1,265	919	416	486	277	156	104	399	69	537	52
$20,000 and over	14,822	2,261	2,721	2,177	2,177	1,759	837	921	461	251	126	419	126	502	84
All levels	$1,389	$467	$248	$162	$141	$114	$64	$41	$47	$28	$26	$16	$13	$15	$7

Source: National Resources Committee, *Consumer Expenditures in the United States, Estimates for 1935–36* (1939), p. 23.

income levels are divided into three groups, lower third, middle third, and upper third. These tables illustrate also the use of percentage figures to facilitate their interpretation.

CHARTS

Quick visualization of many rather complex situations can be readily achieved by merely looking at a simple chart. It is said that nowadays the first step toward using a series of data for any sort of analysis is to represent the figures by a line drawn on a chart. So useful is the chart in giving a quick grasp of the

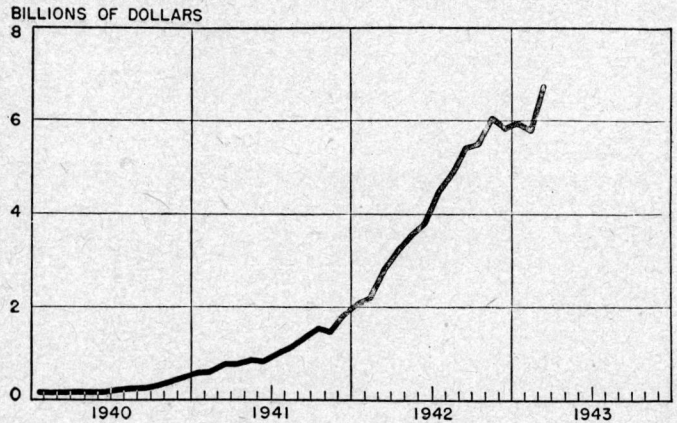

Fig. 11.—Federal expenditures for war activities. (*From data published in Daily Statement of the United States Treasury Department.*)

characteristics of data that it has been adopted in many popular books, in magazines, and in the financial section of metropolitan newspapers. Figures 11 and 12 illustrate dramatically the manner in which charts are used to aid in visualizing important developments during wartime. In peacetime the trends of data, even though less sensational, are watched with care, and charts greatly facilitate their analysis.

The invention in 1786 of charting is claimed by William Playfair, who set forth its advantages as follows:[1] "As the eye is the

[1] *The Commercial and Political Atlas* (3d ed., London, 1801), p. x. Playfair's claim to be "actually the first who applied the principles of geometry to matters of Finance" is made on pages *viii* and *ix*. Cited from W. C. Mitchell, *Business Cycles—The Problem and Its Setting,* p. 209. In *An Enquiry into the Decline and Fall of Nations* Playfair is said to have been the first to employ graphical devices in the treatment of sociological discussion.

best judge of proportion, being able to estimate it with more quickness and accuracy than any other of our organs, it follows, that wherever relative quantities are in question, a gradual increase or decrease of any . . . value is to be stated, this mode of representing it is peculiarly applicable; it gives a simple, accurate, and permanent idea, by giving form and shape to a number of separate ideas, which are otherwise abstract and unconnected."

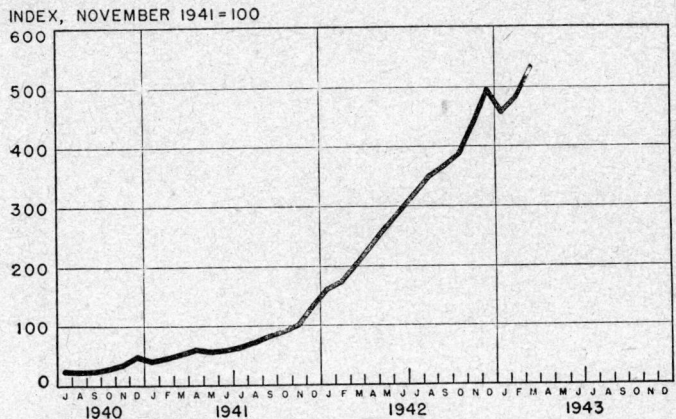

INDEX, NOVEMBER 1941=100

Fɪɢ. 12.—Production of munitions, including ships, planes, tanks, guns, ammunition, and all field equipment.   (*Data from War Production Board.*)

While the idea underlying the use of charts is quite old, the general use of charts for wide public consumption is of much more recent origin and probably owes its present-day popularity to inventions having to do with the plating of charts for printing. From being largely a hand-labor process, the making of plates for the reproduction of charts has come in recent years to be a photoelectric process, with the result that today the most expensive part of the charts in a book, newspaper, or magazine article consists in the mental and hand labor involved in the original construction of the chart.

There are five kinds of charts: (1) pictograms, (2) cartograms, (3) frequency curves, (4) bivariate charts, and (5) curves picturing time series.

"William Playfair was, one may say, the Sir William Petty of the Edinburgh group . . . ."   Lancelot T. Hogben, *Dangerous Thoughts* (1939), p. 283.

Pictograms. There are four kinds of pictograms: (1) linear pictograms, in which the comparison is a linear one; (2) areal pictograms, in which the comparison is one of areas; (3) cubic pictograms, in which the comparison is one of cubes, or three-dimensional objects; and (4) sectors and circles, in which a circle is used to represent a whole and its various sectors are parts of the whole.

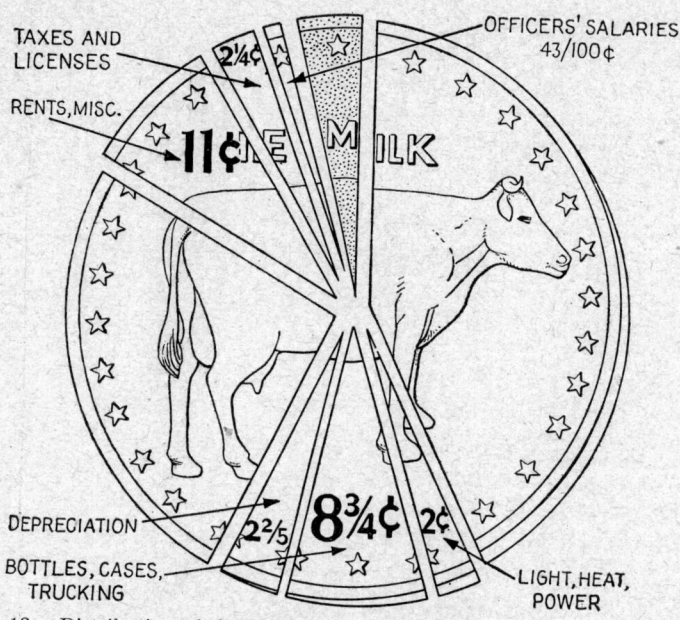

Fig. 13.—Distribution of the milk dollar. (*Data from The Milk Dollar, Milk Industry Foundation.*)

The purpose of pictograms is to aid in rapid visualizing of coordinate comparisons of magnitudes. For example, a pictogram might represent by a picture of a man the population of the United States, accompanied by a picture of proportionately smaller men representing, respectively, the populations of France and Germany. Sometimes pictograms are used to aid in visualizing the proportional parts of a whole magnitude, or comparison of component parts, as where a dollar is shown divided into sectors, representing the way in which the "public dollar" is spent. Figure 13 is an illustration of a pictogram showing the "milk dollar." The small obscured piece at the top represents 2.98 cents of profit for the New York City distributors.

Areal and cubic comparisons are not frequently used because, instead of simplifying the comparison desired, they are likely

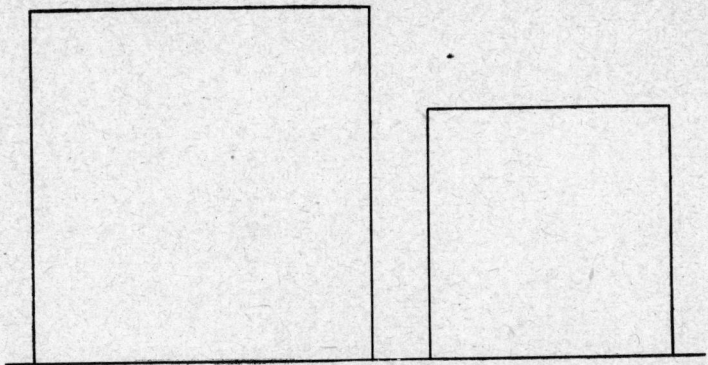

Fig. 14.—Area comparison.

to confuse it. This is because the mind finds difficulty in quickly differentiating sizes of areas or of cubes. Figure 14 shows two areas in the form of squares. One of these areas is actually one-half as large as the other; but, at first glance, it seems to be more than half as large. Consequently, if com-

Fig. 15.—Cubic comparison.

parison of two quantities is desired by charting, areal presentation is not a desirable method of obtaining easy comprehension of the differences that it is desired to stress.

The difficulty is increased if the attempt is made to chart differences of magnitude by the use of cubes, for it is still more difficult for the eye and mind to grasp geometric comparative magnitudes in three dimensions. This is shown in Fig. 15, which depicts two cubes, one of which is one-half as large as the other, though a first glance makes it appear to be two-thirds as large. For this reason the use of pictures for making comparisons is not considered to be the best practice. For example, the presentation for quick visualization of different-sized men in uniform to represent the relative fighting strength of various countries or of different-sized battleships to represent the relative size of navies will confuse the interpretation that the eye and mind will give to the relative sizes compared, even though the relative size is given purely a linear setting in the actual drawing of the figures.[1] Only the height of the uniformed men may be varied, but this might lead to comically proportioned men and an illusion of armies of tall thin men vs. armies of short fat men. If the uniformed men are properly proportioned for their varying heights, this results in an areal comparison.

Consequently, the most generally used types of pictogram are those involving merely linear comparisons and the use of purely abstract linear distances. Rows of soldiers, each soldier representing a specified number of men, may be used to advantage, however, the longer row representing the larger army. Similarly, large and small navies can properly be compared by rows of ships, each ship representing a specified tonnage of that type of warship. Such pictograms are really linear comparisons as also are bar charts and sectors of circles.

Bar Charts and Sectors of Circles. The use of bar charts and sectors of circles is widely practiced and finds its application whenever it is desired to compare two or more differing magnitudes with each other or to give quick visualization of component parts of a given magnitude. Extensive use of vertical or horizontal bars is made by the United States Bureau of the Census in the *Statistical Atlas of the United States*, one of which was issued in 1914 and another in 1924. In addition, many modern writings, especially in the fields of the social sciences, attempt to portray by charts the statistics it is desired to present for popular reading.

---

[1] *Cf.* CROXTON, F. E., and HAROLD STEIN, "Graphic Comparisons by Bars, Squares, Circles and Cubes," *Journal of the American Statistical Association*, Vol. 27 (1932), pp. 54–60.

Figure 16 is a graphic portrayal of the budget expenditures of the Federal government, based upon legislation in effect in February, 1943, in which the blacked-out portion of the vertical bars reveals in a striking manner the expected increases from year to year in expenditures for war activities.

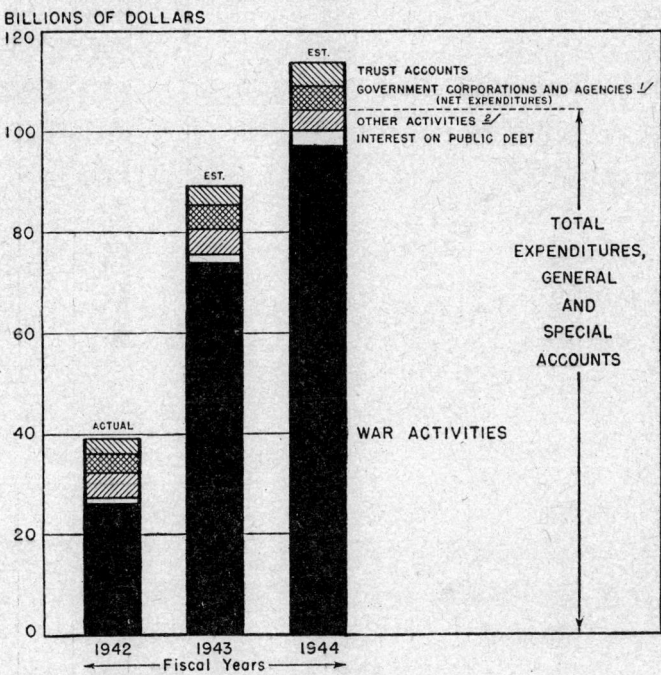

¹ Transactions in checking accounts.
² Includes statutory public debt retirement.

FIG. 16.—Budget expenditures of the Federal government, based upon legislation as of February, 1943. (*The Budget of the United States Government.*)

The use of horizontal bars is illustrated in Fig. 17, which shows graphically the statistical data in Table 4. The differences between distribution of income among nonrelief families in metropolitan areas as compared with that among families on farms is seen at a glance, and a slight scrutiny of the bars brings out the less dramatic but clear differences in the distribution of income in small cities compared with that in the larger ones.

Another government publication contains data, shown in Table 6, from which charts were drawn that illustrate the use

of the component-part bar chart. The data that appear in
these tables are shown in component bars in Fig. 18, where
the length of the bar is varied in accordance with the income

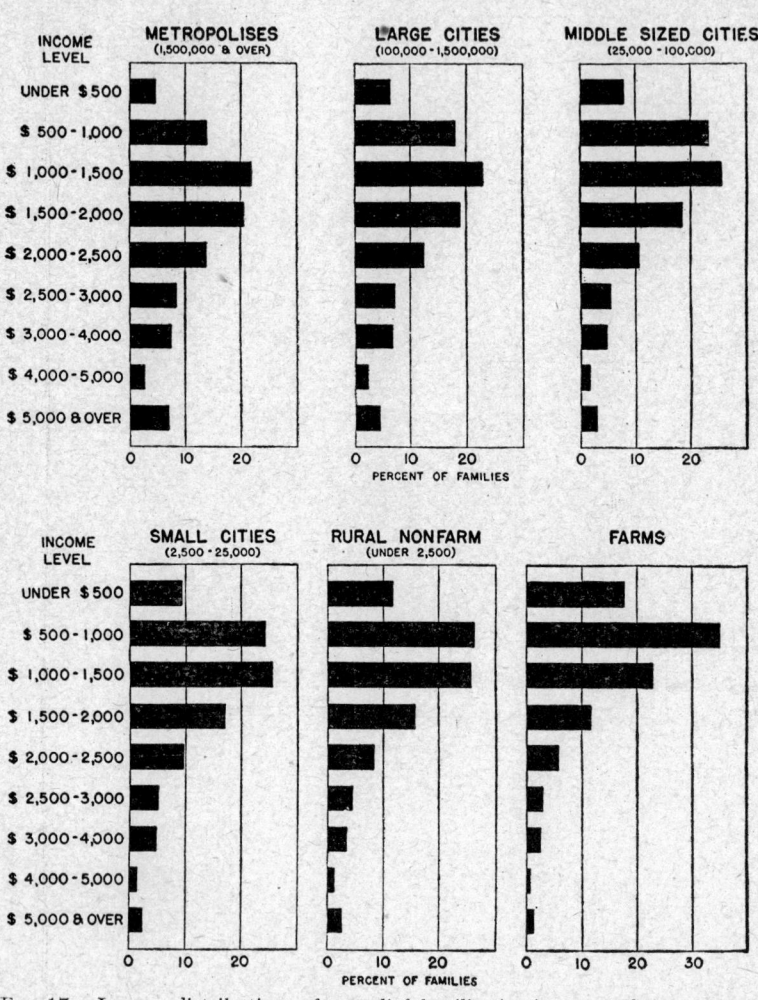

FIG. 17.—Income distributions of nonrelief families in six types of community,
1935–1936. (Based on Table 4.)

level. This makes possible the visual comparison of the average
total family expenditure at various income levels. For example
at the income level of $2,000 to $2,500 the aggregate family
expenditure averages a little over $2,000. At the same time,

the amount spent for various purposes can be seen from the differently crosshatched parts of each bar. Throughout the bars one kind of crosshatching represents a specified kind of

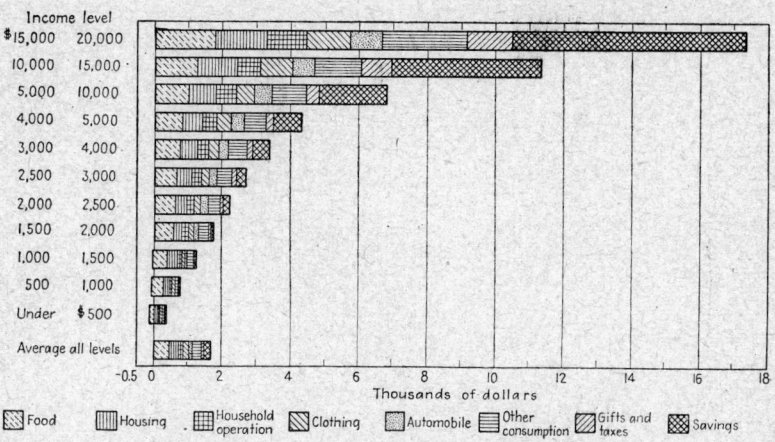

FIG. 18.—Use of income by American families at different income levels, illustrating the use of bar diagrams. (Based on Table 6.)

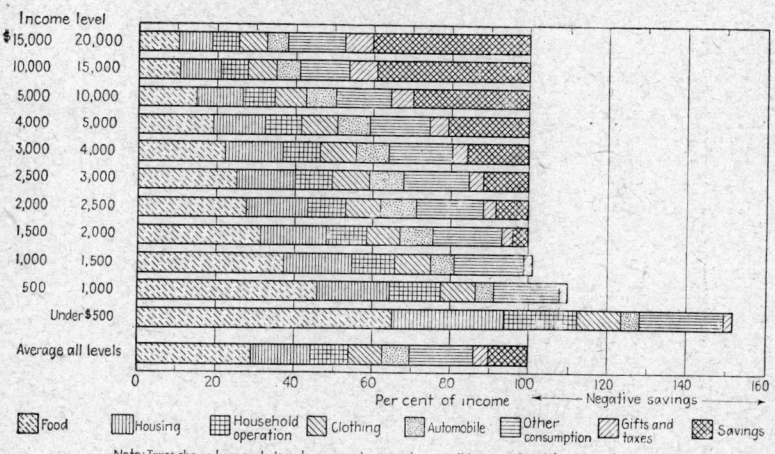

FIG. 19.—Percentage use of income by American families at different income levels, 1935–1936, illustrating the use of 100 per cent bar diagrams. (Based on Table 6.)

expenditure. The second desirable comparison is still more quickly grasped by the use of 100 per cent component part bars, which is illustrated in Fig. 19. When such a chart is drawn, it is always advisable to warn readers that 100 per cent bar charts are being used; in addition, the table of actual figures should be given for the actual figures are completely concealed in the relative figures if only the chart is given. It will be noticed that clever arrangement of crosshatching, placing contrasting types adjacent to each other, aids greatly in the reading of the chart. Figures 20 and 21 are interesting uses of the bar

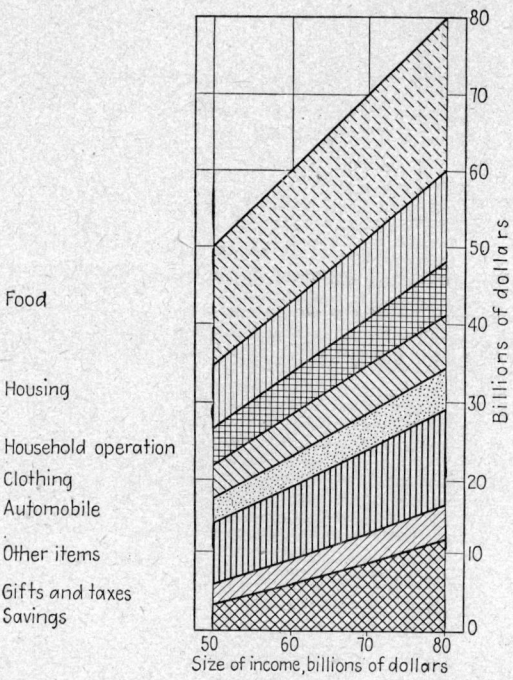

Fig. 20.—Variation in expenditures with income, illustrating the use of a cross-hatched zone diagram. [*National Resources Committee, Consumer Expenditures in the United States, Estimates* 1935–1936 (1939), *pp.* 165–166.]

chart, virtually in the form of zones, to show the distribution of the consumer food dollar on the assumption of four different total national income levels. The same data are shown in Fig. 21 in the form of a 100 per cent bar or zone chart. The use of the zone effect has the advantage of aiding the eye to make the principal indicated comparisons.

There are many examples of the use of sectors of circles in the *Statistical Atlas of the United States*, census of 1920, and a number in the publications of the census of 1930. Figure 22 is an example of a single circle divided into sectors representing component parts in the utilization of milk in the United States in 1929. As in the case of the component bar charts, so also in the case of sectors of a circle, it is possible to represent changes

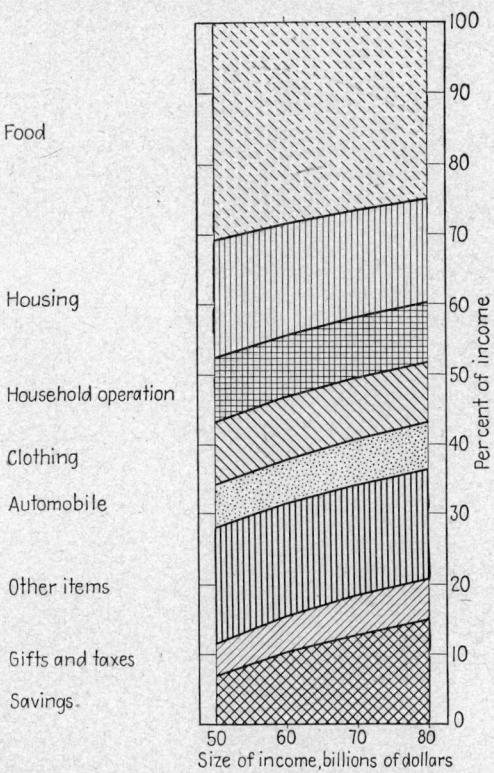

Fig. 21.—Variation in percentages of various expenditures with income, illustrating the use of a 100 per cent crosshatched zone diagram. [*National Resources Committee, Consumer Expenditures in the United States, Estimates 1935–1936* (1939), *pp.* 165–166.]

from time to time in percentage components by the use of a series of circles. It is not advisable to use the sectors and circles as bars were used in Fig. 21, namely, to picture relative change and total change simultaneously. To do this with sectors and circles involves areal comparisons that are not grasped by the readers of the charts. In Fig. 23, which is presented to illustrate the use of sectors and circles, the attempt

has been made to show also such an areal comparison.   While
most people would see at a glance that the circle for the End of
1938 is smaller than the circle for the End of 1930, presumably
to indicate that the total United States long-term investments
in foreign countries was smaller in 1938 than in 1930, few could
see from the areal comparison of the circles how much smaller.

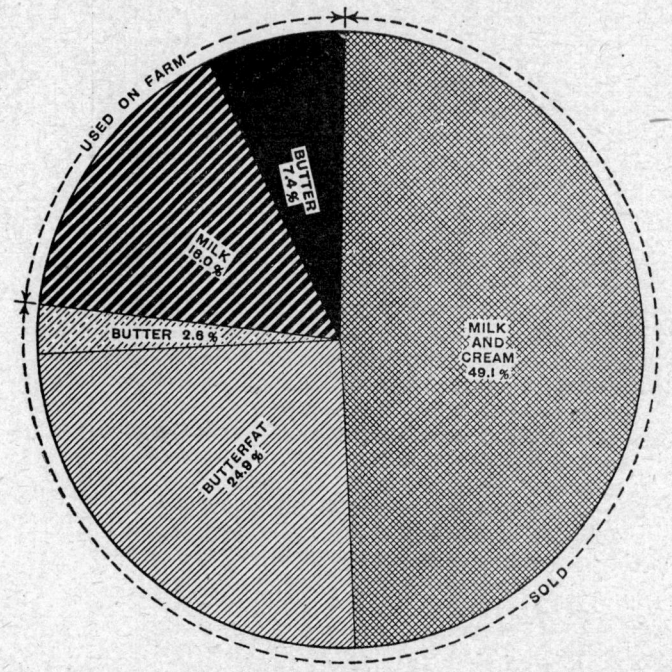

Fɪɢ. 22.—Utilization of milk in the United States, 1929, illustrating the use
of sectors of circles.   Based on value.   (*Fifteenth Census of the United States,
1930, Vol. 4, Agriculture.*)

Perhaps it is sufficient to have the smaller 1938 circle call attention to the fact and then assume that the reader will be led
thereby to note the figures, which are shown in a separate table.
But the figure shown in each sector of the circles is a component
percentage and does not throw light on aggregate amount.

For the purpose of showing graphically the component parts
of a total, the split-bar chart is a promising new device.   Figure
24 illustrates its use to show the distribution of the consumer
food dollar.   Comparison between consumer dollars of varying

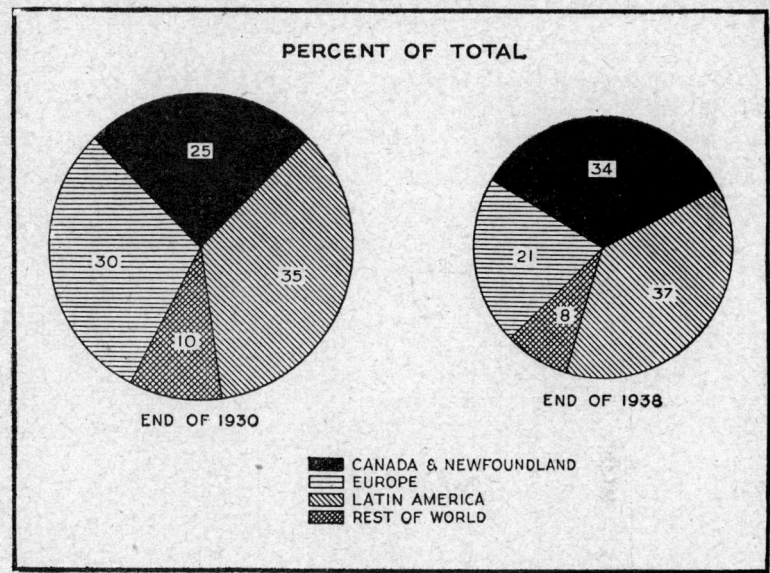

FIG. 23.—The United States' long-term investments in foreign countries, end of 1930 and end of 1938, illustrating use of circles of different sizes. (*Bureau of Foreign and Domestic Committee, " The Balance of International Payments of the United States in 1938," p.* 49.)

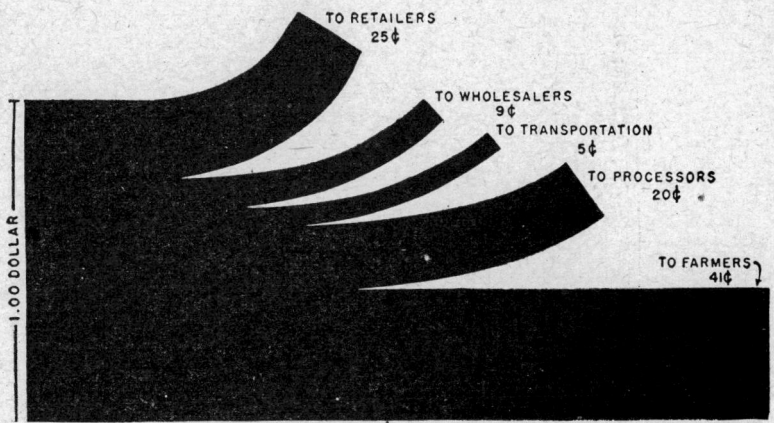

FIG. 24.—Distribution of consumer food dollar, 1935, illustrating use of a split-bar chart. [*National Resources Committee, The Structure of the American Economy, Part* I, (1939), *p.* 68.]

purchasing power could be shown by differences in the over-all lengths of the bars used.

Simple bar charts and sectors of circles, it will be noted, do not involve areal comparisons to depict component parts; the bars and sectors are areas, it is true, but it is not the areas that are compared. The comparisons are between the varying lengths of the bars, because the bars are of uniform width. Bars of varying widths would complicate the comparisons and make them areal. Moreover, sectors of circles do not involve areal comparisons, because the comparisons visualized are the arcs cut on the circle by the angles from the center of the circle. The visual comparison is therefore a linear one. Everyone is used to estimating the size of a piece of pie.

Cartograms. As the name indicates, cartograms are maps. Generally, outline maps are used and various devices employed to picture varying characteristics of different parts of the country. All are familiar with the colored maps that show the mountainous sections in brown shaded off to the green of the lowlands, the light brown in between being the higher plateaus, but not mountains. The same principle is used in a variety of ways to present statistics regarding geographically classified characteristics of the country by the use of maps. These will be classified and briefly described and illustrated.

Cartograms by Dots, or Points. Dots varying in size for different quantities are used in the first class of cartogram of this type. Because of the necessity of making areal comparisons, that is, of using different-sized circles, this type of cartogram is not widely employed and is considered not a good method of presenting subjects in cartogram form. An example in Fig. 25, however, shows clearly the areas of geographical concentration in 1935 of wage earners in manufacturing industries of the United States. An attempt is made to facilitate the areal comparisons involved in this cartogram by supplying a key, in the lower right corner of the map.

In the second kind of cartogram of this type dots of uniform size are used, each dot indicating an aggregate specified. When dots of this sort are used, they can be counted to figure out the total. Sometimes a dot is quarter or half shaded to indicate a quarter or half the amount of a full dot. When thus used, the

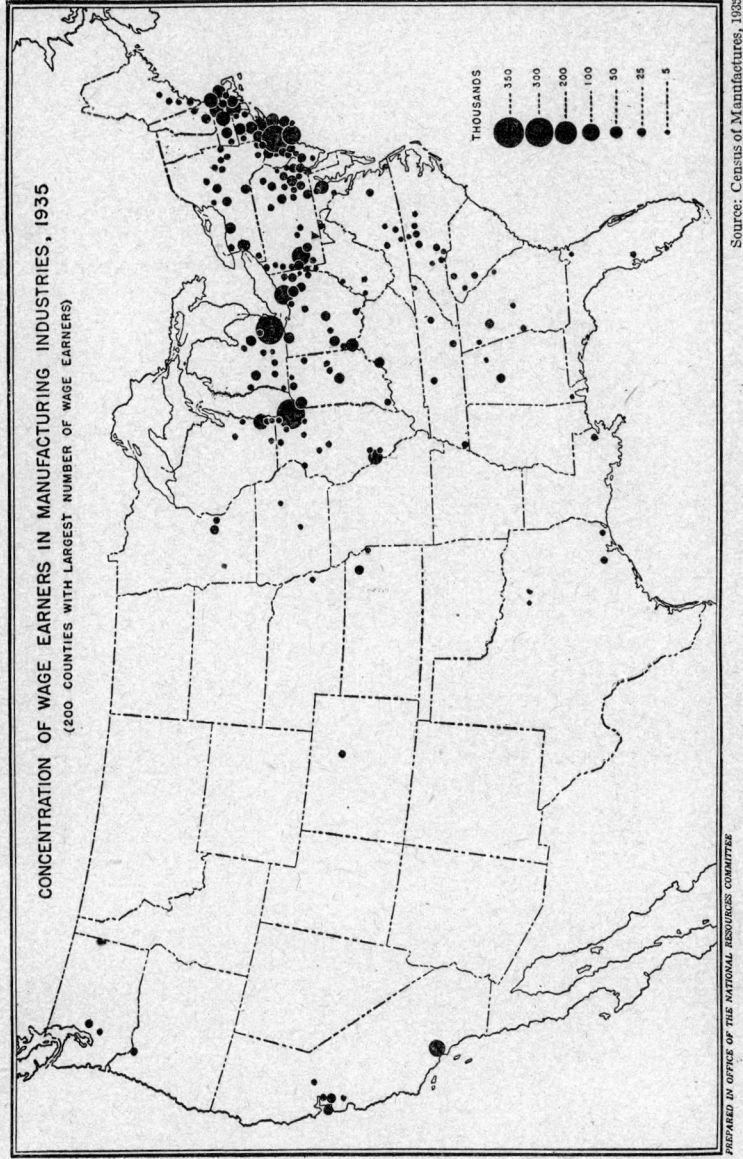

CONCENTRATION OF WAGE EARNERS IN MANUFACTURING INDUSTRIES, 1935
(200 COUNTIES WITH LARGEST NUMBER OF WAGE EARNERS)

PREPARED IN OFFICE OF THE NATIONAL RESOURCES COMMITTEE

Source: Census of Manufactures, 1935.

FIG. 25.—Illustrating the use of dots of varying sizes to show the concentration of wage earners in manufacturing industries, 1935. *(Reproduced from National Resources Committee, The Structure of the American Economy, Part I, (1939), p. 37.)*

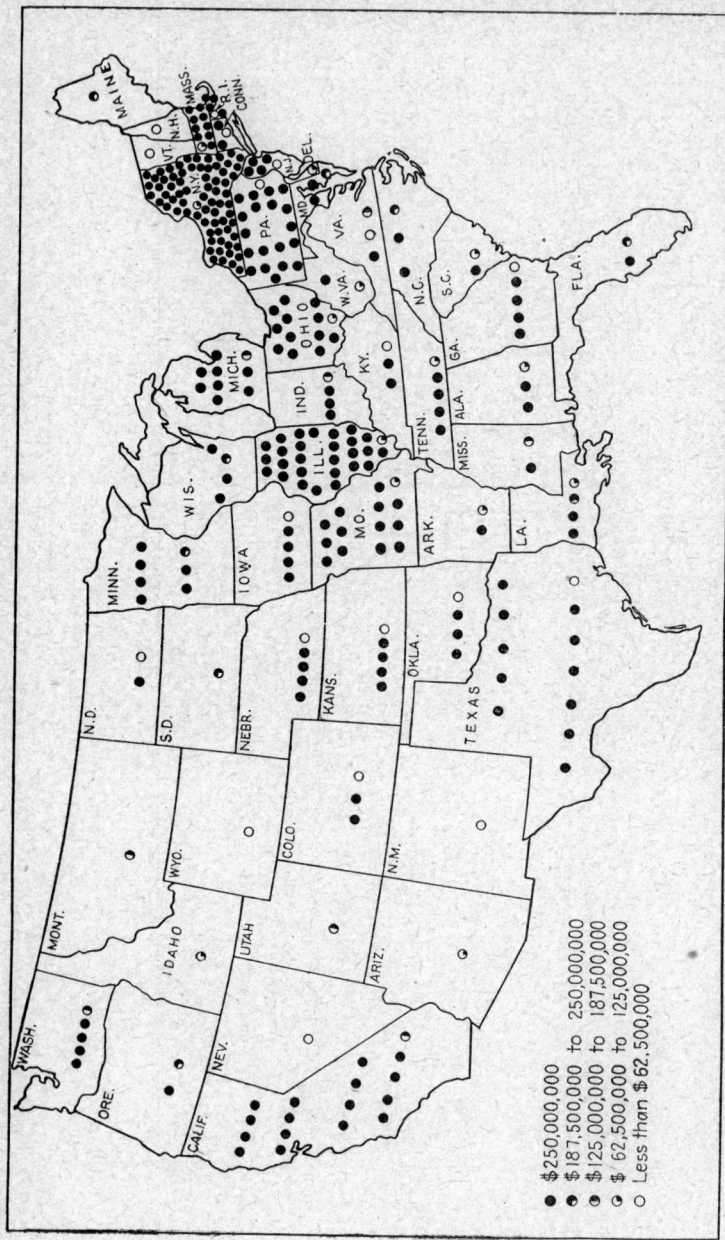

Fig. 26.—Wholesale trade in the United States, 1930, illustrating use of equal-sized dots.

$250,000,000
$187,500,000 to 250,000,000
$125,000,000 to 187,500,000
$ 62,500,000 to 125,000,000
○ Less than $62,500,000

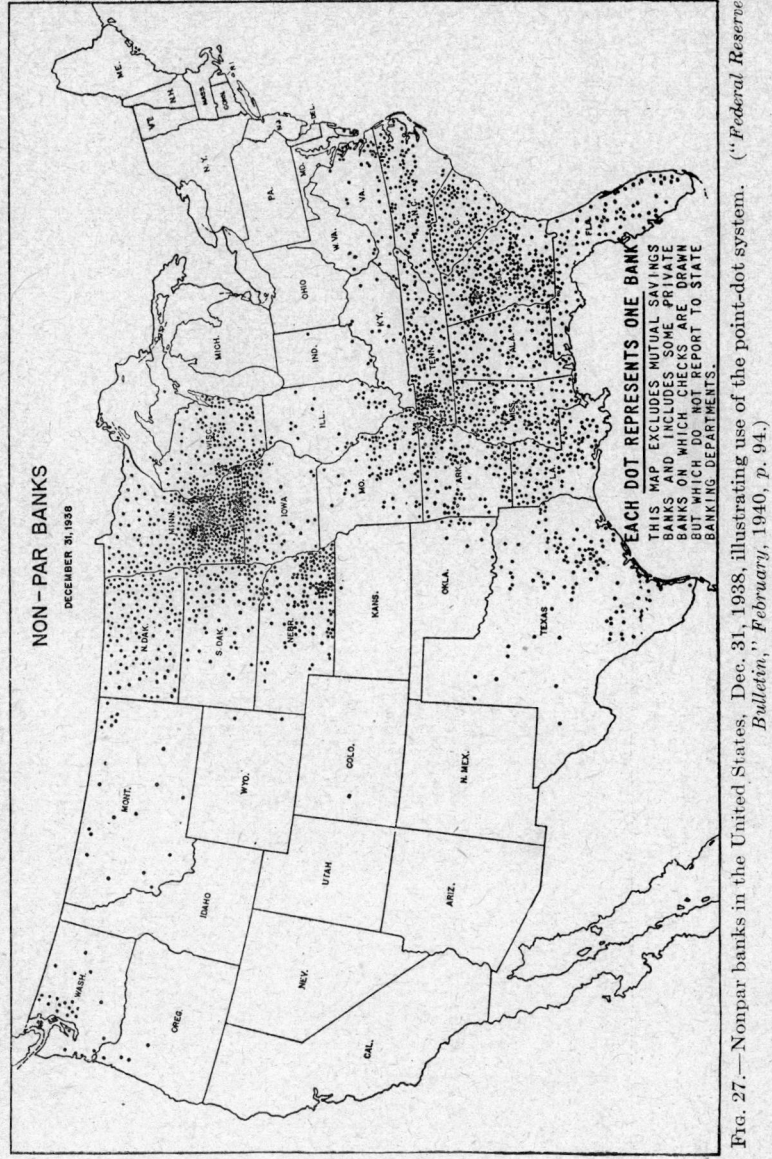

NON-PAR BANKS

DECEMBER 31, 1938

EACH DOT REPRESENTS ONE BANK

THIS MAP EXCLUDES MUTUAL SAVINGS BANKS AND INCLUDES SOME PRIVATE BANKS ON WHICH CHECKS ARE DRAWN BUT WHICH DO NOT REPORT TO STATE BANKING DEPARTMENTS.

Fig. 27.—Nonpar banks in the United States, Dec. 31, 1938, illustrating use of the point-dot system. (*"Federal Reserve Bulletin," February, 1940, p. 94.*)

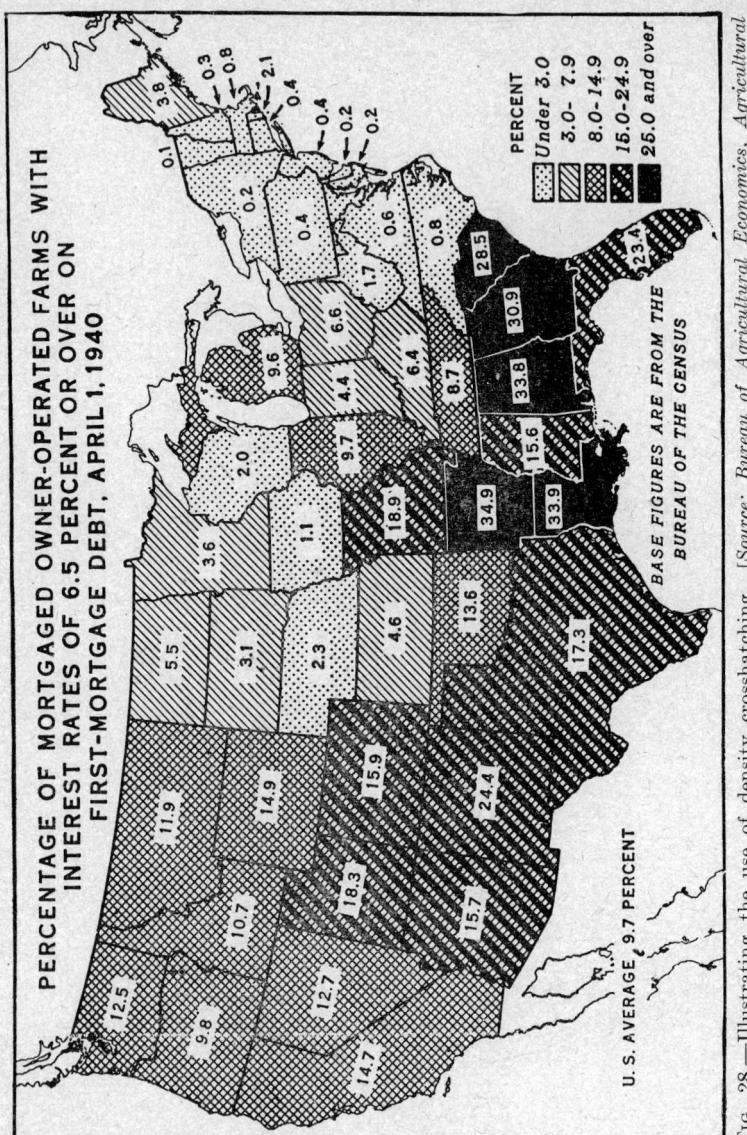

PERCENTAGE OF MORTGAGED OWNER-OPERATED FARMS WITH INTEREST RATES OF 6.5 PERCENT OR OVER ON FIRST-MORTGAGE DEBT, APRIL 1, 1940

PERCENT
Under 3.0
3.0- 7.9
8.0-14.9
15.0-24.9
25.0 and over

BASE FIGURES ARE FROM THE BUREAU OF THE CENSUS

U. S. AVERAGE 9.7 PERCENT

Fig. 28.—Illustrating the use of density crosshatching. [Source: Bureau of Agricultural Economics, Agricultural Financial Review, Vol. 5 (1942), p. 62.]

dots should be of sufficient relative size so that there will not be
too many of them. An example is shown in Fig. 26.

The chief difficulty in the use of this kind of cartogram is the
mechanical one of arriving at the proper magnitude to assign

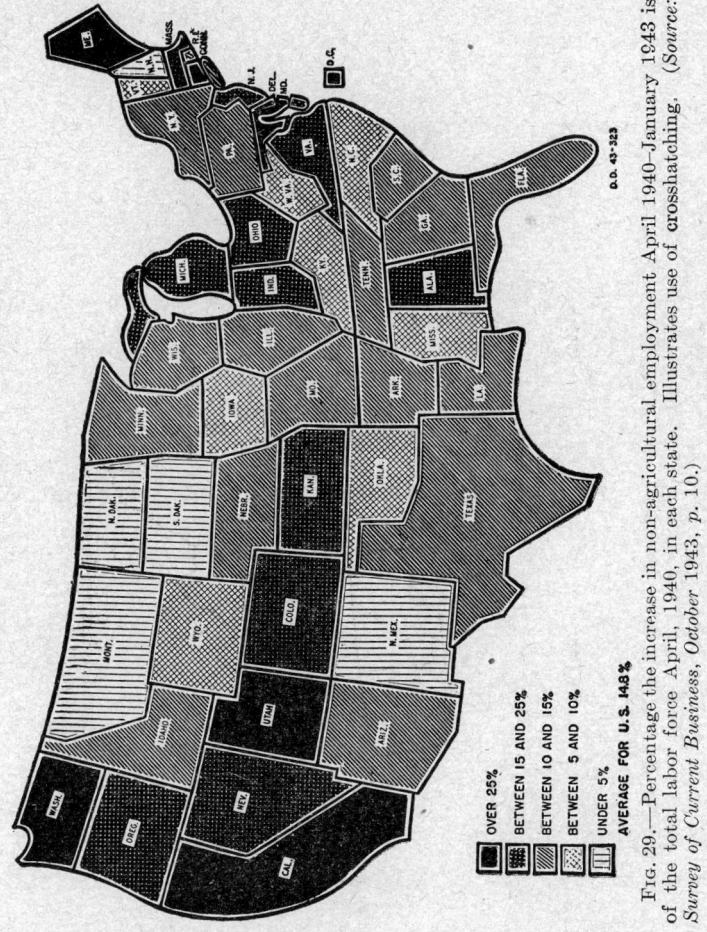

FIG. 29.—Percentage the increase in non-agricultural employment April 1940–January 1943 is
of the total labor force April, 1940, in each state. Illustrates use of crosshatching. (*Source:
Survey of Current Business, October 1943, p. 10.*)

to each dot of uniform size. If the magnitude assigned to each
dot is too large, it becomes difficult to show graphically the
small quantities relating to geographical locations where the
characteristic is scarce. On the other hand, if the magnitude
assigned to each dot is too small, this results in too great a crowd-
ing of the dots in areas where the characteristic is very plentiful.

In Fig. 26, this is illustrated by the attempt to picture the volume of wholesale trade of the state of New York, compared with the rest of the country. The dots are so dense that it is hardly possible to count their number. While the general

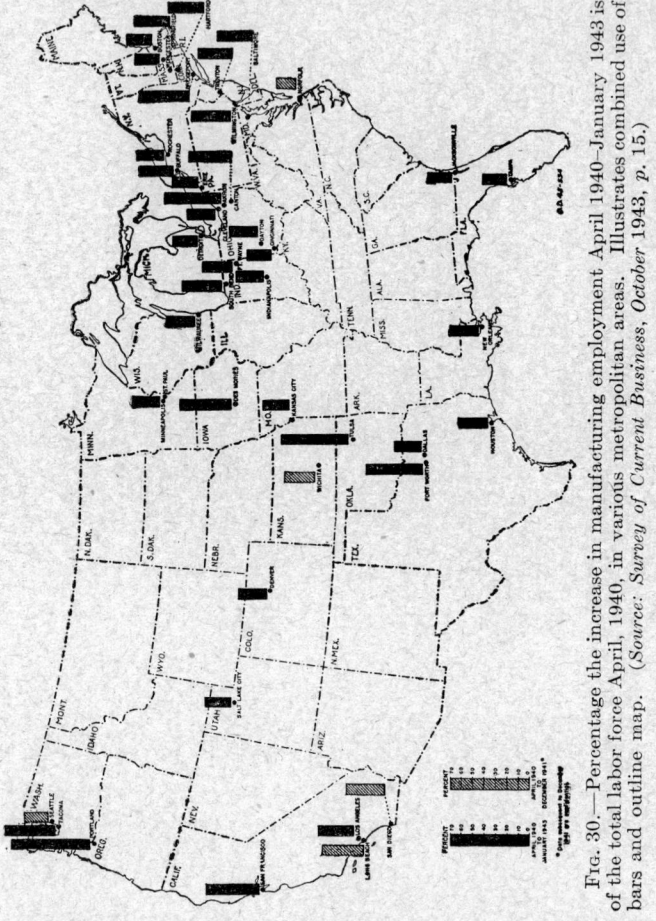

Fig. 30.—Percentage the increase in manufacturing employment April 1940–January 1943 is of the total labor force April, 1940, in various metropolitan areas. Illustrates combined use of bars and outline map. (*Source: Survey of Current Business, October 1943, p. 15.*)

picture of relative density is quickly visualized from such a map, this purpose can be better served by the use of the point-dot map. Another objection to the dot of uniform size map for this particular purpose is that it may convey the impression that the concentration of wholesale trade is over the whole state of New York, whereas it is known to be concentrated in the

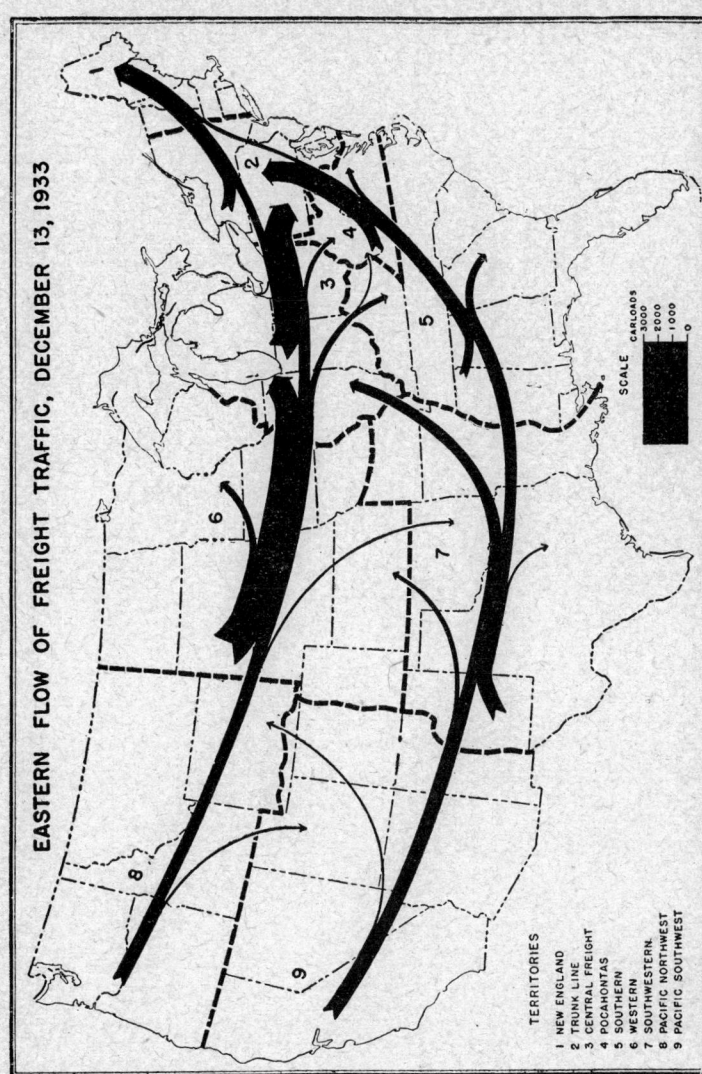

EASTERN FLOW OF FREIGHT TRAFFIC, DECEMBER 13, 1933

TERRITORIES

1 NEW ENGLAND
2 TRUNK LINE
3 CENTRAL FREIGHT
4 POCAHONTAS
5 SOUTHERN
6 WESTERN
7 SOUTHWESTERN.
8 PACIFIC NORTHWEST
9 PACIFIC SOUTHWEST

SCALE
CARLOADS
3000
2000
1000
0

100   0   100   200   300   400   500   600 Miles

Prepared in office of the National Resources Committee

Interstate Commerce Commission.

FIG. 31.—Illustrating uses of bars of varying width to depict traffic. (*Reproduced from National Resources Committee, The Structure of the American Economy, Part I, p. 38.*)

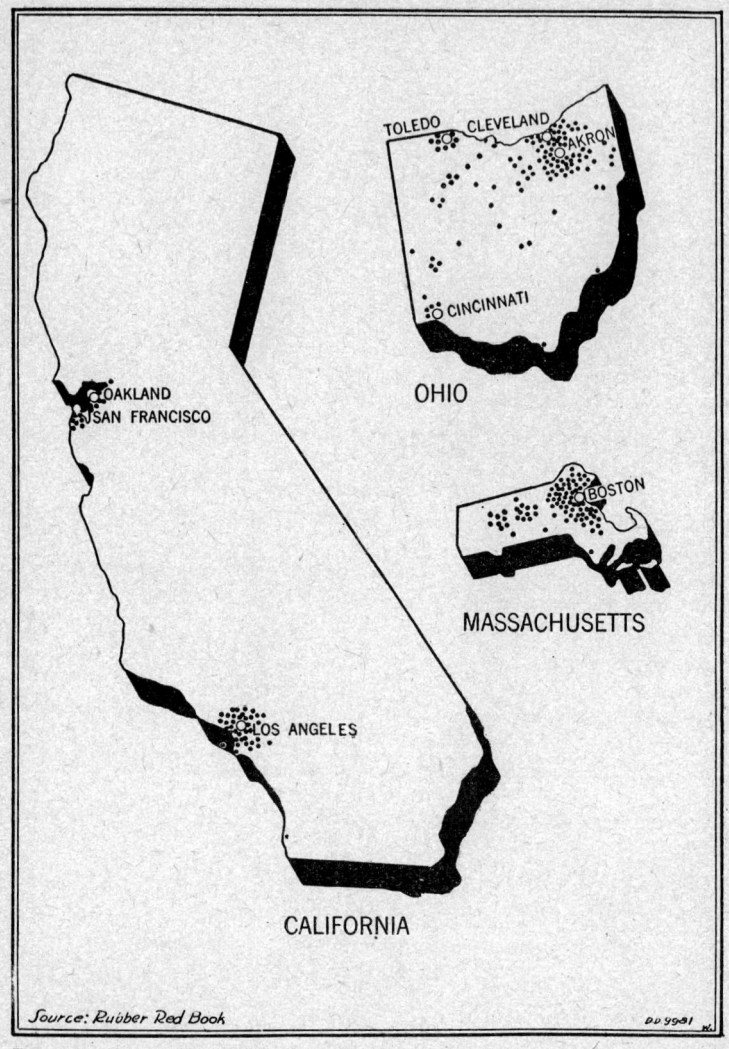

Fig. 32.—Distribution of rubber manufacturing in three leading states in 1937, illustrating a dramatic use of a point-dot map. [*Reproduced from Barker, P. W., and E. G. Holt, Rubber Industry of the United States, 1938–1939 (Bureau of Foreign and Domestic Commerce), p. 20.*]

metropolitan area of New York City. This conception is more clearly brought out by the use of the device of using large dots of varying size.

The third type is the point-dot cartogram, in which each dot means a certain quantity, but the dots are so small that they cannot be conveniently counted. The significance lies in presenting the idea of relative density of dots. Figure 27 shows the concentration in the Southeast and the Northern Middle states of nonpar banks of the United States.

Cartograms by Colors and Shades. Obviously, the same effect can be produced by the use of colors and shades as by the use of dots, but the former are expensive to reproduce in print and therefore are not extensively employed. The *Statistical Atlas* of the eleventh and twelfth censuses of the United States contains numerous such cartograms.

Cartograms by Crosshatching. Making comparisons relating to geographical location by crosshatching maps has increased in popularity during recent years. It is more effective than the method of dots and is cheaper than coloring and shading. Figure 28 makes it easy for the reader to visualize the variation in different parts of the United States in the proportion of mortgaged owner-operated farms paying rates of interest as high or higher than 6.5 per cent. Figure 29 shows at a glance the variation from state to state in the percentage increase in nonagricultural employment from 1940 to 1943.

Figure 30 is an interesting experiment in the combined use of a map and bar chart to show variation in the percentage increase in manufacturing employment in various metropolitan areas from 1940 to 1943. Figure 31 shows the use of a map and bars to depict flow of freight traffic in the United States. In Fig. 32 the geographical concentration of the rubber-manufacturing industry in three states of the United States is dramatically emphasized by showing outline maps of only those three states.

CHAPTER V

STATISTICS—A STUDY OF VARIATION

Ubiquitous Variability. Only in the abstract sense is there such a thing as a fixed quantity; in all cases, with reference both to physical and to psychic things, practical quantitative expressions are variables. However fixed the true quantity may be, no human measuring device is capable of giving the exact quantity; hence, all measurements obtained are approximations. In both physical sciences and social sciences, the raw materials amenable to the techniques of statistics are quantitatively expressed variations. The methods of analysis are likely to be complex when the scientist is faced with complex variability. This fact for the social sciences is recognized in the following quotation:[1] "The social scientist is limited by the fact that he does not deal with rational material but with the rational and irrational conduct of man. The host of variables which this fact introduces multiplies the obstacles to his work and sets limits to the applicability of results."

USE OF SYMBOLS

Simplification of the complex methods that need to be used in statistics is accomplished by the use of symbols. Because symbols are used for various purposes, beginners may have a natural psychological reaction unfavorable to the study of statistics. The uninitiated may be mystified and frightened away from the subject on account of the symbolic presentation. It is important, therefore, to realize that the symbols used in statistics are quite simple and that there are not very many of them. Furthermore, they are easily learned and remembered, as soon as their real purpose of simplification is understood.

[1] FOSDICK, RAYMOND, B., *A Review for* 1939—*The Rockefeller Foundation*, pp. 41–42. This foundation contributes extensively to the support of research in many scientific fields; for example, it contributes to such research organizations as the Brookings Institution and the National Bureau of Economic Research, discussed in Chap. III.

The Variable X. The study of variation is the meat and bones of the craft. The *variable X* is not a new idea to anyone who has gone as far as a first course in algebra and who has on many occasions said, "Let X equal . . . ." Symbols enter into statistical analysis in only three ways:

1. To represent variation in size with time; in such a case the data measuring the variable are designated "time series."

2. To represent variation in order of magnitude, from smallest to largest, or vice versa (if time is involved, it is disregarded, as the variable is rearranged or reclassified upon the basis of magnitude); in such a case the data measuring the variable are designated "frequency series."

3. To represent variation in quality or attribute (for example, occupation, geographical location, or race).

In symbolic language, it is purely a matter of convention that the variable may be referred to as X or as Y or as Z. In a given problem, if the nomenclature of X is assigned to a given variable, it is necessary to retain that symbol for that particular variable throughout the problem. In the theory of statistics conventions have arisen as to the use of symbols; for example, variables are commonly designated by the letters at the end of the alphabet, while constants or known figures are designated by the letters at the beginning of the alphabet.

One convention widely followed is to use a bar over a letter to designate the arithmetic mean, so that $\bar{X}_i$ (read "X_i bar") is the symbol for the mean of a series of X's. Another group of X's would be X_j and their mean $\bar{X}_j$. The subscripts i and j, respectively, symbolize subgroups. For example, all the X's may refer to the I.Q.'s of college freshmen; X_i refers to the I.Q.'s of male freshmen; and X_j refers to the I.Q.'s of female freshmen. Accordingly, $\bar{X}_i$ symbolizes the mean I.Q. of male freshmen, and $\bar{X}_j$ symbolizes the mean I.Q. of female freshmen. It is then conventional to designate the mean of all the X's, both X_i and X_j, as $\bar{X}$ (called "X bar").

Another commonly used convention is to designate an estimated figure by a letter followed by prime. According to this convention if an estimate is made of the value of X (for example, the coming crop yield of wheat based upon reports to the United States Department of Agriculture), the estimate is symbolically designated X'. Similarly, if an estimate of X (the price of wheat, for example) is made from information on supply and demand data, it is called X'. The small Greek letter sigma (σ) is used to designate standard deviation.[1] A special estimate of the standard deviation is symbolized by $\breve{\sigma}$.

It is a common practice to use certain other Greek letters to symbolize statistics. Accordingly, $\mu_1, \mu_2, \mu_3, \ldots, \mu_n$ (the Greek letter mu) symbolize the series of statistics called "moments" about a mean of a sample. The symbol π refers to the constant 3.1416. The symbols $v_1, v_2, \ldots, v_n$ (the Greek letter nu) refer to moments about an arbitrary origin.

While the use of symbols has become fairly well standardized in some respects along the conventional lines indicated, complete uniformity and consistent systematization are far from realized. Even the simple conventions above enumerated are not universally followed. Nevertheless, the student will find it an advantage to have his attention directed to these trends in symbolic representation.

TIME SERIES

Conventional Use of X and T to Symbolize Passage of Time. A convention in times-series analysis is that X is used to refer to the passage of time. T is also used for this purpose.[2] It happens that the same symbol, X, is conventionally used in geometry, trigonometry, and the like, to refer to the horizontal axis in a plane. The unification of these two conventions results in the convention in statistics that, in making graphs of statistical time series, the X-axis (the horizontal axis) is used to represent the passage of time. Thus, the passage of time may be indicated by a series of X's: $X_1, X_2, X_3, \ldots, X_n$, as shown in Fig. 33, where X refers to years

1940	1941	1942	1943	...
X_1	X_2	X_3	X_4	...

Fig. 33.

or as shown in Fig. 34 where X refers to months.

Jan.	Feb.	Mar.	Apr.	...
X_1	X_2	X_3	X_4	...

Fig. 34.

[1] For further discussion of the standard deviation, see Chap. VI.
[2] See Chaps. XIX–XXIV.

As indicated, T_1, T_2, T_3, . . . , T_n may also represent the passage of time.

Lower-case letters x and t refer to deviation from the mean; that is, $X - \bar{X} = x$; $T - \bar{T} = t$.

Where the Variable Fluctuates in Size with Time. When the statistician is dealing with a variable that fluctuates in size with the passage of time, he refers to this variable as Y. This is a convention; there is no logical reason for it except that he has already used the symbol X or T to refer to time and wants to have a different symbol for the variable being studied as it fluctuates through time. This situation is described in technical language by saying that the variable is a "function" of time, by which is meant merely that, as time passes, the variable fluctuates in magnitude, one way or another. The simple symbolic way of saying exactly the same thing (where X refers to time and Y refers to the variable) is

$$Y = F(X)$$

There is nothing mysterious to be read into this expression. It is merely a use, slightly different from the ordinary one, of the equality sign; and the whole expression means that Y is a function of X, or the variable which is being studied is a function of time, meaning that it fluctuates with the passage of time. This may be illustrated by one or two examples, imaginary figures being used.

TIME PASSES IN 1944

The unit that constitutes the variable is the price of sugar per pound in the New York City market (average for the month of prevailing daily prices).

X		Y	
X_1	January	Y_1	3 cents
X_2	February	Y_2	2 cents
X_3	March	Y_3	4.3 cents
X_4	April	Y_4	5 cents
X_5	May	Y_5	4 cents
X_6	June	Y_6	2.8 cents

Thus X_1 is the first unit of time (January), and Y_1 is the measurement of the variable Y at that time according to the designated unit of description; in other words, Y_1 is the price in January. Similarly, Y_2 is the price in February (X_2, or the second unit of time), and so on.

The unit of time may be the week, as where the unit that constitutes the variable is the amount of rainfall in inches in New York City per week.

X	Y
First week	0.1 inch
Second week	4.0 inches
Third week	0.3 inch
Fourth week	0.7 inch

In this illustration, X_1 refers to the first week, X_2 to the second week, etc., while Y_1 refers to the inches of rainfall in the first week, Y_2 to the inches of rainfall in the second week, etc.

The unit of time may be the year, as where the unit that constitutes the variable is the net worth of a business enterprise on Jan. 1 of each year.

X	Y
1936	$20,001.00
1937	$28,546.00
1938	$21,527.00
1939	$20,250.00
1940	$27,430.00
1941	$35,240.00

It is customary in geometry, trigonometry, etc., to let the vertical axis represent the Y variable; fluctuations in Y are shown by vertical distances. The unification of this custom with statistical presentation results in the convention that, when a graph is made of a variable that is a function of time, fluctuations in the Y variable are shown by vertical distances while time change is indicated along the X-axis, or horizontally.

Figure 35, showing comparative changes in cash farm income, farm-mortgage debt, and value per acre of farm real estate for years 1910–1942, is an illustration of the graph of a time series.

Careful Description of Units Involved. One or two matters concerning the units involved in time series should be noted. Sometimes the variable refers to an average value over a specified period of time; in the first illustration above, the average price of sugar per pound in New York City is an average over a period of a month. In other instances, the variable refers to a total for a given period of time; in the second illustration above, the inches of rainfall are given by totals per week. In still other problems, the variable refers to a quantity at the beginning of a period of time or at the end of a period of time; in the third illustration, the net worth of a business enterprise on Jan. 1 of successive

years was used.   In Fig. 35, cash farm income is in totals for
calendar years, each year's total being expressed as a percentage
of the average 1910–1914 yearly income.   Farm-mortgage debt
is in amounts as of Jan. 1 each year, expressed as a percentage
of the average 1910–1914 annual amounts.   Value per acre of
farm real estate is in amounts as of Mar. 1 each year, expressed
as percentages of the average 1912–1914 annual amounts.

It is important in connection with the study of time series to
know exactly how the variable is being used.   Of equal impor-

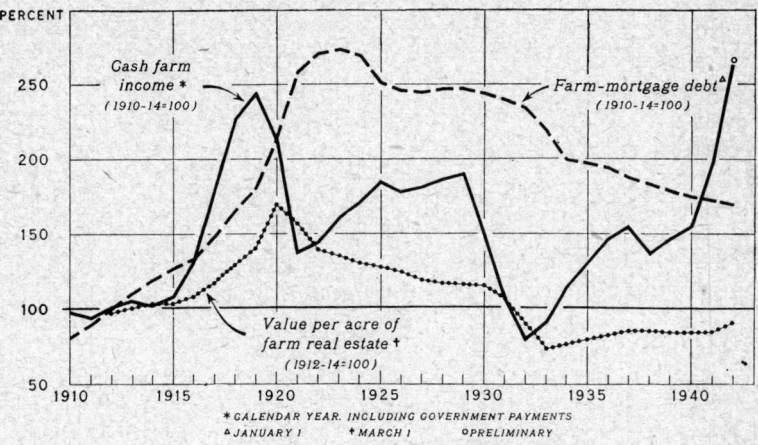

FIG. 35.—Cash farm income, farm-mortgage debt, and value per acre of farm real
estate, index numbers, United States, 1910–1942.

tance is it that exact indication of this should be given.   Every
good statistician invariably indicates either in titles of tables or
in footnotes just what his variables mean.   He should do this
no matter how expert a statistician he is and no matter how clear,
without such explanation, his work may seem to him.

Cumulative and Noncumulative Data.   Another important
matter is the difference between cumulative and noncumulative
data in time series.   The fundamental distinction between
cumulative and noncumulative data is really the difference
between data of "condition" and data of "change."   Cumulative data are the data of change.   It is possible to add the data
on weekly rainfall and thus obtain data on monthly rainfall

or yearly rainfall. Sales of a store by the week can be added to get sales by the month or by the year. It is possible to cumulate the number of births daily in order to get the total number of births per month or per year. Income and outgo figures are cumulative data. To those who have studied accounting, a convenient analogy is to the profit and loss statement—figures in the profit and loss statement in the main represent cumulative data.

Noncumulative data are those describing a condition and are not subject to the additive treatment. The average price of sugar per week cannot be cumulated to obtain the average price of sugar per month or per year. It is necessary to resort to averaging. The daily figures on population cannot be added in order to get the monthly population figures. A balance of $3,000 in the bank in January and of $5,000 in March do not give you a balance of $8,000 for the two months. These are items of condition and cannot be added. In order to obtain significant summary results in the case of noncumulative data over several periods of time, it is necessary to average rather than to add.

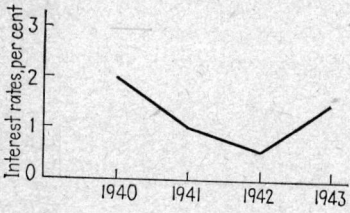

Fig. 36.—Chart of a time series.

The method of averaging is applicable, not only to the noncumulative, but to the cumulative type of data. It is significant to speak of the average daily rainfall during a given month or year, or the average weekly rainfall during a given month or year, or the average weekly sales of a given year, etc.

Another way of referring to a time series is to describe it as the situation in which a variable is classified according to the time of its occurrence. The basis of classification is time; and the most logical arrangement of the data in question is that basis. As will be seen, the data of a time series may be reclassified, for certain purposes, upon a different basis, and when this is done they no longer constitute a time series.

Charting Time Series. When a time series is graphed, the X-axis is used to represent passage of time, while the Y-axis is used to represent varying magnitudes. Thus, in Fig. 36, the points plotted would represent a magnitude equal to 2 in 1940, equal to 1 in 1941, and equal to $\frac{1}{2}$ in 1942, rising to $1\frac{1}{2}$ in 1943. It is conventional to represent time series by lines or curves connecting the plotted points. In graphic phraseology these lines may be drawn through the plotted points as polygons (*e.g.*, Fig. 36), or the changes in direction may be curved.

Two kinds of charts are in general use for the graphic presentation of time series: (1) arithmetic charts and (2) ratio charts.

ARITHMETIC AND RATIO CHARTS

Arithmetic Charts. The arithmetic chart pictures arithmetic changes in magnitude. For illustration, in Fig. 37 is shown a

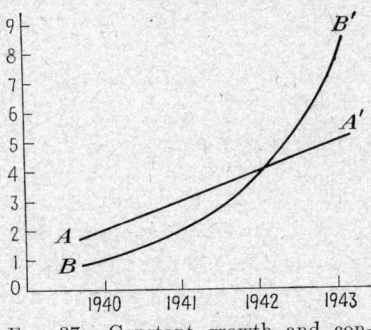

FIG. 37.—Constant growth and constant rate of growth.

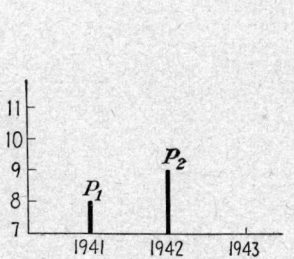

FIG. 38.—Showing effect of omitting zero line.

variable magnitude represented by the line AA', increasing by 1 during each time interval. This produces a straight line. On such a scale any variable increasing at a constant rate would give a straight line; but any variable increasing at a constant relative rate would produce an ever-steeper curve. This is illustrated by BB', which shows a magnitude doubling in each interval, that is, increasing at a constant rate.

The significant comparison in such a chart is always with zero, and hence the zero line should invariably be included in the chart. Leaving out the scale between zero and the point where the curve reaches its lowest point will give a deceptive appearance to the changes that occur. This is illustrated in Fig. 38, where P_2 is really $1\frac{1}{8}$ larger than P_1 (see scale) but appears in the figure to be twice as great because only part of the vertical scale is shown.

An arithmetic chart may also be a graph of relative figures, in which change from time to time relative to some base is

pictured. Such a graph is Fig. 35. In this kind of graph, the
base is usually called arbitrarily 100 per cent and the relative
changes above and below that base are graphed as percentages
of it. Figure 39 shows a magnitude at 105 in 1941 (5 per cent
above the base), at 95 in 1942, at 90 in 1943, and at 105 again in
1944. It is an extensive practice to convert time series into

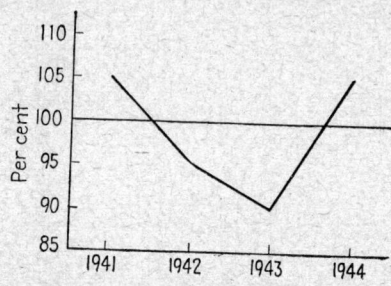

FIG. 39.—Chart of time series in relatives.

relatives, using some particular point in time as the base; and
when such relative series or "indexes" (as they are sometimes
called) are charted, the chart assumes the form indicated in
Fig. 39. The point of departure for reading such a chart is the
100 per cent line, which should be emphasized—the zero point
does not have to be shown on such a chart. The relative chart

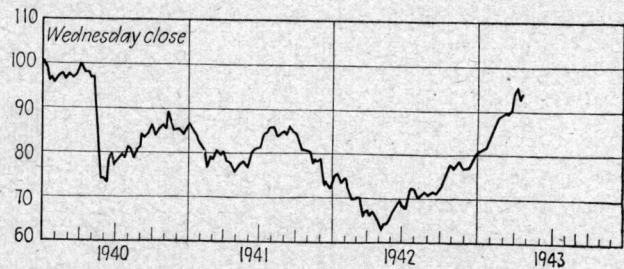

FIG. 40.—The percentage changes in the prices of 354 industrial stocks (1935–
1939 = 100). (*Survey of Current Business, Weekly Supplement, Apr.* 29, 1943.)

should not be confused with the case in which raw data are
already in the percentage form and the zero per cent may be
the significant point of departure rather than 100. Thus the
raw data may be percentages of population paying income taxes
in successive years. In such a case the zero line is important,
the raw data themselves being in percentage figures.

Figure 40 is an illustration of a graph of a relative time series. It shows the month-to-month variation, compared with the average of monthly figures, 1935–1939, in the prices of 354 industrial stocks; thus the average 1935–1939 equals 100 per cent.

Ratio Charts. The second type of chart for graphing time series is the ratio chart, which is designed to picture relative rate of change. According to Wesley C. Mitchell, the idea of the ratio chart was introduced by Jevons in 1863–1865.[1] But the ratio chart did not come into general use until its advantages were explained by Prof. Irving Fisher and James A. Field, in 1917.[2]

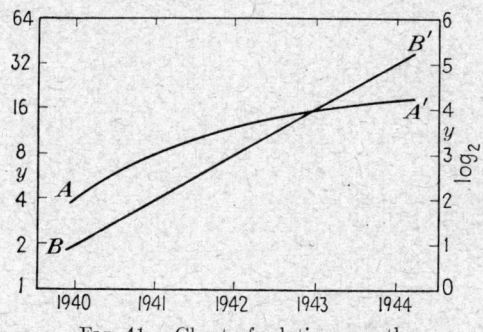

FIG. 41.—Chart of relative growth.

The great popularity in recent years of the ratio chart has been largely due to the fact that special graphing paper has been made for the purpose, the work of making such a chart being thus vastly simplified.

In the case of the arithmetic chart, equal rises on the chart per unit of time represent a constant rate of increase—in the case of the ratio chart, equal rises per unit of time represent a constant relative rate of increase. This is illustrated by the comparison of the left with the right scale in Fig. 41. This figure is a simple illustration showing a magnitude changing at the same relative rate, *BB'*, and a magnitude changing at a constant rate, *AA'*, both plotted on a ratio scale. The *BB'*

---

[1] MITCHELL, W. C., *Business Cycles*, p. 209.

[2] FISHER, IRVING, "The 'Ratio' Chart for Plotting Statistics," *Publications of the American Statistical Association*, Vol. 15 (June, 1917), pp. 577–601; FIELD, JAMES A., "Some Advantages of the Logarithmic Scale," *Journal of Political Economy*, Vol. 25 (October, 1917), pp. 805–841. Cited from Mitchell, *op. cit.*, p. 209.

magnitude doubles in each time period. The AA' magnitude increases in each time period by the constant difference of 4.

Notice the scale of logarithms at the right, which corresponds to the scale of natural numbers at the left. These logarithms are to the base 2. Thus, the $\log_2$ of 64 is 6 because $2^6 = 64$; $\log_2$ of 32 is 5 because $2^5 = 32$; etc. It is evident, of course, that while the scale at the left is in geometric progression the scale at the right is in arithmetical progression. This is a characteristic of ratio paper. Ratio charts have no zero line, and there is no point of emphasis. The attention is directed to the shape and fluctuations in the curve. In the case of the arithmetically ruled chart, growth at a constant difference is a straight line—the greater the difference, the steeper the line—but it is still a straight line if the difference is constant. In the case of the ratio chart, growth at a constant relative rate is a straight line—the greater the constant relative rate, the steeper the line—but it is still straight.

On arithmetical paper, changes in differences produce curves or irregular lines. On ratio paper, changes in relative rates of change produce curves or irregular lines. The vertical scale of the arithmetical chart is an arithmetic progression. The vertical scale of the ratio chart is in geometric progression; but the logarithms of the natural scale on a ratio chart are in arithmetical progression. For this reason, the ratio chart is often called the semilogarithmic chart. One method of plotting a ratio chart is to find the logarithms of the raw data and then plot the logarithms on arithmetically ruled paper. The results are the same as if the natural data were plotted on a ratio scale. The labor of looking up logarithms is avoided by having the scale made into a logarithmic one, upon which the plotting of natural data will produce the same effect as if the logarithms were found and plotted. This is shown in a very simple case in Fig. 41, in which the scale in logarithms is at the right and the scale in raw data units is at the left. As already explained above, the line BB' represents a variable that increases at a constant relative rate, while the line AA' represents a variable that increases by a constant quantity. In Fig. 41 the vertical distance between each of the scale markings on the left represents just double the absolute amount of the same vertical distance immediately below it and just half the absolute amount of the same vertical distance immediately above it. In this figure the variable that doubles every year follows the straight line BB' (it was a curve in Fig. 37). A variable that increases by the same aggregate amount each year and hence follows a straight line in Fig. 37 would follow a curved path on a ratio chart, such as line AA' of Fig. 41.

Since the logarithm of the ratio between two quantities is equal to the difference between their logarithms, ratio paper can be easily "calibrated" by the use of a logarithmic scale. Thus, if equal vertical distances are taken to measure equal aggregate differences between logarithms, then these same vertical distances will represent equal relative distances (equal ratios) between the antilogarithms of the logarithmic scale. In Fig. 41, for example, the unit vertical distance is taken to be a unit difference between logarithms to the base 2, and the logarithmic scale on the right reads, 2, 3, 4, etc. Since the antilogarithm of a number to the base 2 is equal to 2 raised to the $\log_2$ power, the antilogarithms of the logarithmic scale become 1, 4, 8, 16, etc. This is the scale shown on the left. It is evident that while the scale on the right is in arithmetic progression the scale on the left is in geometric progression. Accordingly, if paper is ruled so as to be in arithmetic progression with respect to some logarithmic scale but is marked or calibrated in terms of the antilogarithms of the logarithmic scale, any variable plotted on this paper in accordance with the antilogarithmic scaling will indicate a constant rate of growth or decline wherever it traces out a straight line.

Most ratio paper is ruled in accordance with a logarithmic scale to the base 10, since this is the base of common logarithms. An example of this kind of "semilogarithmic paper" (as it is often called because the vertical scale is logarithmic while the horizontal scale is arithmetic) is shown in Fig. 42. The reason common logarithms are to the base 10 is that numbers are arranged upon a decimal system and, by taking the base 10 for logarithms, the integral part of the logarithm (characteristic) is a mere record of the position of the decimal point in the original number. The number 10 raised to the zero power is 1, and so the logarithm of 1 is zero; the number 10 raised to the second power is 100, and so the logarithm of 100 is 2; the number 10 raised to the third power is 1,000, and so the logarithm of 1,000 is 3; and so on, indefinitely. Likewise any number between 1 and 10 will have a logarithm (to the base 10) whose characteristic is 0; any number between 10 and 100 will have a logarithm whose characteristic is 1; etc. The fractional part of a logarithm (its mantissa) is the same for all similar successions of similar digits. The fractional part of the logarithm to the base 10 for the number 2 is the same as the fractional part of the logarithm for 20 or 200 or 2,000, etc., namely, 0.3010; but the characteristic of the logarithm of 2 is 0, the characteristic of the logarithm of 20 is 1, the characteristic of the logarithm of 200 is 2, and so on. Thus, the entire logarithm of 2 is 0.3010; the entire logarithm of 20 is 1.3010; the entire logarithm of 200 is 2.3010; etc. Hence, when the base of the logarithm is 10, logarithmic markings of -2, -1, 0, 1, 2, 3, etc., represent antilogarithmic markings of 0.01, 0.1, 1, 10, 100, 1,000, etc.

Semilogarithmic paper to the base 10 is usually ruled to represent either one logarithmic unit and the fractional parts thereof, corresponding to equal tenths on the antilogarithmic scale (called "one-cycle paper"), or two logarithmic units and the fractional parts of each, corresponding to equal tenths on the antilogarithmic scale (called "two-cycle paper"), or three logarithmic units and the fractional parts of each, corresponding to equal tenths on the antilogarithmic scale (called "three-cycle paper"). All three of these types of logarithmic rulings are shown in the right part of Fig. 42. Since the logarithmic scale is in arithmetic progression, these rulings would be the same for any logarithm differing by one, two, or three units; they would apply to logarithms running from -2 to 0, as well as from 0 to 2. Thus the corresponding antilogarithmic scale can be selected by the statistician in accordance with his needs. If his data run from 2 to 800, for example, he would select three-cycle semilogarithmic paper and make his scale as indicated on the left of Fig. 42. If his data ran from 200 to 80,000, he would also select three-cycle semilogarithmic paper and make his scale from 100 (at the bottom) to 100,000 at the top. If his data ran from 0.2 to 8, he would choose two-cycle semilogarithmic paper and make his scale from 0.1 (at the bottom) to 10 (at the top).

Figure 42 is an illustration of a three-cycle ratio scale for the plotting of a time series by months for 6 years. The scale as drawn reads from 1 to 1,000, but it could be made to read from

10 to 10,000, or from 100 to 100,000, etc. At the right of the figure are shown the three most generally used types of ratio scales, the three-cycle ratio scale, the two-cycle ratio scale, and the one-cycle ratio scale. If the extreme fluctuations of a time series are 60 and 3,000, it would be necessary to use three-cycle

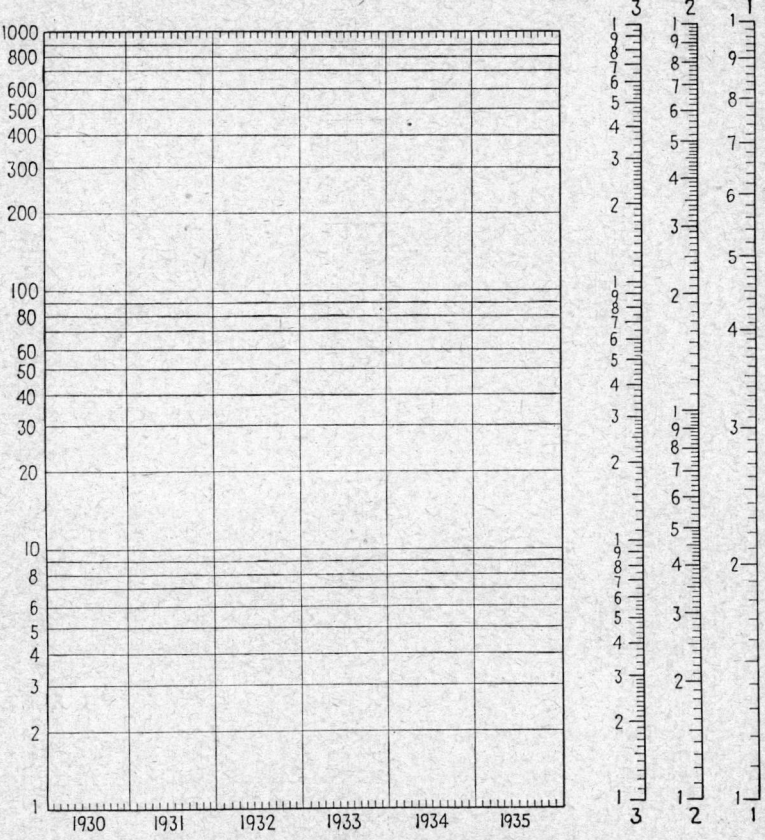

FIG. 42.—Three-cycle semilogarithmic paper.

paper; on the other hand, if the extreme fluctuations are 60 to 500, it would be necessary to use only two-cycle paper.

Figures 43 and 44 are intended to illustrate the advantages and disadvantages of the ratio chart. Figure 43 shows the comparative growth of some famous cities of the United States on an arithmetic scale, and Fig. 44 shows the same data plotted on a ratio scale. These data are also shown in Table 7. It will be

noticed that on an arithmetic scale it is not possible to bring the
New York City population growth curve. into the picture.   On
the ratio paper this is possible.   Of course, on the arithmetically
ruled paper New York City population could be plotted on a
different scale; but then the arithmetic comparison between
New York City and the other cities would be lost, since the
height of the curve from the zero line is what counts in the comparison on arithmetic paper.

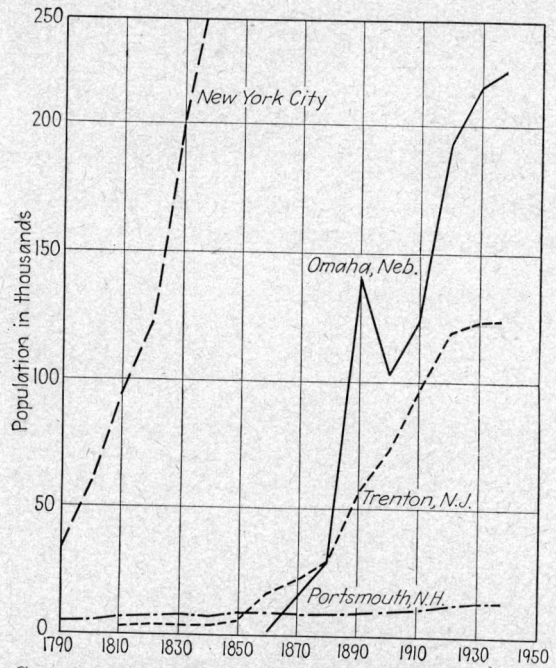

Fig. 43.—Growth of certain cities in the United States (arithmetic scale).

The advantage of the ratio chart is threefold.   (1) It makes
possible a quick answer to the question as to whether a magnitude
is changing its rate of growth.   (2) It clearly pictures the relative significance of. fluctuations—for example, arithmetic differences of small magnitudes appear as important as the same
relative differences of large magnitudes.   On an arithmetic chart
the latter would appear much larger.   If an arithmetic chart of
almost any item of production in the United States, say from
1800 to 1940 by years, is constructed, the fluctuations in the

curve for the earlier period will be minute, while the fluctuations in the curve for the latter part will loom very large. In such cases, the inclusion has therefore sometimes been reached that instability is greater now than formerly. Plotting the same data on ratio paper would in most cases show that the earlier fluctuations were relatively as great as or greater than the modern ones. (3) It facilitates comparisons between time series in order to detect correlation between them.

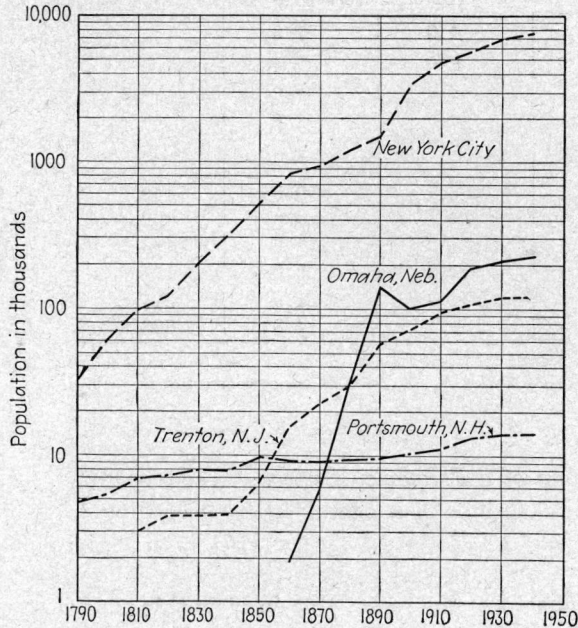

FIG. 44.—Growth of certain cities in the United States (logarithmic, or ratio, scale).

The disadvantage of the ratio chart is that it is not possible to make magnitude comparisons. For illustration, if the attempt were made to compare the actual size of Trenton, N.J., and New York City in 1930, an entirely incorrect impression would be created—Trenton would appear from the ratio chart to be about half as large as New York City in 1940 if vertical distance were assumed to be magnitude. When the ratio chart is used, such magnitude comparisons must be made by the use of the raw figures themselves, which should always be given in a table of figures along with the chart.

TABLE 7.—POPULATION OF SPECIFIED CITIES IN THE UNITED STATES FROM
EARLIEST CENSUS TO 1940

(In thousands)

Census date	Trenton, N. J.	Portsmouth, N. H.	Omaha, Neb.	New York City[1]
1790	.....	4.7	.....	49.4
1800	.....	5.3	.....	79.2
1810	3.0	6.9	.....	119.7
1820	3.9	7.3	.....	152.1
1830	3.9	8.0	.....	242.3
1840	4.0	7.9	.....	391.1
1850	6.5	9.7	.....	696.1
1860	17.2	9.3	1.9	1,174.8
1870	22.9	9.2	16.1	1,478.1
1880	30.0	9.7	30.5	1,911.7
1890	57.5	9.8	140.5	2,507.4
1900	73.3	10.6	102.6	3,437.2
1910	96.8	11.3	124.1	4,766.9
1920	119.3	13.6	191.6	5,620.0
1930	123.4	14.5	214.0	6,930.4
1940	124.7	14.8	223.8	7,455.0

Source: Sixteenth Census of the United States, 1940, Vol. I, *Population*, pp. 32 and 660.
[1] Refers to New York City and its boroughs as constituted in 1940.

FREQUENCY SERIES

Definition of a Frequency Series. A convenient arrangement of any set of data is a classification according to magnitude, that is, from smallest to largest. In the case of a time series, time seems to be the most logical and workable basis of classification, because it seems reasonable to view things as they occur in time. There is a rationality about such a procedure. But another aspect of data, unrelated to time, may be important. For example, how many different prices of sugar during a given week differed from the average price for that week, and in what respect did they differ, or from how wide a range of fluctuations in price during the week were the respective average weekly prices calculated? This particular aspect would have no reference to time, except as a matter of definition of the unit involved (one would not take prices of the third week in March to study the average price in the first week of March). When the arrangement of data according to time of occurrence is not significant, it seems rational to classify the data in a series from smallest to largest. When this is done, the resulting series of data is called an "array."

Following is an example of an array:[1]

AN ARRAY OF 10 CHILDREN IN THIRD GRADE, BY AGE

	Age, Years
X_1	$7\frac{1}{4}$
X_2	$7\frac{1}{2}$
X_3	$7\frac{3}{4}$
X_4	8
X_5	$8\frac{1}{4}$
X_6	$8\frac{1}{2}$
X_7	$8\frac{3}{4}$
X_8	9
X_9	$9\frac{1}{4}$
X_{10}	$9\frac{1}{2}$

Variable X arranged according to magnitude, where X = age of children in third grade, X_1 = age of youngest child, etc., until X_{10} is age of oldest child.

The situation may be one where there are a number of children of each age, for example:

AN ARRAY OF 18 CHILDREN IN THIRD GRADE, BY AGE

	Age, Years	
X_1	$6\frac{1}{4}$	}1
X_2	$6\frac{1}{2}$	}2
X_3	$6\frac{1}{2}$	
X_4	$6\frac{3}{4}$	}3
X_5	$6\frac{3}{4}$	
X_6	$6\frac{3}{4}$	
X_7	7	}4
X_8	7	
X_9	7	
X_{10}	7	
X_{11}	$7\frac{1}{4}$	}3
X_{12}	$7\frac{1}{4}$	
X_{13}	$7\frac{1}{4}$	
X_{14}	$7\frac{1}{2}$	}3
X_{15}	$7\frac{1}{2}$	
X_{16}	$7\frac{1}{2}$	
X_{17}	$7\frac{3}{4}$	}1
X_{18}	8	}1

[1] The particular magnitude here taken is "age." Any other common characteristic could be taken as the magnitude for comparison of the chil-

From the array, it is noticed that there is 1 child $6\frac{1}{4}$ years old, and there are 2 children $6\frac{1}{2}$ years old, 3 children $6\frac{3}{4}$ years old, etc.

Inasmuch as there are really only eight variations of the variable X, some of which occur more than once, the above is more conveniently summarized as follows:

NUMBER OF CHILDREN OF SPECIFIED AGE, AMONG 18 CHILDREN IN THIRD
GRADE

Age, Years, of Children in Third Grade X		Number of Children of Specified Age F	
X_1	$6\frac{1}{4}$	1	F_1
X_2	$6\frac{1}{2}$	2	F_2
X_3	$6\frac{3}{4}$	3	F_3
X_4	7	4	F_4
X_5	$7\frac{1}{4}$	3	F_5
X_6	$7\frac{1}{2}$	3	F_6
X_7	$7\frac{3}{4}$	1	F_7
X_8	8	1	F_8
		$\overline{18} = N = \Sigma F$	

This is called a "frequency series" or a "frequency distribution"; the variable is listed in a column in the form of an array, and in a second column the frequencies of each variation are set down. It is merely a condensed form of the array and is particularly convenient, as may be readily imagined, when a large number of cases is studied. It will be noticed that a new symbol is introduced, but it is a very simple one and one that readily suggests itself. F_1 refers to the number of times X_1 occurs, F_2 the number of times X_2 occurs, etc. F stands in general for the frequency of occurrence of a variation; 18 is the total number of cases and is therefore the sum of the F's, and this is written ΣF. $(F_1 + F_2 + F_3 + \cdots + F_n = \Sigma F.)$ However, a more general way to symbolize the total number of cases is to use a large N. Either ΣF or N could be used, but it is conventional in statistics to use N to represent ΣF. This Σ is the capital Greek letter sigma, and it is always used in statistics to designate "sum" or "total of."

Nature of a Frequency Distribution and Illustration. The idea of the array and of the frequency distribution in its barest

---

dren, for example, height or weight. The basis must be a common characteristic or attribute that is a variable magnitude capable of quantitative measurement.

simplicity has been illustrated. From the example, it is seen that the frequency distribution is merely the commonplace and rational arrangement of a set of data in order of magnitude. As indicated elsewhere, this form of arrangement discloses a natural order that appears to persist in all things,[1] namely, that in a large number of observations of a common characteristic of a thing the following tendencies exist:

1. A large number of frequencies cluster about a central magnitude or average, which occurs most frequently.

2. Small variations above and below this central magnitude are numerous.

3. Large variations are much less frequent.

4. Extreme variations are rare.

Following is an example of a frequency distribution showing the number of cities of 100,000 or more population that have specified death rates from puerperal causes:

TABLE 8.—MATERNAL MORTALITY IN CITIES OF 100,000 OR MORE POPULATION IN THE UNITED STATES, 1938

Death Rates (Number per 1,000 Live Births) X	Number of Cities F
1–	2
2–	16
3–	18
4–	20
5–	15
6–	10
7–	4
8–	6
9–	0
10–	2
	93

Source: Bureau of the Census, "Vital Statistics," *Special Reports*, Vol. 9, No. 7 (Feb. 10, 1940), pp. 125–126.

The average maternity death rate for these 93 cities is 4.8 per 1,000 live births. It will be noted that, instead of writing X_1, X_2, X_3, . . . , for each variant of the variable X, the symbol X is written at the head of the column, indicating that the column consists of X_1, X_2, X_3 . . . X_n. The symbol F is handled in a similar manner. Furthermore, in this illustration, class intervals

[1] See Chaps. VI and VII.

of 1 are used, which is signified by the dash after each of the numbers in the X column. This is because fractional rates are given in the source and not merely rounded numbers. For example, the death rate from puerperal causes in 1938 in the city of Akron, Ohio, was 4.0; in the city of Albany, N.Y., it was 3.1; in the city of Atlanta, Ga., it was 4.4. Since the death rates are given to one decimal place, if class intervals were not used for the frequency table, it would require some hundred or more rows of figures to place the death rates in an array. The symbol for the class interval is i. In this case, $i = 10$ decimal units, or 1. The average 4.8 was calculated by assuming that cases in any class interval all had the value of the mid-point of the interval.[1]

Discrete and Continuous Frequency Series. A discrete frequency series is one in which the units of measurements are more or less fixed by the character of the data. The phenomena actually occur in such a manner that their variations in size proceed by distinct jumps or steps. The unit of measurement is fixed by this fact. An example of such a series is a frequency distribution of interest rates, in which the quoted variations in rates are likely to fluctuate by $\frac{1}{4}$ or $\frac{1}{8}$ per cent jumps and there are few if any intermediate variations. The variation in the range of the actual cases is consequently by distinct steps of $\frac{1}{4}$ or $\frac{1}{8}$ per cent. The variation throughout the range is not by infinitesimal amounts. The very character of the data determines the unit of measurement and its degree of refinement. Where variation proceeds in this manner, by discrete steps of considerable magnitude as compared with the whole range of variation, it is probably best not to use a class interval. If the number of different values of X that occur are too numerous for convenience, however, then the data may be grouped into class intervals. Great care should be employed in this case to see that the class intervals are chosen so that the possible values of X are placed in a balanced position throughout the intervals. For example, if values of X occur at 0, 2, 4, 6, 8, etc., then, if grouping is desired, a class interval of size 4 might be chosen running from 1 up to but not including 5, from 5 up to but not including 9, etc. These would balance the actual X values

---

[1] For a more complete discussion of the class interval and calculation of averages, see Chap. VII.

around the center of each interval.   On the other hand, intervals of 4, running from 0 up to but not including 4, from 4 up to but not including 8, etc., would result in the actual X values occurring at the lower limit and middle of each interval, causing an upward bias if the cases are assumed to be concentrated at the mid-points of the intervals, as is usual.[1]   If the discrete data vary by steps that are small in relation to the range of variation in the data (*e.g.*, in steps of 1 cent over a range of $100), then the data might reasonably be treated as if they were continuous.

A continuous series is one representing a phenomenon that varies by infinitesimal amounts. It may have the appearance on the statistical table of the same discreteness as the discrete series; but this is because the arbitrarily discrete character of the unit of measurement eclipses the actual continuous character of the data. In a continuous series the range of the interval is obtained by a process of testing and finding the one that appears best to smooth the data, following the general rules for determining the class interval discussed later.[2] Frequency series of all growth phenomena are of the continuous type. For example, the frequency distributions of weights or heights of people of some specified age are continuous in character. In passing from one height to another, the individual must necessarily pass through every minute difference between; and accordingly in measuring the heights of individuals at the same age (or of mature people) the variants will be by minute or infinitesimal differences. The units of measurement, however, will make them appear discrete in character.

Charts of Frequency Distributions. A frequency table is the presentation of a series of variable magnitudes, usually arranged from smallest to largest, in such a manner as to record the frequencies of the different magnitudes. For purposes of graphing it is conventional to use the x-axis for the variable magnitude and the y-axis for the frequencies. For illustration, in Fig. 45, the x-axis shows the variations of magnitude (death rates from puerperal causes in 1938) and the y-axis the frequencies (the number of cities of 100,000 or more population) of those death rates—so that the points appearing from the left to the right signify the following:

[1] *Cf.* Chap. VII.
[2] See Chap. VII.

Death rates in 1938 from puerperal causes:
2 cities have death rates between 1 and 2 per 1,000 live births.
16 cities have death rates between 2 and 3 per 1,000 live births.

. . . .

6 cities have death rates between 8 and 9 per 1,000 live births.
0 cities have death rates between 9 and 10 per 1,000 live births.
2 cities have death rates between 10 and 11 per 1,000 live births.

The points are plotted over the mid-points to indicate that the frequencies cover the class interval and not merely the rounded quantities shown on the scale. Accordingly, F_1, or 2,

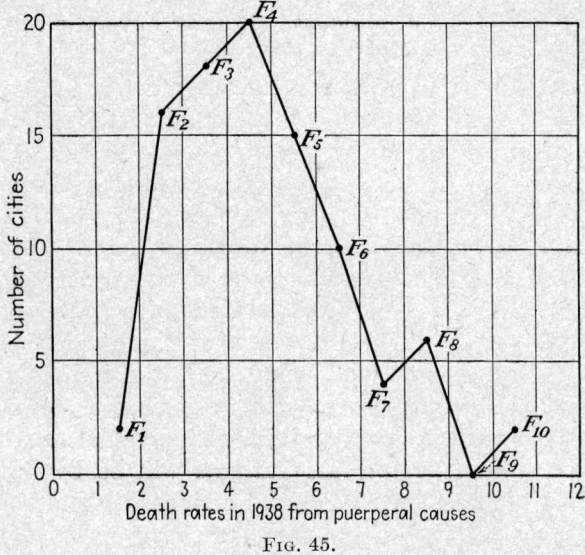

Fig. 45.

is plotted directly over 1.5; F_4, or 20, is plotted directly over 4.5; etc. It is easily seen from the figure that the peak of the frequencies is in the interval containing the average. It can also be seen that numerous small variations from the average occur, but large variations from the average are few in number—that is, the frequency polygon slopes rapidly downward on each side of the average where the frequency is highest. Variations of 1 below average death rate (death rate of about 3.8) lie in the class interval having 18 cases; variations of 1 above average death rate (death rate of about 5.8) lie in the class interval having 15 cases. Variations of 3 below and above average are much less frequent—only 2 cases are in the class interval containing death rate 1.8, and only 4 cases are in the class interval containing death rate 7.8.

Instead of a polygon to trace the direction of frequencies, the practice of using bars to depict frequency distributions is often followed. Figures 46 to 48 are illustrations of such graphs of frequency distributions. It is possible also to fit a curve to the points either by freehand or by mathematical means and

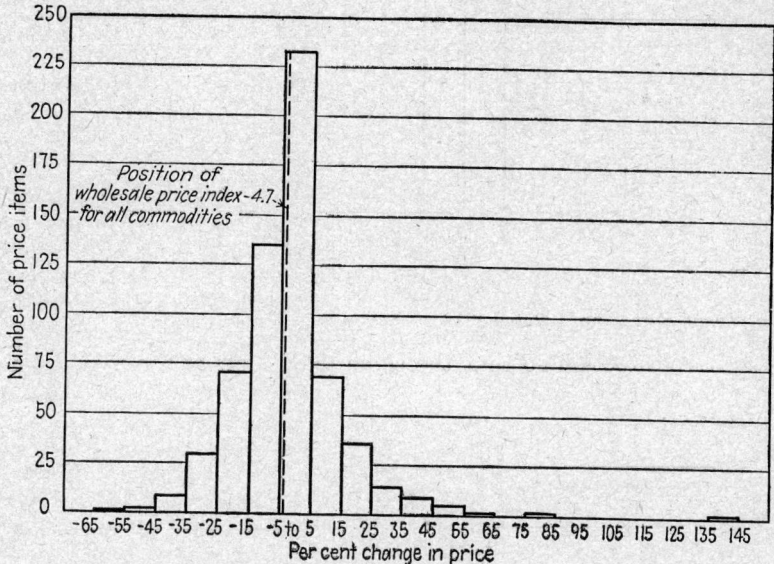

Fig. 46.—Distribution of 617 wholesale price items by percentage of price change, 1926–1929. (*National Resources Committee, The Structure of the American Economy, Part I, pp. 128 and 131.*)

thus describe graphically the frequency distribution by a curve, which is called a "frequency curve."[1]

In Figs. 46 to 48 it is interesting to compare the concentration of percentage changes in the three different periods, namely, 1926–1929, when prices and economic activity were comparatively stable; 1929–1932, when prices and economic activity were on the decline; and 1932–1937, when prices and economic activity were increasing. Figure 46, depicting the distribution of percentage price changes, 1926–1929, is quite symmetrical, and the slope on each side of the maximum frequency is rapid; the position of the mean (wholesale price index for all commodi-

[1] See Chap. VI.

ties, or −4.7) is close to midway between the two extreme ranges of the variable. In Figure 47, however, there is no such symmetry. On the contrary, there is a piling up of cases in the

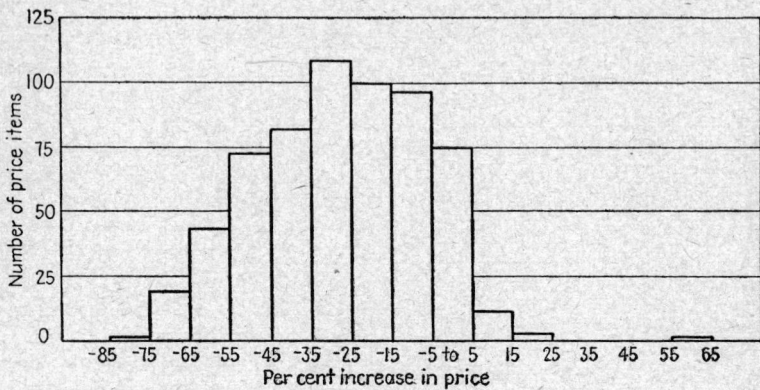

Fig. 47.—Distribution of 617 wholesale price items by percentage of price change, 1929–1932. (*National Resources Committee, The Structure of the American Economy, Part* I, *pp.* 128 *and* 131.)

negative direction so that the slope to the left of the maximum frequency is gradual while the slope to the right is parabolic; the distribution appears to have a tail in the negative direction.

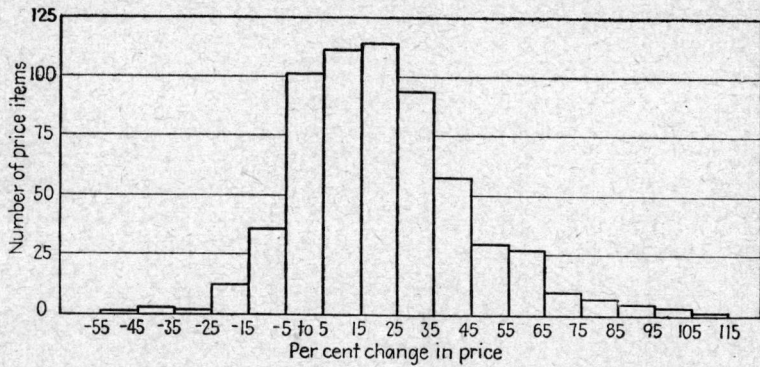

Fig. 48.—Distribution of 617 wholesale price items by percentage of price change, 1932–1937. (*National Resources Committee, The Structure of the American Economy, Part* I, *pp.* 128 *and* 131.)

Figure 48, on the other hand, shows the opposite tendencies, with the appearance of a tail extending in the positive direction.

Figures 49 and 50 illustrate the use of frequency curves in chemical studies.

Figures 51 and 52 are illustrations of the use of frequency histograms in biochemical studies.

While the frequency distribution in Fig. 45 is in the form of a polygon, those of Figs. 46 to 48 and 51 and 52 are shown by outline bars. When a frequency distribution is drawn with bars, the graph is called a "histogram."

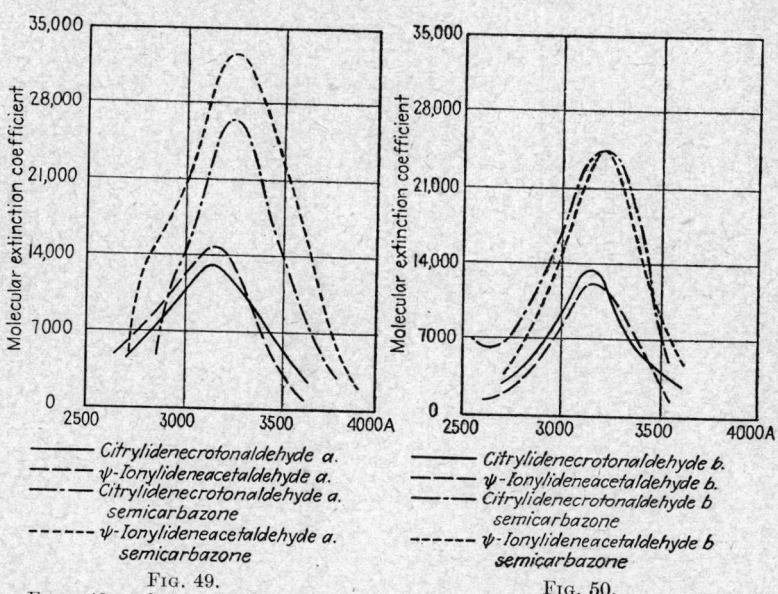

Citrylidenecrotonaldehyde a.
——— *ψ-Ionylideneacetaldehyde a.*
——— *Citrylidenecrotonaldehyde a.*
  semicarbazone
----- *ψ-Ionylideneacetaldehyde a.*
  semicarbazone

Citrylidenecrotonaldehyde b.
——— *ψ-Ionylideneacetaldehyde b.*
——— *Citrylidenecrotonaldehyde b*
  semicarbazone
----- *ψ-Ionylideneacetaldehyde b*
  semicarbazone

Fig. 49.   Fig. 50.

Figs. 49 and 50.—Analysis of the semicarbazone, melting point 178–179°, proved it to be derived from an aldehyde $C_{15}H_{22}O$. The position of its absorption maximum at 3250 A. and that of the free aldehyde (3150 A.) regenerated on hydrolysis with phthalic anhydride are in excellent agreement with the positions found for citrylidenecrotonaldehydes and their semicarbazones. [*Burraclough, E., J. W. Batty, I. M. Heilbron, and W. E. Jones,* "Studies in the Polyene Series, Part I," *Journal of the Chemical Society* (London), *October,* 1939, p. 1551.]

Frequency Distribution Plotted on a Ratio Scale. At an earlier point in this chapter (page 131) the effect of plotting a time series on a ratio scale (semilogarithmic paper) was discussed. For some purposes the use of similar paper for the plotting of a frequency series is desirable. Figure 53 shows the effect of plotting on a ratio scale the frequency distribution showing the number of cities having specified death rates from puerperal causes. The frequency distribution when plotted on the arithmetic scale as shown in Fig. 45 appears to be unsymmetrical, with a steep slope on the left side and a gradual slope on the right side. The use of a ratio scale for the variable

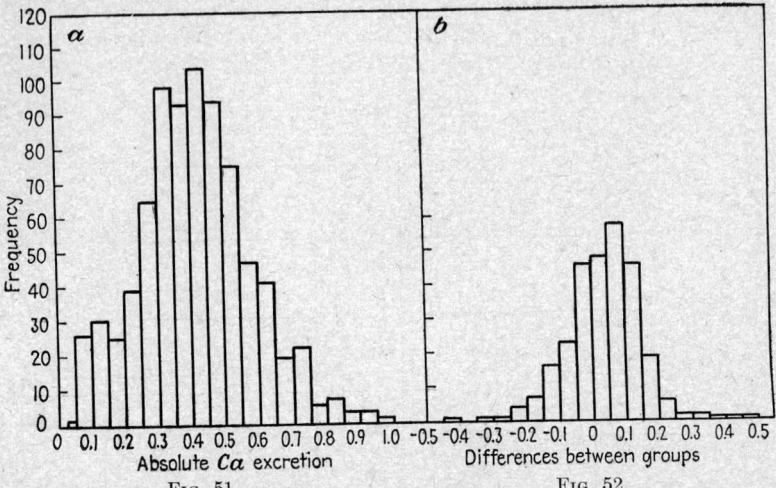

FIG. 51.   FIG. 52.

FIGS. 51 and 52.—Showing distribution of daily Ca excretion for groups of rats. Figure 51 shows results of 792 determinations of urinary Ca (mg./100 g./24 hr.) under standard conditions. Figure 52 shows differences (283 values) between test- and arbitrarily selected control groups. In both cases the results correspond with a normal distribution. [*Truszkowski, R., J. Blauth-Opieńska, and J. Iwanowska*, "Parathyroid Hormone," *The Biochemical Journal (London), Vol.* 33 (1939), *p.* 1007.]

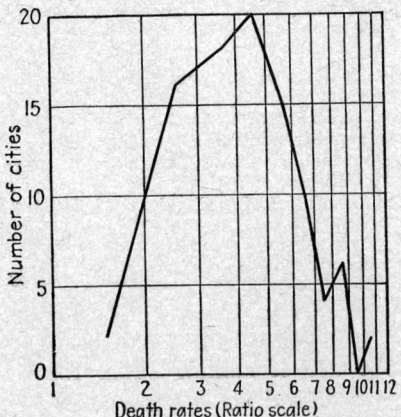

FIG. 53.—Death rates in 1938 from puerperal causes.   (*Cf.* Fig. 45.)

magnitude (continuing the use of an arithmetic scale for the frequencies), as illustrated in Fig. 53, has reduced this contrast to such an extent that the slopes on either side are almost the same and the frequency polygon appears to be almost symmetrical.

An interesting application of logarithmic frequency-distribution analysis has recently been made in entomology,[1] by C. B. Williams, who says:

> Mr. Yule shows that the frequency distribution of sentence length (*i.e.*, number of words between successive full stops) is of the skew type and by comparing two different manuscripts . . . he is able to produce convincing mathematical evidence on the identity or otherwise of their authorship. . . . When I converted some of Yule's tables into diagrams I was struck by their general resemblance to skew distributions with which I have recently been dealing in some entomological problems, . . . which distributions, I found, became normal and symmetrical if the logarithm of the number was taken as a basis for subdivision into groups instead of the number itself.

Taking the logarithm of the number as a basis for subdivision into groups instead of the number itself accomplished the same end as the plotting of the original groups on a logarithmic or ratio scale.

GROWTH CURVES

Not all curves shaped like frequency polygons or curves are in truth graphs of frequency distributions. Some growth curves assume shapes very similar to frequency curves.[2] Figure 54 is an illustration of a growth curve, showing the increase in *Chlorella vulgaris* cultures over a period of hours. The two curves contrast the peak of growth for two different-sized inoculums; in both cases the rate of multiplication per cell varied inversely with the density of population, not only in the early stages of growth but throughout the growth period in each culture.

BIVARIATE SERIES

Bivariates are cross classifications of two variable characteristics possessed in common by the objects being studied. Graphs of bivariates are sometimes confused with frequency

---

[1] WILLIAMS, C. B., "A Note on the Statistical Analysis of Sentence-length as a Criterion of Literary Style," *Biometrika*, Vol. 31 (1940), Parts III, IV, pp. 356–361.

[2] For other types of growth curves, see Chap. XX.

distributions because in some cases their shape resembles the frequency curve. Charts of bivariates, however, may assume almost any shape, and the center of the distribution may have no more importance than any other part of it. Good examples of bivariate comparisons may be found among the great variety of vital events when they are related to the different ages by their frequency of occurrence.

Table 9 and Fig. 55 present a set of such distributions. These are clearly bivariate comparisons. The x scale in these charts

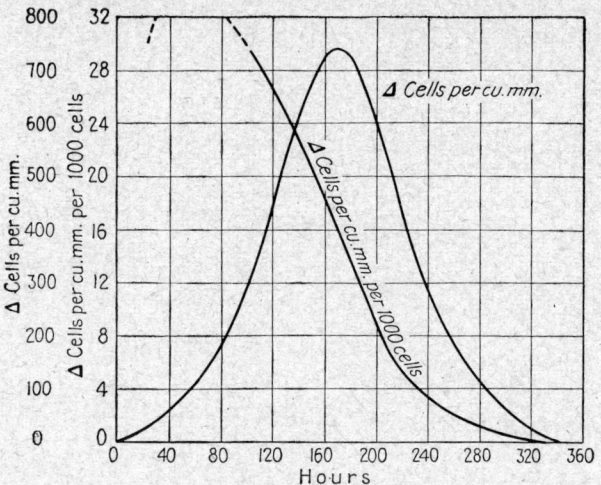

Fig. 54.—Growth curve showing the rate of increase in population in *Chlorella vulgaris* cultures as a function of time. [*Pratt, Robertson*, "*Influence of the Size of the Inoculum on the Growth of Chlorella Vulgaris in Freshly Prepared Culture Medium*," *American Journal of Botany, Vol.* 27 (*January*, 1940), *p.* 54.]

is the variation in age, from childhood to old age, representing a heterogeneous scale with respect to many vital events, such as susceptibility to certain types of disease, accident, etc. Difference in age constitutes in itself an attribute introducing lack of homogeneity where such a reference is made of it. With reference to many types of diseases, man at very tender ages and at old ages is a different being from man at middle life or in the prime of youth. Such bivariates have no reference to central tendencies—the matter of central tendencies is irrelevant. What is sought is a picture of the association between the two variables, and the very character of the data is such that there can be no expectation of a piling up of frequencies about one

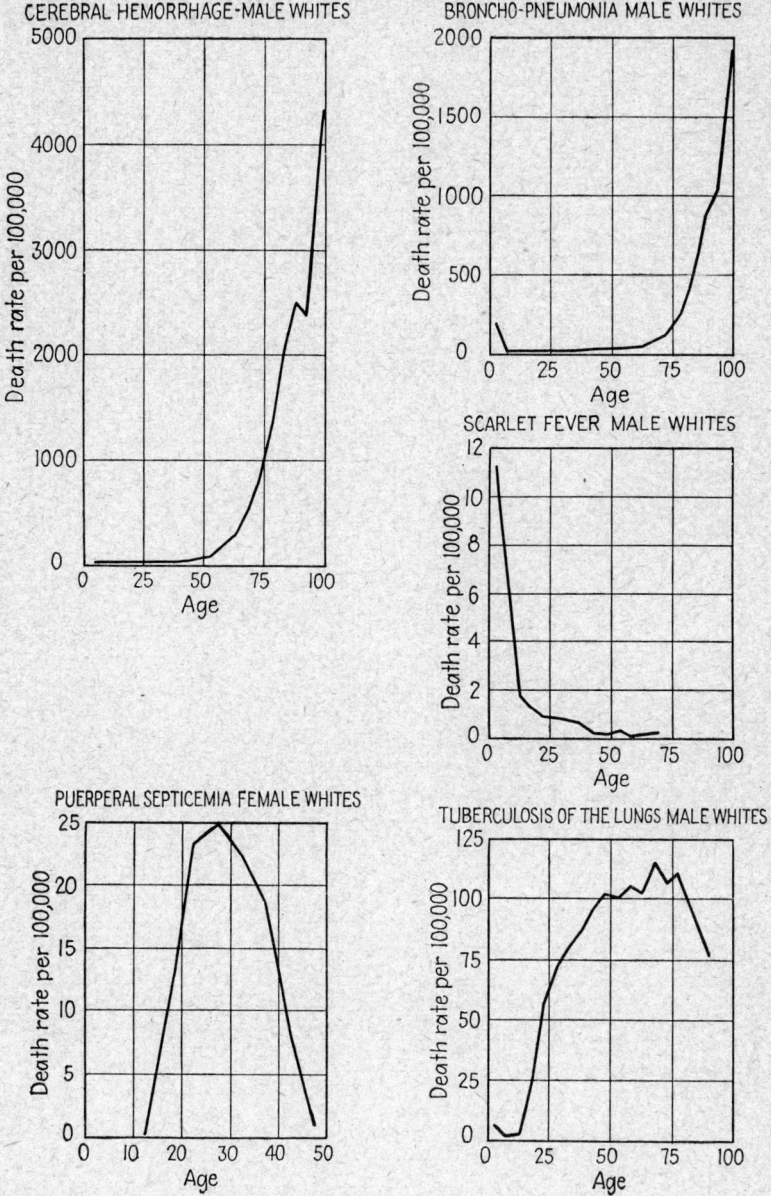

Fig. 55.—Examples of bivariate comparisons.

average or central tendency. Figure 55 is presented to show a number of examples of bivariate charts. It is readily seen that when the purpose is understood such charts are very useful as a method of picturing vital statistics; but merely because the shape of the two last examples resembles the frequency polygon it does not follow that these are true frequency distributions.

TABLE 9.—DEATH RATES PER 100,000 POPULATION IN THE UNITED STATES, 1929, FROM SPECIFIED CAUSES, BY AGE*

Age group	Tuberculosis of the lungs, male whites	Scarlet fever, male whites	Cerebral hemorrhage, male whites	Broncho-pneumonia, male whites	Puerperal septicemia, female whites
0–	7.01	11.29	2.06	182.00	
5–	2.27	5.81	0.59	6.44	
10–	3.13	1.74	0.47	2.85	0.15
15–	22.37	1.11	0.83	3.42	9.94
20–	56.33	0.94	1.50	4.33	23.01
25–	72.28	0.92	2.19	4.66	24.72
30–	80.34	0.79	4.24	6.70	22.25
35–	86.17	0.60	9.95	9.38	18.48
40–	95.66	*0.19*†	21.47	13.91	8.18
45–	101.08	*0.18*	45.22	16.47	0.99
50–	100.32	*0.28*	85.37	22.38	
55–	105.27	*0.09*	170.99	29.77	
60–	102.63	*0.17*	286.15	46.03	
65–	114.62	*0.23*	506.14	77.05	
70–	106.77	.....	814.09	124.62	
75–	110.39	.....	1,323.92	238.82	
80–		.....	2,015.65	445.22	
85–		.....	2,477.50	845.00	
90–	76.09	.....	2,365.00	1,035.00	
95–		.....⎱	4,320.00	1,920.00	
100–		.....⎰			

* The rates in this table were calculated from data on total deaths by ages in the total registration area of the United States in 1929 according to the Bureau of the Census (1932), Thirteenth Annual Report on Mortality Statistics, 1929, pp. 196–197, 198–199; 202–203, 206–207, 210–211; and population of the United States by age groups as reported in the *Abstract of the Census* (1930), p. 183. In 1929, the death registration area of continental United States included 95.7 per cent of the total population.

† Rates in italics based on less than 10 deaths.

The odd shapes that may be assumed by bivariate charts are shown by these illustrations. They may be U shaped; they may be J shaped; they may be S shaped; and, of course, they may be shaped like an ordinary frequency distribution, but when they are this is a matter of coincidence, without significance.[1]

Figure 56 is an illustration of a bivariate chart of data in the field of the natural sciences, which is shaped like a frequency curve and which even uses the word "frequency" in the title of one of its units, though it is not a frequency curve. It is a chart of a bivariate comparison—the amplitude in centimeters compared with frequency in cycles per second.

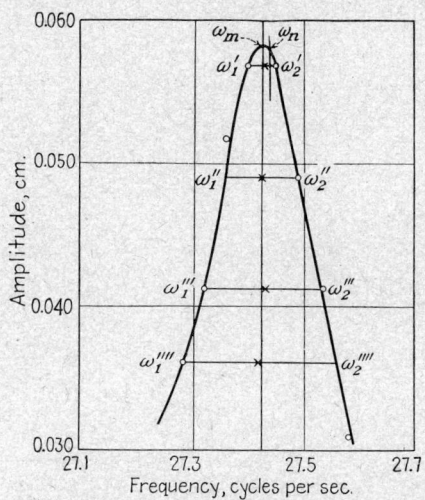

FIG. 56.—Another bivariate comparison. [*Clark, A. L., and L. Katz, "Resonance Method for Measuring the Ratio of the Specific Heats of a Gas, C_p/C_v," Canadian Journal of Research, Vol.* 18 (*February,* 1940), *p.* 30.]

Figure 57 shows the relationship between inventories and shipments of all manufacturing industries in the United States and is a bivariate chart. The dotted line on the figure represents the average relationship of inventories to shipments based on the $2\frac{1}{2}$-year period from 1939 through the second quarter of 1941. Deviations from this relationship by the quarterly items were small during the base period, the expansion of inventories being generally in proportion to the expansion of shipments. In contrast, inventories increased phenomenally in relation to shipments during the latter half of 1941 and the first half of

[1] *Cf.* also such a type of frequency distribution as that described by Thomas V. Pearce, "An Unusual Frequency Distribution—the Term of Abortion," *Biometrika,* Vol. 22 (1930–1931), pp. 250–252.

1942. Protective buying replaced immediate production needs as a motive for much of the inventory accumulation during this second period, and stocks expanded far out of line with the indi-

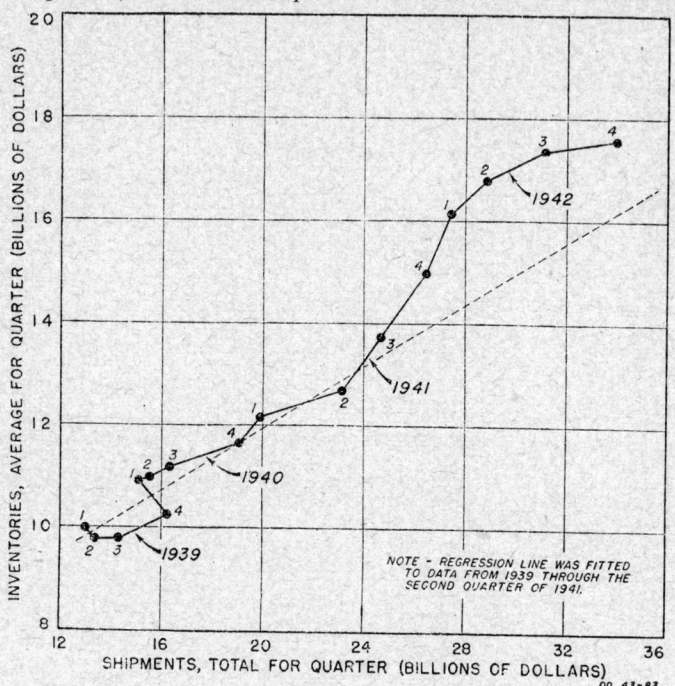

Fig. 57.—A third example of a bivariate comparison. [*Source: Survey of Current Business, Vol.* 23 (1943), pp.3–9.]

cated requirements of production, assuming that the shipments give an indication of requirements for production.

STATIC VARIATION AND DYNAMIC VARIATION

In statistical analysis there are two general forms of variation. The static form of variation is that occurring at a given point in time or occurring in such a manner that time may be rationally regarded as irrelevant to the variation. Where the variations that occur are a function of time, however, the variation is dynamic and requires different methods of analysis. In the main, the methods of analysis of static variation center in the treatment of the frequency distribution, whereas the methods of analysis of dynamic variation call for a different application of principles. The same fundamentals, however, are used in the analysis of dynamic variation or time series as those used for the analysis of frequency distributions; only the applications differ.

Rational Frequency Distributions. A rational frequency distribution is one in which that arrangement of the data is suggested by the nature of the matter observed. Such a frequency distribution is rational also because the variability of a common characteristic is chosen as the basis of the particular classification and this basis remains comparable among the objects measured. Frequently, the same idea is expressed by saying that the data are homogeneous; thus a rational frequency distribution means one in which the variable is homogeneous.

Homogeneity may be defined as the condition prerequisite to comparability of data with respect to the attribute or factor being considered. The negative aspect of this condition is that attributes not being considered are judged unimportant for the purposes of the study in hand. The positive aspect of this condition is that attributes or factors judged important for the purpose of the study are taken into consideration.

For example, if the attribute height of human beings is being considered, color of eyes may be judged irrelevant and therefore is not considered. But, for a homogeneous study, age, sex, and perhaps race are attributes that must be considered because they are all correlated with the attribute height and cannot therefore be judged unimportant in studying height. Unimportant attributes (those ignored) have zero correlation with the attribute studied. Attributes correlated with the attribute studied must be taken into consideration in order to obtain homogeneous data. In the example of heights, homogeneity is obtained by classification, that is, by taking heights of a particular class in which the correlated attributes are constants. Thus, heights of mature Caucasian males may be taken as one homogeneous group; another homogeneous group would be heights of mature Caucasian females; another would be sixteen-year-old Caucasian males; etc.

An important result of homogeneity is that no particular cause of bias or cumulated variation is present. On the contrary, the causes of variation consist of many minute mutually uncorrelated (or independent) causes of variation that occur according to the law of large numbers, in other words, in a random manner.[1]

Irrational Frequency Distributions.   By disregarding the element of time present in a time series, whose natural arrangement is according to time occurrence, the data may be reclassified and arranged in an array, or a frequency distribution.   Such a rearrangement would conceal the natural time sequence originally present in time-series data when in their natural or rational order. This type of frequency distribution is irrational as a method of summarization.   The multiple forces affecting variability in a time series are not usually operative at random or in a mutually independent manner.   On the contrary, the causes of variation may and usually do form a cumulative series of mutually dependent variations.   It is to be noted in passing that Figs. 46 to 48 are not distributions of time series.   In the data for each of these frequency distributions the attribute summarized is for a specified time and all the variables are for that specified time—thus time is held constant, and the variation shown in the histogram is uncorrelated with time.   These are rational frequency distributions.   But as soon as the data are viewed in their dynamic aspect, that is to say, are correlated with time, the many biasing attributes or factors of time destroy homogeneity in the data.[2] For example, with respect to the price of sugar taken as a time series, the supply at a subsequent period might tend to be larger as a result of the relatively high price existing at the earlier period; and as a consequence the previous high price is a cause of a later lower price.   The existence of a price situation, morever, at a given time may produce technological changes in the production and distribution of sugar that in turn will be a dominant factor in the determination of a subsequent price.

In spite of the fact that the procedure of reclassifying time series and arranging the data in frequency distributions is irrational, it has legitimate uses in statistical analysis.   There is a place for irrational procedure in the progressive development of knowledge; but, when used, the user should be conscious of the irrationality involved.[3]

---

[1] For careful consideration of the law of large numbers, see Chaps. IX–XI; also see J. G. Smith and A. J. Duncan *Sampling Statistics and Applications*, pp. 101–103, hereafter referred to by the short title *Sampling Statistics*.

[2] For further discussion of time-series analysis see Chaps. XIX–XXV.

[3] FISCHER, LUDWIG, *The Structure of Thought*, p. 360.   *Cf.* for illustrations of such rearrangement of time series, Dickson H. Leavens, "Frequency

VARIABLE QUALITIES, OR ATTRIBUTES

When statisticians have to deal with variable qualities, such as different colors, different races, different climatic conditions, different geographical locations, or different intellectual or moral capacities, their problems are principally questions of the consistent use of class or group distinctions. Usually there is no need for elaborate quantitative treatment. Yet, so far as possible, statisticians strive to convert quality, or attribute, differences into quantitative terms, and when that is accomplished, their analysis is similar to the analysis of frequency series. It has been found, for example, that certain tests can be made to provide quantitative measures of differences in intelligence, native or acquired; and a large scope for statistical analysis lies in the field of education and psychology through the use of these tests.

Distributions Corresponding to Time Series," *Journal of the American Statistical Association*, Vol. 26 (1931), pp. 407–415.

PART II

Analysis of Frequency Distributions

CHAPTER VI

SUMMARIZATION AND COMPARISON

For summarization and comparison of static variation the fundamental tool of analysis is the frequency distribution, its graphic presentation, and the analysis of its characteristics. The frequency distribution portrayed in a table or in a graph gives a picture of the whole of the variation relative to some particular matter; but how can comparisons be made? The frequency table, especially if large numbers of magnitudes are involved, even though it is admittedly better than a haphazard arrangement of the data, requires study before the mind can grasp its full significance. If two frequency distributions of heights (*e.g.*, of mature males in New Jersey in 1800 and of mature males in New Jersey in 1900) are to be compared, the frequency table could be used, but the total number of cases measured might be different in each year taken, which would make it more difficult to discern the similarity or lack of similarity of the two distributions. To make comparisons, a chart could be drawn; but a chart may be large or small depending on the scale used, and differences would then appear from purely arbitrary, mechanical causes having no real significance. Moreover, if the heights of these same males and also their weights are to be compared, a comparison of nonhomogeneous units (inches of height and pounds of weight) is required. Clearly some method or methods of summarization and comparison of frequency distributions must be devised.

Use of Frequency Distributions. The common practice of attaining a summary figure by "averaging" is familiar to all, but it should be clear that an average, taken by itself, is indeed a

158

very "summary" expression for a variable. It is one value, used to represent a whole series of variations; and a study of the variations about the average may be as important as or more important than the study of the average alone. In statistics and in most of the fields of study that use statistics and statistical methods, the average is generally a convenient point of departure for a more adequate analysis of the variable.[1]

Types of Comparison. There are six possible ways in which it may be desirable to obtain summary figures and to make comparisons. This may be explained by the use of diagrams, as follows:

In Fig. 58, the central tendency, or average, is located at A, which is plumb with the peak of the frequency curve. In this figure the central tendency is typical, in the sense that it is a magnitude that occurs more frequently than other magnitudes. It may be looked upon quite rationally as a norm, or typical value. In such a case, the average value has a significance for itself, as a summary

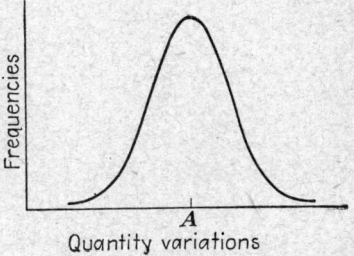

FIG. 58.—A central tendency as a norm.

value, but its principal use is still a comparative one. For example, suppose that in Fig. 58 the quantity variations (the x scale) are heights of children of a specified age while the curve represents the number of children having the indicated heights. The question is asked whether or not a certain child is normal in height. If the child has less height than height A, how much less must he be so that lack of development in this respect indicates need for medical advice? At once it is suggested that it is important to determine how much on the average children vary from this normal height. Accordingly, the principal use of the average as a summary figure, when used as a norm, is to compare individual variations with the average and to compare individual variations with the average amount of variation to be expected.

The second type of comparison is the difference in central tendencies existing between two distributions a and b, as illustrated

[1] FISHER, R. A., *Statistical Methods for Research Workers* (1941), Section 1. References to section numbers are valid for any edition of this book.

in Fig. 59. This difference is measured by comparing the averages of the two distributions; for example, by the comparison of the average height of children in third grade with the average height of children in sixth grade. Such a comparison is rational only where the units of the two frequency distributions are comparable.

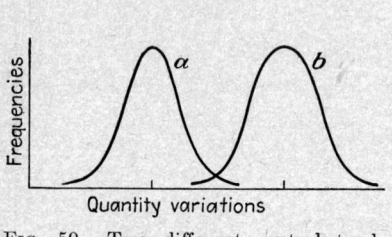

Fig. 59.—Two different central tendencies.

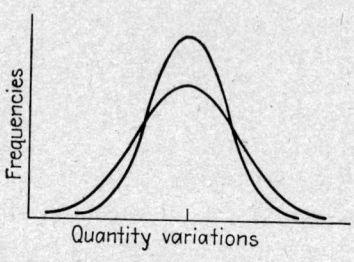

Fig. 60.—Similar central tendencies but different variability about the central tendencies.

The third type of comparison is illustrated in Fig. 60, in which some sort of measurement of the variability of the variations about the average is required for making the comparison; for example, an average of the variations from the central tendency could be used. Such measures are called "measures of variability."

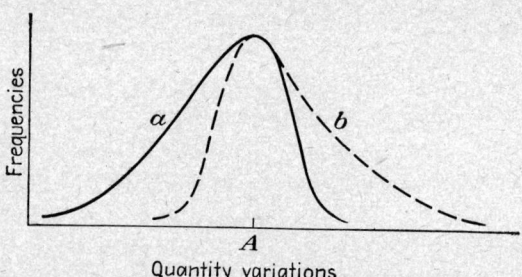

Fig. 61.—Similar central tendencies, but different types of skewness of distribution about central tendencies.

Figure 61 illustrates the fourth type of comparison. Frequency curves a and b have peaks plumb with the same quantity, A, but a is skewed to the left and b is skewed to the right. The central tendency A is a value of greatest frequency in both curves, but the lower range of curve a is farther from A than is the lower range of b; and the upper range of a is much nearer to *A* than is the upper range of *b*. School grades sometimes have a frequency distribution like *a*, with the most common grade around 70 or 80 and with very few above 90, yet with some grades below 20 or even as low as 10. Personal incomes are distributed like curve *b*, with the most common income at an amount near to the lowest and a few incomes of amounts far above the most common amount. When frequency curves like *a* or *b* in Fig. 61 are encountered, it is desirable to have some way to measure skewness and evaluate its importance in connection with the interpretation of other statistics about the frequency curve.

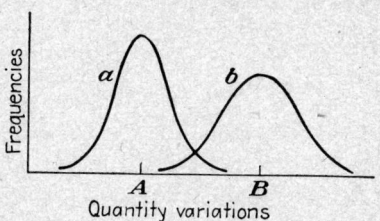

FIG. 62.—Different central tendencies and different variabilities.

In the fifth type of comparison, illustrated by Fig. 62, not only may it be desirable to compare average with average and variability with variability in aggregate terms, but it may be essential also to find a way to compare relative variability. The variability in *b* relative to its average may not be so much larger than the relative variability in *a* as the graph seems to show. The graph shows that the absolute variability in *b* is greater; but it may be that the relative comparison is the more significant one. To make the relative comparison requires the calculation of further information.

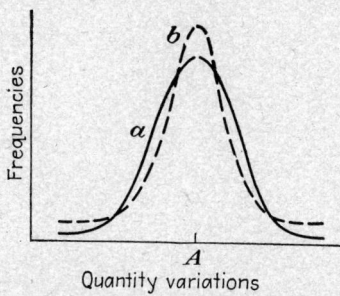

FIG. 63.—Similar central tendencies, similar variabilities, and absence of skewness, but different concentrations at center and along tails.

Curves *a* and *b* in Fig. 63, which illustrates the sixth type of comparison, have the same central tendencies and approximately the same average deviations about their central tendencies; but *b* has a relatively greater concentration of small variations close to the central tendency and also relatively more extreme variations than does *a*. Another way of looking at this difference is to note that the shoulders of *a* are broader than the shoulders of *b* and that the top of *a* is flatter than the top of *b*. The relative flatness of top or breadth of shoulder of a distribution is called "kurtosis." The measurement of this characteristic is important in determining the relative importance of small variations from average in the two curves.

It appears to follow from the above discussion of six types of comparison that the analysis of frequency distributions requires the calculation of the average and, in addition, the calculation of measures of dispersion.[1]

THEORETICAL SIGNIFICANCE OF FREQUENCY CURVES

Histograms and Frequency Curves. It has been noted that a frequency distribution may be graphed in the form of a histogram, that is, a figure in which the frequency of any class interval is represented by a rectangle erected on that interval as a base and with a height equal to the observed frequency.[2] If the data are continuous in character, that is, if they change by very small jumps, it may become reasonable to represent the frequency distribution by a smooth frequency curve rather than by a broken histogram.

Area Histograms. It is possible to make certain modifications in the form of the ordinary histogram to represent the frequency of cases occurring in any class interval, not by the height of the rectangle, but by the area of the rectangle. If the class interval is equal to unity, an area histogram is identical with one in which frequencies are represented by heights, since the altitude multiplied by the base equals the area. But if the class interval is greater than unity, the height of an area histogram will be proportionately reduced; if the class interval is less than unity, the height will be proportionately increased. This follows because in an area histogram the frequency of any class interval is given by the height of the rectangle erected on it, multiplied by the length of its base (that is, by the size of the class interval). In histograms of the area type, it follows that the total area of the histogram always equals the total number of cases, N.

Relative Frequencies. The histogram may be further modified by making it represent relative or proportional frequencies, rather than absolute frequencies. Following is a table showing a proportional frequency distribution:[3]

[1] See pp. 168–195.
[2] For illustrations, see Figs. 64 and 66, pp. 187–188.
[3] *Cf.* p. 141.

MATERNAL MORTALITY IN CITIES OF 100,000 OR MORE POPULATION IN THE
UNITED STATES, 1938

Death rates (number per 1,000 live births)	Number of cities	Relative number of cities	
		Expressed as proportions $\frac{F}{N}$	Expressed as percentages $\left(\frac{F}{N}\right) \times 100$
X	F		
(1)	(2)	(3)	(4)
1–	2	0.022	2.2
2–	16	0.172	17.2
3–	18	0.193	19.3
4–	20	0.215	21.5
5–	15	0.161	16.1
6–	10	0.108	10.8
7–	4	0.043	4.3
8–	6	0.064	6.4
9–	0	0.000	0.0
10–	2	0.022	2.2
	93	1.000	100.0

In the above table the figures in column (3) represent the proportionate frequencies, namely, the proportionate number of cities having the specified maternal mortality rates. Since this illustration has a class interval of 1, an area histogram could be obtained by plotting the frequencies of column (2) in the form of vertical bars, with the heights equal to the respective frequencies. A proportional area histogram could be obtained by similarly plotting the frequencies shown in column (3); because in the resulting histogram, the area of each rectangle would represent the proportion of the total number of cases falling in a class interval; it would represent F/N instead of F. The total area of such a histogram will always equal unity, just as the total of column (3) equals unity. This will be true no matter what the form or shape of the histogram, because $\Sigma F = N$.

Frequency Curves. Suppose that the data, from which the histogram has been constructed, are a sample from a very large set of cases, theoretically an infinite set. For instance, the data might be the heights of 100 adult males of the white race, instead of the mortality statistics above illustrated. The 100 heights, then, would be a sample of the heights of all adult men of that race, presumably millions of men. In such a relatively small sample, the size of the class interval cannot be reduced without causing the histogram to show very irregular fluctuations. If, however, many cases are added to the number in the sample, say heights of 200 men, the size of the class interval could be reduced, for example, from 10 units to 5 units, without causing the occurrence of such irregularities. In fact, if the number in the sample is made larger and larger and at the same time the size of the class interval is continuously reduced, the histogram will tend to become more and more regular and the tops of the rectangles, which are getting narrower and narrower, will come closer and closer to forming a smooth continuous curve (a frequency curve). In such a manner the frequency curve may be viewed as the limit that an area histogram of relative frequencies approaches as the number of cases is increased and the size of the class interval is reduced indefinitely. The frequency curve is the distribution of a theoretically infinite set of data, with a theoretically infinitesimal class interval.

Being the limit approached by an area histogram of relative frequencies, the frequency curve has a total area (between the curve and the x-axis) that is always equal to unity. Furthermore, any section of area under the curve[1] will give the relative frequency of the cases falling within the class interval marking off that section of area. It is upon this basis that tables of relative frequencies are constructed for certain well-known frequency curves.[2]

Uses of Frequency Curves. Frequency curves are hypothetical, but they are idealizations of frequency distributions that are real. They serve many useful purposes and in the theory of statistics they are indispensable. One important use of frequency curves is the graduation of frequency distributions obtained from actual observation. Suppose, for example, that a frequency distribution has been constructed, using a class interval of 10 units. Suppose further that the number of cases is such that any smaller class interval would introduce marked irregularities into the distribution, irregularities that, it is believed, would not be present

[1] See Fig. 91, p. 264 and Fig. 94, p. 277.
[2] See Appendix, Table VI.

if an infinitely large number of cases were observed. In this case a frequency curve fitted to the distribution (histogram) may be the best means of estimating the true frequency for any given class interval. In other words, the frequency curve affords a graduation for the frequency distribution. The frequency curve makes it possible to interpolate values not given directly by the original sample frequency distribution.

Besides serving to graduate a given set of data, frequency curves facilitate in other ways the description and comparison of frequency distributions. For instance, the peakedness or flatness of a particular frequency curve, called the "normal frequency curve," is taken as the standard to which the peakedness or flatness of a given distribution is generally referred. Again, theoretical analysis shows that data affected by certain kinds of forces will tend to be distributed in the form of particular types of frequency curves. Certain types of curves, therefore, become the expected norm for all data affected by particular kinds of forces. As a consequence, the hypothesis that variations in a given set of data have resulted from certain forces may be tested by noting how well the distribution of the data conforms to the type of frequency curve that these forces may be expected to produce. In such instances frequency curves help to explain the underlying causes of variation. Such an analysis is of special importance when it is assumed, as it is in so many statistical procedures, that chance is the fundamental cause of variation. It is to be noted that a difference in the general form of two frequency distributions may in some cases be looked upon as of more fundamental importance than a mere difference in their averages, dispersion, and the like, because such a difference in form may indicate a contrast in the type of forces causing variation in the data. To detect a fundamental difference of this kind frequency curves are used.

Still another useful purpose served by frequency curves is in sampling analysis. Since a chapter is subsequently devoted to a discussion of sampling, it need merely be touched upon and simply illustrated in very general terms at this point.[1] For

[1] See Chap. XII; see also SMITH, J. G., and A. J. DUNCAN, *Sampling Statistics*, pp. 107–109, Parts II and III.

illustration, suppose that a large number of balls, each with a number written on it, are placed in a big bowl and thoroughly mixed. Suppose that 10 balls are drawn at random from the bowl and their numbers read off and averaged. Suppose that this sampling operation is repeated over and over again, the balls being replaced and thoroughly mixed after each set of drawings. Experience shows that unless the distribution of numbers is freakish, the distribution of sample averages will approximate the so-called "normal" frequency curve. If, instead of the average of the respective 10 readings, a certain measure of the variation around their averages, known as the "variance," had been recorded in each instance, then the frequency distribution of these measurements of variation would have tended to conform to a frequency curve known as the "χ^2 curve."[1] The significant thing is that "sampling distributions" of this kind tend to conform to specific frequency curves that may be described by definite mathematical formulas. In general, these formulas are expressed in terms of the characteristics of the "population" (in the illustration, the bowl of numbers) from which the samples are drawn. The consequence is that if a random sample has been obtained from an unknown population, it is possible from knowledge of the sampling distributions of various sample measurements to make certain inferences regarding the nature of the population from which the sample has been drawn. This is probably the most important use that is made of frequency curves in statistical analysis.

MEASUREMENTS OF SUMMARIZATION AND COMPARISON

Population, Parameters, and Statistics. *Population.* To say that the population of the United States is one hundred and thirty million people is a familiar use of the word "population." In statistics the word is used in the same familiar sense, but it is also used in a more general sense, referring to the count of persons or of animals of any kind or even to the count of inanimate things. To statisticians the term means all the things, animate or inanimate as the case may be, of a given kind in the known universe or in a specified universe, for example, all the people on the earth, or all the people in the United States if the

---

[1] This is read "chi square"; the letter is the Greek small chi.

universe is more specific. An example of an inanimate population would be all the petroleum in the known universe or, if a more specific universe is considered, all the petroleum in the United States.

Parameters and Statistics. In the theory of statistics the measurements of the characteristics of the population are called "parameters." The average height of all people living in the United States is a parameter of the population. No one has ever actually measured the heights of all the people living in the United States, and it is not likely that anyone ever will do so. Nevertheless, this population does exist. In practice, it is much easier to estimate the average height of all the people by taking the average of a sample of the people. This latter average, the average of the sample, is called a "statistic." Accordingly, parameters are measures of the characteristics of the population, and the corresponding sample measures are statistics commonly used to estimate these parameters. A statistic is thus a value computed from an observed sample in order to characterize the population from which it is drawn. Parameters are the characters of the population.[1]

In accordance with this terminology, the quantities to be obtained as measures of central tendencies are "statistics," the arithmetic mean is a "statistic," the range (difference between the highest and lowest magnitude) of a frequency distribution is a "statistic."

Averages. There are several kinds of averages. The one most familiar is the arithmetic mean. The others most generally presented are the median, mode, geometric mean, and harmonic mean. The most commonly used averages are the mean, the median, and the mode. In this chapter each will be viewed in its simplest aspect, and at the same time the symbolic language associated with the analysis of frequency distributions will be introduced.

The Arithmetic Mean. By definition, *the arithmetic mean is the sum of the cases divided by the number of cases.* For example, taking a simple case of ungrouped data, *i.e.,* where the frequencies are 1 throughout (each X occurs once), $F_1, F_2, \ldots ,$ F_7 each $= 1$:

---

[1] FISHER, *op. cit.*, pp. 7–8, 41.

	X		F
X_1	2	F_1	1
X_2	3	F_2	1
X_3	4	F_3	1
X_4	6	F_4	1
X_5	8	F_5	1
X_6	9	F_6	1
X_7	10	F_7	1
$\Sigma X = 42$		$\Sigma F = 7$	

The sum of the variable magnitudes in this case is 42. The number of variable magnitudes is 7. Hence, by definition, the arithmetic mean is $\frac{42}{7}$, or 6.

Symbolically,

$$42 = \Sigma X, \; i.e., \; X_1 + X_2 + \cdots + X_7$$
$$7 = \Sigma F = N, \; i.e., \; F_1 + F_2 + \cdots + F_7$$

The arithmetic mean is represented by the symbol $\bar{X}$, and hence

$$\bar{X} = \frac{\Sigma FX}{N} \tag{1}$$

In frequency distributions the F is not equal to 1 throughout but varies. An illustration of the calculation of the arithmetic mean of a frequency distribution is shown below:

X	F	FX
2	3	6
3	3	9
4	6	24
5	9	45
6	6	36
7	3	21
ΣF or $N = 30$		$\Sigma FX = 141$

It should be noted that the sum of the X's cannot be obtained by adding the first column because the various X's occur 3, 6, or 9 times. Consequently, the sum of the X's is obtained by multiplying each X by its respective frequency and then adding the products.

$$\Sigma FX = 141$$
$$\Sigma F \text{ or } N = 30$$

and therefore, by definition,

$$\bar{X} = \tfrac{141}{30} = 4.7$$

If the frequencies of a frequency distribution are expressed in relative numbers, *i.e.*, if each frequency is expressed relative to the total number of cases, F_1/N, F_2/N, . . . , F_n/N, the arithmetic mean is merely the sum of the third column, as follows:

X	$\dfrac{F}{N}$	$\dfrac{F}{N}X$
2	0.1	0.2
3	0.1	0.3
4	0.2	0.8
5	0.3	1.5
6	0.2	1.2
7	0.1	0.7
	1.0	4.7

Following the definition, the arithmetic mean is the sum of the third column divided by the sum of the second column; but the sum of the second column is 1, by definition. Consequently, the arithmetic mean is the sum of the third column.

$$\bar{X} = \sum \frac{F}{N} X \qquad (1a)$$

This modified form of the definition of the arithmetic mean is very convenient in certain statistical problems.

The sum of the deviations of the cases from the arithmetic mean is equal to zero. This may be demonstrated as follows: Given the variable X_1, X_2, . . . X_n, $\bar{X} = \Sigma FX/N$.

$$F_1(X_1 - \bar{X}) = F_1 x_1$$
$$F_2(X_2 - \bar{X}) = F_2 x_2$$
$$\cdot \quad \cdot \quad \cdot \quad \cdot \quad \cdot \quad \cdot$$
$$\underline{F_n(X_n - \bar{X}) = F_n x_n}$$
$$\Sigma FX - N\bar{X} = \Sigma Fx \qquad \text{by adding}$$

The small x is used regularly to refer to the deviations of the variable from the arithmetic mean.

When added, $\Sigma F\bar{X}$ becomes $N\bar{X}$ because $\bar{X}$ is constant and ΣF is equal to N.

If the value of $\bar{X}$ given in Eq. (1) is substituted in

$$\Sigma FX - N\bar{X} = \Sigma Fx$$

it becomes

$$\Sigma FX - N\frac{\Sigma FX}{N} = \Sigma Fx$$

By canceling the N, this becomes

$$\Sigma FX - \Sigma FX = \Sigma Fx$$

and hence

$$\Sigma Fx = 0 \qquad (2)$$

The Median and the Quartiles. In its original simplicity and by definition the median is not a mathematical concept like the arithmetic mean. On the contrary, the median is a position average. By definition, *the median is that value than which there is an equal number of cases larger and smaller.* When the cases are arranged in an array, the median is either the value of the middle one (when there is an odd number) or some value between the two middle ones (when there is an even number). Normally, in the latter instance, the arithmetic mean of the two middle cases is taken as the median value. To illustrate from a very simple example with an odd number of cases:

$$
\begin{array}{c}
X \\
1 \\
2 \\
3 \\
6 \\
7 \\
8 \\
9
\end{array}
$$

X_4, or 6, is the median by definition, because it is the middle one in the array. $Mi = 6$ (Mi is the conventional symbol for median).

It is to be noted that $\bar{X} = 5.143$.

In this illustration it is seen that 1, the first case, is 5 smaller than the median, while 9, the last case, is only 3 larger than the median. This preponderance of smallness of the variable results in an arithmetic mean smaller than the median. By definition, the arithmetic mean is affected by every variation and consequently by extreme variations. It is affected by the size and the number of cases above and below it. The median, on the other hand, by definition, is not affected by the size of the cases above or below it.

When the frequencies vary, the median may be found as in the following illustration:

X	F	Cumulated F
1	2	2
2	4	6
3	5	11
4	8	19
5	7	26
6	3	29
7	2	31
	31	

Thus, there are 2 cases where $X = 1$; there are 4 cases where $X = 2$; etc. In all, there are 31 cases ($\Sigma F = 31 = N$), and the middle one is the sixteenth. Mi $= 4$. That the median is 4 is quickly seen by the examination of the cumulated frequencies in the third column. This is equivalent to taking the median equal to the $(N + 1)/2$th case, a procedure often adopted when dealing with ungrouped data.[1]

In general terms, the first quartile Q_1 is that value below which one-fourth of the cases fall and above which three-fourths of the cases fall. Similarly, the third quartile Q_3 is that value below which three-quarters of the cases fall and above which one-fourth of the cases fall. The median is the second quartile, or Q_2. In the above frequency distribution, $N/4 = 7\frac{3}{4}$ and $3N/4 = 23\frac{1}{4}$. Q_1 should thus be some value below which $7\frac{3}{4}$ cases fall and above which $23\frac{1}{4}$ cases fall. For this distribution, it happens that the seventh and eighth cases are identical, and it therefore follows that the value of Q_1 is the common value of the seventh and eighth cases, or $Q_1 = 3$. If the seventh and eighth cases had not been the same, then Q_1 could be taken as a value between the values of the seventh and the eighth case to be found by interpolation.

For ungrouped data, it is recommended that a uniform and systematic method of interpolation be adopted, as follows:[2]

---

[1] When the data are grouped, it is simplest to find the median by interpolation within the class interval for the $N/2$th case. This method is described and illustrated in the next chapter. See pp. 218–220.

[2] For the method of interpolation when the data are grouped, see pp. 218–220.

Take Q_1 as the $(N/4 + \frac{1}{2})$ case, Q_2, or Mi, as the $(N/2 + \frac{1}{2})$ case, and Q_3 as the $(3N/4 + \frac{1}{2})$ case. Consider, for example, the cases 5, 9, 11, 16, 25, 31, 38, 43, 45, and 49. The $(N/4 + \frac{1}{2})$ case would be the $(\frac{10}{4} + \frac{1}{2})$ or third case; *i.e.*, $Q_1 = 11$. The median would be the $(\frac{10}{2} + \frac{1}{2})$ or $5\frac{1}{2}$th case. Since there is no $5\frac{1}{2}$th case, however, but only a fifth case, 25, and a sixth case, 31, the median is taken as the value that lies just halfway between the fifth and sixth cases, *i.e.*, $\mathrm{Mi} = 25 + \dfrac{(31 - 25)}{2} = 28$. The third quartile would be the $(\frac{30}{4} + \frac{1}{2})$ or eighth case; *i.e.*, $Q_3 = 43$.

As another illustration, suppose 51 is added to the set of numbers, making a total of eleven instead of ten numbers. Then the first quartile would be the $(\frac{11}{4} + \frac{1}{2})$ or the $3\frac{1}{4}$th case. But there is no $3\frac{1}{4}$th case, only a third case, 11, and a fourth case, 16. Hence, Q_1 is taken as the value that lies one-fourth of the distance between the third and fourth cases. The difference between the third and fourth cases is $16 - 11 = 5$, and Q_1 is therefore taken as $11 + \frac{5}{4} = 12\frac{1}{4}$. Similarly, Mi is the $(\frac{11}{2} + \frac{1}{2})$ or sixth case, which is 31.

The Mode. As in the case of the median, the mode is not a mathematical concept. Moreover, it is not a "position average." The mode is an average that is described in terms of relative frequency of occurrence. It is defined as the magnitude that occurs more frequently than any other. The mode is the most probable magnitude and might be considered a "probability average," because it is often thought of in terms of probabilities. It may be illustrated as follows:

X	F
2	1
3	2
4	4
6	7
7	8
8	5
9	4
10	3
	34

By definition the mode (Mo) is 7, because this value occurs more frequently than any of the others. The probability of the mode is $\frac{8}{34}$ and is greater than the probability of any other value of X.

It is to be noted that the $\bar{X}$ of this example is 6.706 and the median is 7. The mode is not affected by the size of the cases above or below it, nor is it affected by the number of cases above or below it, within certain rational limits. For example, in the illustration, two magnitudes ($X = 8$) could be added to the distribution and the mode would remain 7, as before; but if five magnitudes ($X = 8$) were added to the distribution, then 8 would become the mode, as its frequency would then be 10.

It has been established that, when the distribution is only moderately skewed, the mode can be estimated from the mean and median by the following approximate formula:

$$\text{Mo} = \bar{X} - 3(\bar{X} - \text{Mi}) \tag{3}$$

Accordingly, the mode may be estimated if the mean and the median have been calculated. In actual problems involving grouped data the mean and the median are both more accurately determinable than is the mode, and for this reason the above formula often gives more satisfactory results than any convenient direct procedure. This is called the "mathematical mode." It should be emphasized that the formula should not be used, however, if the distribution is very skewed.

The Geometric Mean. The geometric mean (G.M.) is a mathematical concept and is defined as the *nth root of the product of n variables* X. Accordingly, the geometric mean of 5, 8, and 25 is $(5 \times 8 \times 25)^{\frac{1}{3}} = 10$. The geometric mean may also be defined as the antilogarithm of the arithmetic mean of the logarithms of the variable X, *i.e.*,

$$\log \text{G.M.} = \frac{\Sigma \log X}{N} \tag{4}$$

This may be illustrated as follows:

$$
\begin{array}{rl}
\log 5 = & 0.69897 \\
\log 8 = & 0.90309 \\
\log 25 = & \underline{1.39794} \\
\frac{\Sigma \log X}{N} = & 3)\overline{3.00000} \\
& \overline{1.00000}
\end{array}
$$

The antilogarithm of 1.00000 is 10; hence, G.M. = 10.

Just as the arithmetic mean balances the aggregate deviations so the geometric mean balances the ratios of the variations; that is,

$$\frac{X_1}{G.M.} \times \frac{X_2}{G.M.} \times \cdots \times \frac{X_n}{G.M.} = 1 \qquad (5)$$

For, by taking logarithms, this expression becomes

$$\log X_1 + \log X_2 + \log X_3 + \cdots + \log X_n - N \log G.M. = 0$$
$$\text{or} \qquad \Sigma \log X - N \log G.M. = 0$$

But from Eq. (4),

$$N \log G.M. = \Sigma \log X$$

and hence the expression is shown to be true.

In some types of problems the geometric mean gives more satisfactory results than the arithmetic mean. For example, it is necessary to use the geometric mean to average percentage increases of population over successive years or decades or to average percentage changes in income, production, and the like.[1] Thus, in the column marked X of the following table the estimated national income of each year is expressed as a percentage of the preceding year:

Year	Estimated national income produced in the United States,[1] billions of dollars	Increase in national income expressed as percentage of previous year X
1933	47.3	
1934	54.6	115.43
1935	59.2	108.42
1936	68.9	116.39
1937	73.1	106.10
1938	67.0	91.66
1939	69.7	104.03

[1] *Survey of Current Business*, Vol. 20 (March, 1940), p. 19; (April, 1940), p. 11.

If the average annual percentage increase is obtained by calculating the arithmetic average, the answer obtained is $642.03/6 = 107.01$, which represents an average annual percent-

[1] CHADDOCK, R. E., *Principles and Methods of Statistics* (1925), pp. 126–127; CROXTON, F. E., and D. J. COWDEN, *Applied Business Statistics* (1939), pp. 225–226.

age increase of 7.01 per cent. Now, if 7.01 is used as a constant annual percentage increase from 1933, the following figures would be obtained:

Year	Constant 7.01 Percentage Increase from 47.3 in 1933
1934	107.01 per cent of 47.3 = 50.62
1935	107.01 per cent of 50.62 = 54.17
1936	107.01 per cent of 54.17 = 57.97
1937	107.01 per cent of 57.97 = 62.14
1938	107.01 per cent of 62.14 = 66.50
1939	107.01 per cent of 66.50 = 71.16

But in 1939 the actual figure, as shown in the preceding table, was 69.7; and the average percentage yearly increase could not have been so large as 7.01. To obtain the correct percentage increase, the geometric and not the arithmetic mean should be calculated in this instance. Following the formula given above for the geometric mean, it is calculated for this problem as follows:

Year	Estimated national income produced in the United States, billions of dollars	Logarithm of the percentage increase $\log X$
1933	47.3	
1934	54.6	2.06232
1935	59.2	2.03511
1936	68.9	2.06591
1937	73.1	2.02572
1938	67.0	1.96218
1939	69.7	2.01716

If the average annual percentage increase is now obtained by calculating the geometric mean of the rates of increase, by first taking the arithmetic mean of the logarithms

$$\frac{12.16840}{6} = 2.02807$$

and then taking the antilogarithm (antilogarithm of 2.02807) the answer obtained is 106.68 or an average annual percentage increase of 6.68 per cent. If 6.68 is assumed to be the average annual percentage increase since 1933, the following figures would be obtained:

	Constant 6.68 Percentage Increase from 47.3 in 1933
Year	
1934	106.68 per cent of 47.3 = 50.46
1935	106.68 per cent of 50.46 = 53.83
1936	106.68 per cent of 53.83 = 57.43
1937	106.68 per cent of 57.43 = 61.27
1938	106.68 per cent of 61.27 = 65.36
1939	106.68 per cent of 65.36 = 69.73

In 1939 the actual figure, as shown above, was 69.7, to which 69.73 is a close approximation; and hence the average annual percentage increase apparently was in fact close to 6.68.

The Harmonic Mean.   The harmonic mean (H.M.) *is the reciprocal of the average of the reciprocals of observations of the variable X,* thus:

$$\text{H.M.} = \frac{N}{\sum \frac{1}{X}} \tag{6}$$

Accordingly, the harmonic mean of 5, 8, and 25 would be found as follows:

From a table of reciprocals or by calculation, the reciprocals of 5, 8, and 25 are determined—0.200, 0.125, and 0.040—and hence the harmonic mean, by definition, is

$$\frac{3}{0.200 + 0.125 + 0.040} = \frac{3}{0.365} = 8.22$$

The geometric mean of these three numbers, as discovered above, is 10; the arithmetic mean is $5 + 8 + 25 = 38$ divided by 3, or 12.67.   It is thus seen that the arithmetic mean is the largest, the geometric mean next, and the harmonic mean the smallest of these three averages.   It is always true that[1]

$$\text{H.M.} < \text{G.M.} < \bar{X} \tag{7}$$

The usefulness of the harmonic mean arises in connection with certain types of problems in which variable quantities of one variable are compared with a constant quantity of another. For illustration, speeds may be looked upon as variable numbers of miles per minute (a constant quantity of time) or as variable amounts of time required to cover a given distance.   Similarly,

---

[1] For a proof see G. R. Davies and W. F. Crowder, *Methods of Statistical Analysis in the Social Sciences*, p. 313.

prices may be looked upon as variable amounts of money per unit of goods sold (a constant quantity of goods) or as variable amounts of goods that can be purchased with $1. In many such problems the choice of the variable for which the quantity is always constant is optional, depending upon the type of information it is desired to emphasize. There is a nice distinction between the mean and the harmonic mean wherever such interchangeability is present. This will be illustrated by examples.

The accompanying table shows data on prices of corn.

WHOLESALE PRICE OF NO. 3 YELLOW CORN

Year	Dollars per Bushel
1913	0.61
1919	1.59
1929	0.93
1939	0.50

Source: *Survey of Current Business*, April, 1940, p. 18.

In the table the amount of money varies, but the quantity of corn is constant. The average price per bushel may be calculated directly from this table, thus: $\frac{3.63}{4} = 0.9075$. In order to obtain the harmonic mean, the reciprocals of these prices must first be calculated.

WHOLESALE PRICE OF NO. 3 YELLOW CORN

Year	Bushels per Dollar
1913	1.64
1919	0.63
1929	1.08
1939	2.00

The average of these reciprocals must be computed, thus:

$$\frac{5.35}{4} = 1.3375.$$

The reciprocal of the latter number must be obtained, namely, 0.74766. This last number is the harmonic mean of the prices expressed in dollars per bushel. The harmonic mean, therefore, of the prices per bushel of No. 3 yellow corn is approximately 75 cents; and it is the price per bushel of the average amount of No. 3 yellow corn that could have been purchased for $1, or, in other words, it is the reciprocal of the average amount of No. 3

yellow corn that could have been purchased for $1. If the reciprocal of the mean price, 0.9075, is taken, a figure of quite different significance is obtained, namely, 1.102. This reciprocal is the average number of bushels that could have been bought at the mean price.

In deciding whether to use the arithmetic or the harmonic mean in any given problem, it should be determined which magnitude should be regarded as the constant (for example, the amount of corn bought or the amount of money spent), a matter that can usually be decided without difficulty in a practical problem. If the data are recorded with the appropriate quantity constant, the arithmetic mean may be used. If the appropriate item is made a variable as the data are tabulated, the harmonic mean must be used.

Another illustration will serve to clarify further the use of the harmonic mean. The efficiency of a fighting airplane may be determined, in part at least, by its speed, which can be expressed either as the number of miles flown per minute or the amount of time required to fly a mile. Following are the results of tests of a plane under trial:

RESULTS OF TESTS

Miles per minute............................ 6, 4, 7, 6, 5

Is the significant measure the rate at which a plane flies or the amount of time required to fly a number of miles? If it is admitted that the rate at which the plane flies is the important consideration (that is, the number of minutes required to fly a mile), the reciprocal of the harmonic mean is the relevant measure, inasmuch as the recorded data make the time element constant and not the distance flown. The arithmetic mean, if calculated, would not be lacking in significance, but its reciprocal should not be compared with rate measures in which the number of miles is constant and the time varies. The average number of miles per minute is $\frac{28}{5} = 5.6$. The reciprocal of this number, 0.17857, is not the harmonic mean, and it is not the average time that it takes to travel a mile. On the contrary, 0.17857 minute is the amount of time it requires to go a mile when traveling at the average number of miles per minute. The average amount of time required to travel a mile is a different thing, namely, the average of $\frac{1}{6}$, $\frac{1}{4}$, $\frac{1}{7}$, $\frac{1}{6}$, and $\frac{1}{5}$ minutes, or 0.179 minute. While the two results are close together in value, it would make a large difference in calculations having to do with hours of time if the arithmetic mean were used when the harmonic mean ought to have been used.

The Concept of an Average as a Summary Figure. The general significance of an average as a summary figure may be illustrated. Suppose that information concerning the heights of mature males in Newark, N.J., is desired. Heights of all the mature males in Newark are therefore measured to the nearest $\frac{1}{8}$ inch. The data collected will constitute complete information about the heights of mature males in Newark. But this knowledge, in untabulated form without summary figures, is not easy to comprehend. It is necessary to analyze this total knowledge in some manner so that it may become more significant. The manner in which the analysis will proceed depends upon the object in mind; for example, an answer to any one of the following questions may give a more significant view:

1. What height will coincide with the greatest number of recorded observations? The answer to this question is, of course, the mode.

2. What is the height such that greater and smaller heights have been recorded with equal frequency? The answer to this question is the median.

3. What is the height such that the sum of the squares of the differences between it and the recorded observations is a minimum? Or what is the height such that the algebraic sum of the differences between it and the recorded observations is zero? The answer to this question will be the arithmetic mean.

4. What is the height H such that the product of the ratios of the recorded observations to H is unity? The answer to this question will be the geometric mean.

5. If several rates of speed were given in miles per second, how many seconds on the average will be required to travel 1 mile? The answer is the reciprocal of the harmonic mean. (Heights could not be used as an illustration because the harmonic mean is significant only in the dual-variable type of quantity expression, as explained above.)

The term "average" is a generic term, and any one of these summary figures may be called an average; the decision as to which average should be used depends upon what question is to be answered.   If the median height is known and the height of a man is greater than the median, it can be inferred that the man is taller than most men.   If a man's height is equal to the mode, it is known that he has the most common, or usual, height.   If height is analyzed in the abstract, as it might be in research on the effects of heredity and environment, the arithmetic mean is likely to be used, for such analyses ordinarily involve the solution of problems in mathematical terms.

MOMENTS

Definition.   In physics, "moment" is a measure of a force with respect to its tendency to produce rotation.   The strength of the tendency depends on the amount of force and the distance from the origin of the point at which the force is exerted.   If a number of forces, $F_1, F_2, \ldots, F_n$, at distances $X_1, X_2, \ldots X_n$, are applied, the moment of the first force about the origin is F_1X_1, the moment of the second force is F_2X_2, etc.   These moments are additive so that ΣFX is the total moment about the origin.   If the total moment is divided by the total force, the quotient is termed "a moment coefficient."   The formula is $\Sigma FX/N$, where $N = \Sigma F$ is the total force.

It will be recognized that the formula for a moment coefficient is identical with that for an arithmetic mean.   This identity has lead statisticians to speak of the arithmetic mean as the "first moment about the origin."   Technically the mean is a moment coefficient and not a total moment, but in the case of frequency curves, with which mathematical statistics is primarily concerned, the total frequency N is generally taken as unity,[1] so that the total moment and the moment coefficient are identical. In any case, it has become customary in statistics to speak of the mean $\bar{X} = \Sigma FX/N$ as the first moment about the origin, and the distinction between total moment and moment coefficient is ignored.

The concept of moments is also extended to higher powers. Thus in statistics $\Sigma FX^2/N$ is termed the "second moment about the origin," and $\Sigma FX^3/N$ is called the "third moment about the origin," etc.   In general, the moments about zero are as follows:

[1] See pp. 276–277 and Appendix, Table VI.

$$\nu_1 = \frac{\Sigma FX}{N}$$

$$\nu_2 = \frac{\Sigma FX^2}{N}$$

$$\cdot \quad \cdot \quad \cdot \quad \cdot \quad \cdot$$

$$\nu_n = \frac{\Sigma FX^n}{N}$$

$$(8)$$

When the moments are calculated, not from zero, but from the mean, or "centroid," they are defined as follows:

$$\mu_1 = \frac{\Sigma Fx}{N}$$

$$\mu_2 = \frac{\Sigma Fx^2}{N}$$

$$\mu_3 = \frac{\Sigma Fx^3}{N}$$

$$(9)$$

$$\cdot \quad \cdot \quad \cdot \quad \cdot \quad \cdot$$

$$\mu_n = \frac{\Sigma Fx^n}{N}$$

where $x = X - \bar{X}$. It will be noted that it is a convention in statistics to use small x to represent deviations from the arithmetic mean.

The first moment about the mean is the sum of the deviations from the mean multiplied by their respective frequencies and divided by the number of cases in the frequency distribution. The second moment is similarly obtained except that the deviations are squared before adding. To obtain the third moment the deviations are cubed, multiplied by their respective frequencies, added, and divided by the number of cases; to obtain the fourth moment the deviations are raised to the fourth power; to obtain the nth moment the deviations are raised to the nth power. This is indicated in the above equations. As already demonstrated above,[1] the first moment about the mean is equal to zero. In mechanics, the square root of the second moment is the radius of gyration of a set of s equal particles, with respect to a given centroidal axis.[2]

Purpose of Moments. For statistics the moments serve primarily as intermediary values. The moments about the

[1] See pp. 169–170.
[2] *Cf.* RIETZ, H. L., *Mathematical Statistics* (1936), p. 20.

mean are intermediary values useful for calculating measures of variability, skewness, and other characteristics of the frequency distribution. Because of their great convenience in obtaining measures of the various characteristics of a frequency distribution, the calculation of the first four moments about the mean may well be made the first step in the analysis of a frequency distribution. This valuable feature will be illustrated in the ensuing pages and in the next chapter. Following are important generalizations concerning moments measured from the arithmetic mean for all frequency distributions,

$$
\left.
\begin{aligned}
\mu_0 &= 1 \\
\mu_1 &= 0 \\
\mu_2 &= \sigma^{2*}
\end{aligned}
\right\} \quad (10)
$$

and in symmetrical distributions,

$$
\left.
\begin{aligned}
\mu_3 &= 0 \\
\mu_5 &= 0 \\
\mu_7 &= 0 \\
&\ \cdot\quad\cdot\quad\cdot\quad\cdot
\end{aligned}
\right\} \quad (11)
$$

for all "odd" numbered moments.

VARIABILITY

It was indicated above that the chief interest of statistics is in variability; summary figures such as averages are useful as points of departure for further study of the frequency distribution. It may be noted that the principle of averaging is fundamental throughout; for all the various methods of summarizing, whether it be central tendencies or variations from points of central tendencies, use the principle of averaging as a method of summarization or measurement.

The Range. The most obvious method of measuring variability is to take the difference between the highest value and the lowest value; this difference is called the "range." Thus in a set of several hundred grades, if the highest grade is 92, and the lowest 13, the range is $92 - 13 = 79$. The range is easily understood and easy to compute, but it is dependent entirely on the two extreme items. It is therefore seldom used as the measure of variability when accuracy and stability of results are

* Read "sigma square."

desired. It is better to use some measure of variability that is dependent on more than just two, if not all, of the cases.[1]

The Average Deviation. The average deviation (A.D.) is the arithmetic average of the variations of the data from their central tendency. This measure of variability may be illustrated as follows:

Variable	Deviations from the Mean $(\bar{X} = 6)$
X	x
2	-4
3	-3
4	-2
6	0
8	2
9	3
10	4
	$+9$
	-9
	$\Sigma|x| = 18$

The deviations have to be added without regard to sign—otherwise, their sum is zero. In this example there are seven deviations (one of which is zero), and hence the average deviation is $\frac{18}{7}$, or 2.57.

$$A.D._{\bar{x}} = \frac{\Sigma|x|}{N} \qquad (12)$$

where $x = X - \bar{X}$.

The average deviation could be measured from the median or the mode, as well as from the arithmetic mean. In fact, it is usually measured from the median since it is least when so computed.[2] Let $X - Mi = x'$. Then the formula for the average deviation from the median is

$$A.D._{Mi} = \frac{\Sigma|x'|}{N} \qquad (12a)$$

Mi is used as a subscript to A.D. to indicate that the average deviation is measured from the median. It is to be noted that the average deviation is a measure of variability that is based on all the observed cases.

---

[1] See, however, Smith and Duncan, *Sampling Statistics*, pp. 294–296, for the use of the range in sampling analysis.

[2] *Cf.* KELLEY, TRUMAN, *Statistical Method* (1923), p. 74.

In the foregoing example each X occurred only once, and so the F's were all unity. When there is more than one of any X, the formulas are

$$A.D._{\bar{x}} = \frac{\Sigma|Fx|}{N}$$

$$A.D._{Mi} = \frac{\Sigma|Fx'|}{N}$$

Standard Deviation. The most generally used measure of variability, however, is the standard deviation. This will be readily understood when it is seen that the standard deviation is easily treated mathematically; the average deviation has very distinct limitations in this respect owing to the disregard of plus and minus signs. In the case of the standard deviation this defect is overcome by squaring the deviations before they are averaged and then taking the square root of the average. The symbol for the standard deviation is the small Greek letter σ, read "sigma." By definition, *the standard deviation is the square root of the average of the squared deviations from the mean.* Symbolically,

$$\sigma = \sqrt{\frac{\Sigma F x^2}{N}} \tag{13}$$

As may be seen by comparing this definition with the definition of the moments about the mean [Eqs. (9)], the standard deviation is the square root of the second moment; *i.e.*,

$$\sigma = \mu_2^{\frac{1}{2}} \tag{13a}$$

Following is an illustration of the computation of the standard deviation:

Variable	Deviations from the Mean ($\bar{X} = 5$)	Deviations Squared
X	x	x^2
1	-4	16
2	-3	9
3	-2	4
4	-1	1
5	0	0
6	1	1
7	2	4
8	3	9
9	4	16
		$\Sigma x^2 = 60$

In the above illustration the standard deviation is $(\frac{60}{9})^{\frac{1}{2}}$, or 2.58. It will be noted here that the F's are all unity and therefore do not enter into the calculations.

Variance. The square of the standard deviation is called the "variance." Since $\sigma^2 = \Sigma F x^2 / N$, the variance is merely another name for the second moment about the mean [see the definition of this in Eqs. (9)]. The second moment is smaller when calculated from the mean than when calculated from any other point.[1]

SKEWNESS

Definition and Significance. "Skewness" means asymmetry. Frequency distributions that have extreme variations resulting in a longer tail in one direction from the peak than in the other direction from the peak are asymmetrical in appearance. Such distributions are called "skewed distributions." Up to this point the discussion has concerned methods for measuring central tendencies (averages) and methods for measuring variability (average deviation and standard deviation). The significance of an average may be considerably modified when considered in comparison with the average deviation or standard deviation; but, in addition, the significance of the averages depends upon the symmetry or lack of symmetry in the distribution of individual cases. Measures of skewness are accordingly desirable.

Skewness Measured by Relationship between the Mean, the Median, and the Mode. Skewness is most easily measured by the relationship between the mean, the median, and the mode; for it will be recalled that the mode is not affected by the magnitudes or number of variations above or below it. The median is affected by the number of variations, but not by their magnitudes. The mean is affected by both the number and the magnitudes of the variations from it. Consequently, it would be expected that

1. The mode, by definition, will remain at the point of greatest frequency, whether or not distribution is skewed.

2. The median will be pulled away from the mode in distributions that are skewed, since the larger number of items on one side pull it from the point of greatest frequency.

[1] *Cf.*, for proof, p. 215.

3. The mean in such distributions will be pulled away from the mode still farther since the larger number and extreme magnitude of the items on one side pull it farther away from the point of greatest frequency.

These points are illustrated in the following frequency distributions:[1]

1. SYMMETRICAL		2. SKEWED POSITIVELY		3. SKEWED NEGATIVELY	
X	F	X	F	X	F
1	3	1	6	1	1
2	4	2	8	2	2
3	6	3	9	3	3
4	9	4	8	4	5
5	10	5	7	5	7
6	9	6	5	6	9
7	6	7	3	7	10
8	4	8	2	8	8
9	3	9	1	9	6
	54		49		51

(1)	(2)	(3)
$\bar{X} = 5$	$\bar{X} = 3.92$	$\bar{X} = 6.10$
$Mi = 5$	$Mi = 3.69$	$Mi = 6.33$
$Mo = 5$	$Mo = 3$	$Mo = 7$
$\sigma = 2.08$	$\sigma = 2.05$	$\sigma = 2.01$

Figures 64 to 66 show in graphic form the frequency distributions given on this page. The relationship between the three averages will be more clearly visualized from these figures.

In Fig. 64, for example, all three averages equal 5. In Fig. 65, which is the positively skewed frequency distribution, the three differ from each other; the mode is 3, the median is 3.69, and the mean is 3.92. The extreme variations toward the higher values give the frequency distribution a longer tail to the right, or toward the higher values of X, and this pulls the median and the mean in that direction from the mode.

In Fig. 66 a negatively skewed frequency distribution is illustrated. This histogram is a graph of the third set of figures shown on this page. In this figure, too, the averages differ from each other, but here the mode is the largest. The extreme variations toward the lower values give the frequency distribution a longer tail to the left, or toward the lower values of X,

[1] Calculations of averages were made on the assumption that the x values are mid-points of class intervals of unity.

and this pulls the median and the mean in that direction from the mode; so while the mode is 7, the median is 6.33 and the mean is 6.10.

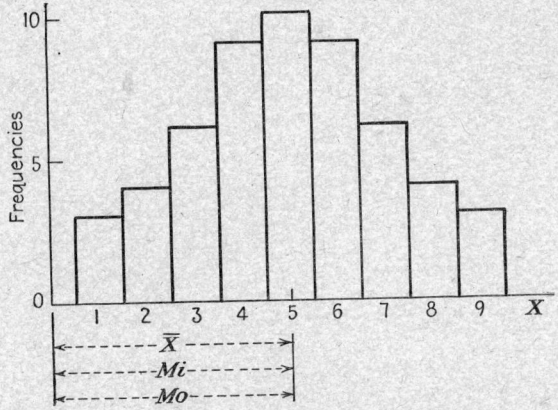

Fig. 64.—A symmetrical frequency distribution.

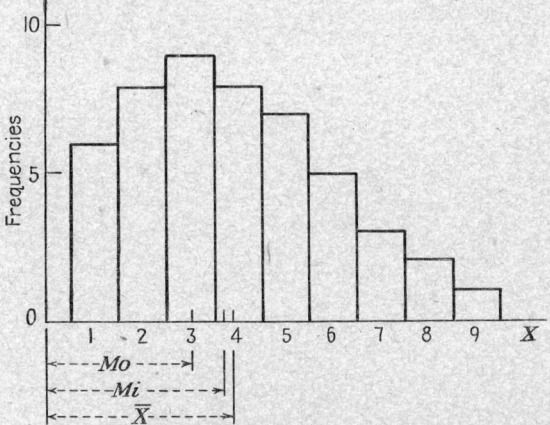

Fig. 65.—A positively skewed frequency distribution.

Skewness may accordingly be measured by the difference between the mean and the mode. For the above examples,

$$\bar{X} - \text{Mo} = 0 \qquad \bar{X} - \text{Mo} = +0.92 \qquad \bar{X} - \text{Mo} = -0.90$$

This is a measure of the aggregate amount of skewness, but how significant is this amount? One device to weigh this is to compare the aggregate amount of skewness with the standard deviation and thereby to obtain a coefficient of skewness, as follows:

For example (2)

$$\text{sk} = \frac{\bar{X} - \text{Mo}}{\sigma} = \frac{0.92}{2.05} = 0.45 \tag{14}$$

For example (3)

$$\text{sk} = \frac{\bar{X} - \text{Mo}}{\sigma} = \frac{-0.90}{2.01} = -0.45$$

The relative amount of skewness, or asymmetry, in these two distributions comes out equal, although one is positive and the other is negative.

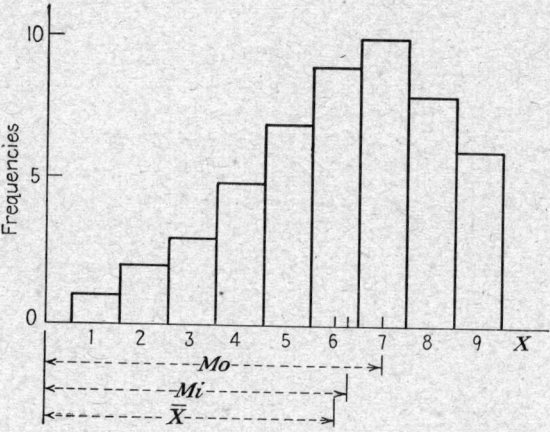

FIG. 66.—A negatively skewed frequency distribution.

Another measure of skewness is based on the median and the mean. It has been established that in a moderately asymmetrical distribution, if the mean is pulled a distance P away from the mode, the median is pulled approximately two-thirds P away from the mode in the same direction; that is,

$$\bar{X} - \text{Mo} = 3(\bar{X} - \text{Mi})$$

Hence, skewness can also be measured by three times the distance between the mean and the median, as follows:

$$\text{sk} = \frac{3(\bar{X} - \text{Mi})}{\sigma} \tag{14a}$$

The second equation has the advantage over (14) in that the median is often easier to locate than the mode. The mode is frequently difficult to locate in a sample distribution and is subject to wide fluctuations of sampling; in addition, its location is often dependent merely upon the selection of the class interval.

Skewness Measured by the Medians and Quartiles. A simple measure of skewness, and one that is easily comprehended, is obtained by comparing the location in a frequency distribution of its median and quartiles. This can be illustrated by taking the same three distributions used above and calculating their respective first and third quartiles (the medians are already calculated). From Fig. 67 it is seen that in the symmetrical distribution the first quartile is smaller than the median by the

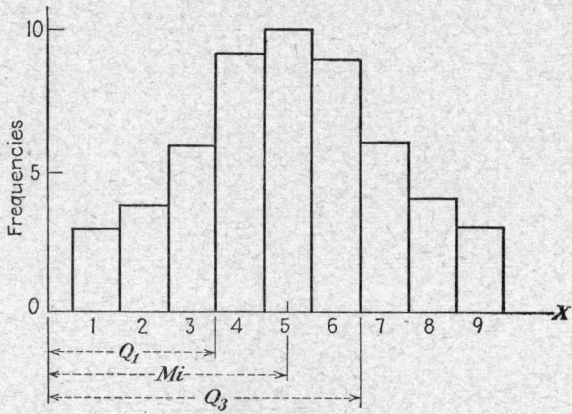

Fig. 67.—Relation between the first and third quartiles and the median of a symmetrical distribution.

same amount that the third quartile is larger than the median— Q_1 and Q_3 are equidistant from the median; accordingly,

$$Q_3 - \text{Mi} - (\text{Mi} - Q_1) = 0$$

If the terms are rearranged, this may be written

$$Q_1 + Q_3 - 2\text{Mi} = 0$$

From Fig. 68, the positively skewed case, it is seen that the first quartile is smaller than the median by an amount considerably less than the amount by which the third quartile is larger than the median; accordingly,

$$Q_3 - \text{Mi} - (\text{Mi} - Q_1) = +0.222$$

From Fig. 69, the negatively skewed distribution, it is seen that the first quartile is smaller than the median by an amount considerably larger than the amount by which the third quartile is larger than the median; for $Q_3 - \text{Mi} - (\text{Mi} - Q_1) = -0.154$.

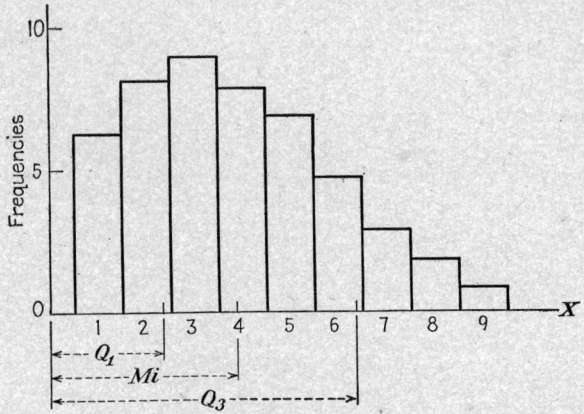

Fig. 68.—Relation between the first and third quartiles and the median of a positively skewed distribution.

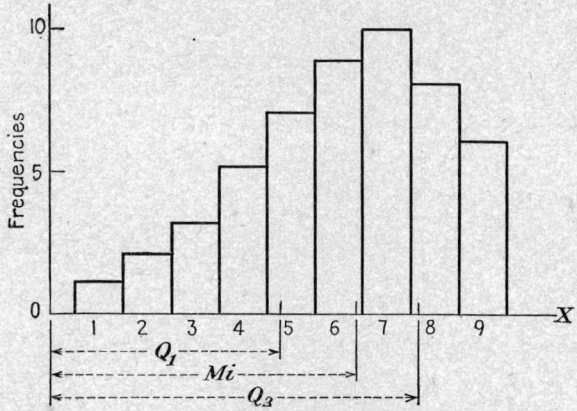

Fig. 69.—Relation between the first and third quartiles and the median of a negatively skewed distribution.

If the location of the quartiles compared with the location of the median, in each distribution, is now compared with half the distance between the two quartiles (*i.e.*, the average distance of the two quartiles from the median), a coefficient or relative measure of skewness is obtained and the formula that measures skewness is as follows:

$$\text{sk} = \frac{Q_3 - \text{Mi} - (\text{Mi} - Q_1)}{\dfrac{Q_3 - Q_1}{2}} = \frac{Q_3 + Q_1 - 2\text{Mi}}{Q} \qquad (15)$$

where Q is used as a symbol signifying the semiquartile range.

Not only is the coefficient of skewness based upon the median and quartiles a good one because these are usually easy to find, but also this coefficient of skewness has the advantage that it has value limits between $+2$ and -2. It can be no greater than $+2$, that is, when positive skewness is so great that the median equals the first quartile. It can be no greater than -2, that is, when negative skewness is so great that the median equals the third quartile. In Figs. 68 and 69, respectively, the coefficients of skewness are $+0.146$ and -0.106 expressed as ratios. Expressed as percentages of skewness, they are $+14.6$ per cent and -10.6 per cent.

Third Moment as a Measure of Skewness. The cube root of the third moment is also a good measure of skewness. This is due to the fact that (1) if the distribution is symmetrical, ΣFx^3 will be zero; but (2) if the distribution is not symmetrical, the third moment will not be equal to zero but will have a positive or negative value according to whether the distribution is skewed positively or negatively. This is illustrated by simple examples showing a symmetrical and a positively skewed distribution. The negatively skewed distribution is left to the student to work out.

1. SYMMETRICAL DISTRIBUTION

X	F	x	Fx	Fx^2	Fx^3
1	2	-3	-6	18	-54
2	3	-2	-6	12	-24
3	4	-1	-4	4	-4
4	5	0	0	0	0
5	4	1	4	4	4
6	3	2	6	12	24
7	2	3	6	18	54
	23		$\Sigma Fx = 0$	$\Sigma Fx^2 = 68$	$\Sigma Fx^3 = 0$

2. Positively Skewed Distribution

X	F	x	Fx	Fx²	Fx³
1	6	−2	−12	24	−48
2	8	−1	− 8	8	− 8
3	10	0	0	0	0
4	4	1	4	4	4
5	3	2	6	12	24
6	2	3	6	18	54
7	1	4	4	16	64
	34		$\Sigma Fx = 0$	$\Sigma Fx^2 = 82$	$\Sigma Fx^3 = 90$

In the second example, the third moment is equal, not to zero, but to $\frac{90}{34}$. The measures of skewness by this method would be $\frac{90}{34}$. Symbolically, this measure of skewness is

$$\text{sk} = \sqrt[3]{\frac{\Sigma Fx^3}{N}} = \mu_3^{\frac{1}{3}} \qquad (16)$$

It may be seen from the definition of the third moment [Eqs. (9)] that this measurement of skewness is the cube root of the third moment. Expressed as a coefficient of skewness, where the aggregate amount of skewness is in terms of the standard deviation, this measure of skewness is as follows:

$$\text{sk} = \frac{\mu_3^{\frac{1}{3}}}{\sigma}$$

The Beta Coefficients. This last measure of skewness is of particular interest, not only because it is based on a wholly mathematical procedure (it is not dependent on nonmathematical summaries like the median and quartiles or the mode), but also because it is directly related to one of the so-called "beta coefficients." The beta coefficients are functions of the moments of the frequency distribution that have been found very useful in describing and distinguishing various types of frequency distributions.[1] The two principal beta coefficients are β_1 and β_2, which are defined as follows:

$$\beta_1 = \frac{\mu_3^2}{\mu_2^3} \qquad \beta_2 = \frac{\mu_4}{\mu_2^2}$$

It will be noted that the sixth root of β_1 is identically the coefficient of skewness, $\text{sk} = \mu_3^{\frac{1}{3}}/\sigma$, for $\mu_2 = \sigma^2$. Frequently $\sqrt{\beta_1}$ is itself

---

[1] Smith and Duncan, *Sampling Statistics.*

taken as a measure of skewness, the square root being given the same sign as ΣFx^3 from which the third moment is calculated.

When the beta coefficients are used to describe a frequency curve according to a formula developed by Karl Pearson,[1] the skewness for this curve as measured by $\dfrac{\bar{X} - \text{Mo}}{\sigma}$ is found to be equal to

$$\text{sk} = \frac{\sqrt{\beta_1}\,(\beta_2 + 3)}{2(5\beta_2 - 6\beta_1 - 9)} \qquad (17)$$

When the data are such as to warrant the fitting of a smooth frequency curve, this is an excellent formula for measuring skewness. The curve, of course, does not have to be fitted to make use of the formula as a measure of skewness.

When β_1 is small, *i.e.*, when the skewness is slight, and when β_2 is approximately equal to 3, as it is in the case of a normal distribution,[2] this last equation shows that $\sqrt{\beta_1}$ is approximately equal to twice $\dfrac{\bar{X} - \text{Mo}}{\sigma}$, the mode being that of the fitted Pearsonian curve. When the latter is calculated by the approximate formula $\text{Mo} = \bar{X} - 3(\bar{X} - \text{Mi})$, the calculation of half the square root of β_1 will in certain cases serve as a rough check on the computation of skewness from the formula $\text{sk} = \dfrac{\bar{X} - \text{Mo}}{\sigma}$.

The importance of the second beta coefficient lies in the fact that it is a measure of kurtosis.

KURTOSIS

Definition.   Kurtosis is described by Karl Pearson as follows:[3]

Given two frequency distributions which have the same variability as measured by the standard deviation, they may be relatively more or less flat-topped than the normal curve. . . . A frequency distribution may, in other words, be symmetrical, but it may fail to be mesokurtic (equally flat-topped with the normal curve), and thus the Gaussian curve cannot describe it.

[1] *Cf.* Smith and Duncan, *Sampling Statistics*, pp. 134–137.
[2] See the next section.
[3] "Skew Variation, A Rejoinder," *Biometrika*, Vol. 4 (1906), p. 173. Cited from H. M. Walker, *Studies in the History of Statistical Method*, p. 182.

The "normal curve" to which this quotation refers is represented by the equation

$$y = \frac{1}{\sigma \sqrt{2\pi}} e^{-\frac{(X-\bar{X})^2}{2\sigma^2}}$$

(18)

Because this curve has arisen so frequently in statistics and because it has been used as a type with which to compare other

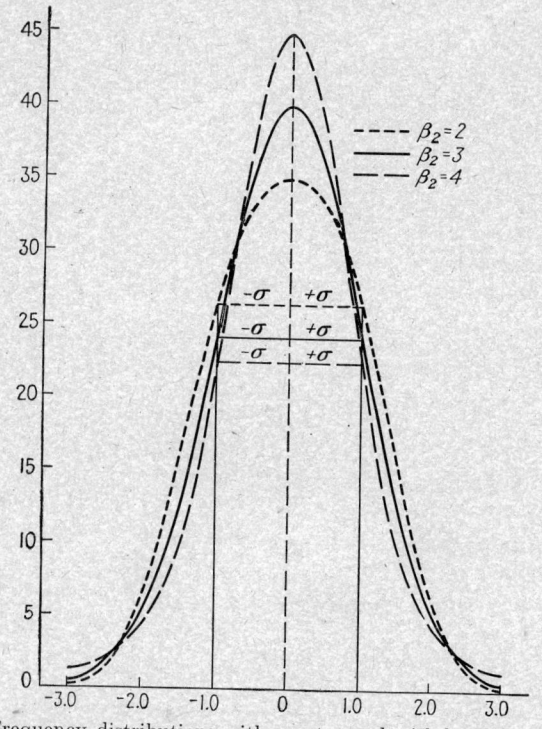

Fig. 70.—Frequency distributions with greater and with less kurtosis than the normal curve.

frequency curves, it has come to be known as the normal curve. Also, since Gauss early recognized its importance, it is sometimes called the Gaussian curve.[1]

As shown in graphic form earlier in this chapter (Fig. 63), when there is a marked concentration of very small variations about the central tendency, the frequency curve rises to a high peak, unlike the normal, or Gaussian, curve, which has a certain

[1] *Cf.* pp. 294–295.

roundness at the top. Kurtosis is a measure that makes it possible to describe the relative degree to which this characteristic exists with reference to any frequency distribution. For the normal curve, the relationship between the second and the fourth moments is as follows:

$$\beta_2 = \frac{\mu_4}{\mu_2^2} = 3$$

If the ratio of the fourth moment to the square of the second moment is less than 3, the curve is flatter than the normal curve; and if the ratio is greater than 3, the curve is more peaked than the normal curve. Figure 70 shows three frequency distributions, with β_2 equal, respectively, to 2, 3, and 4; the standard deviations of the three curves are equal. It should be noted that the smaller area at the peak of the flat-topped distribution is accompanied by a loss of area at the tails of the distribution. This loss of area at the peak and the tails is compensated by the fact that the curve is higher than the normal curve on each side

TABLE 10.—COMPUTATION OF THREE FREQUENCY CURVES[1]

$$\beta_2 = 2 \qquad \beta_2 = 3 \qquad \beta_2 = 4$$

$\dfrac{x}{\sigma}$	ϕ_0 $\beta_2 = 3$	ϕ_4	$\frac{1}{24}\phi_4$	$-\frac{1}{24}\phi_4$	$\beta_2 = 4$	$\beta_2 = 2$
(1)	(2)	(3)	(4)	(5)	(6)	(7)
0.0	0.3989	1.1968	0.0499	−0.0499	0.4488	0.3490
0.2	0.3910	1.0799	0.0450	−0.0450	0.4360	0.3460
0.4	0.3683	0.7607	0.0317	−0.0317	0.4000	0.3366
0.6	0.3332	0.3231	0.0135	−0.0135	0.3467	0.3197
0.8	0.2897	−0.1247	−0.0052	0.0052	0.2845	0.2949
1.0	0.2420	−0.4839	−0.0202	0.0202	0.2218	0.2622
1.2	0.1942	−0.6925	−0.0288	0.0288	0.1654	0.2230
1.4	0.1497	−0.7364	−0.0307	0.0307	0.1190	0.1804
1.6	0.1109	−0.6440	−0.0268	0.0268	0.0841	0.1377
1.8	0.0790	−0.4692	−0.0195	0.0195	0.0595	0.0985
2.0	0.0540	−0.2700	−0.0112	0.0112	0.0428	0.0652
2.2	0.0355	−0.0927	−0.0039	0.0039	0.0316	0.0394
2.4	0.0224	0.0362	0.0015	−0.0015	0.0239	0.0209
2.6	0.0136	0.1105	0.0046	−0.0046	0.0182	0.0090
2.8	0.0079	0.1379	0.0057	−0.0057	0.0136	0.0022

[1] Columns (2), (6), and (7) give the ordinates of the three curves. Column (6) = (2) + (4), and column (7) = (2) + (5), account being taken of the signs. The figures are derived from the formula for a Gram-Charlier frequency curve. See SMITH and DUNCAN, *Sampling Statistics*, pp. 84, 142–144.

between the peak and the tails. In other words, it is flat both at the peak and at the tails and is high in the shoulders. In contrast, the more peaked frequency curve is higher than the normal curve at both the peak and the tails and lower than the normal curve on each side between the peak and the tails. Its shoulders are lower than those of the normal curve.

SUMMARY

There are two ways in which frequency distributions differ from the so-called "normal" frequency distribution.[1] (1) Frequency distributions may have a higher or lower peak than the normal frequency distribution. This relative flatness or lack of flatness of the peak relative to the normal curve is called "kurtosis." (2) Frequency distributions may have a preponderance of variability to the large values or to the small values. This lack of symmetry in variability is called "skewness." The normal distribution and the concepts connected with its analysis constitute a convenient point of departure for the general analysis of variability. In this study of variability, the characteristics of kurtosis and skewness are of great importance for the reason that a large part of the phenomena studied have characteristics producing frequency distributions that are not "normal." Even as early as the time when Sir Francis Galton was developing his theory of correlation (1877–1889), writers on mathematical statistics realized that the univariate normal law of De Moivre and Laplace could not be regarded as a universal law of frequency distribution; the presence of skewness in homogeneous material was certainly as common as that of normality.[2]

It is important to realize that the function of frequency-distribution analysis is not primarily to define and measure averages but to define, describe, and measure variability. Simple averages have relatively limited uses and may lead to misinterpretation rather than clarification if used without reference to the measures of variability, skewness, and kurtosis.

---

[1] For further description of the normal curve, see Chaps. X and XI.
[2] PRETORIUS, S. J., *Biometrika*, Vol. 22 (1930–1931), pp. 109–223. *Cf.* ELDERTON, W. PALIN, *Frequency Curves and Correlation* (1927). RIETZ, H. L., *Handbook of Mathematical Statistics*, Chap. VII, Frequency Curves, pp. 92–119, by H. C. Carver, and pp. 288–239 by W. A. Shewhart.

In this chapter some of the most generally used methods of analysis of frequency distributions have been presented in elementary form, in order to keep clear of the complications of practical application. It will now be easier to see how these methods are applied and just what complications enter into their application to real problems. The following chapter gives an example of such an analysis, using data from real life. But it will be well to close this chapter with a summary of the symbols that have thus far been used and that include by far the majority of all the symbols used in statistics. Most of the symbolic language can be learned from this chapter. If they are mastered, the few additional ones will be easy to learn.

SUMMARY OF SYMBOLS

A variable $X_1, X_2, X_3, \ldots, X_n$ or in general X

Frequencies $F_1, F_2, F_3, \ldots, F_n$ or in general F

Sum of Σ (Greek capital sigma)

Number of cases N (equals ΣF)

Arithmetic mean $\bar{X}$

Deviations from the mean $x_1, x_2, x_3, \ldots, x_n$ or in general
$$x \text{ (equals } X - \bar{X})$$

Median   Mi

First quartile Q_1

Third quartile Q_3

Mode   Mo

Deviations from the median $x_1', x_2', x_3', \ldots, x_n'$ or in general
$$x' \text{ (equals } X - \text{Mi)}$$

Geometric mean   G.M.

Harmonic mean   H.M.

Average deviation   A.D.

Standard deviation σ (Greek small sigma)

Chi square χ^2 (Greek small chi)

Skewness   sk

Moments:

   a. About arbitrary origin:

$$\nu_1, \nu_2, \nu_3, \ldots, \nu_n$$

   b. About the arithmetic mean:

$$\mu_1, \mu_2, \mu_3, \ldots, \mu_n$$

Kurtosis β_2 (Greek small beta)

Following is a summary of the formulas that have been used in this chapter:

SUMMARY OF FORMULAS

(1) $\bar{X} = \dfrac{\Sigma FX}{N}$ also $\bar{X} = \Sigma \dfrac{F}{N} X$

(2) $\Sigma Fx = 0$

(3) $\text{Mo} = \bar{X} - 3(\bar{X} - \text{Mi})$

(4) $\log \text{G.M.} = \dfrac{\Sigma \log X}{N}$

(5) $\dfrac{X_1}{\text{G.M.}} \times \dfrac{X_2}{\text{G.M.}} \times \cdots \times \dfrac{X_n}{\text{G.M.}} = 1$

(6) $\text{H.M.} = \dfrac{N}{\Sigma \dfrac{1}{X}}$

(7) $\text{H.M.} < \text{G.M.} < \bar{X}$

(8) $\nu_1 = \dfrac{\Sigma FX}{N},\ \nu_2 = \dfrac{\Sigma FX^2}{N},\ \nu_n = \dfrac{\Sigma FX^n}{N}$

(9) $\mu_1 = \dfrac{\Sigma Fx}{N},\qquad \mu_2 = \dfrac{\Sigma Fx^2}{N},\qquad \mu_n = \dfrac{\Sigma Fx^n}{N}$

(10) $\mu_0 = 1,\ \mu_1 = 0,\ \mu_2 = \sigma^2$

(11) $\mu_3 = 0,\ \mu_5 = 0,\ \mu_7 = 0,\ \ldots$ in a symmetrical distribution

(12) $\text{A.D.}_{\bar{X}} = \dfrac{\Sigma |Fx|}{N},\qquad \text{A.D.}_{\text{Mi}} = \dfrac{\Sigma |Fx'|}{N}$

(13) $\sigma = \sqrt{\dfrac{\Sigma Fx^2}{N}} = \mu_2^{\frac{1}{2}}$

(14) $\text{sk} = \dfrac{\bar{X} - \text{Mo}}{\sigma}$ also $\text{sk} = \dfrac{3(\bar{X} - \text{Mi})}{\sigma}$

(15) $\text{sk} = \dfrac{Q_3 + Q_1 - 2\text{Mi}}{Q}$

(16) $\text{sk} = \mu_3^{\frac{1}{2}}$

(17) $\text{sk} = \dfrac{\sqrt{\beta_1}\,(\beta_2 + 3)}{2(5\beta_2 - 6\beta_1 - 9)}$

(18) $y = \dfrac{1}{\sigma\sqrt{2\pi}} e^{-\frac{(X-\bar{X})^2}{2\sigma^2}}$

CHAPTER VII

ILLUSTRATION OF FREQUENCY-DISTRIBUTION ANALYSIS

Data for a Frequency Distribution. Data selected to illustrate frequency distribution analysis are presented in Table 11. Heights in inches of 300 members of the freshman class of 1943 were obtained from the records of the Department of Health and Physical Education, Princeton University. As presented in the table the data are not arranged in a frequency distribution; they are listed at random. In order to make a frequency distribution of the data it is necessary first to decide on the size and limits of the class interval to be used in the construction of the distribution; for the frequency distribution per se is a method of summarization compared with the manner of presentation of the data in Table 11.

CONSTRUCTION OF A FREQUENCY DISTRIBUTION

The Class Interval. *Rules for Determining the Class Interval.* The class interval is the unit of the frequency distribution; in other words, it is the size of the groups in which the data are summarized. In the data selected for illustration should the groups be 1-inch, $\frac{1}{2}$-inch, $\frac{1}{4}$-inch, or $\frac{1}{10}$-inch groups? That is, should the class interval be 1 inch, a half inch, a quarter inch, or a tenth of an inch?

A general rule for selecting the class interval is that it should be such as to make possible, without serious error, the treatment of all values assigned to any one of the classes as if they were equal to the mid-point or mid-value of the class. The lower limit of the class intervals also should be so selected as to facilitate this end. If the cases are concentrated, in fact, at the mid-point of the class interval or are evenly distributed throughout, it may, without serious errors in calculation, be assumed that all cases in the class are equal in value to the mid-value.

Another guide in the selection of the class interval is that it should be as large as possible subject to the first condition and

ANALYSIS OF FREQUENCY DISTRIBUTIONS

to the condition that the interval should not be so large as to conceal too much of the character of the variability. Indeed, the most important purpose of the class interval is so to summarize

TABLE 11.—HEIGHTS, 300 EIGHTEEN-YEAR-OLD MEMBERS OF THE CLASS OF 1943, PRINCETON UNIVERSITY
(In inches)

71.00	76.50	70.25	68.75	74.40	70.50	74.00
71.50	69.00	71.00	69.50	73.00	67.50	70.50
70.00	67.50	71.25	70.00	69.80	66.75	68.50
67.50	75.00	72.80	70.75	63.00	72.00	72.50
72.50	69.00	65.75	67.00	70.25	69.00	71.25
70.50	70.50	68.25	69.70	66.00	69.75	69.00
72.00	70.30	72.00	73.20	69.00	71.75	72.00
72.25	72.60	68.50	71.20	70.50	67.50	74.40
67.25	72.80	66.50	68.00	70.50	70.50	70.70
71.00	71.50	69.70	73.50	68.00	67.50	71.75
72.25	70.75	70.50	67.75	70.50	72.00	67.25
66.50	75.75	66.90	73.00	69.50	68.25	70.75
73.75	65.50	70.75	69.20	73.25	70.75	73.00
69.70	70.00	72.50	71.75	71.60	72.50	70.80
75.75	70.50	75.50	75.75	70.75	71.00	69.75
71.50	72.75	69.20	70.25	69.50	71.00	67.50
72.00	67.50	73.20	73.75	68.50	70.00	77.25
67.00	68.75	71.30	73.50	72.00	71.00	69.00
71.00	69.50	74.10	70.50	70.75	72.00	66.50
65.75	73.00	66.25	71.00	70.75	68.20	67.75
75.25	71.70	69.50	67.75	73.50	74.20	72.50
67.25	67.50	70.75	70.75	67.00	72.00	67.00
69.50	69.25	67.50	69.30	74.30	67.00	70.40
70.25	67.00	66.50	72.00	70.25	68.70	71.75
70.10	69.50	67.25	66.75	72.50	71.30	66.50
69.20	69.75	68.50	69.75	68.75	70.10	74.00
68.00	69.00	72.50	73.75	70.00	68.10	68.25
71.00	74.50	72.75	71.40	71.25	73.00	71.50
69.00	71.50	68.50	72.80	72.00	71.00	71.50
62.00	68.00	74.75	69.25	73.25	64.25	75.25
70.00	70.50	68.25	67.90	70.75	70.75	72.50
74.00	71.00	72.50	69.50	72.00	71.20	69.50
67.00	72.00	71.50	68.25	69.00	72.00	69.50
73.50	71.30	70.70	67.50	63.60	72.50	72.50
70.50	71.30	69.75	68.50	71.00	71.00	71.00
71.25	67.50	69.75	69.25	66.50	69.00	68.50
73.00	68.00	69.50	69.25	74.00	67.50	67.00
68.50	73.25	68.50	74.25	73.70	72.00	69.00
68.00	71.00	68.80	70.00	69.50	71.75	68.50
70.00	69.00	67.00	68.50	71.75	73.00	69.75
75.20	74.00	69.50	70.00			
72.80	67.75	69.30	70.00			
69.40	70.50	66.75	73.40			
68.50	68.00	76.25	67.80			
68.50	74.75	71.75	65.00			

the data in a frequency distribution as to disclose more clearly the character of the variability. If a very small class interval is chosen, the character of the variability will not be visible unless a

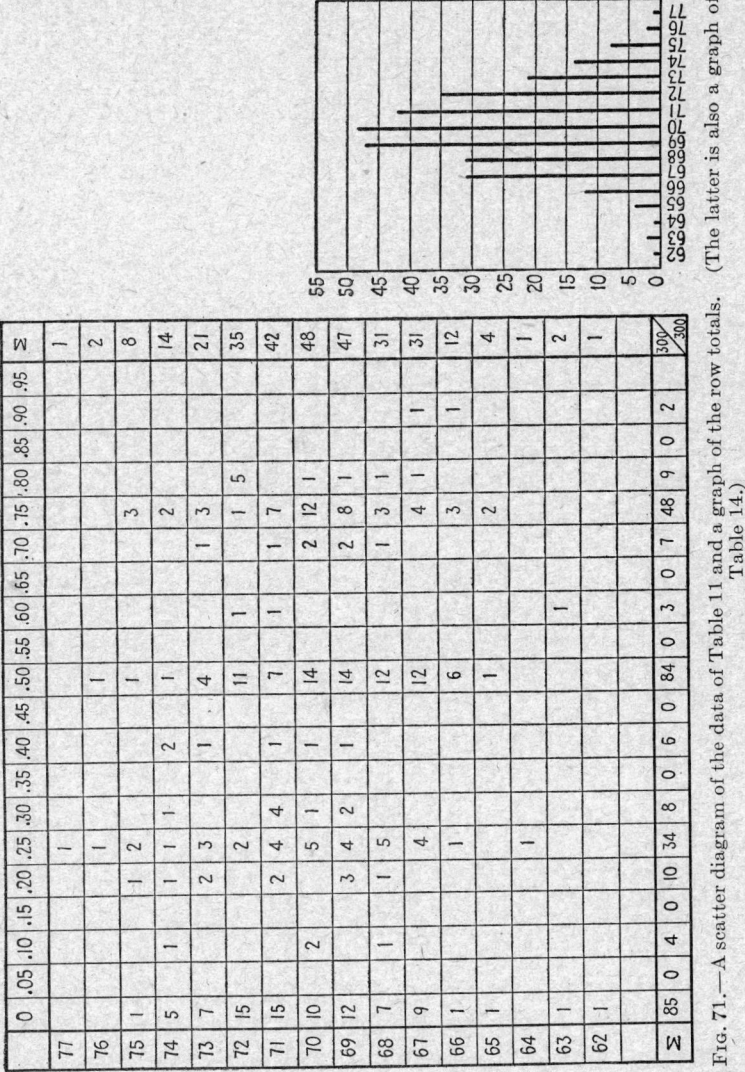

Fig. 71.—A scatter diagram of the data of Table 11 and a graph of the row totals. (The latter is also a graph of the column totals. Table 14.)

very large number of cases are measured; if a very large class interval is chosen, significant irregularities in the data may be concealed.

Ordinarily, the size of the class interval should be uniform throughout, because different-sized class intervals will complicate calculations. In some cases, however, it is necessary to use different-sized class intervals in order to give a proper picture of variability.

If other more important rules are not thereby violated, in the interests of simplicity the position of the class interval in the range should be such that the limits of the intervals are integers or such that the mid-values of the class intervals are integers. Where marked concentration about certain values exists, as is sometimes the case in dealing with discrete data, these values should so far as possible be made the mid-points of class intervals.

An Array of the Data. Intelligent determination of the class interval is aided by study of the data arranged in an array or scatter diagram such as Fig. 71, which is presented to illustrate the determination of the proper class interval. In the figure, the heights shown in Table 11 are arranged in an array. Because inspection of the data in Table 11 led to the suspicion that concentration points were present at the $\frac{1}{4}$-, $\frac{1}{2}$-, and $\frac{3}{4}$-inch values, the array is presented in rows with these concentration points plumbed. Summing the columns as well as inspection of the detail of the scatter diagram show the concentration of frequencies at these values.

Frequency Distribution with Too Many Class Intervals. Examination of Fig. 71 suggests that a $\frac{1}{4}$-inch class interval beginning at 61.875 inches, as shown in Table 12, might be a good class interval for the data of Table 11, for the $\frac{1}{4}$-inch class interval with the lower limits as shown in Table 12 places the mid-values of class intervals at points of concentration. Such a frequency distribution contains over 60 rows, however, and, in addition, is uneven and irregular in appearance. Ten frequencies occur in the interval 66.875–; only five frequencies occur in the interval 68.625–; twelve frequencies occur in the intervals immediately below and above 68.625–. Moreover, it is not clear whether the modal class interval is $69\frac{1}{2}$, $70\frac{1}{2}$, $70\frac{3}{4}$, 71, or 72 inches; because an equal number (15) have each of these five heights.

The $\frac{1}{4}$-inch class interval is too small in this instance to disclose clearly the nature of variation in freshman heights.

A Larger Class Interval Reveals the Character of Variation. If 1 inch is taken as the class interval, the frequency distribution

TABLE 12.—FREQUENCY DISTRIBUTION OF THE HEIGHTS OF 300 PRINCETON FRESHMEN, CLASS OF 1943

Heights of freshmen X		Number of freshmen having specified heights F
Interval	Mid-value	
61.875–	62.00	1
62.125–	62.25	0
62.375–	62.50	0
62.625–	62.75	0
62.875–	63.00	1
63.125–	63.25	0
63.375–	63.50	1
63.625–	63.75	0
63.875–	64.00	0
64.125–	64.25	1
64.375–	64.50	0
64.625–	64.75	0
64.875–	65.00	1
65.125–	65.25	0
65.375–	65.50	1
65.625–	65.75	2
65.875–	66.00	1
66.125–	66.25	1
66.375–	66.50	6
66.625–	66.75	3
66.875–	67.00	10
67.125–	67.25	4
67.375–	67.50	12
67.625–	67.75	5
67.875–	68.00	9
68.125–	68.25	6
68.375–	68.50	12
68.625–	68.75	5
68.875–	69.00	12
69.125–	69.25	9
69.375–	69.50	15
69.625–	69.75	11
69.875–	70.00	12
70.125–	70.25	6
70.375–	70.50	15
70.625–	70.75	15
70.875–	71.00	15
71.125–	71.25	10
71.375–	71.50	9
71.625–	71.75	8
71.875–	72.00	15
72.125–	72.25	2
72.375–	72.50	12
72.625–	72.75	6
72.875–	73.00	7
73.125–	73.25	5
73.375–	73.50	5
73.625–	73.75	4
73.875–	74.00	6
74.125–	74.25	3
74.375–	74.50	3
74.625–	74.75	2
74.875–	75.00	1
75.125–	75.25	3
75.375–	75.50	1
75.625–	75.75	3
75.875–	76.00	0
76.125–	76.25	1
76.375–	76.50	1
76.625–	76.75	0
76.875–	77.00	0
77.125–	77.25	1
		300

will contain 17 classes and will appear as shown in Table 13. In this frequency distribution the lower limits of the class intervals are so chosen that mid-values are at the 0.625-inch points ($\frac{5}{8}$ inch), which is a balancing center of the concentration points at the $\frac{1}{4}$-inch intervals because at $\frac{5}{8}$ inch each mid-value has two $\frac{1}{4}$-inch concentration points below it and two above it in the

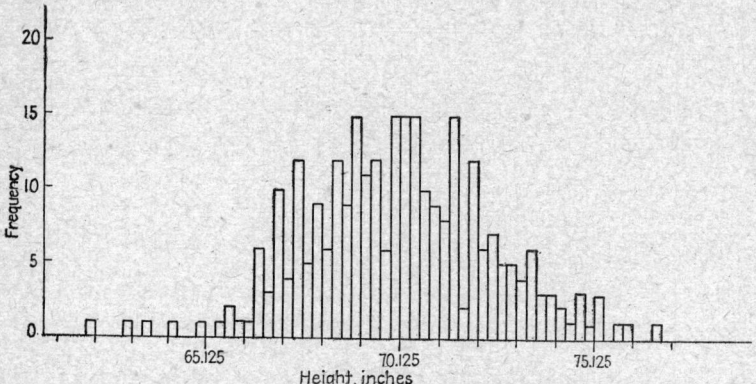

FIG. 72.—Distribution of heights of 300 Princeton freshmen.   (Class interval = $\frac{1}{4}$ inch.)

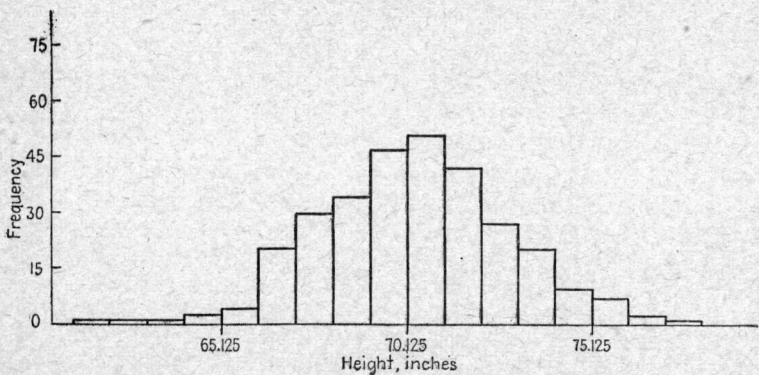

FIG. 73.—Distribution of heights of 300 Princeton freshmen.   (Class interval = 1 inch.)

1-inch class interval. This balancing position of the $\frac{5}{8}$-inch points can be readily seen by an examination of Fig. 71.

In order to contrast the irregularities in the frequency distribution using too small a class interval with the regular appearance of the same frequency distribution using a larger class interval, Figs. 72 and 73 are presented. Figure 72 is a graph of the frequency distribution of heights of 300 Princeton freshmen, using a ¼-inch class interval. Figure 73 is a graph of the frequency distribution of heights of 300 Princeton freshmen, using 1-inch class interval.

The argument for a class interval centered at the ⅝-inch point has been based on the assumption that measurements have been made to the nearest ¼ inch. In other words, a height recorded as 64.25 might be anything between 64.125 and 64.375. If measurements were always made to the lowest ¼ inch, then some other mid-point would be warranted such as the ½-inch points, or integral values. Table 14 is one based on this assumption. Since the exact method of measurement is not known and since Table 14 is simplest in form, it is adopted for subsequent analysis. A graph of the distribution has already been shown in Fig. 71.

In frequency Tables 12 to 14, the class interval has been listed in two ways. (1) It has been described by writing on each line the lower limit of the class interval, followed by a dash. (2) It

TABLE 13.—FREQUENCY DISTRIBUTION OF THE HEIGHTS OF 300 PRINCETON FRESHMEN, CLASS OF 1943

Heights of freshmen X		Number of freshmen having specified heights F
Interval	Mid-value	
61.125–	61.625	1
62.125–	62.625	1
63.125–	63.625	1
64.125–	64.625	2
65.125–	65.625	4
66.125–	66.625	20
67.125–	67.625	30
68.125–	68.625	35
69.125–	69.625	47
70.125–	70.625	51
71.125–	71.625	42
72.125–	72.625	27
73.125–	73.625	20
74.125–	74.625	9
75.125–	75.625	7
76.125–	76.625	2
77.125–	77.625	1
		300

TABLE 14.—FREQUENCY DISTRIBUTION OF THE HEIGHTS OF 300 PRINCETON FRESHMEN, CLASS OF 1943

Heights of freshmen X		Number of freshmen having specified heights F
Interval	Mid-value	
62–	62.5	1
63–	63.5	2
64–	64.5	1
65–	65.5	4
66–	66.5	12
67–	67.5	31
68–	68.5	31
69–	69.5	47
70–	70.5	48
71–	71.5	42
72–	72.5	35
73–	73.5	21
74–	74.5	14
75–	75.5	8
76–	76.5	2
77–	77.5	1
		300

has been described by writing in the next column the mid-value. Obviously, both methods of describing the class interval need not always be employed; the conventional procedure is to use the lower-limit description rather than the mid-value description. The mid-value can always be calculated by adding one-half the class interval to the lower limit of the class interval.

WORK SHEET FOR FREQUENCY-DISTRIBUTION ANALYSIS

The frequency distribution having been constructed, the procedure for frequency-distribution analysis will now be described. Table 15 is a work sheet for the analysis of a frequency distribution; in columns (1) and (2), under X and F, is copied the frequency distribution from Table 14. Entries in the remaining columns will be explained below. The work sheet is so constructed that advantage may be taken of certain economies in calculation. These economies arise from two sources: (1) the reduction in calculation, due to the use of a short method that involves the calculation of the moments about an "arbitrary origin" and (2) a reduction in calculation, due to the use of class intervals as units of deviation from the arbitrary origin.

Saving Calculation by Obtaining Moments about an Arbitrary Origin. In applying the short method, an arbitrary origin, which may be called A, is selected. While zero may be taken as an arbitrary origin (and often is in certain statistical problems), in the analysis of frequency distributions the amount of calculation is reduced by selecting a value for A somewhere near the middle of the range. The moments about the arbitrary origin are then calculated by measuring deviations from A in class-interval units, that is, in d/i's. Sometimes d' is used to symbolize $\frac{d}{i}$. The savings in calculation are due to the fact that all desired mathematical statistics can then be computed by the use of formulas from the four moments about the arbitrary origin.

Saving Calculation by Using Class-interval Units. Saving in the amount of calculation to obtain the various statistics results if the class-interval unit is used, particularly if the variable is in complex or fractional units or in large numbers. This economy is brought about by expressing the deviations in terms of class intervals instead of in original units, *i.e.*, in d/i's instead of in d's. As pointed out above, this saving is augmented by selecting the arbitrary origin near the middle of the frequency distribution. If the arbitrary origin is at or near the middle class interval, the largest deviation in terms of class-interval units will then be no greater than half the number of class intervals in the frequency distribution. Since the deviations must be raised to the fourth power in order to calculate the fourth moment, substantial saving in calculation is secured by keeping class-interval deviations as small as possible by placing the arbitrary origin near the middle of the frequency distribution. It will be observed in Table 15 that the frequency distribution has been copied on the work sheet in such a position that the arbitrary origin is near the middle of the frequency distribution. It can also be seen that, when the class interval is uniform in size, recording the class-interval deviations in column (3) is merely a matter of proceeding by count above and below the arbitrary origin, that is, -1, -2, -3, etc., for successive smaller class-interval values, and $1, 2, 3$, etc., for successive larger class-interval values.

Entering the Frequency Distribution on the Work Sheet. The frequency distribution of freshmen heights shown in Table 14 has 16 class intervals; and if the mid-value of the central class interval is to be selected as the arbitrary origin, the first class interval, 62–, will be entered in column (1) under "Interval" on the line opposite −7 in column (3) ($d/i = -7$). The remaining class intervals will be entered in succeeding lines until 77– will be opposite 8 in column (3) ($d/i = 8$). The mid-value of the central class interval is 69.5, which is opposite 0 in column (3) ($d/i = 0$). The corresponding frequencies are then entered in column (2). Full description of the data and their source is entered in the space provided at the top of the work sheet.

Saving Calculation in Use of Work Sheet. The amount of calculation involved in the entries required for columns (4) to (9) can be reduced to a minimum by the following procedure:

In column (4), headed $F(d/i)$, enter the class-interval deviations multiplied by the frequencies [*i.e.*, items in column (3) multiplied, respectively, by items in column (2)]. The algebraic sum of the figures in column (4), divided by N, equals the first moment (in class-interval units) about the arbitrary origin.

The figures in column (5), headed $F(d/i)^2$, are obtained by multiplying the items in column (4), respectively, by the corresponding items in column (3). The sum of figures in column (5), divided by N, equals the second moment (in class-interval units) about the arbitrary origin.

The figures in column (6), headed $F(d/i)^3$, are most easily obtained by multiplying the items in column (5), respectively, by the corresponding items in column (3). The algebraic sum of figures in column (6), divided by N, equals the third moment (in class-interval units) about the arbitrary origin.

The figures in column (7), headed $F(d/i)^4$, are obtained by multiplying the items in column (6), respectively, by the corresponding items in column (3). The sum of figures in column (7), divided by N, equals the fourth moment (in class-interval units) about the arbitrary origin.

The figures in column (8), headed $\left(\frac{d}{i} + 1\right)^4$, are obtained by adding 1, respectively, to each figure in column (3) and raising the result to its fourth power. All figures in this column are readily obtained by using a table of powers of numbers.[1] The sum of column (8) is not used.

The figures in column (9), headed $F\left(\dfrac{d}{i} + 1\right)^4$, are obtained by multiplying the items in column (8), respectively, by corresponding items in column (2). The sum of column (9) is used to check the arithmetical accuracy of all calculations in the work sheet.

When the work sheet is completed, it will show the following values:

$$A, \; i, \; N, \; \Sigma F\left(\frac{d}{i}\right), \; \Sigma F\left(\frac{d}{i}\right)^2, \; \Sigma F\left(\frac{d}{i}\right)^3, \text{ and } \Sigma F\left(\frac{d}{i}\right)^4$$

In addition, by means of columns (8) and (9), the work sheet provides a cross check on its internal calculations, since the expansion of $\Sigma F\left(\dfrac{d}{i} + 1\right)^4$ gives the following terms:

$$\Sigma F\left(\frac{d}{i}\right)^4 + 4\Sigma F\left(\frac{d}{i}\right)^3 + 6\Sigma F\left(\frac{d}{i}\right)^2 + 4\Sigma F\left(\frac{d}{i}\right) + \Sigma F$$

It follows that on a correctly constructed work sheet the sum of column (9) equals the sum of column (7) plus four times the sum of column (6) plus six times the sum of column (5) plus four times the sum of column (4) plus the sum of column (2). This is called a "Charlier check" after the name of the man who first suggested its use as a checking device.

For Table 15 the Charlier check is as follows:

Σ [column (2)]	=	300
4Σ [column (4)] $= 4 \times$	$292 =$	1,168
6Σ [column (5)] $= 6 \times$	$2,140 =$	12,840
4Σ [column (6)] $= 4 =$	$5,590 =$	22,360
Σ [column (7)]	=	45,088
Sum $=$ Σ [column (9)]	=	81,756

[1] *Cf. Mathematical Tables from Handbook of Chemistry and Physics,* pp. 153–173. For use in making calculations there are a number of convenient devices such as the slide rule and calculating machines, as well as logarithms. There are also several useful printed tables such as Barlow's *Tables of Squares, Cubes, Square-roots, Cube-roots, and Reciprocals of Integers up to 10,000* and Karl Pearson's *Tables for Statisticians and Biometricians;* A set of logarithms will be found in Appendix, Table I.

TABLE 15.—WORK SHEET FOR MAKING CALCULATIONS IN THE ANALYSIS OF A FREQUENCY DISTRIBUTION

DESCRIPTION OF DATA: Heights of 300 Princeton University Freshmen, Class of 1943

SOURCE OF DATA: Princeton University's Department of Health and Physical Education

$i = 1$ in.

$A = 69.5$ in. (Mid-point of class interval near center of distribution)

(1)		(2)	(3)	(4)	(5)	(6)	(7)	(8)	(9*)
X									
Interval	Mid-point	F	$\frac{d}{i}$	$F\left(\frac{d}{i}\right)$	$F\left(\frac{d}{i}\right)^2$	$F\left(\frac{d}{i}\right)^3$	$F\left(\frac{d}{i}\right)^4$	$\left(\frac{d}{i}+1\right)^4$	$F\left(\frac{d}{i}+1\right)^4$
			−12						
			−11						
			−10						
			−9						
			−8						
62–		1	−7	− 7	49	−343	2,401	1,296	1,296
63–		2	−6	−12	72	−432	2,592	625	1,250
64–		1	−5	− 5	25	−125	625	256	256
65–		4	−4	−16	64	−256	1,024	81	324
66–		12	−3	−36	108	−324	972	16	192
67–		31	−2	−62	124	−248	496	1	31
68–		31	−1	−31	31	−31	31	0	0
69–	69.5	47	0	0	0	0	0	1	47
70–		48	1	48	48	48	48	16	768
71–		42	2	84	168	336	672	81	3,402
72–		35	3	105	315	945	2,835	256	8,960
73–		21	4	84	336	1,344	5,376	625	13,125
74–		14	5	70	350	1,750	8,750	1,296	18,144
75–		8	6	48	288	1,728	10,368	2,401	19,208
76–		2	7	14	98	686	4,802	4,096	8,192
77–		1	8	8	64	512	4,096	6,561	6,561
			9						
			10						
			11						
			12						
Σ		300		292	2,140	5,590	45,088		81,756

* Columns (8) and (9) are for checking purposes. [Σ column (9)] = Σ[Column (2)] + 4Σ[Column (4)] + 6Σ[Column (5)] + 4Σ[Column (6)] + Σ[Column (7)].

Moments about the Arbitrary Origin. The moments about an arbitrary origin can be quickly calculated from the sums of columns (4) to (7), because by definition the moments about an arbitrary origin are as follows:

$$\nu_1 = \frac{\Sigma Fd}{N}$$

$$\nu_2 = \frac{\Sigma Fd^2}{N}$$

$$\nu_3 = \frac{\Sigma Fd^3}{N}$$

$$\nu_4 = \frac{\Sigma Fd^4}{N}$$

$$\cdot \quad \cdot \quad \cdot$$

$$\nu_n = \frac{\Sigma Fd^n}{N}$$

where $X - A = d$.

If A were zero, d would equal X; and the moments would then reduce to the form shown in Chap. VI.

When, as in Table 15, the deviations have been taken in class-interval units rather than in original units, the formulas for the moments about an arbitrary origin, would be written as follows:[1]

$$\nu_1' = \frac{\Sigma F\left(\frac{d}{i}\right)}{N}$$

$$\nu_2' = \frac{\Sigma F\left(\frac{d}{i}\right)^2}{N}$$

$$\nu_3' = \frac{\Sigma F\left(\frac{d}{i}\right)^3}{N}$$

$$\cdot \quad \cdot \quad \cdot$$

$$\nu_n' = \frac{\Sigma F\left(\frac{d}{i}\right)^n}{N}$$

$$(1)$$

where $X - A = \frac{d}{i}(i)$, in which i is the class interval.

[1] *Cf.* p. 181. The prime on ν means that the ν is in class-interval units; *i.e.*, $\nu' = \nu/i$, $\nu_2' = \nu_2/i^2$, etc.

Accordingly, the moments in class-interval units about an arbitrary origin are obtained from the sums of columns (4) to (7) of the work sheet by dividing each by N [the sum of column (2)].

In Table 15, the moments about the arbitrary origin in class-interval units are as follows:

$$\nu_1' = \frac{292}{300} = 0.97333$$

$$\nu_2' = \frac{2,140}{300} = 7.13333$$

$$\nu_3' = \frac{5,590}{300} = 18.63333$$

$$\nu_4' = \frac{45,088}{300} = 150.29333$$

Moments about the Arithmetic Mean. When the moments about an arbitrary origin are obtained, the moments about the mean are obtained from the following equations:[1]

$$\left.\begin{aligned}
\mu_1' &= \nu_1' - \nu_1' = 0 \\
\mu_2' &= \nu_2' - \nu_1'^2 \\
\mu_3' &= \nu_3' - 3\nu_2'\nu_1' + 2\nu_1'^3 \\
\mu_4' &= \nu_4' - 4\nu_3'\nu_1' + 6\nu_2'\nu_1'^2 - 3\nu_1'^4
\end{aligned}\right\} \quad (2)$$

The moments about the arbitrary origin having been calculated for the frequency distribution of freshmen heights in Table 15, the moments about the arithmetic mean in class-interval units may now be obtained by the use of Eqs. (2), as follows:

$$\mu_1' = \quad 0.97333 - 0.97333 = 0$$
$$\mu_2' = \quad 7.13333 - (0.97333)^2 = 7.13333 - 0.94737 = 6.18596$$
$$\mu_3' = \quad 18.6333 - 3(7.13333)(0.97333) + 2(0.97333)^3$$
$$= \quad 18.6333 - 20.82924 + 1.84420 = -0.35171$$
$$\mu_4' = 150.2933 - 4(18.63333)(0.97333) + 6(7.13333)(0.97333)^2$$
$$- 3(0.97333)^4$$
$$= 150.29333 - 72.54552 + 40.54740 - 2.69253 = 115.60268$$

Equations (2) for finding the moments about the mean from the moments about an arbitrary origin may be proved as follows:

[1] $\mu_1' = \mu_1/i, \ \mu_2' = \mu_2/i^2, \ u_3' = \mu_3/i^3$, etc.

Since, in Eqs. (1) for moments about an arbitrary origin, $i(d/i) = X - A$, it follows that

$$F_1\left(\frac{d_1}{i}\right) i = F_1(X_1 - A) = F_1 X_1 - F_1 A$$

$$F_2\left(\frac{d_2}{i}\right) i = F_2(X_2 - A) = F_2 X_2 - F_2 A$$

$$\cdots \cdots \cdots \cdots \cdots$$

$$F_n\left(\frac{d_n}{i}\right) i = F_n(X_n - A) = F_n X_n - F_n A$$

By adding,

(a) $$\Sigma F\left(\frac{d}{i}\right) i \qquad = \qquad \Sigma FX - NA$$

since $\Sigma F = N$.

Because A is a constant, $d_1, d_2, \ldots, d_n$ will vary in proportion as $X_1, X_2, \ldots, X_n$ vary. Also, since A is a constant, the sum of the A's may be written as the constant multiplied by the total frequencies, or NA. If now Eq. (a) is divided by N,

(b) $$\frac{\Sigma F\left(\dfrac{d}{i}\right)}{N} (i) = \frac{\Sigma FX}{N} - A$$

But, by definition,

$$\frac{\Sigma F\left(\dfrac{d}{i}\right)}{N} (i) = \nu'_1(i) = \nu_1$$

and

$$\frac{\Sigma FX}{N} = \bar{X}, \text{ the arithmetic mean}$$

Therefore, by substitution and transposing, Eq. (b) becomes

$$\bar{X} = A + \nu'_1(i) \qquad \text{or} \qquad \bar{X} = A + \nu_1 \qquad (3)$$

Accordingly the arithmetic mean of the frequency distribution of 300 freshmen heights shown in Table 15 is as follows:[1]

[1] The result of calculation is 70.47333; but since the beginning data were significant to only two places beyond the decimal, the figures beyond .47

$$\bar{X} = 69.5 + 0.97333, \qquad \text{since } i = 1$$
$$= 70.47 \text{ in.}$$

It has thus been proved that the arithmetic mean equals any arbitrary quantity plus the first moment about that arbitrary quantity. In other words, *the arithmetic mean of a series of magnitudes is equal to any arbitrary quantity plus the mean of the deviations from the arbitrary quantity.* From Eq. (3) and from the fact that $d = X - A$, it follows that $A = X - d$ and that $\bar{X} = X - d + \nu_1$. Therefore, $X - \bar{X} = d - \nu_1$, and

(c) $$x = d - \nu_1$$

or if d is in class-interval units,

$$x = \left(\frac{d}{i} - \nu'_1\right) i$$

This value for x may be substituted in the equations defining the moments about the mean, as follows:[1]

$$\mu_1 = \frac{\Sigma F x}{N} = \frac{\Sigma F \left(\dfrac{d}{i} - \nu'_1\right)}{N} \quad (i)$$

$$\mu_2 = \frac{\Sigma F x^2}{N} = \frac{\Sigma F \left(\dfrac{d}{i} - \nu'_1\right)^2}{N} \quad (i^2)$$

$$\mu_3 = \frac{\Sigma F x^3}{N} = \frac{\Sigma F \left(\dfrac{d}{i} - \nu'_1\right)^3}{N} \quad (i^3)$$

$$\mu_4 = \frac{\Sigma F x^4}{N} = \frac{\Sigma F \left(\dfrac{d}{i} - \nu'_1\right)^4}{N} \quad (i^4)$$

(4)

are not significant. The manner in which the figures are written in Table 11, which was taken from the source of the data, indicates accuracy to two decimal places. Had the numbers been rounded off to the nearest inch, the calculated mean would have significant figures to the nearest inch. Nevertheless, if the value of the mean is to be used for making further mathematical calculations to obtain other statistics, it should be carried out to several more decimal places in order to give an accurate result to two places in the additional statistics.

[1] For definition of moments about the mean, *cf.*, p. 181.

After expanding and collecting like terms, these equations become

$$\mu_1 = \frac{\Sigma F \left(\frac{d}{i}\right)}{N} (i) - \nu_1$$

$$\mu_2 = \frac{\Sigma F \left(\frac{d}{i}\right)^2}{N} (i)^2 - (\nu_1)^2$$

$$\mu_3 = \frac{\Sigma F \left(\frac{d}{i}\right)^3}{N} (i)^3 - 3 \frac{\Sigma F \left(\frac{d}{i}\right)^2}{N}(i)^2\nu_1 + 2(\nu_1)^3$$

$$\mu_4 = \frac{\Sigma F \left(\frac{d}{i}\right)^4}{N} (i)^4 - 4 \frac{\Sigma F \left(\frac{d}{i}\right)^3}{N} (i)^3\nu_1$$

$$+ 6 \frac{\Sigma F \left(\frac{d}{i}\right)^2}{N} (i)^2(\nu_1)^2 - 3(\nu_1)^4$$

$$(5)$$

From values given for ν_1, ν_2, ν_3, and ν_4 in Eqs. (1), Eqs. (5) may now be written as follows:

$$\mu_1 = \nu_1 - \nu_1 = 0$$
$$\mu_2 = \nu_2 - \nu_1^2$$
$$\mu_3 = \nu_3 - 3\nu_2\nu_1 + 2\nu_1^3$$
$$\mu_4 = \nu_4 - 4\nu_3\nu_1 + 6\nu_2\nu_1^2 - 3\nu_1^4$$

which it was said at the beginning of this section would be proved. An important corollary follows from the above derivation of the second moment (or "variance," as it is sometimes called). Since

$$\mu_2 = \nu_2 - \nu_1^2$$

it follows that *the mean square deviation about the mean of the observations is less than the mean square deviation about any arbitrary quantity;* that is, the mean square deviation (σ^2) about the mean is a minimum—smaller than it would be if calculated from any other average. This is obvious from the equation; since ν_1^2 is a positive quantity, being a square, μ_2 must be less than ν_2.

The Standard Deviation. The standard deviation about the arithmetic mean may now be quickly calculated, since it is by definition the square root of the second moment. For the frequency distribution of heights of 300 freshmen the standard deviation is as follows:

$$\frac{\sigma}{i} = \mu_2'^{\frac{1}{2}} = 2.487 \text{ or } 2.49 \text{ in.}$$

Since the moments were calculated in class-interval units (see page 212), this result is also in class-interval units. The standard deviation in original units is found by multiplying by i. In the present problem, $i = 1$; hence, $\sigma = \sigma/i = 2.49$ in.

The Beta Coefficients. For the frequency distribution of heights of 300 freshmen, the first two beta coefficients are as follows:

$$\beta_1 = \frac{\mu_3^2}{\mu_2^3} = 0.00052$$

$$\beta_2 = \frac{\mu_4}{\mu_2^2} = 3.02102$$

Since the betas are ratios having i raised to the same power in both numerator and denominator, the fact that the moments are in class-interval units instead of original units may be disregarded.

Measures of Skewness and Kurtosis. Measures of skewness and kurtosis are also readily determined from the moments about the mean. In the frequency distribution of heights of 300 freshmen, the measure of kurtosis, β_2, calculated above, is 3.021, slightly larger than 3. Hence the frequency distribution is somewhat less flat-topped than the normal curve.[1]

Skewness in heights of the 300 freshmen, measured by the cube root of the third moment, is -0.7057 class intervals. Since $i = 1$ in., this is -0.7057 inch.

CALCULATION OF OTHER STATISTICS

Averages and Measures of Variability. *Difficulties in Locating the Median and the Mode.* Consideration of the median, the mode, and the quartiles has been left to the last for the reason that, in the analysis of frequency distributions with class intervals, these values must be estimated. By definition, the median is the value at the center of the distribution, the first quartile

---

[1] Figure 101, p. 295, is a graph comparing the frequency distribution with the ideal normal curve.

is the value midway between the lower limit of the range and the median, and the third quartile is the value midway between the median and the upper limit of the range. The mode is the value that occurs with the greatest frequency. The calculations of these statistics are not based on the work sheet shown in Table 15.

Because they are concealed in the class interval among a group of other cases in the same class interval, the quartiles, the median, and the mode must be obtained by estimation. Where within the range of the class interval is the median? Where within the range of the class interval with the largest frequency is the mode? These questions have to be answered by interpolation, and the value so obtained becomes an abstract quantity—as abstract and mathematical in character as the mean, but without the latter's precision.

The Mode. In the case of the mode, a further difficulty arises in finding the correct answer to the question: Which class interval should be considered to contain the mode? If different-sized class intervals are taken in each of several frequency distributions of the same data, the modal class interval will be observed to shift around. The mode, by definition the simplest of the several measures, is actually the most difficult average to locate. Its accurate computation is more highly mathematical than that of the arithmetic mean. If a Pearsonian curve gives a good fit to the data, the ideal method of obtaining the mode is to find the mode of this curve. A formula for this is given on the next page. The disadvantage of this method is that there is no way of telling whether a curve is a good fit or not until it is actually fitted, and this involves a considerable amount of calculation just for the sake of finding the mode.

But simpler measures of the mode are often used. These are interpolated values, on the assumption that the mode lies in the modal class interval, that is, the class interval that has the highest frequency. It is assumed that the general shape of the distribution affects the distribution of cases at the point of greatest concentration in the following manner: All the frequencies below the modal class interval are pulling the mode near the lower limit of that class interval, and all the frequencies above the modal class interval are pulling the mode toward the upper limit of the interval. The mode is equal to the lower limit of the modal class interval plus the interpolated part of the class interval established by the relationship of the frequencies above and below that class interval.   In the frequency distribution of freshmen heights (Table 15), the modal class interval, that is, the class interval with the greatest concentration of cases, is 70–.   There are 129 cases pulling the mode toward the lower limit of the class interval 70–, and 123 cases pulling the mode toward the upper limit.   Consequently,

$$\text{Mo} = 70 + \tfrac{123}{252} \times 1 = 70.488 \text{ or } 70.49 \text{ in.}$$

The so-called "mathematical mode," an approximation of the mode of the Pearsonian curve that is invalid if the frequency curve is very skewed, is calculated from the following equation:[1]

$$\text{Mo} = \bar{X} - 3(\bar{X} - \text{Mi})*$$

For the frequency distribution of 300 freshmen heights, the mathematical mode is calculated as follows:

$$\text{Mo} = 70.47333 - 3(70.47333 - 70.4375) = 70.366 \text{ or } 70.37 \text{ in.}$$

The mode of the Pearsonian curve fitted to the data is given by the formula:

$$\text{Mo} = \bar{X} - \sigma \text{sk}$$

where $\text{sk} = \dfrac{\sqrt{\beta_1}\,(\beta_2 + 3)}{2(5\beta_2 - 6\beta_1 - 9)}.$

For the frequency distribution of 300 freshmen heights, the mode calculated by this equation is as follows:

$$\text{Mo} = 70.50 \text{ in.}$$

The Median and the Quartiles.   Determination of the median and the quartiles by interpolation is reasonably accurate if, as it is assumed, the cases are evenly distributed within the class interval containing the median and the two quartiles, respectively.   The calculation of the median and the quartiles is facilitated by making a column of cumulated frequencies as shown in Table 16.   The median is equal to the lower limit of the class containing the $N/2$th case plus an interpolated amount within the class interval determined by the ratio of the fre-

[1] *Cf.* p. 173.
* The median is 70.4375.   *Cf.* the next section.

quencies in the interval to the balance of frequencies necessary to make up $N/2$ frequencies. In the frequency distribution of freshmen heights (Table 16), $N/2 = 150$. The frequencies are counted cumulatively from the lower limit of the first class interval (top of the table). By this count, there are 129 cases to the lower limit of the class interval 70–. When the point 70 is reached on the quantity scale, 129 cases have been counted; but the median is the value of the 150th case, that is, 21 cases beyond 70. From 70 to 71 there are 48 cases. Consequently, the ratio of interpolation within the class interval is $\frac{21}{48}$. Accordingly, the estimate of the median in freshmen heights is as follows:

$$Mi = 70 + \tfrac{21}{48} \times 1 = 70.4375 \text{ or } 70.44 \text{ in.}$$

TABLE 16.—FREQUENCY DISTRIBUTION OF THE HEIGHTS OF 300 PRINCETON FRESHMEN, CLASS OF 1943
(In inches.   Class interval 1 in.)

X	F	Cumulative F
62–	1	1
63–	2	3
64–	1	4
65–	4	8
66–	12	20
67–	31	51
68–	31	82
69–	47	129
70–	48	177
71–	42	219
72–	35	254
73–	21	275
74–	14	289
75–	8	297
76–	2	299
77–	1	300
	300	

1. There are 129 cases to $X = 70$.

2. Since $N/2 = 150.0$, this leaves $150.0 - 129$, or 21.0 cases to go, of the 48 cases in the next class interval (70–71).

3. The interpolated amount of the class-interval range is therefore $\frac{21}{48} \times 1$.

The third and first quartiles are calculated by interpolating in a similar manner for the values of the $3N/4$th and the $N/4$th cases. In the frequency distribution of the heights of 300 freshmen, following are the values of the quartiles:

$$Q_1 = 68 + \tfrac{24}{31} \times 1 = 68.774 \text{ or } 68.77 \text{ in.}$$
$$Q_3 = 72 + \tfrac{6}{35} \times 1 = 72.171 \text{ or } 72.17 \text{ in.}$$

The Average Deviation. The average, or mean, deviation is a measure of dispersion that has its minimum value when deviations are measured from the median. To compute the average deviation from the median, subtract each of the N values of X from the median, add the absolute values of the deviations, and divide by N. Thus,

$$\text{A.D.} = \frac{\Sigma|X - \text{Mi}|}{N} \tag{6}$$

The average deviation is simpler in concept than any other measure of dispersion. It is less affected by extreme deviations than the more popular standard deviation, and for this reason it probably has greater sampling reliability from extremely leptokurtic universes. In spite of these advantages the average deviation is not a popular measure of dispersion, partly because of several widely accepted but mistaken notions concerning its properties.

It is often said that it is illogical to neglect the signs of deviations to be averaged and that this fallacy is avoided in the case of other measures of dispersion. It is true that the mean deviation from the median is the mean of absolute deviations from some average, but every other measure of dispersion is also equal (or proportional) to an average of absolute deviations from some average. The quartile deviation is the median of absolute deviations from the mid-quartile, and the standard deviation is the quadratic mean of absolute deviations from the mean.

It has been said that the sampling reliability of the average deviation is less than that of the standard deviation. This may be true for normal universes, but it can hardly be true for all types.

Grouped Data—Mid-value Assumption in Calculating Average Deviation. When data are grouped in the form of a frequency distribution with equal class intervals, the average deviation can be written in the simple form

$$\text{A.D.} = \frac{i(\Sigma |Fd/i|)}{N} \tag{7}$$

where d is the deviation of class mid-values from the mid-value of the class interval containing the median. Although Eq. (7) is the exact value of the average deviation from the median according to the assumption that all observations in every class interval are equal to the mid-value of the interval (the same assumption commonly used for the standard deviation), many statisticians consider it unsatisfactory as a formula for the average deviation. The chief reason for the dissatisfaction seems to be that the mid-value assumption, which implies that the median is the mid-value of the median interval, is inconsistent with the ordinary notion of the interpolated median.

In applying the simple formula in practice, several corrections may be used, some of which will be illustrated below. Each of these corrections deals with a separate aspect of the problem of approximating the average deviation of ungrouped data from a frequency distribution. The two most important corrections are usually of the same order of magnitude, but opposite in sign, so that they tend to offset each other. For this reason, it is usually advisable to use the simpler formula without correction, because of its simplicity, unless the problem is of great importance so that minor adjustments are worth making.

Grouped Data—Histogram Assumption in Calculating Average Deviation. The average deviation of the histogram considered as a continuous frequency function is often used in preference to the simple formula for the average deviation presented in Eq. (7). This corresponds to the assumption on which the usual interpolated median is based. The median is the abscissa of the vertical line that divides the histogram into two equal areas. When the left half of the histogram is folded along this vertical line, over the half on the right, the average deviation is the first moment about the line of folding.

To simplify the derivation, let d/i represent deviations from the mid-value of the median interval, and let

$$\text{Mi} = L + ci \tag{8}$$

where L is the lower limit of the median interval, i is the width of the class interval, and c is the proportion of observations in the median interval that are less than Mi. It is to be noted that the cases are assumed to be distributed uniformly through the interval.

In these terms the formula for average deviation can be written as follows:

$$\text{A.D.} = i\left(\frac{\Sigma\left|F\frac{d}{i}\right|}{N} + C_1 + C_2\right) = \frac{i\left[\Sigma\left|F\frac{d}{i}\right| + c(1-c)F_0\right]}{N} \quad (9)$$

in which F_0 is the frequency of the median interval, C_1 is the amount of correction associated with observations above and

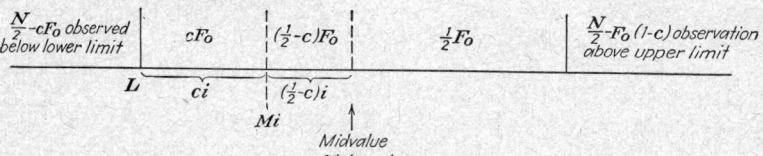

FIG. 74.—Illustration of distribution of cases in and above and below the median interval.

below the median interval, and C_2 is the amount of correction associated with the median interval itself.

To demonstrate the truth of this equation, consider the diagram of the median interval shown in Fig. 74. Since deviations from the mid-value of the median interval are $(\frac{1}{2} - c)i$ too small for observations above the median interval and $(\frac{1}{2} - c)i$ too large for those below the median interval, it follows that

$$C_1 = i\left(\frac{1}{2} - c\right)\left[\frac{N}{2} - (1-c)F_0 - \left(\frac{N}{2} - cF_0\right)\right] \quad (10)$$

$$= i(\tfrac{1}{2} - c)(2c - 1)F_0 = iF_0(2c - 2c^2 - \tfrac{1}{2})$$

The area in the median interval below Mi is cF_0, and its mean deviation from Mi is $ci/2$. Similarly, $(1-c)F_0$ lies above Mi with a mean deviation of $(1-c)i/2$. Hence,

$$C_2 = cF_0\left(\frac{ci}{2}\right) + (1-c)\frac{i}{2}(1-c)F_0$$

$$= iF_0\left[\frac{c^2}{2} + \frac{(1-c)^2}{2}\right] = iF_0\left(c^2 - c + \frac{1}{2}\right) \quad (11)$$

From Eqs. (10) and (11), the combined corrections are found to be

$$C_1 + C_2 = iF_0(2c - 2c^2 - \tfrac{1}{2}) + iF_0(c^2 - c + \tfrac{1}{2})$$
$$= iF_0(c - c^2) = iF_0c(1 - c) \qquad (12)$$

a result that verified Eq. (9).   Equation (9) is probably the most convenient form available for computing the mean deviation according to the histogram assumption.

Calculation of the average deviation by the use of Eq. (9) is illustrated by Table 17 and the ensuing analysis.

TABLE 17.—FREQUENCY DISTRIBUTION OF THE HEIGHTS OF 300 PRINCETON FRESHMEN, CLASS OF 1943

(In inches.   Class interval 1 in.)

X	F	$\dfrac{d}{i}$	$F\left(\dfrac{d}{i}\right)$
62–	1	−8	−8
63–	2	−7	−14
64–	1	−6	−6
65–	4	−5	−20
66–	12	−4	−48
67–	31	−3	−93
68–	31	−2	−62
69–	47	−1	−47
70–	48	0	0
71–	42	1	42
72–	35	2	70
73–	21	3	63
74–	14	4	56
75–	8	5	40
76–	2	6	12
77–	1	7	7
	300		−298
			+290
			Σ (without regard to sign) = 588

When the median and the quartiles were calculated, it was assumed that the frequencies were evenly distributed in the class intervals. This assumption is continued while calculating the average deviation about the median. As shown in Table 17, the sum of the deviations about the arbitrary origin without regard to sign is 588.   That is,

$$\Sigma \left| F\left(\frac{d}{i}\right) \right| = 588$$

where
$$d_1 = X_1 - A$$
$$d_2 = X_2 - A$$
$$\cdot \quad \cdot \quad \cdot \quad \cdot$$
$$d_n = X_n - A$$

The sum desired is the sum without regard to sign of deviations from the median.   That is,

$$\Sigma \left| F\left(\frac{x'}{i}\right) \right|$$

where
$$x'_1 = X_1 - \mathrm{Mi}$$
$$x'_2 = X_2 - \mathrm{Mi}$$
$$\cdot \quad \cdot \quad \cdot \quad \cdot$$
$$x'_n = X_n = \mathrm{Mi}$$

NOTE: x has been used to symbolize the deviations from the arithmetic mean; x' is used to symbolize deviations from the median.

Accordingly, the above sum, 588, which for the illustration chosen is $\Sigma |F(d/i)|$ can be adjusted by a calculated correction that will change the sum to $\Sigma |F(x'/i)|$.   This correction is obtained by using Eq. (9).

From Table 17 and the analysis on pages 221 to 223 it is to be noted that $F_0 = 48$, the frequency of the interval containing the median; $i = 1$; and $c = 0.44$, since the median is 70.44, the lower limit of the interval containing the median is 70, and c is the proportion of observations in the median interval that are less than the median.   Accordingly, the average deviation may be calculated by using Eq. (9), as follows:

$$\begin{aligned}
\text{A.D.}_{\mathrm{Mi}} &= \frac{i\left[\Sigma \left|F\dfrac{d}{i}\right| + c(1-c)F_0 \right]}{N} \\
&= \frac{1[588 + 0.44(0.56)48]}{300} \\
&= \frac{588 + 11.83}{300} \\
&= 2.00 \text{ in.}
\end{aligned}$$

The Semiquartile Range.   The semiquartile range, one-half of the difference between the third quartile and the first quartile, is another statistic that measures variability. Its formula is

$$Q = \frac{Q_3 - Q_1}{2}$$

For the frequency distribution in Table 15, the semiquartile range is calculated as follows:

$$Q = \frac{72.17143 - 68.77419}{2} = 1.69862 \text{ or } 1.70 \text{ in.}$$

Measures of Skewness. From statistics measuring variation and central tendencies, important measures of skewness are obtained. It has been noted that $\bar{X} - \text{Mo}$ is a measure of skewness. In the frequency distribution of 300 Princeton freshmen heights,

$$\bar{X} - \text{Mo} = 70.473333 - 70.36584 = 0.10749 \text{ or } 0.11 \text{ in.}$$

The position of the first and third quartiles in relation to the median is a very convenient statistic measuring skewness, namely,

$$Q_3 - \text{Mi} - (\text{Mi} - Q_1) \qquad \text{or} \qquad Q_1 + Q_3 - 2\text{Mi}$$

For the frequency distribution of heights of 300 Princeton freshmen this statistic is

$$68.7742 + 72.1714 - 2(70.4375) = 0.07 \text{ in.}$$

COEFFICIENTS OF VARIABILITY

The various aggregative measures of variability may conveniently be expressed as relatives or coefficients, as explained in the preceding chapter; indeed, they must be so expressed if comparisons are to be made with other frequency distributions having different types of units. The aggregative measures of variability are converted into relatives or coefficients by dividing the former by the mean, the median, or the average of the two quartiles. For the present problem, the relative measures of variability that would be useful in comparing this frequency distribution with other frequency distributions, are as follows:

$$V_\sigma = \frac{\sigma}{\bar{X}} = 3.53 \text{ per cent}$$

$$V_{\text{A.D.}} = \frac{\text{A.D.}}{\text{Mi}} = 1.38 \text{ per cent}$$

$$V_Q = \frac{Q_3 - Q_1}{Q_1 + Q_3} = 2.41 \text{ per cent}$$

The formula for the V_Q is really the semiquartile range divided by the average of the two quartiles, but the 2's cancel out, leaving merely the difference between the two quartiles in the numerator and their sum in the denominator.

COEFFICIENTS OF SKEWNESS

Statistics measuring skewness are likewise more significant for comparative purposes when expressed as coefficients. The various coefficients of skewness for the frequency distribution in Table 16 are as follows:

Based on mathematical statistics:

$$\text{sk} = \frac{\mu_3^{\frac{1}{3}}}{\sigma} = \frac{-0.32764 \text{ in.}}{2.48716 \text{ in.}} = -0.1317 \text{ or } -13.17 \text{ per cent}$$

$$\text{sk} = \frac{\sqrt{\beta_1}\,(\beta_2 + 3)}{2(5\beta_2 - 6\beta_1 - 9)} = -0.0112, \text{ or } -1.12 \text{ per cent}$$

NOTE: This is given the negative sign because the third moment is negative.

Based on other statistics (using Mo = 70.488):

$$\text{sk} = \frac{\bar{X} - \text{Mo}}{\sigma} = \frac{-0.015 \text{ in.}}{2.487 \text{ in.}} = -0.006 \text{ or } -0.6 \text{ per cent}$$

(If the so-called "mathematical mode," *i.e.*, Mo = 70.366, is used, this coefficient of skewness by the same formula would be +4.32 per cent.)

Using the median and the two quartiles to measure skewness, the following result is obtained:

$$\text{sk} = \frac{Q_3 + Q_1 - 2\text{Mi}}{Q} = \frac{+0.0706 \text{ in.}}{1.69862 \text{ in.}} = +0.0416, \text{ or } +4.16 \text{ per cent}$$

The difficulty of locating the mode, even when quite a large sample is taken, is illustrated by the frequency distribution analyzed in this chapter. In this illustration every mathematical indication is that the mode is larger than the mean, but the non-mathematically calculated mode (the interpolated mode) is smaller than the mean.

GRAPHIC INTERPRETATION OF STATISTICS OF VARIABILITY AND SKEWNESS

Figure 75 shows on a scale the relative location of the median, the two quartiles, and the upper and lower limits found by taking $Mi \pm A.D._{Mi}$, namely, 70.44 ± 2.00. The figure illustrates the fact that, when there is skewness, the location of the quartiles with reference to the median reflects the presence of skewness. If, therefore, the quartiles are used as measures of deviation, they reflect the fact that, in skewed distributions, the deviation

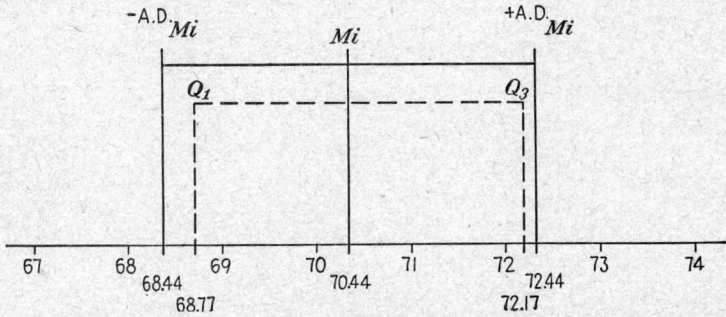

Fig. 75.—Illustration of significance of average deviation and two quartiles as measures of dispersion.

is skewed in one direction or the other. If the average deviation is used as a measure of deviation or variability, the presence of skewness will not be noted in the results. Whenever the distribution is skewed to any extent, the quartiles are unequal distances from the median, as may be noticed in Fig. 75. As the figure also illustrates, the average deviation is conceived as an equal distance on each side of the median.

Figure 76 shows on a scale the relative location of the median and average deviation and the location of the mean and the standard deviation by depicting the upper and lower limits of $Mi \pm A.D._{Mi}$ (as in Fig. 75) and, in addition, the upper and lower limits of $\bar{X} \pm \sigma$. As in the case of the average deviation, so also in the case of the standard deviation, the measure of variability is conceived as an equal distance above and below the mean—that is, an equal distance from the mean on the x-axis in both the positive and the negative directions in Figs.

75 and 76. If the distribution is skewed to a marked extent, it should be evident that care must be exercised in interpreting the significance of the average deviation or the standard deviation.

From Fig. 75 it is noted that the first quartile in the negative direction and the third quartile in the positive direction are less distant from the median than $\pm$ A.D.$_{Mi}$. By definition, the limits of the range between the first and third quartiles include exactly 50 per cent of the cases. For a normal distribution[1] the distance between the upper and lower limits defined by Mi $\pm$ A.D.$_{Mi}$ include approximately 58 per cent of the cases.[2]

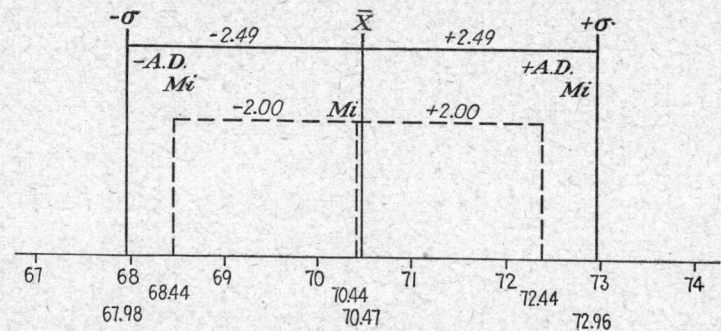

FIG. 76.—Illustration of the standard deviation and average deviation as measures of variability.

It will be noted from Fig. 76 that the limits $\bar{X} \pm \sigma$ are farther, respectively, in the positive and negative directions from the mean than are the limits Mi $\pm$ A.D.$_{Mi}$ from the median. The standard deviation is always larger than the average deviation; in fact, an approximate check[3] on the accuracy of calculation may be used as follows: A.D. $= 0.8\sigma$. In the frequency distribution illustrated, this check works fairly well; for $0.8(2.49) = 1.97$ and the calculated A.D.$_{Mi} = 2.00$. For a normal distribution the distance between the upper and lower limits defined by $\bar{X} \pm \sigma$ includes approximately two-thirds (68 per cent) of the cases.[2]

FREQUENCY DISTRIBUTIONS WITH UNEQUAL CLASS INTERVALS

As remarked earlier in this chapter, the size of the class interval should ordinarily be uniform throughout a given frequency

---

[1] See Chap. XI for description of a normal distribution.

[2] For more precise discussion and explanation, see Chaps. XI and XII.

[3] For distributions that depart widely from the normal form, this check may not be satisfactory.

distribution; but in some cases, usually because there is a large concentration of cases at one or the other extreme of the range, it is considered necessary to use different-sized class intervals for parts of the frequency distribution in order to give a proper picture of variability. Table 18 illustrates such an instance. Of 150 cases distributed over the range 0–51, 106 cases fell within the limits 0–10. Obviously, a small number of class intervals of uniform size would give a wholly erroneous notion of the variation. Occasionally, data at its primary source will be published in a manner similar to that of Table 18, and the statistician has no choice but to utilize the material in frequency distributions that have unequal-sized class intervals. This is particularly true of statistics of wages and income and statistics of hours of labor.

TABLE 18.—DEATHS DUE TO AUTOMOBILE ACCIDENTS IN 150 CITIES,*
FIRST 20 WEEKS OF 1940

Number of deaths due to automobile accidents X		Number of cities whose automobile accident fatalities were as specified F	Calculations of deviations from an arbitrary origin $(A = 15)$ $\frac{d}{i}$†
Intervals	Mid-values		
0–	0.5	11	−1.45
1–	2.0	23	−1.30
3–	4.0	34	−1.10
5–	7.5	38	−0.75
10–	15.0	24	0
20–	25.0	12	1.00
30–	35.0	4	2.00
40–51	45.5	4	3.05
		150	

* New York, Los Angeles, Chicago, and Detroit are excluded from these statistics. United States Bureau of the United States Census, *Weekly Accident Bulletin*, May 24, 1940, pp. 1–4.
† $i = 10$.

If the mid-value of the class interval 10– is taken as the arbitrary origin, that is, $A = 15$, and the "class interval" or abscissa scale unit i is taken equal to 10 (since that size interval predominates), the deviations of class intervals in that part of the frequency distribution where class intervals are equal are readily determined. Where the class intervals are unequal, simple subtraction of mid-values and the division of the answer by the scale unit gives the results in the last column of Table 18.   To illustrate the process, there is a difference of 10.5 between mid-value 35 and mid-value 45.5, a quantity 1.05 times the scale unit.   Accordingly, the deviation advances from 2.0 to 3.05 scale units.   In the lower reaches of the range there is a difference of 7.5 between mid-value 15 and mid-value 7.5, or $\frac{3}{4}$ a scale unit; consequently, the step-deviation change is from 0 to -0.75. From mid-value 7.5 to mid-value 4, the deviation recedes 0.35 a scale unit to -1.10.   From mid-value 4.0 to mid-value 1.5, a distance of $\frac{1}{4}$ an interval, the scale-unit deviation changes from -1.10 to -1.35.   Finally, from mid-value 1.5 to mid-value 0.5, a distance of $\frac{1}{10}$ a scale unit, the scale-unit deviation recedes from -1.35 to -1.45.

From this point on, the analysis of the frequency distribution is the same as it would be were uniform class intervals used, although obviously the uneven numbers add somewhat to the burden of filling in the work sheet according to the plan shown in Table 16.   Once the work sheet has been completed, however, the fact that the class intervals are not uniform ceases to be a consideration in the subsequent computations; the summation figures can be applied in the formulas in precisely the same manner as if the class intervals were uniform.

ACCURACY IN THE CALCULATION OF STATISTICS

Ordinary common sense would dictate that all recording of figures needs to be carefully checked, since there is always a chance of making a mistake in copying.   Such mistakes are not statistical errors to be disregarded under the "theory of errors," which is explained in Chap. XI.   They cannot be disregarded, and every effort should be made to prevent their occurrence. The same applies to all calculations made, but frequently short-cut or cross checks can be devised for these.   While accuracy is essential, a spurious accuracy may be introduced into final answers.   For example, in most cases final figures representing samples should be presented in round numbers, including only the significant figures in the arithmetical answers obtained.[1]

Care must be taken, however, in cases where errors are likely to accumulate through successive steps of calculation.   It may be

[1] The meaning of "significant" is explained on p. 213, note.

necessary to retain the figures in a calculated result for a number of places beyond the significant figures if that calculated result is being used in the process of calculating other statistics. In some statistical problems it is necessary to add a constant successively perhaps fifty or even hundreds of times, or, similarly, to multiply by a constant successively a large number of times. In such instances the constant should be written to several more places than will be used in the final answers in order to avoid an error in significant figures at the end of the process. This is a purely mathematical problem; in every case, the standard of accuracy required, or the number of significant figures, having been decided upon, a simple arithmetical calculation will show to how many places the intermediary calculations must be carried. The final results are then rounded off to the number of significant figures.

In rounding numbers the rule is that a remainder less than half a unit is disregarded, while half or more than half is counted as an additional unit. Exactly half may be changed to the nearest even number—thus 174.5 would be 174 but 175.5 would be 176.

PART III

The Normal Frequency Curve

CHAPTER VIII

PROBABILITY

Up to this point, the discussion has primarily been concerned with "descriptive statistics." Attention has centered upon methods of summarizing and describing statistical variation. Occasionally, theory has been employed to explain certain methods or to indicate why one method is to be preferred to another; but, in general, emphasis has been upon the facts as such, rather than upon any theoretical explanation of or inference to be made from these facts.

In contrast, the next four chapters will be primarily concerned with a particular body of theoretical statistics, namely, the theory of the normal frequency curve. The question now to be considered is not "what" is the character of a given frequency distribution, but "why." The discussion will be abstract and general and will not pertain to actual concrete data, except by way of illustration.

Before this theoretical analysis can be undertaken, however, certain mathematical tools must be acquired and certain fundamental concepts clarified. That is the purpose of this and the next chapters.

PERMUTATIONS AND COMBINATIONS

Permutations Defined and Illustrated. A "permutation" is an arrangement. The word "man," for example, is a special arrangement of the three letters m, a, and n. Other possible arrangements of these three letters are: *mna, nma, nam, anm,* and *amn.* All these arrangements are permutations.

232

In general, if there are N different things, it is possible to form $N!$ different permutations.[1] Consider again the three letters m, a, and n. In making various arrangements of these, it is possible to pick the first letter in three different ways. The first letter having been picked, there are then left two different ways for the selection of the second letter. Finally, the first two letters having been selected, there remains one, and only one, way for the selection of the last letter. Now, each one of the two ways that are open for the selection of the second letter can be combined with each of the three ways that are open for the selection of the first letter, so that there are 3×2 different ways of picking the first and second letters. Since there is only one way left in every case for the selection of the last letter, there are therefore $3 \times 2 \times 1 = 6$ different ways of picking all the three letters. Thus, the number of different permutations of three things is $3! = 6$. If there had been 10 different letters, the number of different permutations of these would have been $10 \times 9 \times 8 \times 7 \times 6 \times 5 \times 4 \times 3 \times 2 \times 1 = 10! = 3,628,800$.

Suppose, now, that among 10 different things 3 are to be selected for some particular purpose, the exact nature of the purpose being immaterial for the analysis. The question is: In how many different ways may a subgroup of 3 be selected from the total of 10; in other words, what is the number of different permutations that can be made of 10 things taken 3 at a time? This question may be answered as follows: It is possible to select the first of the subgroup of 3 in 10 different ways, the second in 9 different ways, and the third in 8 different ways. There are thus altogether $10 \times 9 \times 8$ different ways in which the 3 things may be selected from the total of 10. Accordingly, the number of different permutations of 10 things taken 3 at a time is $10 \times 9 \times 8 = 720$. In general, the number of different permutations of N things taken r at a time is

$$P_r^N = N(N-1) \cdots \qquad \text{to } r \text{ factors}$$

that is,

$$P_r^N = N(N-1)(N-2) \cdots (N-r+1) \qquad (1)$$

Combinations Defined and Illustrated. A "combination" is not the same thing as a permutation. A group of 3 letters con-

---

[1] $N!$ is to be read "N factorial" and signifies the successive product of N by all the integers less than N and greater than zero.

stitutes a combination of these 3 letters; but as has just been seen, this combination can be arranged in 3! different ways. In other words, it is possible to have 3! permutations of a single combination of 3 things. In general, it is possible to have N! permutations of a single combination of N things.

Although a group of N things forms but a single combination, subgroups may be picked in such a way as to constitute different combinations. Suppose, for example, that the board of directors of a given corporation consists of 10 men and the chairman. The chairman wishes to pick a committee of 3 men. In how many different ways can such a committee be constituted, the chairman himself being excluded? This is a question of how many different combinations of 3 men may be taken from a group of 10 men. It will be noted that the order of selection is immaterial, for it is only the constituency of any committee that differentiates it from other possible committees.

The answer to this question is obtained as follows: Let C_3^{10} represent the number of combinations to be calculated, *viz.*, the number of different combinations of 10 things taken 3 at a time. Each one of these combinations, it will be recalled, can be arranged in 3! different ways; *i.e.*, there are 3! different ways in which a given committee can be selected. Accordingly, the total number of ways in which a committee of 3, *i.e.*, just any committee and not a particular committee, can be chosen is equal to $C_3^{10} \times 3!$. But the total number of different ways in which a committee of 3 can be picked from a group of 10 is the number of permutations of 10 things taken 3 at a time, which is equal to $10 \times 9 \times 8$. Therefore, $C_3^{10}\ 3! = 10 \times 9 \times 8$, and $C_3^{10} = \dfrac{10 \times 9 \times 8}{3!}.$ In general, the number of different combinations of N things taken r at a time is

$$C_r^N = \frac{N(N-1)(N-2)\ \cdots\ (N-r+1)}{r!} \tag{2}$$

or if numerator and denominator are both multiplied by $(N-r)!$,

$$C_r^N = \frac{N!}{r!(N-r)!} \tag{3}$$

The Binomial Expansion. A use that is made of combinatorial theory in elementary algebra is to find a formula for the expansion of the binomial $(x + y)^N$. It will be recalled that $(x + y)^2 = (x + y)(x + y)$ is found by multiplying each term of the first factor by each term of the second factor and adding these partial products. Thus

$$(x + y)^2 = x^2 + xy + xy + y^2 = x^2 + 2xy + y^2$$

A higher powered binomial can be evaluated by mere repetition of this process. Thus

$$(x + y)^3 = (x + y)(x + y)(x + y) = (x^2 + 2xy + y^2)(x + y)$$
$$= x^3 + 2x^2y + xy^2 + x^2y + 2xy^2 + y^3 = x^3 + 3x^2y + 3xy^2 + y^3$$

It will be noted that the result in each case consists of a series of terms in diminishing powers of x (or rising powers of y), and this is generally true no matter what the power of the binomial. It will also be noted that the number of times a given term occurs (*i.e.*, its coefficient in the expansion) depends on the number of ways the x's (or y's) that make up that term can be selected from the different factors. Thus in the case of $(x + y)^3$ the term composed of three x's, that is, x^3, can be formed in only one way, namely, by taking an x from each of the three factors. The term x^2y, however, which contains two x's, can be formed in three ways. This is because the number of different combinations that can be made of three x's taken two at a time is $\frac{3 \cdot 2 \cdot 1}{2 \cdot 1 \cdot 1} = 3$. Similarly, the coefficient of xy^2 is the number of different combinations of three x's taken one at a time, which is $\frac{3 \cdot 2 \cdot 1}{1 \cdot 2 \cdot 1} = 3$. Accordingly, the expansion of $(x + y)^3$ might be written $(x + y)^3 = C_3^3 x^3 + C_2^3 x^2y + C_1^3 xy^2 + C_0^3 y^3$, where C_3^3 means the number of combinations of three things taken three at a time, C_2^3 equals the number of combinations of three things taken two at a time, etc.,[1] the evaluation of these quantities to be determined by Eq. (3). If consideration were given to the power of y instead of x, this new method of writing the expansion of $(x + y)^3$ would become

$$(x + y)^3 = C_0^3 x^3 + C_1^3 x^2y + C_2^3 xy^2 + C_3^3 y^3$$

[1] Note that 0! is taken by convention to be 1, so that $C_0^3 = 1$.

In general,

$$(x + y)^N = C_N^N x^N + C_{N-1}^N x^{N-1}y + \cdots + C_2^N x^2 y^{N-2}$$
$$+ C_1^N xy^{N-1} + C_0^N y^N \quad (4)$$

or, on using the second method of expression,

$$(x + y)^N = C_0^N x^N + C_1^N x^{N-1}y + \cdots + C_{N-2}^N x^2 y^{N-2}$$
$$+ C_{N-1}^N xy^{N-1} + C_N^N y^N \quad (4a)$$

Thus

$$(x + y)^4 = C_4^4 x^4 + C_3^4 x^3 y + C_2^4 x^2 y^2 + C_1^4 xy^3 + C_0^4 y^4$$
$$= x^4 + 4x^3 y + 6x^2 y^2 + 4xy^3 + y^4$$

and

$$(x + y)^5 = C_5^5 x^5 + C_4^5 x^4 y + C_3^5 x^3 y^2 + C_2^5 x^2 y^3 + C_1^5 xy^4 + C_0^5 y^5$$
$$= x^5 + 5x^4 y + 10x^3 y^2 + 10x^2 y^3 + 5xy^4 + y^5$$

It is in this way that the combinatorial formulas enter into the binomial expansion. Later it will be seen that a certain frequency distribution is called a "binomial distribution" because its relative frequencies are computed in the same way as the coefficients of the terms of a binomial expansion.

MATHEMATICAL PROBABILITY

The concept of probability has been the subject of much debate among philosophers, mathematicians, and statisticians. To enter into this debate, however, would be beyond the scope of this book.[1] Although the concept of probability presented below appears to be the most suitable for an elementary text and is apparently the one most in favor among statisticians, it must not be thought that other approaches are necessarily invalid or even possibly less fruitful.[2]

[1] A brief review of the classical theory and the frequency theory of R. von Mises is presented in the Appendix, pp. 242–251.

[2] The concept of probability presented in this book is patterned after that presented by J. Neyman in his *Lectures and Conferences on Mathematical Statistics* (Graduate School of the United States Department of Agriculture, Washington, 1937). His views, Dr. Neyman believes, "are shared by E. S. Pearson and other workers attached to the Department of Statistics at University College, London." He also refers to H. Cramer, *Random Variables and Probability Distributions* (Cambridge, 1937); Maurice Frechet, *Recherches theoriques modernes sur la theorie des probabilités* (Gauthiers-Villars, Paris, 1937); A. Kolmogoroff, *Grundbegriffe der Wahrscheinlich-keitsrechnung* (Julius Springer, Berlin, 1933); and D. J. Struik, "On the

Definition. A discussion of probability can best begin with a finite set of objects. Suppose that, in a given set of t objects, m possess a given property and n do not possess this property. Then the probability of an object of this set having the given property is m/t or the relative frequency of these objects in the set. The word "object" as used in this definition is to be interpreted broadly. Besides objects proper, it may be taken to include events that have the property of occurring or even propositions that have the property of being true.

To illustrate the above definition of probability, consider an ordinary deck of 52 playing cards. This will have 26 red cards and 26 black cards; hence the probability of a red card in this deck is $\frac{26}{52} = \frac{1}{2}$. The deck also contains 13 cards of each suit, so that the probability of a heart, say, is $\frac{13}{52} = \frac{1}{4}$. This is also the probability of a diamond, or a spade, or a club.

Description of Fundamental Probability Set. It should be especially noted that in defining a probability the set of objects to which it pertains must be precisely designated and the property of an object to which the probability refers must be carefully distinguished. For example, the probability of an ace in a pinochle deck[1] is $\frac{8}{48} = \frac{1}{6}$ and not $\frac{4}{52} = \frac{1}{13}$, as it is in an ordinary deck. Furthermore, for the same set of cards, the probability of a card of a given color is not the same as the probability of a card of a given suit or of a card of a given value. What is more important is that each of these properties and hence their probabilities pertain to a different classification of the objects of the set. As will be seen later, it is possible to add probabilities pertaining to the same classification of the objects of a given set, but not probabilities pertaining to different classifications, even though the set of objects is the same. A set of objects classified in a given way is called a "fundamental probability set." In all calculations it is very important to define carefully the fundamental probability set that is involved.

In this connection it should be noted that the "probability of a heart in an ordinary deck of cards" is not necessarily the same thing as the "probability of drawing a heart from the deck."

Foundations of the Theory of Probabilities," *Philosophy of Science* (1934), Vol. 1, pp. 50–70.

[1] A pinochle deck consists of 2 aces, 2 kings, 2 queens, 2 jacks, 2 tens, and 2 nines of each suit. There are no cards of lower value.

For the former, the fundamental probability set is precisely designated; it is simply the given deck of cards classified according to suit. The total number in the deck may be readily counted; the hearts may be easily separated from the others; and their relative frequency, *i.e.*, their probability, may be directly computed. But what is the fundamental probability set to which the "probability of drawing a heart from the deck" pertains? To this there are several answers.

Suppose that 100 drawings are made from the given deck, the card drawn each time being replaced in the deck and the whole well shuffled before the next drawing. Let the number of hearts so drawn be 20. Here the fundamental probability set is the set of 100 drawings classified according to suit, and the probability of a heart in this set is $\frac{20}{100} = \frac{1}{5}$. In this case also, the total number of objects can be counted and the number having the given property can be readily ascertained.

The "probability of drawing a heart from the deck" may, however, pertain to a set of 100 drawings to be made in the future. Here the total number of "objects" in the set is given, but there is no way of ascertaining how many of these drawings will yield hearts. In this case, the "probability of drawing a heart from the deck" is simply unknown.

Finally, the "probability of drawing a heart from the deck" may pertain to a set of hypothetical drawings, not actual drawings. If, it may be argued, 100 drawings should be made from the deck in the prescribed manner and if 30 of these should be hearts, then the probability of a heart in this assumed set would be $\frac{30}{100}$. The "probability of drawing a heart from the deck" refers in this case to a hypothetical set.

Infinite Probability Sets. Frequently, probability theory is concerned with an infinite set of objects. These are usually hypothetical sets but may in some cases be real sets, such as the infinity of points on a line. Without going into mathematical refinements, it may be said that the probability of an object of a given property in an infinite set is the percentage of such objects in the set. For the percentage of a particular kind of object in an infinite set may be finite even if the number of objects of the given property and the total number of objects are both infinite. For example, if a coin is tossed indefinitely, both the total number of tossings and the number of tossings yielding heads may be increased without limit. Nevertheless, the ratio of the number of heads to the total number of tossings will stay within finite limits no matter how many tossings are made. For an infinite set, therefore, as well as for a finite set, the probability of an object having a particular property is the relative frequency of such objects in the given set.[1]

PROBABILITY AND THE RELATIVE FREQUENCY
OF ACTUAL EVENTS

In concluding this chapter a few words should be said about the relationship between mathematical probability and the relative frequency of actual events. As defined above, probability is a constant characterizing a given set of objects; it is merely a mathematical abstraction. If the theory of probability is to be of any practical use, however, it must be tied to the relative frequency of actual events. It must help, in other words, in making predictions about real life.

The Law of Large Numbers. The link that ties mathematical probability to the relative frequency of real events is actual experience with mass phenomena. This experience has been called the "law of large numbers," which says that, when a large number of random events is involved, it is usually possible to predict, with reasonable accuracy, the relative frequency of occurrence of a particular event by calculating a certain mathematical probability. To illustrate, consider once again an ordinary deck of playing cards. Mathematically, this can be looked upon as a set of 52 objects for which the probability of a heart is $\frac{13}{52} = \frac{1}{4}$. Let a large number of drawings, say 1,000, be made from this deck, the card drawn each time being replaced and the deck well shuffled before the next drawing. As already pointed out, no exact statement about the number of hearts drawn can be made in advance of the drawings. Experience shows, however, that in random drawings of this kind the relative frequency of hearts drawn approximates fairly well the mathematical probability of a heart in the deck. Hence, in the given instance it may be predicted that of the 1,000 random drawings something close to 250 will be hearts.

---

[1] For a more refined definition of probability, see Neyman, *op. cit.*, pp. 10–11.

The foregoing is a very simple illustration of the law of large numbers. The law appears to be equally valid, however, for more complicated calculations of probability. For example, suppose there are two decks of cards, one an ordinary deck and the other a pinochle deck, and suppose that all possible combinations of two cards are made by combining one card from the ordinary deck with one card from the pinochle deck. Since the first card can be picked in 52 ways and the second in 48 ways, there will be $52 \times 48 = 2,496$ such combinations. Of these 2,496 combinations, $4 \times 8 = 32$ will be pairs of aces; hence, in this set of combinations, $32/2,496 = \frac{1}{78}$ is the probability of a pair of aces.[1] Now let a very large number of drawings be made from each deck of cards, the card drawn each time being replaced and the deck well shuffled before the next drawing. Furthermore, let the first card drawn from the ordinary deck be paired with the first card drawn from the pinochle deck, the second card from the ordinary deck with the second card from the pinochle deck, etc. Then, if the number of random drawings is very large, experience shows that the pairs of aces actually occurring in this large set of drawings will be close to $\frac{1}{78}$ times the total number of drawings. Again the relative frequency of actual events can be approximately predicted by the computation of a mathematical probability. In fact, if random mass phenomena are involved, the whole of the calculus of probability can be employed in the prediction of relative frequencies with satisfactory accuracy.

Empirically Determined Probabilities. It might be pointed out in passing that in many instances the original set of objects is not completely known and the probability of a given property of the set must be determined empirically. For example, the total number of deaths in the United States of white males, age fifty, is not completely known. Indeed, so far as we know, deaths of men, age fifty, will continue to occur indefinitely. Thus of the total number of men who have reached and will reach the age of fifty, the number who have died or will die during their fiftieth year is not precisely known. On the basis of the law of large numbers, however, it seems safe to assume that the many vital statistics that have been accumulated give a very close approximation to the true probability of death at age fifty. That

[1] *Cf.* Chap. X.

this assumption is justified is again verified by actual experience. Thus, if the empirically determined probability of a man dying at age fifty and the empirically determined probability of his wife dying at age fifty are used to calculate[1] the probability of both a man and his wife dying at the age of fifty, experience with large masses of data shows that the relative frequency of such pairs of deaths at age fifty does actually approximate the calculated probability. The calculus of probability can thus be used by life-insurance companies with general success. Similar results have been found true of other empirically determined probabilities. The law of large numbers thus appears to be universally valid.[2]

"*Randomness.*" It will be noted that the law of large numbers applies only to mass phenomena that are "random." This is very important. If it happened, for example, that, in drawing pairs of cards from an ordinary deck and a pinochle deck, some method of selection were used that caused aces to appear in some cyclical order, say an ace on every tenth draw from the ordinary deck and on every fifth draw from the pinochle deck, then the relative number of pairs of aces occurring would not equal the computed mathematical probability. For, in this case, pairs of aces would occur on every tenth draw, and the probability of a pair of aces in the infinite set of drawings would be $\frac{1}{10}$ and not $\frac{1}{78}$, as computed above.

"Randomness" cannot be exactly defined. Fundamentally, it is an intuitive concept. General notions suggest that to be random the occurrence of an event must be related in no way to its property; *e.g.*, the drawing of an ace must be unrelated to its being an ace. Nor must a random series of events show any relationship between the members of the series. In other words, events must occur in complete disorder; they must be unpredictable by any formula. But, after all, these are negative

[1] See Chap. X.

[2] The association between mathematical probability and the relative frequency of real events is not essentially different from the association between mathematical models in other sciences and happenings in the real world. In physics, for example, the closeness of the association is good enough to enable mathematical formulas to be used in the construction of bridges, automobiles, and the like. In other words, the justification of the theory is that it works.

criteria. The positive content of randomness must be left undefined.[1]

APPENDIX

A REVIEW OF THREE IMPORTANT CONCEPTS OF PROBABILITY

As pointed out in the main body of this chapter, various concepts of probability are admissible. Altogether there appear to be three principal concepts that have contended for acceptance by scientists and philosophers. These may be described as the "classical concept," the "frequency concept," and the "intuitive-axiomatic approach" to probability. It is this last that is used in this book. Since it is an outgrowth of the conflict between the other two lines of thought, they will be discussed first.

Classical Concept of Probability. *Historical Background.* Although commercial insurance was practiced by the Babylonians and was well known to the Greeks and Romans, the development of a theory of probability, such as that on which modern insurance practice is based, dates back only to the seventeenth century. Furthermore, it was not in the field of business that the seeds of this probability theory were sown, but in the gambling rooms of the French gentry. In 1654, Antoine Gornbaud, chevalier de Méré, a French gentleman with an interest in mathematics, called upon the French mathematician Pascal for the solution of a particular gambling problem. The ensuing mathematical speculation marked the beginning of the investigation of games of chance. Subsequently there appeared various works by Huygens (1657), Jacques Bernoulli (1713), De Moivre (1718), and Bayes (1764), most of which were concerned with the application of the theory of permutations and combinations to the calculation of probabilities associated with various dice and card games.

Meanwhile, French and English experimentalists, mathematical physicists, and astronomers were concerning themselves with errors of measurements. Simpson (1757) examined the implications of taking the mean of a set of astronomical measurements as the best estimate of the true value, and Lagrange (1770) published a memoir dealing with the "probable error" of the mean.[2] Other names associated with the early development of the theory of errors are Boscovich, Lambert, Euler, Daniel Bernoulli, and Legendre.[3] The development of such concepts as "inverse probability" and probability of "causes" also led at this time to growing philosophical speculations on the theory of probability. Furthermore, the collection of mortality statistics led to the computation of mortality tables and the development of actuarial science.

All these investigations—the analysis of gambling games, the formulation of a theory of errors, and philosophical speculation—reached their culmination in the great work of Laplace, *Théorie analytique des probabilités* (1812).

---

[1] See Smith and Duncan, *Sampling Statistics*, pp. 155–162, for a discussion of various methods employed to get random samples.

[2] *Cf.* LEVY, H., and L. ROTH, *Elements of Probability* (1936), pp. 5–6.

[3] *Cf.* NAGEL, E., *Principles of the Theory of Probability*, p. 10.

This master synthesis contains all the essentials of the classical theory of probability and most of the important deductions from it. From the time of Laplace, developments of probability theory in the fields of philosophy; logic; mathematics; physical, chemical, and biological research; and the social and industrial arts and sciences were all bound to react on each other and to build on the same broad foundation.[1] In the sense that he thus fused together the various lines of development, Laplace may be looked upon as the formulator of the classical theory of probability.

The Classical Concept. The definition of probability given by Laplace and generally adopted by disciples of the classical school runs as follows: Probability, it is said, is the ratio of the number of "favorable" cases to the total number of equally likely cases. For example, if a coin is tossed, there are two equally likely results, a head or a tail; hence the probability of a head is $\frac{1}{2}$. If a die is thrown, there are six equally likely results, and the probability of any particular one of these results, say a five, is therefore $\frac{1}{6}$. Or again, if a die is thrown, the probability of obtaining an even number is $\frac{3}{6} = \frac{1}{2}$, for three of the six equally possible results are even numbers. This last example illustrates how the classical theory derived the addition theorem. For it will be noted that the probability of getting a particular one of the even numbers is in each case $\frac{1}{6}$. But it has just been shown that the probability of any even number is $\frac{3}{6} = \frac{1}{6} + \frac{1}{6} + \frac{1}{6}$; hence, the theorem follows that the probability of any one of a number of mutually exclusive events is the sum of their individual probabilities.

Still another example will illustrate how the classical concept led to the multiplication theorem. Suppose three coins are tossed. Since either one of two results on the first coin can be combined with either one of two results on the second coin and any one of these combinations can be combined with either one of two results on the third coin, there are altogether $2 \times 2 \times 2 = 8$ equally possible results. The number of these eight possible combinations that have all three heads is 1. Hence, the probability of all three heads on the tossing of three coins is $\frac{1}{8}$. But this is the same as the product of the individual probabilities of a head on each coin, *i.e.*, $(\frac{1}{2})(\frac{1}{2})(\frac{1}{2}) = \frac{1}{8}$. In general, the probability of the joint occurrence of independent events[2] is the product of their individual probabilities. These are all illustrations of how the classical theory of probability, in line with its definition of the term, sought in every case to resolve a problem into a set of equally likely cases and then by the application of combination formulas to determine the number of "favorable" cases.

Criticism of the Classical Concept. There is little criticism of the theorems built up by the calculus of probabilities on the basis of the classical definition insofar as they represent merely a set of logical relationships. Generally, the same set of relationships can be demonstrated on the basis of other definitions of probability. Criticism of the classical concept centers

---

[1] *Cf.* LEVY and ROTH, *op. cit.*, p. 8.

[2] The independence of the individual events is necessary for this theorem to hold true. In the given example, the probability of getting a head on any one coin is independent of the results obtained on the other two.

rather in the meaning of the results obtained and the adequacy of the theory for handling problems outside the field of gambling games, as in the statistical analysis of physical, biological, and economic data.

Meaning of "Equally Likely."   The principal line of attack on the classical concept is directed against the terms "equally likely cases." What does "equally likely" mean, it is asked.   Is not "equally likely" merely another way of saying "equally probable," and in that case is not the classical definition of probability a circular one, since it defines probability in terms of itself?   To avert criticism, some rule must be laid down for the determination of "equally likely" or "equally probable" that is independent of "probable."[1]   What then were the rules of the classicists for determining equal likelihood?

In the development of the classical theory, two procedures were offered for the determination of "equally likely" cases.   One was the *principle of sufficient reason* and the other the *principle of indifference*, or the *principle of the equal distribution of ignorance*, as it was sometimes called.   The first procedure was followed when a person examined all available evidence relevant to the event in question and noted that this evidence was symmetrical with reference to the various possible results.   For example, after a thorough examination of a die, including a nice determination of its center of gravity and the moments of inertia about various sides, it might be concluded that the investigator had sufficient reason to consider the die perfectly symmetrical and hence the six possible results equally likely.   According to the principle of indifference, on the other hand, if the investigator knew nothing about the die in question, he had no basis for deeming one side of the die to be different from any other and could therefore assume them all to be equally likely.   This second procedure is subject to particularly severe criticism and will be discussed first.

Principle of Indifference.   Total ignorance about a thing, it may reasonably be argued, can scarcely be a source of any knowledge concerning it, even of that uncertain kind afforded by a probability statement.   In other words, how can something be got out of nothing?   As might be expected, the use of the principle of indifference has frequently led to paradoxical results.   This has been generally true whenever the set of "equally likely" cases was not discrete but was represented by a continuous variable.   Suppose, for example, it is known that the weight of a certain man is at least equal to that of his wife but is not more than double her weight.   If ignorance as to the exact ratio of weights is "evenly distributed," it may be concluded that any ratio of the man's to the woman's weight lying between 1 and 2 is as likely as any other within that interval.   From this it follows that the probability of its lying between 1 and 1.5 is 50 per cent and that the probability of its lying between 1.5 and 2 is also 50 per cent.   Suppose, however, the ratio of the woman's to the man's weight had been taken as the variable.   The limits would then be 0.5 and 1, and according to the principle of indifference all possible values of the ratio lying within this range might be deemed equally likely.   Then, however, it may be concluded that

---

[1] *Cf.* NAGEL, *op. cit.*, p. 46.

the probability of the ratio of the woman's weight to the man's weight lying between 0.5 and 0.75 is just 50 per cent and that the probability of its lying between 0.75 and 0.1 is also 50 per cent. But this second result is in disagreement with the first, for a ratio of the woman's to the man's weight equal to 0.75 is the equivalent of a ratio of the man's weight to the woman's weight equal to 1.33. Thus, according to the second method of distributing ignorance, the probability is 50 per cent that the man is 1 to $1\frac{1}{3}$ times as heavy as the woman; and, according to the first method, the probability is 50 per cent that he is 1 to $1\frac{1}{2}$ times as heavy. In general, when the principle of indifference is employed to determine what is equally likely, a change in the coordinates used to describe a continuous variation in possible results frequently affects the values of the computed probabilities.[1]

Principle of Sufficient Reason. The first method of procedure, *viz.*, that of sufficient reason, puts the theory on a more solid basis. It has been criticized, however, in respect to its practical applicability. Even after the symmetry of a die has been carefully determined, it is still necessary to note any lack of bias in the method of throwing it or again in the surface on which it rolls. To determine these a priori are matters more difficult than the symmetry of the die itself. Much greater, however, is the difficulty of determining equal likelihood when attention is turned from dice, coins, and cards to the phenomena of the scientific laboratories and of everyday life. An insurance company insures the lives of a thousand men; how can it determine a priori whether they are all equally likely to die during the year? Some men are tall, others short; some are fat, some thin; some work outdoors, others indoors. Is there any possibility of the insurance company telling, other than from its actual experience with men of various classes, *i.e.*, a posteriori, whether these individual differences destroy the equal likelihood of death?. Critics of the classical theory answer with an emphatic "no." It is easily seen, they say, why the classical theory developed out of a study of games of chance, for it is in that field alone that there is any reasonable possibility of determining a priori whether a set of possible results are "equally likely." In most other fields it is impossible.[2]

But why insist on a rational a priori determination of equal likelihood, the reader may ask. Why not determine it a posteriori? For example, to determine whether a head or a tail is equally likely for a given coin, why not toss the coin a large number of times and note whether the number of heads is approximately equal to the number of tails? This sounds simple enough until it is studied more closely. Then the question immediately arises: How good an approximation is necessary—how close to 0.5 must the ratio of heads to tails be—before it can be concluded that a head and a tail are equally likely? On the assumption of equal likelihood, the classical theory itself explains that in a finite number of tosses any given result is possible, although of course all results are not equally probable. If N tosses are made, for example, there are 2^N equally possible results,[3] and of

[1] *Cf.* VON MISES, RICHARD, *Probability, Statistics, and Truth* (1939), pp. 114–115.

[2] *Cf.* VON MISES, *op. cit.*, pp. 98–110.

[3] *Cf.* p. 274.

these the number that would have r heads would be the number of combinations of N things taken r at a time,[1] or $C_r^N = \dfrac{N!}{r!(N-r)!}$. Hence, any value of r/N would be possible with a probability of $\dfrac{N!}{r!(N-r)!}\left(\dfrac{1}{2^N}\right)$. If N is large, the probability that r/N should deviate considerably from 0.5 is very small and the general reasonableness of the hypothesis of equal likelihood could be tested by determining the probability of as large a deviation from 0.5 as is actually found.[2]

The empirical results therefore do not provide a certainty that a head or a tail is equally likely. There is no way of telling for sure whether the deviation from an exact value of 0.5 is due merely to chance or whether the coin is actually biased. A similar result might have been produced by a biased coin. In fact, the latter might on occasion produce an exactly equal number of heads and tails, so that, even if the ratio of r to N is exactly 0.5, it is not certain that the coin is perfectly unbiased. If, as suggested above, the hypothesis of equal likelihood is accepted or rejected on the basis of the probability of getting the given deviation from 0.5, then equal probability is being determined in a way that is dependent on the concept of probability and the criticism of circularity in the definition becomes immediately valid.[3]

A still further criticism is this: Suppose that after a careful examination of a die it is found that the die is not symmetrical, what then? If a die is biased, how can the problem be resolved into a set of equally likely cases? True, if it can be determined that, through careful weighing, balancing, rotating, etc., the occurrence of an even number is twice as likely as the occurrence of an odd number, it might be argued that there are nine equally likely results, one of which is a one, two of which are twos, one of which is a three, two of which are fours, one of which is a five, and two of which are sixes, and the various combinatorial formulas might be based on this assumption. Even if the possibility of making such an a priori determination is not questioned, there still remains the problem of how to treat the case where the bias is such that a given result or results is 1.5 or 3.67 or π times as likely as some other result. Laplace himself attempted a solution of this problem but failed to obtain a correct answer.[4] It would seem that the problem is insoluble on the basis of the classical concept.[5]

Subjective Character of Classical Concept. Since the foregoing criticisms have in a way implied that "probability" was more or less objective in character, in all fairness to the classical theory it should be pointed out that Laplace and most of his followers took a subjective view of the concept.

[1] *Cf.* p. 234.

[2] *Cf.* pp. 248–249 for a further discussion of this.

[3] The "frequency" concept expounded below does not suffer from this criticism because, according to this concept, probability is defined as the limit that the ratio of heads to total results approaches as the number of tosses is indefinitely increased. No circularity arises from the need of determining equal probability. See pp. 250–251.

[4] VON MISES, *op. cit.*, p. 102.

[5] *Cf.* NAGEL, *op. cit.*, p. 45.

Probability to them was a "rational degree of belief." They considered the word "probability" as meaning a state of mind regarding a given statement, a future event, or any other thing about which absolute knowledge was not to be had.[1] It was not made clear, by the classicists, however, just how subjective their concept of probability was. If it were a mere measure of degree of (psychological) belief, the theory of probability became a part of the science of psychology and immediately the question arose as to how degrees of belief could be added and multiplied, as called for by the probability calculus. On the other hand, if "rational degree of belief" was to be interpreted as what every intelligent person ought to believe under the given circumstances, then the theory assumed a certain degree of objectivity and all the foregoing criticisms became applicable with respect to the exact content of this standard of "oughtness."[2] It is the contention of the critics of the classical concept that, if probability theory is to be of practical use in statistical science, some objective definition of probability should be adopted. One writer points out that physical thermodynamics had its starting point in the subjective impressions of hot and cold but that its development began when an objective method was used to compare temperatures by means of a column of mercury.[3] In the same way, he concludes, probability should be put upon a physical, objective basis.

Frequency Concept of Probability. If the reader will toss an ordinary coin a large number of times, he will see that the ratio of the number of heads to the total number of tosses will be close to 0.5000, and approximately the same result will be obtained each time the experiment is repeated. This empirical fact, that in mass phenomena the relative frequency of a given attribute often appears to approximate a definite constant, is the cornerstone of the frequency concept of probability. The constant value that the relative frequency tends to approximate is identified with the "probability" of the given attribute.

This frequency approach to the theory of probability goes back at least to the work of J. Venn on the *Logic of Chance* published in London in 1886. In the present day, a leading exponent of this view is Richard von Mises, whose writings[4] constitute one of the most important formulations of the frequency theory of probability. The next section will be devoted to an exposition of his ideas. A subsequent section will discuss the "intuitive-axiomatic" approach, which is similar to von Mises' theory but differs somewhat in its logical basis.

Concept of von Mises. In von Mises' theory, probability is defined only with reference to what he calls a "collective." This is an infinitely large set of "random" elements that possess certain specified characteristics.

[1] *Cf.* Nagel, *op. cit.*, p. 44.

[2] *Cf.* NAGEL, *op. cit.*, p. 46.

[3] VON MISES, *op. cit.*, p. 112.

[4] The most important of these are *Wahrscheinlichkeitsrechnung* (Leipzig, 1931) and *Probability, Statistics, and Truth* (1939), the latter being a translation of an earlier (1928) German edition.

The sequence of results obtained from an indefinite tossing of a coin or throwing of a die, the set of human births running back into the indefinite past and projected into the endless future, the sequence of parts turned out by the continuous operation of a given manufacturing process[1]—all these are examples of collectives. If the elements of such sequences take on varying attributes, such as heads or tails, male babies and female babies, acceptable and unacceptable parts, the first essential characteristic of a true collective is that the relative frequency with which a particular attribute occurs shall approach a fixed limit as the number of elements in the collective is indefinitely increased. Mathematically this means the following: If r/N is the relative frequency of a given attribute among N elements, *e.g.*, the number of heads among N tossings of a coin, and if p is the limit that r/N approaches as N is increased indefinitely, then after some point, say $N = 1,000,000$, the difference between r/N and p becomes, and thereafter remains, less than an arbitrarily chosen positive quantity ϵ, say 0.005. Numerically it means that if r/N is calculated to a given number of decimal places, as N is increased a point is finally reached after which further increases bring no change in the calculated figures. For example, if the ratio of heads to total tossings is calculated to three decimals, then, after some number of tossings, this ratio will always give $r/N = 0.500$. The limit that the relative frequency of a given attribute approaches as the number of elements of a collective is indefinitely increased is defined as the probability of that attribute in the given collective.

The second characteristic of a true collective is its "randomness." Thus the sequence of elements constituting a collective must be free from any regularity; they must be in complete disorder. It is to be noted that the relative frequency of an attribute may approach a limit in a given sequence without that sequence being a random one. If, for example, some special apparatus were constructed so that every fifth tossing of a coin resulted in a head and every other tossing in a tail, the sequence of results would look as follows:

TTTTHTTTTHTTTTHTTTTHTTTTHTTTTHTTTTHTTTTH . . . .

The limit of relative frequency of heads in such a sequence would be $\frac{1}{5}$, but the sequence is obviously not a random one. It is consequently not a true collective, and it cannot be said that the probability of a head under the given conditions is $\frac{1}{5}$. Actually the probability of a head on every fifth tossing is 1, and on every other tossing it is 0.

What precisely constitutes "randomness"? von Mises' answer to this fundamental question is as follows: If subsequences of elements are picked from the original sequence in such a way that the selection of a particular

---

[1] In reality, manufacturing processes change materially from time to time. What is envisaged here is one that remains exactly the same indefinitely. For a discussion of the statistical aspects of manufacturing processes, see W. A. Shewhart, *Statistical Method from the Viewpoint of Quality Control* (Graduate School of the United States Department of Agriculture, Washington, 1939).

element is independent of the attribute assumed by that element and if in all possible subsequences of this kind the limit of relative frequency of a given attribute is the same as in the original sequence, the latter may be said to be random. In the truly random tossing of a coin, for example, the selection of every fifth tossing would yield a subsequence of tossings in which the relative frequency of heads would approach the same limit ($\frac{1}{2}$ if the coin is unbiased) as in the complete sequence. If such a method of selection were applied to the particular sequence of heads and tails given above, the result would obviously be a subsequence consisting of all heads, for which the limit of relative frequency would be 1 and not $\frac{1}{5}$ as in the original sequence. This sequence clearly fails to meet the test of randomness. Another example of randomness is provided by the game of roulette. If the results of the game are influenced solely by chance forces, *i.e.*, if they constitute a truly random sequence, there is no way of placing bets so as to secure better than average results; no formula can be devised to "beat the house." As von Mises puts it, the existence of randomness means the impossibility of devising a gambling "system."

In summary then, a true collective is a mass phenomenon or an endless sequence of observations for which (1) the relative frequencies of the particular attributes of the elements of the collective tend to fixed limits and (2) these fixed limits are the same for any place selection of a subsequence, *i.e.*, a selection that depends only on the location of an element in the collective and not on the attribute it assumes. The existence of such a collective is the fundamental postulate of von Mises' theory of probability.

Criticism of von Mises' Concept. Since the initial formulation of his theory in 1919,[1] von Mises' concept of probability has been the subject of considerable discussion. Some have sought to refine and elaborate von Mises' views; others have contended that they contain serious logical inconsistencies.[2] Here only a brief mention will be made of these criticisms.

Since in real life only finite series can be observed, there has been some objection to a concept of probability based upon the notion of infinite sequences. One writer[3] has attempted to work out von Mises' ideas, using finite series, but the complications are great and the results are not so comprehensive. After all, the concept of an infinite series only aims to give approximate results. It has been a useful mathematical tool in many other sciences; so why not in probability?[4]

Some writers have attacked the existence of limiting values.[5] For example, in accordance with the classical theory of probability, if an unbiased coin is tossed N times, there is always a probability, however small, that the

---

[1] See *Mathematische Zeitschrift*, Vol. 5.

[2] See list of references in von Mises' *Probability, Statistics, and Truth*, pp. 316–318, references 35–51.

[3] BLUME, JOHANNES, *Zur axiomatischen Grundlagung der Wahrscheinlichkeitsrechnung*, 1934 (Dissertation Münster); *Zeitschrift für Physik*, Vol. 92 (1934), pp. 232–252; Vol. 94 (1935), pp. 192–203.

[4] *Cf.* VON MISES, *Probability, Statistics, and Truth*, pp. 121–122.

[5] *Cf.* FRY, T. C., *Probability and Its Engineering Uses*, pp. 88–91.

coin will turn up heads in all, or in a large proportion of, the N tossings. It is consequently argued that, whatever point is selected in the infinite sequence of tossings, there is always the possibility that the next N tossings will turn up such a large proportion of heads that the ratio of heads to total tossings will differ from the supposed limit p by more than the arbitrarily selected quantity ϵ and hence contradict the mathematical criterion for the existence of a limit.[1] The answer to this criticism is that it is based upon another (the classical) concept of probability and is a proposition concerning the possible results obtained from a finite number of tossings. It is not in contradiction to another proposition that begins with a different view of probability and postulates the existence of a limit in an infinite sequence of tossings.[2]

More serious criticism of von Mises' theory has been directed against the condition of randomness. There is the question, for example, whether a series that is in complete disorder and cannot accordingly be described by a mathematical formula can logically be conceived to exist. Still further, there is the question whether limits to relative frequencies in an infinite sequence can coexist with von Mises' definition of randomness. Recent mathematical investigations, however, appear to have resolved this difficulty. It is claimed that, with a more carefully drawn and slightly less comprehensive definition of randomness, the type of collective described by von Mises can for all practical purposes be conceived to exist.[3]

THE INTUITIVE-AXIOMATIC APPROACH TO PROBABILITY

The theory of probability presented in the main body of this text is based upon the intuitive notion that theorems derived from axioms relating to relative frequencies approach satisfactorily the occurrence of events in real life. It may therefore be called the "intuitive-axiomatic" approach to probability. It is the concept of probability accepted by such men as Neyman, Fréchet, and Kolmogoroff.[4] Lying between the classical concept of Laplace and the pure frequency theory of von Mises, it may be called a "compromise" concept.

[1] See p. 248.

[2] *Cf.* von Mises, *Probability, Statistics, and Truth,* pp. 126–128, and the whole of the fourth lecture. Also, see Nagel, *op. cit.,* pp. 37.

[3] The fundamental papers supporting this claim are those of A. H. Copeland, *American Journal of Mathematics,* Vol. 50, pp. 535–552; Vol. 51, pp. 612–618; Vol. 53, pp. 153–162; and Vol. 58, pp. 181–192, and a paper by A. Wald, *Ergebnisse eines mathematischen Kolloquiums,* Wien, No. 8, pp. 38–72. See, however, the recent criticism of Maurice Fréchet, *Journal of Unified Science,* Vol. 8, pp. 1–22. He refers to an example by Ville in which a given set is so defined that it meets all the conditions laid down by Wald and yet contains the regularity that the relative frequency always converges to its limit by values that are greater than p. He admits, however, that von Mises does not feel that this creates any difficulty in his theory.

[4] See footnote (2), p. 236.

The intuitive-axiomatic approach to probability differs from the classical theory in that it avoids the circularity of "equal likelihood." It merely definies probability as a relative frequency of a certain attribute in a given set of objects without any statement as to whether these are "equally likely." It consequently avoids introducing any subjective elements into the definition of probability.[1]

On the other hand, the intuitive-axiomatic approach differs from von Mises' approach in that it does not identify probability with the mathematical limit approached by the relative frequency of a given attribute in an infinite random sequence of actual events. It may indeed take the relative frequency of a certain attribute in a hypothetical infinite set as the probability of that attribute, but this need not be the mathematical limit approached by the relative frequency of any actual type of event. It merely says that, if relative frequencies of random mass data are treated as if they were mathematical probabilities of some hypothetical infinite set, then the calculations derived on this assumption will be satisfactorily close to the relative frequencies of various combinations of these data. "Randomness" is left as an undefined, intuitive concept.

[1] The subjective elements and even the concept of equal likelihood enter to some extent, however, in the determination of "randomness" (see pp. 241–242).

CHAPTER IX

PROBABILITY DISTRIBUTIONS

A description of a fundamental probability set giving the various categories, or classes, into which the members of the set are grouped, together with the probabilities of each group, is called a *probability distribution*. The property of a member of a given group may be spoken of as an "attribute," and a probability distribution may be said to show how the total probability is distributed among the various attributes. Since the attributes of a fundamental probability set are necessarily mutually exclusive and since a member of a set must possess some one of the given attributes, it follows that the total probability, *i.e.*, the sum of the probabilities of the various attributes, must equal 1. In other words, the percentages (probabilities) of the cases falling in the various groups must add up to 100 per cent.

For example, the distribution of probability among the four suits of an ordinary playing card deck is

Spades	$\frac{1}{4}$	or	25 per cent
Hearts	$\frac{1}{4}$	or	25 per cent
Diamonds	$\frac{1}{4}$	or	25 per cent
Clubs	$\frac{1}{4}$	or	25 per cent

The quality of being a spade, heart, diamond, or club is the attribute of a card. Since a card cannot be both a spade and a heart, say, these attributes are mutually exclusive; and since a card must belong to one of the four suits, the total probability is 1.

Similarly, the distribution of probability among the six faces of an ordinary die is

.	$\frac{1}{6}$
..	$\frac{1}{6}$
...	$\frac{1}{6}$
::	$\frac{1}{6}$
:.:	$\frac{1}{6}$
:::	$\frac{1}{6}$

The quality of being a 1, 2, 3, 4, 5, or 6 is the attribute of a face. Since a face of a die cannot be both a 2 and a 6, say, these attributes are mutually exclusive, and since a face must have one of the markings listed above, the total probability is again 1.

Discrete Probability Distributions. When the attributes of a set are qualitative in character, such as spades or hearts in the case of a deck of cards or heads or tails in the case of coins, or when they are represented by a set of numerical values that do not vary continuously, such as the number of spots on the face of a die, the distribution of probability is said to be "discrete." If the attributes are represented by points on a horizontal axis and their probabilities measured along a vertical axis, a discrete

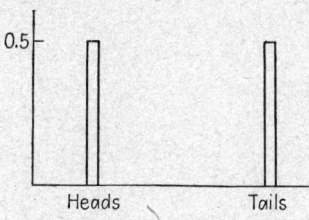

Fig. 77.—Distribution of probability of heads and tails on a coin.

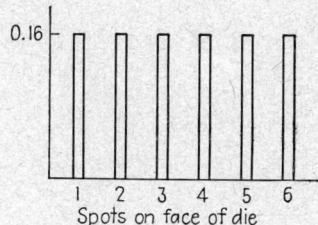

Fig. 78.—Distribution of probability of the spots on the faces of a die.

probability distribution may be pictured by a series of lines or bars as in Figs. 77 and 78. It will be noted that it is the height of the bar in each case that measures the probability of the attribute at which it is erected.

Continuous Probability Distributions. If the members of a set consist of the numerical figures obtained by the repeated measurement of the length of a given table or the continued measurement of the heights of adult white males, living now and in the future, the attributes assumed by the members may form a continuous variable. In such a case, the total probability of 1 can be considered to be distributed over the whole range of variation; it will thus form a "continuous" distribution of probability. More exactly, the range may be divided into small class intervals, and location within one of these intervals may be taken as the attribute of a member of the set. In this instance, the probability of a member belonging to a given interval may be represented by the area of a rectangle erected over that interval, and the total distribution may be pictured as a set of such rectangles in the manner shown in Fig. 79. If, now, the class intervals are made smaller and smaller, the tops of these rectangles will tend to sketch out a smooth curve (*cf.* Fig. 80). A probability curve of this sort can be looked upon as the limit

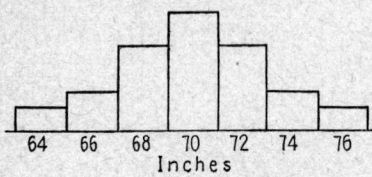

Inches

approached as the class intervals into which the range is divided are made infinitesimally small.

Frequency Distributions as Probability Distributions.

Fig. 79.—A continuous distribution of probability.

From the definition of probability given above, it follows that any frequency distribution in which the frequencies are expressed as a percentage of the total number of cases is a distribution of probability of the given set of cases. It likewise follows that a frequency curve that represents the distribution of relative frequency of an infinite population of cases[1] is also a probability curve.

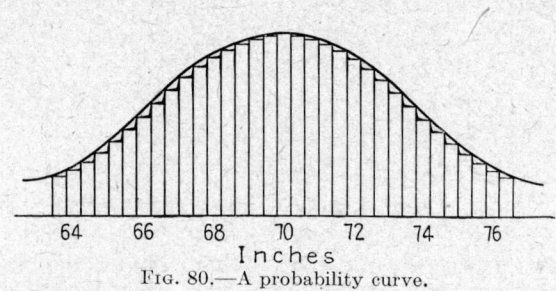

Inches

Fig. 80.—A probability curve.

Since a distribution of relative frequency and a distribution of probability are thus one and the same thing, all the measures of the various characteristics of frequency distributions automatically apply to probability distributions. Thus a probability distribution has a mean, a standard deviation, a coefficient of skewness, and a coefficient of kurtosis, like any frequency distribution.

[1] See p. 238.

ALGEBRAIC AND GRAPHIC REPRESENTATION OF THE NORMAL FREQUENCY CURVE

Functional Relationships. Before entering upon a mathematical and graphic representation of frequency and probability curves, it may be well to review briefly the algebraic and geometric description of simple functional relationships. This is the purpose of the present section.

If one quantity varies when a second varies, the first is said to be a "function" of the second. The pressure of air in an automobile tire, for example, varies with the temperature; pressure is thus a function of temperature. Again, the quantity of butter bought varies with its price; hence, the purchase of butter is a function of its price.

Functional relationships of this kind are described symbolically by such expressions as $y = f(x)$, $y = F(x)$, $y = G(x)$, $y = \varphi(x)$, and $y = \psi(x)$—all of which are to be read "y is a function of x" or, more specifically, "y is the f function of x," "y is the F function of x," etc. The expressions $y = f(x)$ and $y = F(x)$ are the most common; the others are often used, however, when a problem involves more than one functional relationship. For example, if y and z are both functions of x, this may be expressed by $y = f(x)$ and $z = g(x)$.

Frequently a quantity varies, not merely with one, but with a number of other quantities. The former may then be said to be a "joint function" of the latter. Thus the volume of gas in a tube is a function of the pressure and the temperature (Boyle's law); the quantity of butter bought is a function of the price of butter and the income of its purchasers. Joint functional relationships of this kind are expressed by $y = f(x,z)$, $y = F(x,z)$, $y = \varphi(x,z)$, etc.,—all to be read "y is a function of x and z."

Explicit and Implicit Functions. The functional relationships so far considered are "explicit" functions. In explicit functions one variable is selected as the dependent variable, and the other or others as the independent variables; this is indicated by writing the dependent variable to the left of the equal sign. Often, however, it is convenient to talk of two variables as being functionally related without indicating which is to be taken as dependent and which as independent variable. Such a functional relationship is indicated by $f(x,y) = 0$, $F(x,y) = 0$, $\varphi(x,y) = 0$, etc., or if there are more than two variables, by $f(x,y,z,) = 0$, $F(x,y,z) = 0$, $\varphi(x,y,z) = 0$, etc. These all mean that x and y or x, y, and z are "functionally related." Functions of this kind are called "implicit" functions. An explicit function can often (although not always) be derived from an implicit function by merely solving the latter for the variable selected as dependent.

The simplest type of functional relationship is expressed by a polynomial. A polynomial in x means such expressions as x (strictly speaking a monomial), $a + x$, $a + bx$, and $a + bx + cx^2$. The "degree" of the polynomial is the highest power of x that occurs in the expression. Thus $a + bx$ is a polynomial of the first degree; $a + bx + cx^2$ and $a + cx^2$ are polynomials of the second degree; and $a + bx + cx^2 + dx^3$, $a + bx + dx^3$, $a + cx^2 + dx^3$, and $a + dx^3$ are polynomials of the third degree. Polynomials in two variables, say x and z, are illustrated by $a + bx + gz$, $a + bx + cx^2 + gz + hz^2$, $a + bx + gz + mxz$, and $a + bx + kz^3$, the first being of the first degree, the second and third of the second degree, and the last of the third degree.

If y varies by a constant absolute amount every time x varies by a fixed given amount, the function that expresses this relationship is a first-degree polynomial in x, such as $y = a + bx$. For every time x increases (or decreases) by one unit, y increases (or decreases) by b units. Thus, if $y = 10 + 2x$, y increases (or decreases) by two units every time x increases (or decreases) by one unit. If b is negative, then the variation in y is opposite in direction to that of x. For example, if $y = 10 - 2x$, then y decreases (or increases) by two units every time x increases (or decreases) by one unit. The quantity a is the value of y when x equals 0; if $y = 0$ when $x = 0$, then a must be zero.

When a functional relationship can be represented in this way by a first-degree polynomial, such as $y = a + bx$, then y is said to be a "linear" function of x. This continues to hold true when there is more than one independent variable. Thus $y = a + bx + gz$ is said to express y as a linear function of x and z. If the change in y that accompanies a given change in x varies with the value of x, then the functional relationship can no longer be expressed by a first-degree polynomial in x. The function is in this case "nonlinear," and a higher degree polynomial or some more complex expression must be employed to indicate the relationship. A nonlinear relationship between y and two or more variables, such as x and z, must also be expressed by some function other than a first-degree polynomial in these two variables.

Graphs of Simple Functions. A pair of values, x and y, may be represented by a point in a plane. The point P in Fig. 81, for example, represents the value $x = x_0$ and $y = y_0$; *i.e.*, the coordinates of P are (x_0, y_0).

First-degree Polynomials. The graph of a first-degree polynomial is a straight line (hence the name "linear" relationship),

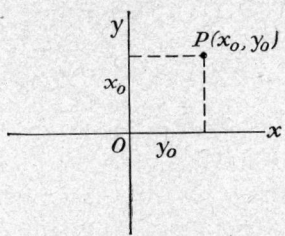

FIG. 81.—Plotting of a point.

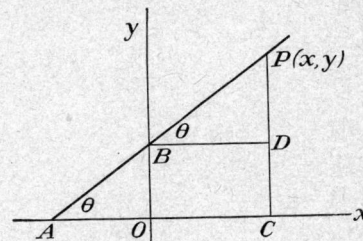

FIG. 82.—Graph of a straight line.

and conversely every straight line may be represented algebraically by a polynomial of the first degree. The simplest way to comprehend this relationship between the algebraic and the geometric presentation is to think of a straight line in reference to (1) the angle it makes with the x-axis and (2) the intercept it cuts on the y-axis. Thus, in Fig. 82, let θ represent the angle CAB that the line makes with the x-axis at A. The tangent of this angle is the slope of the line AB. Let b represent this slope; then $b = \tan \theta$. It is evident that a straight line is determined when its slope b and its y intercept, a (or OB), is found, as follows: Let P (whose coordinates are any x, y) be a representative point of the line. Take PC, the perpendicular to Ox, from P, and BD, the perpendicular to PC, from B. Then,

$$\tan DBP = \frac{DP}{BD}$$

or

$$DP = \tan DBP \times BD \qquad (1)$$

But

$$DP = CP - CD = CP - OB = y - a$$

Also,

$$BD = OC = x \quad \text{and} \quad \tan DBP = \tan CAP$$

and

(similar triangles)

$$\tan CAP = \tan \theta = b$$

Now, since $DP = y - a$, and $\tan DBP = \tan \theta = b$, and $BD = x$, then, upon substituting in Eq. (1),

$$y - a = bx \quad \text{or} \quad y = a + bx \tag{2}$$

A straight line thus represents y as equal to a polynomial in x of the first degree. When the line passes through the origin, $a = 0$ and the functional relationship becomes simply $y = bx$.

Second-degree Polynomials. If the functional relationship between x and y takes the form of a second-degree polynomial,

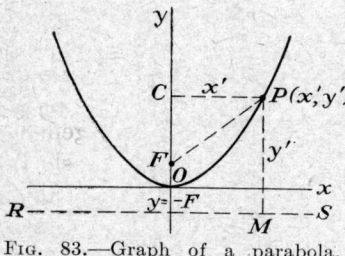

such as $y = a + bx + cx^2$, its graph will be a parabola. By definition, a parabola is the locus of all points equidistant from a fixed point called the "focus" and a fixed line called the "directrix." In Fig. 83, the focus is the point (F), and the directrix is the line RS ($y + F = 0$). Take any point on the parabola, $P(x',y')$, and

Fig. 83.—Graph of a parabola, $y = cx^2$ ($c > 0$).

draw from it a line perpendicular to RS, at point M; then draw a line from the focus (F) to the point P.

At the point $x = 0$, $y = 0$, it is obvious that the parabola is equidistant from the directrix $y + F = 0$, or $y = -F$, and the focus at $x = 0$, $y = F$.

Now, if a line were drawn from P perpendicular to the y-axis, at C, it is clear that $\overline{FP}^2 = (y' - F)^2 + (x')^2$, since $FC = y' - F$ and $PC = x'$. This is true since the square of the hypotenuse is equal to the sum of the squares of the other two sides of a right-angled triangle. Furthermore, it can be seen from Fig. 83 that $\overline{MP}^2 = (y' + F)^2$ because MP is $y' + F$. By hypothesis, $\overline{MP}^2 = \overline{FP}^2$, and hence, by substitution,

$$(y' + F)^2 = (y' - F)^2 + (x')^2$$

which is true for any value of x' and y'; that is, any x and y, and which by transposition and simplification becomes

$$x^2 = 4Fy \qquad \text{or} \qquad y = \frac{x^2}{4F}$$

This is of the general form of $y = cx^2$. If the curve had not passed through the origin, its equation would have been of the form $y = a + cx^2$; and if its vertex had come either to the right or left of the y-axis, its equation would have been

$$y = a + bx + cx^2 \tag{3}$$

If the value of c is negative, the curve turns down as in Fig. 84 instead of up as in Fig. 83. These parabolic curves thus illustrate the form of a functional relationship in which y is set equal to a second-degree polynomial in x.

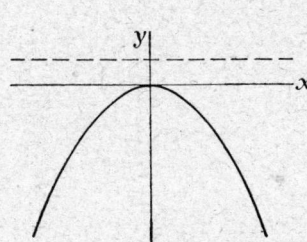

FIG. 84.—Graph of a parabola, $y = -cx^2$ $(c > 0)$.

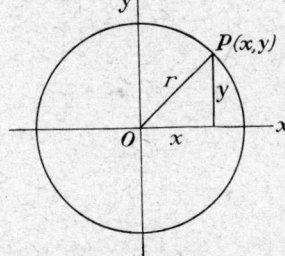

FIG. 85.—Graph of a circle, $x^2 + y^2 = r^2$.

The Circle. The implicit functional relationship

$$x^2 + y^2 - r^2 = 0 \tag{4}$$

is of interest in that its graph is a circle. By definition, a circle is the locus of all points equidistant from a fixed point called the "center." In Fig. 85, the center is taken at the origin. By the property of right-angle triangles, the square of the distance of any point P from the center at O (the origin) is simply $x^2 + y^2$. Since by definition this must be the same for all points on the circle, the equation of the circle is simply $x^2 + y^2 = r^2$, where r is the radius. By transposition, this becomes $x^2 + y^2 - r^2 = 0$. If the center of the circle had been at the point (a,b) instead of at the origin, its equation would have been

$$(x - a)^2 + (y - b)^2 - r^2 = 0$$

An implicit functional relationship, therefore, in which two variables enter to the second degree with identical coefficients but in which there is no cross-product term (such as xy) is simply the algebraic expression for a circle.

The Ellipse. If the functional relationship represented by a circle is modified so that the coefficients of the second-degree terms are no longer identical (but still retain the same signs), its geometric counterpart is distorted so as to become an ellipse. Thus the graph of the implicit functional relationship

$$ax^2 + by^2 - r^2 = 0 \qquad (5)$$

is an ellipse whose semimajor axis is $r/\sqrt{a}$ and whose semiminor axis is $r/\sqrt{b}$ (*cf.* Fig. 86). If b is less than a, then the ellipse runs the other way, as in Fig. 87.

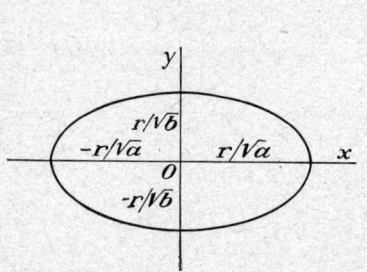
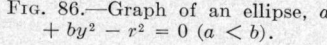
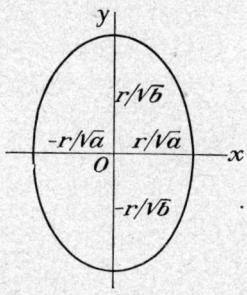

FIG. 86.—Graph of an ellipse, $ax^2 + by^2 - r^2 = 0$ ($a < b$).   FIG. 87.—Graph of an ellipse, $ax^2 + by^2 - r^2 = 0$ ($a > b$).

It will be noted that, if either of the implicit relationships $x^2 + y^2 - r^2 = 0$ or $ax^2 + by^2 - r^2 = 0$ is solved for y, the resulting solution gives y, not as a single-valued function of x, but as a double-valued function. Thus, in the case of the circle, $y = \pm\sqrt{r^2 - x^2}$, which shows that, for each value of x, there are two values of y. Likewise, for the ellipse, $y = \pm\sqrt{\dfrac{r^2}{b} - \dfrac{ax^2}{b}}$, which again gives two values of y for each value of x. Geometrically this means that a line perpendicular to the x-axis cuts the circle and ellipse at two different points. In contrast, the straight line and the parabola express y as a single-valued function of x. The difference is due to the fact that, in the case of the circle and ellipse, it is y^2 and not y that is expressed as a polynomial in x and when the square root is taken two values of y result.

Rising Exponential Function. A simple function that does not express y or y^2 as a polynomial in x is the exponential, or "compound-interest," function. Suppose that a sum of \$1 is put out at interest at 6 per cent per year compounded for 3 years; then the value of this sum at the end of the 3 years would be as follows:

$$\text{Value at end of 3 years} = (1 + 0.06)(1 + 0.06)(1 + 0.06)$$
$$= (1 + 0.06)^3$$

In general, if \$1 is put out at interest for x years and compounded at the rate of r per annum, its value at the end of the x years would be as follows:

$$\text{Value at end of } x \text{ years} = (1 + r)^x$$

If the interest is compounded every 6 months instead of every year, then the value at the end of x years would be as follows:

$$\text{Value at end of } x \text{ years} = \left(1 + \frac{r}{2}\right)^{2x}$$

for the interest rate for 6-months is just half the rate for a year and the number of 6-month periods is just double the number of years. If the interest is compounded every quarter, then the value of the \$1 at the end of x years would be $\left(1 + \frac{r}{4}\right)^{4x}$; and if the interest is compounded every $1/n$th of a year, the value at the end of x years would be $\left(1 + \frac{r}{n}\right)^{nx}$, r always being the rate of simple interest per year. This last may be written

$$\left(1 + \frac{1}{\frac{n}{r}}\right)^{\frac{n}{r}rx}$$

If, now, n is made infinitely large, in other words, if the period of compounding (that is, $1/n$th of a year) is made infinitesimally small, so that the operation of compounding may be viewed as practically continuous, then the quantity $\left(1 + \frac{1}{\frac{n}{r}}\right)^{\frac{n}{r}}$ is equal approximately to e, the base of the Napierian system of logarithms. For, by definition, e is the limit of $\left(1 + \dfrac{1}{m}\right)^m$ as m approaches infinity. The value of \$1 at the end of x years when interest at r per annum is compounded continuously is therefore e^{rx}.

The quantity e, it will be recalled, is a numerical constant equal approximately[1] to 2.7183, so that the value of a sum compounded continuously for x years is given by a function of the form $y = a^{bx}$, where a and b are merely constants. The compound-interest function is thus an "exponential" function,

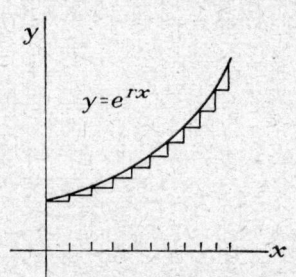

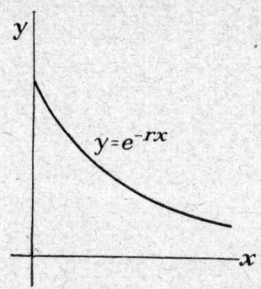

Fig. 88.—Graph of a rising exponential function, $y = e^{rx}$ $(r > 0)$.

Fig. 89.—Graph of a declining exponential function, $y = e^{-rx}$ $(r > 0)$.

for the variable x enters into the function as an exponent. A graph of this function for a positive value of $b(= r)$ is shown in Fig. 88.

Declining Exponential Function. The "present value" of \$1 due x years hence, interest being compounded continuously at the rate of r per annum, would be equal to e^{-rx}. For since the sum of \$1 would accumulate to e^{rx} dollars at the end of x years, the sum of $e^{-rx}(= 1/e^{rx})$ dollars would accumulate to

$$e^{-rx} \cdot e^{rx} = e^0 = 1 \text{ dollar}$$

---

[1] This may be easily proved by putting increasingly large values of m in the formula $e = \left(1 + \dfrac{1}{m}\right)^m$. Thus,

for $m = 10$, $e = (1 + \tfrac{1}{10})^{10} = (1.1)^{10} = 2.594$;
for $m = 50$, $e = (1 + \tfrac{1}{50})^{50} = (1.02)^{50} = 2.691$;
for $m = 1{,}000$, $e = \left(1 + \dfrac{1}{1{,}000}\right)^{1{,}000} = (1.001)^{1{,}000} = 2.7171$;

for $m = 10{,}000$, $e = (1 + 1/10{,}000)^{10{,}000} = (1.0001)^{10{,}000} = 2.7182$, the calculations being carried out by logarithms (see Appendix, Table I).

at the end of that time, and hence the present value of \$1 due x years hence is e^{-rx}. This "discount" function, as it may be called, is thus a negative exponential function. Its graph is shown in Fig. 89.

Whereas the exponential functions are not themselves poly-nomials, it will be noted that the expression that constitutes the "exponent of e" is a first-degree polynomial in x (more accu-rately, the monomial x). This suggests that interesting modi-fications of the exponential func-tion might be obtained by making the exponent of e a second or higher degree poly-nomial in x. A function of this kind that is of very great impor-tance in the theory of frequency curves is $y = e^{-cx^2}$. Figure 90

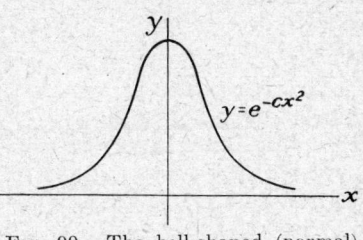

FIG. 90.—The bell-shaped (normal) curve, $y = e^{-cx^2}(c > 0)$.

shows how well this function represents the general shape of a frequency distribution; as will be seen shortly, it is the kernel of the formula for the normal frequency curve.

Formula for the Normal Frequency and Probability Curves. Formulas for frequency and probability curves may be written in two ways. The first, which may be symbolized by $y = \varphi(X)$, merely expresses the ordinate of the curve y as a function of the attribute X whose frequency is being measured. (φ is used here to signify "function of," instead of the usual F or f, in order to avoid confusion with the employment of the latter to indicate frequencies.) In this form the formula simply describes the locus of the points that constitute the frequency or probability curve.

The second method of writing a frequency or probability formula is $d(F/N)$ or $dP = \varphi(X)\,dX$. In this form, the prob-ability or relative frequency of a case lying between X and $X + dX$ is expressed as a function of the attribute X. It will be recalled that a probability or frequency curve is the limit approached by an area histogram as the class interval is made infinitesimally small. The expression $d(F/N)$ or $dP = \varphi(x)\,dX$ merely says that, when the class interval (of size dX)[1] is made

---

[1] The letters dX, dP, $d(F/N)$, etc., are to be read as a single symbol and not as the product d and X or d and P, etc. The symbol dX means an

infinitesimally small, the area under the curve for any class interval [that is, $d(F/N)$ or dP] is approximately equal to the area of a small rectangle whose base is dX and whose height is the ordinate of the curve $\varphi(X)$ at X (cf. Fig. 91). This second method is, strictly speaking, the proper method for describing a

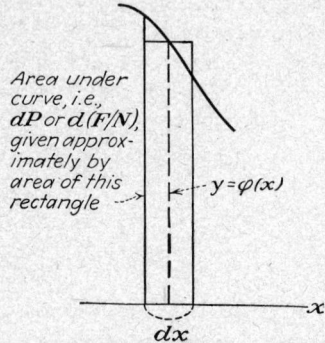

Area under curve, i.e., dP or d(F/N), given approximately by area of this rectangle ⟶

$y = \varphi(x)$

x

dx

FIG. 91.—Graphical representation of a probability function.

"probability" or "frequency" curve, since it is this and not the first which actually expresses the probability or frequency of a given class interval as a function of the attribute X. The former gives merely an algebraic expression for the curve and not the area under the curve.[1]

The Normal Curve. One curve occurs very often in statistical analysis, especially in the theory of sampling. This is the normal frequency curve. Its algebraic and graphic representation may profitably be illustrated by a brief description.

The mathematical formula for the normal curve is

$$dP = \frac{1}{\sigma\sqrt{2\pi}} e^{\frac{-(X-\bar{X})^2}{2\sigma^2}} dX \qquad (6)$$

where $e(= 2.7183+)$ is the base of the Napierian system of logarithms, $\bar{X}$ is the mean of the distribution, and σ is its standard deviation. Pictures of the curve are given in Figs. 92a and 92b. It will be noted that the curve is symmetrical and generally bell-shaped.

Owing to its symmetry, the center of the curve comes at the mean point $X = \bar{X}$. Here the curve also reaches its greatest height, *viz.*, $\dfrac{1}{\sigma\sqrt{2\pi}}$, and from there it slopes gradually downward on each side as the factor $e^{\frac{-(X-\bar{X})^2}{2\sigma^2}}$ assumes greater and greater

infinitesimally small part of the X range, the symbol dP means an infinitesimal probability, and the symbol $d(F/N)$ means an infinitesimal relative frequency.

[1] The first method of description is, however, the only form that is appropriate for a discrete distribution.

significance.[1] The points of inflection, *i.e.*, the points at which
the left and right branches change from concave to convex
downward fall at $X = \bar{X} \pm \sigma$. About two-thirds of the area
under the curve lies between these two points of inflection, and
about 95 per cent between $\bar{X} - 2\sigma$ and $\bar{X} + 2\sigma$. The average
deviation equals 0.7979 times the standard deviation, and the
fourth moment equals three times the square of the second
moment (hence $\beta_2 = 3$).

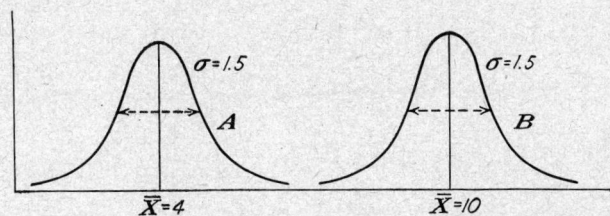

F<small>IG</small>. 92*a*.—Graphs of normal frequency curves with different means but same
standard deviations.

As will be noted from the formula, a particular normal curve
is determined when its mean $\bar{X}$ and its standard deviation σ are
given. Different normal curves, then, will have either different
means or different standard deviations, or both. If the means
are different, the curves will have different positions on the X-
axis; if the standard deviations are different, the curves will be
of different widths. This is illustrated in Figs. 92*a* and 92*b*.

Although normal curves may thus differ in respect to their
means and standard deviations, they all possess the essential
"normal" form. This may be brought out by measuring the
attribute X, not in original units, such as pounds or dollars, but
as a deviation from the mean of X measured in standard-devia-

[1] It will be noted that $e^{\frac{-(X-\bar{X})^2}{2\sigma^2}} = \dfrac{1}{e^{\frac{(X-\bar{X})^2}{2\sigma^2}}}.$ When $X = \bar{X}$, this becomes

$1/e^0 = \frac{1}{1} = 1$. As X moves away from $\bar{X}$ in either direction, $e^{\frac{(X-\bar{X})^2}{2\sigma^2}}$
becomes larger and larger and hence $\dfrac{1}{e^{\frac{(X-\bar{X})^2}{2\sigma^2}}}$ becomes smaller and smaller.

All the ordinates are positive since the exponent of *e* is squared.

tion units, *i.e.*, as $\dfrac{X - \bar{X}}{\sigma}$ or $\dfrac{x}{\sigma}\cdot$ Whenever this is done, all normal curves become one and the same curve.

Suppose, for example, that X in one case represents pounds and in another quarts. In both cases the probability or relative frequency is "normally" distributed, but the mean of the first distribution is 4 pounds and its standard deviation is 1.5 pounds. This distribution is represented by curve A in Fig. 92a. The second distribution has a mean of 6 quarts and a standard deviation of 0.5 quart; it is represented by curve D in Fig. 92b. If, however, the unit adopted for the measurement of the attribute of an element is in the first case $\dfrac{X \text{ lb.} - 4 \text{ lb.}}{1.5 \text{ lb.}}$ and in the

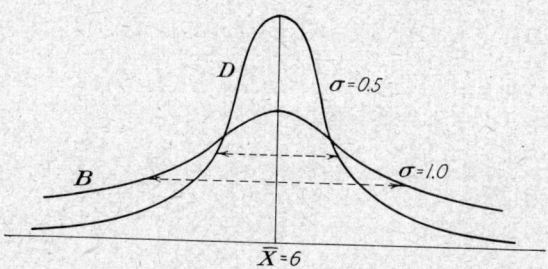

Fɪɢ. 92b.—Graphs of normal frequency curves with same mean, but different standard deviations.

second case $\dfrac{X \text{ qt.} - 6 \text{ qt.}}{0.5 \text{ qt.}}$, then in terms of these $\dfrac{X - \bar{X}}{\sigma} = \dfrac{x}{\sigma}$ units the two distributions will be identical. It is thus possible to reduce all normal distributions to a standard normal form[1] (see Fig. 93).

Consider now the relationship between the mathematical formula for the curve and this standard normal form. In the individual or nonstandard form, the formula for the curve is that given above, *viz.*, $dP = \dfrac{1}{\sigma\sqrt{2\pi}}\, e^{-\frac{(X - \bar{X})^2}{2\sigma^2}}\, dX$. This says that the infinitesimal portion of the total area under the curve dP cut off by the infinitesimal class interval X to $X + dX$ is approximately equal to the area of an infinitesimal rectangle whose

---

[1] It will be noted that in the standard form the height of the middle ordinate is $1/\sqrt{2\pi} = 0.3989$.

height is $\dfrac{1}{\sigma\sqrt{2\pi}}\,e^{-\frac{(X-\bar{X})^2}{2\sigma^2}}$ and whose base is dX. If now the attribute is expressed in $\dfrac{X-\bar{X}}{\sigma} = \dfrac{x}{\sigma}$ units, the mathematical formula becomes,

$$dP = \frac{1}{\sqrt{2\pi}}\,e^{-\frac{1}{2}\left(\frac{x}{\sigma}\right)^2} d\left(\frac{x}{\sigma}\right)$$

In this case, the infinitesimal portion of the total area cut off by the infinitesimal class interval $\dfrac{x}{\sigma}$ to $\dfrac{x}{\sigma} + d\left(\dfrac{x}{\sigma}\right)$ is expressed as the area of a rectangle whose height is $\dfrac{1}{\sqrt{2\pi}}\,e^{-\frac{1}{2}\left(\frac{x}{\sigma}\right)^2}$ and whose

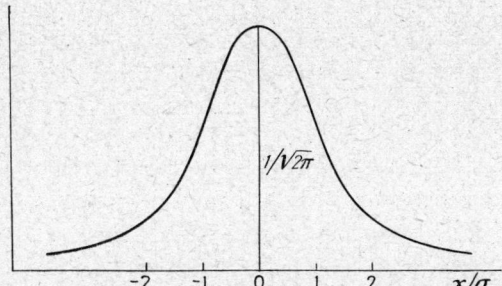

Fig. 93.—Graph of a standard normal curve.

base is $d(x/\sigma)$. In other words, the effect of measuring the attribute in x/σ units instead of X units is to change the size of the unit class interval on which the rectangle rests but at the same time to change its height proportionately so its area dP remains the same.

A table giving the value of $\dfrac{1}{\sqrt{2\pi}}\,e^{\frac{-x^2}{2\sigma^2}}$ for various values of x/σ will be found in the Appendix, Table VII. These are the ordinates of the standard normal curve. It was by means of this table that Fig. 93 was plotted; its use in "fitting" the normal curve to an actual set of data will be explained in the next chapter.[1]

[1] See pp. 277 and 295–304.

CHAPTER X

PROBABILITY CALCULUS

Two Fundamental Theorems. There are two fundamental theorems in the calculus of probabilities. These are the addition theorem and the multiplication theorem. There is also a special form of the latter that pertains only to "independent" attributes.

Addition Theorem. The addition theorem pertains to the summation of the probabilities of one and the same probability set. Since the several attributes of a given probability set are necessarily mutually exclusive, it follows that the relative frequency of cases having either one of two attributes is the sum of the relative frequencies of the separate attributes. For example, there are 13 hearts in an ordinary deck of 52 playing cards, and also 13 diamonds. The relative frequency of a heart is therefore $\frac{13}{52}$, and the relative frequency of a diamond is also $\frac{13}{52}$. The relative frequency of a red card, *i.e.*, either a heart or a diamond, is $\frac{26}{52}$, which equals $\frac{13}{52} + \frac{13}{52}$. Since the relative frequencies of the attributes are by definition their probabilities, it follows that the probability of a member of a set having either one of several attributes is simply the sum of the individual probabilities. The probability of a heart or a diamond is thus $\frac{13}{52} + \frac{13}{52} = \frac{26}{52} = \frac{1}{2}$. This addition theorem is valid for infinite probability sets as well as for finite sets.

Algebraically the addition theorem may be expressed as follows: If the attributes of a given set are $X_1, X_2 \ldots, X_s$ (representing either qualitative or quantitative characteristics) and their probabilities are $p_1, p_2, \ldots, p_s$, then the probability of $X_1, X_2,$ or X_3, say, that is, the attribute of being any one of these X's, is simply $p_1 + p_2 + p_3$. If the variation in attributes within the set is continuous and if the distribution of probability is described by a formula such as $dP = \varphi(X)\, dX$, then the probability of an attribute within any one of a number of small ranges dX whose sum constitutes the range X_1 to X_2 is given by $\Sigma\, dP = \Sigma\varphi(X)\, dX$, or, in the symbolism of the integral calculus, $\int dP = \int \varphi(X) \, dX$. The significance of this theorem will become clearer when its application to particular problems is considered.

The addition theorem is sometimes stated as follows: The probability of either one of two mutually exclusive events (attributes) is the sum of their individual probabilities. This version of the theorem is perfectly valid if it is understood that the two attributes belong to the same set. It will be recalled that all the attributes of a set are mutually exclusive.[1] It is not true, however, that all mutually exclusive attributes belong to the same set. To illustrate this point von Mises gives the following example:[2]

Suppose that the probability of a man dying between his fortieth and forty-first birthdays is 0.011 and the probability of his marrying between his forty-first and forty-second birthdays is 0.009. These events are mutually exclusive, but it cannot be said that the probability of a man either dying in his fortieth year or marrying in his forty-first year is $0.011 + 0.009 = 0.02$. The two events do not belong to the same set, and the addition theorem can be validly applied only to attributes of one and the same set.

Multiplication Theorem. The multiplication theorem pertains to the calculation of a probability of a "derived" or "second-order" probability set from the probabilities of two or more "first-order" sets. Consider, for example, an ordinary deck of playing cards and a pinochle deck. Each may be said to constitute a "first-order" probability set. In the first set the probability of an ace is $\frac{4}{52} = \frac{1}{13}$, and in the second the probability of an ace is $\frac{8}{48} = \frac{1}{6}$. Let the third set be formed from these two first-order sets by combining each card of one first-order set with each card of the other first-order set. Furthermore, let the attribute of any pair be the values of the cards making up the pair, such as a king and a nine, an ace and a queen, a two and a ten, and the like. The probability of any one attribute in this second-order set, say the probability of a pair consisting of two aces, is the relative frequency of such pairs among all possible pairs that might be formed. It is the purpose of the multiplication theorem to give a general rule by which a probability of a

---

[1] See p. 252.

[2] *Probability, Statistics, and Truth*, p. 54.

second-order set of this kind can be computed from the probabilities of the first-order sets.

In deriving the multiplication theorem, two cases must be distinguished, one pertaining to independent probabilities and the other to dependent probabilities. Consider first the case of independent probabilities. Suppose that in finding all the various pairs of cards that might be composed of one card from each deck there is no limitation on how the cards might be matched. Then each card of the ordinary deck will have associated with it every card of the pinochle deck. Hence the set of pinochle cards that are paired with the ace of spades, say, from the ordinary deck will be the same as the set of pinochle cards paired with the jack of diamonds, say, or in fact with any other card from the ordinary deck.

Since the set of pinochle cards paired with each card of the ordinary deck is thus the same as the set of pinochle cards paired with every other card from the ordinary deck and since this common set is identical with the original pinochle set, it follows that the probability of any given pinochle card in the set paired with any given card of the ordinary deck is the same as the probability of that pinochle card in the original pinochle deck. This being the case, the probability of a card from the pinochle deck is said to be independent of the attribute of the card from the ordinary deck.

In general, the probabilities of set II are said to be independent of the attributes of probability set I if, when the members of the two sets are paired together, the probability of an attribute in the subset of members of set II paired with any given member of set I is the same as the probability of that attribute in the original set II. Symbolically, $P(B)$ is independent of A if $P(B/A)$, that is, the probability of B given A, equals $P(B)$, that is, the probability of B.

Consider once again the given example. Since each card of the ordinary deck is associated with each card of the pinochle deck, the total number of different[1] pairs of cards that can be formed is

[1] Different in the sense that the cards going to make up any pair are not precisely the same cards as those making up any other pair. This means that the two aces of spades, the two kings of spades, the two jacks of diamonds, etc., in the pinochle deck must be considered as different cards, even though their value and suit are the same.

52 × 48, for there are 52 ways in which the first card can be picked and 48 ways in which the second card can be picked. Likewise, the number of combinations that would consist of two aces would be 4 × 8 = 32. Hence the probability of a pair of aces in the whole set of pairs of cards is $32/2{,}496 = \frac{1}{78}$. But from the calculations this is seen to be equal to $\frac{4}{52} \times \frac{8}{48} = \frac{1}{78}$. In other words, the probability of a pair of aces in the second-order probability set is equal to the probability of an ace in the ordinary deck times the probability of an ace in the pinochle deck.

The multiplication theorem for independent probabilities may thus be stated as follows: If p_a is the probability of a member of set I having the attribute A and if q_b is the probability of a member of set II having the attribute B, and if q_b is independent of the attribute assumed by a member of set I, then the probability of a member of the derived set I-II having the attribute AB, that is, the probability of a pair AB among all possible pairs of two elements from each of the two sets I and II, is the product of the probabilities p_a and q_b. In simpler form, if $P(B)$ is independent of A, the joint probability of A and B is equal to the probability of A times the probability of B, that is, $P(AB) = P(A) \cdot P(B)$.

Consider next the case of dependent probabilities. Suppose that, in picking pairs of cards from the two decks, the following modification is introduced. Suppose that every time the card picked from the ordinary playing card deck is an ace, a king, a queen, or a jack and that, before any selection is made from the pinochle deck, an ace, a king, and a queen from each suit is discarded from the deck and is replaced by a jack, a ten, and a nine of each suit. The pinochle deck would then contain the same number of cards as before, but it would have 4 aces, kings, and queens instead of 8, and 12 jacks, tens, and nines instead of 8. After the pinochle deck has been modified in this way, let a card be selected from it and combined with the ace, king, queen, or jack picked from the ordinary deck. If the card picked from the ordinary deck is not an ace, a king, a queen, or a jack, let no modification be made in the pinochle deck. The effect of this modification in the method of forming pairs of cards is to make the attributes of the second set dependent on those of the first. For the set of cards of the pinochle deck associated with an ace, a king, a queen, or a jack of the ordinary deck is different from the set of cards of the pinochle deck associated with other cards of the ordinary deck. The probability of a given type of card from the pinochle pack now depends on the card from the ordinary deck; no longer does $P(B/A) = P(B)$.

The number of different pairs of cards that can be made in the way just described is 52×48 as before, for the first card can still be selected in 52 ways and the second in 48 ways. The number of pairs of cards consisting of two aces, however, is now 4×4 instead of 4×8 as in the previous example. Hence the probability of a pair of aces among the whole set of pairs is

$$\frac{4 \times 4}{52 \times 48} = \frac{1}{156}$$

It will be noted, however, that this probability of a pair of aces is the product of the probability of an ace in the ordinary deck (that is, $\frac{4}{52}$) times the probability of an ace in the *modified* pinochle deck (that is, $\frac{4}{48}$). In other words, the probability of a pair of aces is the probability of an ace in the ordinary deck times the probability of an ace in the pinochle deck given the selection of an ace from the ordinary deck.

The multiplication rule for dependent attributes may thus be stated as follows: If members of probability set II are paired with members of probability set I in such a way that the probability of an attribute in the subset of members of set II paired with any given member of set I varies with the attribute of that member of set I, then the probability of the pair AB in the whole set of paired values is equal to the product of the probability of A in set I times the probability of B in that subset of set II associated with the given attribute A. Symbolically, the multiplication rule for dependent attributes is

$$P(AB) = P(A) \cdot P(B/A)$$

that is, the probability of AB equals the probability of A times the probability of B given A. Since, when $P(B)$ is independent of A, $P(B/A) = P(B)$, the multiplication rule for independent probabilities is a special case of the general formula

$$P(AB) = P(A) \cdot P(B/A)$$

The multiplication theorem for both dependent and independent probabilities is valid for infinite sets as well as finite sets.

The significance of independence and dependence may be illustrated by a case pertaining to real life. Suppose that one probability set consists of American fathers of the white race and the other probability set consists of their eldest sons. Suppose the attributes distinguished in each set are dying from cancer, dying from heart disease, dying from tuberculosis, and dying from other causes. If, now, the probability of a son dying from tuberculosis, say, is greater, among those sons whose fathers died of tuberculosis, than among the whole group of sons, then the probability of a son dying from a certain cause is not independent of the cause of death of his father. If, on the other hand, the probability of a son dying from any particular cause is the same for the sons whose fathers died from cancer, the sons whose fathers died from heart disease, the sons whose fathers died from tuberculosis, and the sons whose fathers died from other causes, *i.e.*, if the probability of a son dying from any particular cause is the same, whatever the cause of the father's death, then the probability of a son's death is independent of the cause of death of his father. For example, a case of dependence would be the following:

	Probability of death of eldest son from			
	Cancer	Heart disease	Tuberculosis	Other causes
Eldest sons whose fathers died of				
Cancer....................	0.310	0.102	0.030	0.558
Heart disease..............	0.218	0.151	0.041	0.590
Tuberculosis...............	0.220	0.118	0.093	0.569
Other causes..............	0.215	0.112	0.042	0.631
All eldest sons.............	0.228	0.120	0.046	0.606

A case of independence would be that in which the figures in every row of every column were the same and these in turn were the same as the figures for "All sons." If the probability of a father dying from cancer was 0.228, from heart disease 0.120, from tuberculosis 0.046, and from other causes 0.606, then, in the case of dependence represented by the above table, the probability of both a father and an eldest son dying from heart disease would be $(0.120)(0.151) = 0.018$. In the case of independence, on the other hand, the probability of both a father and an eldest son dying of heart disease would be

$$(0.120)(0.120) = 0.014$$

Illustrations. The following examples will help to illustrate the use of the addition and multiplication theorems in the calculation of desired probabilities. Some will also serve to illustrate the use of the normal probability curve.

Examples Involving Discrete Distributions. Suppose that a gambling game consists of the random tossing of five coins. You agree to pay your opponent a predetermined sum of money whenever all five coins turn up heads; he agrees to pay you a predetermined sum whenever any other result occurs. The question is: What should the odds be to make the game a fair one? The answer is obtained as follows:

Assume that the character of the coins and the method of tossing are such as to cause each coin to tend to turn up heads and tails in equal proportion. In a large number of tossings, therefore, the probability of a head on each coin may be taken as $\frac{1}{2}$. Assume, also, that the method of tossing is such as to make the tosses of each coin independent of the others. Then the probability of heads on all five coins is

$$(\tfrac{1}{2})(\tfrac{1}{2})(\tfrac{1}{2})(\tfrac{1}{2})(\tfrac{1}{2}) = (\tfrac{1}{2})^5 = \tfrac{1}{32}$$

Accordingly, the fair odds are 31 to 1. That is, the game will be fair if you agree to pay your opponent $31 every time five heads occur and he agrees to pay you $1 every time some other result occurs. Of course, in an actual game the assumption regarding the character of the coins and the method of tossing would have to be checked by examination of the coins and by trial tossings. This is an illustration of the multiplication theorem for independent probabilities.

Another gambling game consists of the throwing of two dice. You agree to pay your opponent a predetermined sum whenever a combination totaling 7 appears, and he agrees to pay you a predetermined sum whenever another result appears. Again the problem is to determine fair odds. This may be done by a combined application of the multiplication and addition theorems.

Assume again that the dice are of such a character and are so thrown that all faces tend to turn up in equal proportions. The probability of any given result for each die is therefore $\frac{1}{6}$. The six possible combinations that add up to 7 are (1,6), (2,5), (3,4), (4,3), (5,2), and (6,1). If it is assumed that the dice are thrown so as to give independent results, then, by the multiplication theorem for independent probabilities, the probability of each one of the above combinations is $(\frac{1}{6})(\frac{1}{6}) = \frac{1}{36}$. Any one of the combinations, however, will yield a total of 7. The probability of a total of 7 is therefore the probability of any one of these combinations, which, by the addition theorem, is

$$(\tfrac{1}{36}) + (\tfrac{1}{36}) + (\tfrac{1}{36}) + (\tfrac{1}{36}) + (\tfrac{1}{36}) + (\tfrac{1}{36}) = \tfrac{6}{36} = \tfrac{1}{6}$$

Hence, fair odds are 5 to 1; that is, the game will be fair if you pay your opponent \$5 every time a 7 occurs and he pays you \$1 every time some other total occurs. Again, in a real game the character of the dice and the method of throwing should be checked to see if the above assumptions are warranted.

Consider still a third gambling game. Suppose that two cards are drawn at random from a well-shuffled pack, the suit is noted, the cards are returned to the pack, the latter is shuffled, and the whole operation is repeated. Each time the cards are all spades you agree to pay your opponent a predetermined sum; if they are otherwise, he pays you. What are fair odds?

Assume as in the other games that the method of drawing cards and the method of shuffling are such that all cards tend to be drawn in equal proportion. The probability of a spade among the first cards drawn will thus be $\frac{13}{52}$, assuming the usual deck of 13 spades, 13 hearts, 13 diamonds, and 13 clubs. If the first card drawn is a spade, the remainder of the deck contains 12 spades and 13 of each of the other suits. If in a large set of drawings each of these remaining cards tends to turn up in the same proportion as every other card, then the probability of a spade among the second cards drawn will be $\frac{12}{51}$. This is the probability of a spade on the second draw, assuming a spade on the first draw. Then, according to the multiplication theorem for dependent probabilities, the probability of a spade on both the first and second draws is $(\frac{13}{52})(\frac{12}{51}) = \frac{3}{51}$. The odds will be fair, therefore, if you pay \$48 every time two spades are drawn and your opponent pays \$3 every time any other combination is drawn.   Again the assumptions would have to be checked in a real game.

Examples Involving Continuous Distributions.   All the examples so far have been concerned with discrete probability distributions.   Much of the practical work in statistics, however, is concerned with continuous distributions.   As the first example of this kind, consider the distribution of heights of eighteen-year-old boys.   The fitting of a normal curve to the heights of 300 eighteen-year-old Princeton freshmen[1] suggests that in general the forces of nature are such as to cause a "normal" distribution of heights.   If this is assumed to be the case, then the normal curve can be employed to calculate the probability of an eighteen-year-old boy having a height lying between any given range. This is done as follows:

As indicated above,[2] if the distribution of probability follows the normal law, then the probability of an attribute ranging from x/σ to $x/\sigma + d(x/\sigma)$ is given by the formula

$$dP = \frac{1}{\sqrt{2\pi}} \, e^{\frac{-x^2}{2\sigma^2}} \, d\left(\frac{x}{\sigma}\right)$$

where x/σ represents a deviation of the attribute from the mean attribute measured in σ units, σ is the standard deviation of the distribution, and $d(x/\sigma)$ is an infinitesimally small range.   This represents approximately the area under the curve for the infinitesimal range x/σ to $x/\sigma + d(x/\sigma)$.   A finite range running, say from x_1/σ to x_2/σ, can be conceived as made up of a number of infinitesimal ranges of size $d(x/\sigma)$; and the probability of an attribute ranging from x_1/σ to x_2/σ is (by the addition theorem) merely the sum of the probabilities for each of these infinitesimal ranges, *viz.*,

$$\sum_{\frac{x_1}{\sigma}}^{\frac{x_2}{\sigma}} \frac{1}{\sqrt{2\pi}} \, e^{\frac{-x^2}{2\sigma^2}} \, d\left(\frac{x}{\sigma}\right)$$

or, in the notation of the integral calculus,

$$\int_{\frac{x_1}{\sigma}}^{\frac{x_2}{\sigma}} \frac{1}{\sqrt{2\pi}} \, e^{\frac{-x^2}{2\sigma^2}} \, d\left(\frac{x}{\sigma}\right)$$

[1] See pp. 295–306 and especially Fig. 101.
[2] See pp. 264–267.

In other words, the probability of an attribute ranging from x_1/σ to x_2/σ is simply the area under the curve for this range. This is graphically shown in Fig. 94 and is a direct result of the addition theorem.

The area under the normal curve for any given range, might, as indicated, be found by evaluating the "integral"

$$\int_{\frac{x_1}{\sigma}}^{\frac{x_2}{\sigma}} \frac{1}{\sqrt{2\pi}} e^{\frac{-x^2}{2\sigma^2}} d\left(\frac{x}{\sigma}\right)$$

This is not an easy task, however, even for those who understand advanced mathematics. Consequently, tables have been pre-

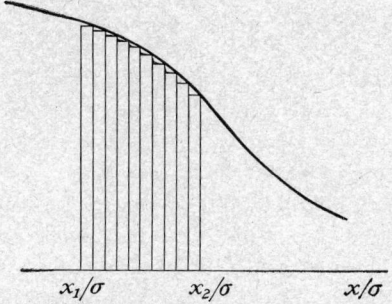

x_1/σ x_2/σ x/σ

FIG. 94.—Illustration of computation of probability of an x/σ lying between x_1/σ and x_2/σ.

pared that give the approximate areas under the normal curve for certain specified ranges and that permit by simple arithmetical operations the calculation of areas for all other ranges. Such a table is Table VI of the Appendix, page 693. This gives the proportionate area under the positive half of the normal curve from the mean ($x/\sigma = 0$) to various selected points. Thus from the table it is seen that the proportion of the area lying under the normal curve from $x/\sigma = 0$ to $x/\sigma = 0.2$ is 0.07926.

In addition, since the proportion of the area under the normal curve from $x/\sigma = 0$ (the mean) to infinity is 0.50000, the proportion of area under the curve from any selected point to infinity can be readily calculated. Thus the proportion of the area under the curve from $x/\sigma = 0.2$ to infinity is 0.42074 (*i.e.*, 0.50000 − 0.07926), the proportion of area from $x/\sigma = 1.96$ to infinity is 0.02500 (*i.e.*, 0.50000 − 0.47500), etc. Owing to the symmetry of the curve, the same values hold true for areas from $x/\sigma = 0$ to

$x/\sigma = -\infty$. Thus the proportion of the area for the range from $x/\sigma = -0.2$ to $x/\sigma = -\infty$ is $0.50000 - 0.07926 = 0.42074$.

To find proportionate areas for other ranges, it is necessary merely to add or subtract proportionate areas given directly by the table. Thus, the proportion of area from the range $x/\sigma = 0.2$ to $x/\sigma = 0.3$ is the difference between the proportionate area from $x/\sigma = 0.3$ to the mean, and the proportionate area from $x/\sigma = 0.2$ to the mean, *i.e.*, $0.11791 - 0.07926 = 0.03865$. Likewise, the proportionate area under the curve for the range $x/\sigma = -0.2$ to $x/\sigma = +0.3$ is simply the sum of the proportionate area from $x/\sigma = -0.2$ to $x/\sigma = 0$, and the proportionate area from $x/\sigma = 0$ to $x/\sigma = 0.3$, *i.e.*, $0.07926 + 0.11791 = 0.19717$. Proportionate areas for obscure points not given directly or indirectly by the table may be obtained by interpolation; usually, straight-line interpolation (*i.e.*, the calculation of simple proportionate differences) gives satisfactory results.

To make use of Table VI in a given problem it is merely necessary to convert the original measurements into deviations from the mean expressed in σ units, *i.e.*, to convert original units into σ units. The mean height of eighteen-year-old boys, for example (as estimated from the heights of eighteen-year-old Princeton freshmen of the class of 1943), is 70.47 inches, and the standard deviation of heights is 2.49 inches. Hence the probability of an eighteen-year-old boy 72 to 73 inches tall is given by the area under the normal curve from

$$\frac{x}{\sigma} = \frac{72 - 70.47}{2.49} = 0.61 \qquad \text{to} \qquad \frac{x}{\sigma} = \frac{73 - 70.47}{2.49} = 1.02$$

This, in accordance with the method outlined in the previous paragraph for calculating such an area, is 0.11707. Similarly, the probability of a boy taller than 74 inches is given by the area under the normal curve from $\dfrac{x}{\sigma} = \dfrac{74 - 70.47}{2.49} = 1.42$ to infinity, which the table shows to be $0.50000 - 0.42220 = 0.07780$. Again, the probability that two boys picked at random should be taller than 74 inches is the product of the two individual probabilities (the multiplication theorem for independent probabilities) or

$$(0.07780)(0.07780) = 0.00605$$

Table VI thus readily facilitates the calculation of probabilities whenever the primary distribution or distributions follow the normal law.

CHAPTER XI

SYMMETRICAL BINOMIAL DISTRIBUTION AND THE NORMAL CURVE

INTRODUCTION

The preceding chapters have been concerned with probability and the probability calculus. These were discussed for the purpose of providing tools for subsequent analysis. In this chapter the tools will be employed in developing a theoretical explanation of the normal frequency curve. The line of attack will be as follows.

The argument will begin with an abstract study of a simple problem in combinatorial analysis. The basic data will be 10 coins, each of which has two sides. These sides will be marked with a head or a tail, and each coin will have one head and one tail.

The combinatorial problem will be the determination of the relative frequencies or probabilities of various types of combinations in the whole set of combinations that might be made from various arrangements of the given set of coins. Thus the theoretical problem will be the determination of the relative frequencies or probabilities of combinations having 0, 1, 2, . . . , 10 heads in the whole set of combinations that might be constructed from various arrangements of the 10 coins.

In the terminology of probability, this combinatorial problem consists of the derivation of a certain second-order probability set from the elementary probability set. To put this in another way, the problem is to find the type of frequency or probability distribution that results from the combination of certain elementary frequency or probability distributions. Attention will in particular center upon the form of the derived frequency or probability distribution. Exact and approximate formulas will be determined for this distribution.

The purely theoretical part of the theory of the normal curve will thus be a set of problems in the probability calculus. What is ultimately desired, however, is the explanation that this distribution affords of some of the frequency distributions that appear in real life, such as the frequency distributions of the heights of adult white males, the frequency distribution of samples from a given population, and the like. This explanation will be undertaken after the completion of the combinatorial analysis.

SYMMETRICAL BINOMIAL DISTRIBUTION

Derivation. As already suggested, the discussion of the theory of the normal frequency curve will begin with the analysis of a simple problem involving 10 coins. Each coin, it will be assumed, has two sides, one of which is a head, the other a tail. Since the probability of an object has been defined as its relative frequency in the set of objects to which it belongs, it may be said that for each coin the probability of a side being a head is $\frac{1}{2}$ and the probability of its being a tail is also $\frac{1}{2}$. The problem to be considered is this: If the 10 coins are combined in all possible ways, the selection of a head or a tail for any one coin being independent of the selection for other coins, what are the various types of combinations of heads and tails that will be produced and what will be the probability of each type in the set of all possible combinations? This is a straightforward problem in the theory of combinations and may be solved as follows.

To facilitate the analysis, let the 10 coins be distinguished by the letters A, B, C, D, E, F, G, H, I, and J. A combination having 0 heads, for example, will be represented as follows,

A	B	C	D	E	F	G	H	I	J
T	T	T	T	T	T	T	T	T	T

a combination having 4 heads as follows,

A	B	C	D	E	F	G	H	I	J
H	T	T	H	H	T	T	T	H	T

etc.

Consider first the combination having 0 heads. Since the probability of a tail on each coin is $\frac{1}{2}$, the probability of 0 heads is $(\frac{1}{2})^{10}$. For the probability of A being a tail is $\frac{1}{2}$, and the same is true for B, C, D, E, F, G, H, I, and J. Furthermore, since the probability of a tail for any one coin is independent of what the other coins are, the probability of the above result is, by the multiplication theorem, the product of the 10 independent probabilities, or $(\frac{1}{2})(\frac{1}{2})(\frac{1}{2})(\frac{1}{2})(\frac{1}{2})(\frac{1}{2})(\frac{1}{2})(\frac{1}{2})(\frac{1}{2})(\frac{1}{2}) = (\frac{1}{2})^{10}$. Finally, it is to be noted that this result can be obtained in only one way. Hence it is to be concluded that the probability of 0 heads is $1/2^{10} = 1/1{,}024$.

Consider next the following combination:

A	B	C	D	E	F	G	H	I	J
H	T	T	T	T	T	T	T	T	T

This is a case of 1 head. Since the probability of A being a head is $\frac{1}{2}$ and the probability of each of the other coins being a tail is also $\frac{1}{2}$ and since each of these results is independent of the others, it follows that the probability of this particular combination of heads and tails is again $(\frac{1}{2})^{10}$. But there are also other combinations having only 1 head. Such are

A	B	C	D	E	F	G	H	I	J
T	H	T	T	T	T	T	T	T	T
T	T	H	T	T	T	T	T	T	T
T	T	T	T	T	T	T	T	T	H

In fact, it is readily seen that there are 10 combinations altogether in each of which a different coin is the one being a head. The probability, therefore, of any one of these 10 combinations, *i.e.*, the probability of a head on some one and only one of the 10 coins is, by the addition theorem, $10(\frac{1}{2})^{10} = 10/1{,}024$.

Consider now the combination

A	B	C	D	E	F	G	H	I	J
H	H	T	T	T	T	T	T	T	T

This is a case of 2 heads. Since the probability of A being a head is $\frac{1}{2}$, the probability of B being a head is $\frac{1}{2}$ and the probability of each of the other coins being a tail is likewise $\frac{1}{2}$; and since each of these results is independent of all the others, it follows once more that the probability of this particular combination is $(\frac{1}{2})^{10}$.

But, as previously, this is not the only combination having 2 heads. The reader himself will be able to write down a number of other combinations in which only 2 heads appear. The question is how many different combinations of the 10 coins have 2 and only 2 heads? This is answered by the theory of

permutations and combinations outlined in Chap. X.[1] Thus
the number of different combinations of 10 coins taken 2 at a
time is

$$C_2^{10} = \frac{10!}{2!\,8!} = 45$$

[*Cf.* Eq. (3), page 234.] There being, therefore, 45 different
combinations, each of which has a probability of $(\frac{1}{2})^{10}$, it follows
that the probability of any one of them is

$$45\left(\frac{1}{2}\right)^{10} = \frac{45}{1,024}$$

The probability of other possible combinations is determined
in a similar manner. In general, the probability of N_1 heads is

$$\frac{(10)!}{(N_1)!(10 - N_1)!}\left(\frac{1}{2}\right)^{10}$$

Thus the probability of 3 heads and 7 tails is

$$\frac{10!}{3!\,7!}\left(\frac{1}{2}\right)^{10} = 120\left(\frac{1}{2}\right)^{10}$$

The probability of 6 heads and 4 tails is

$$\frac{10!}{4!\,6!}\left(\frac{1}{2}\right)^{10} = 210\left(\frac{1}{2}\right)^{10}$$

etc. The results obtained by use of this formula may be tabulated as follows:

TABLE 19.—PROBABILITIES OF VARIOUS COMBINATIONS AMONG ALL POSSIBLE
COMBINATIONS OF 10 COINS

Combinations Having	Probability
0 head	1/1,024 = 0.00098
1 head	10/1,024 = 0.00977
2 heads	45/1,024 = 0.04394
3 heads	120/1,024 = 0.11719
4 heads	210/1,024 = 0.20508
5 heads	252/1,024 = 0.24609
6 heads	210/1,024 = 0.20508
7 heads	120/1,024 = 0.11719
8 heads	45/1,024 = 0.04394
9 heads	10/1,024 = 0.00977
10 heads	1/1,024 = 0.00098

[1] See pp. 232–234.

It will be noted that the series of probabilities of 0, 1, 2, . . . , 10 heads may be obtained by the expansion of $(\frac{1}{2} + \frac{1}{2})^{10}$. This distribution of probability is consequently called a "binomial" distribution.[1] If N coins had been used instead of 10, the probabilities of the distribution would have been given by the terms of the expansion of $(\frac{1}{2} + \frac{1}{2})^N$. Thus the probability of a combination having N_1 heads among all possible combinations of N coins is[2]

$$P(N_1) = \frac{N!}{N_1!(N - N_1)!} \left(\frac{1}{2}\right)^N$$

or if N_2 is set equal to $N - N_1$,

$$P(N_1) = \frac{N!}{N_1!N_2!} \left(\frac{1}{2}\right)^N \tag{1}$$

This is the general formula for a symmetrical binomial distribution.

Character of the Symmetrical Binomial Distribution. A graph of the probabilities given in Table 19 is presented in Fig. 95.   It will be noted from the table and also from the figure that the probability of 0 heads is the same as the probability of 10 heads, that the probability of 1 head is the same as the probability of 9 heads, etc.   In other words, the distribution of probabilities is symmetrical about a central point, in this case the point representing 5 heads.   This symmetry is the reason for the name "symmetrical" binomial distribution.

Mathematical analysis shows that in general the symmetrical binomial distribution has the following characteristics:[3]

$$\left.\begin{array}{c} \text{Mean} = \dfrac{N}{2} \\[2mm] \sigma = \sqrt{\dfrac{N}{4}} \\[2mm] \beta_1 = 0 \\[2mm] \beta_2 = 3 - \dfrac{2}{N} \end{array}\right\} \tag{2}$$

[1] *Cf.* p. 234.
[2] *Ibid.*
[3] These formulas are derived in Smith and Duncan, *Sampling Statistics*, pp. 65–67.

It will be sufficient to check these equations here by finding the mean, standard deviation, β_1, and β_2 of the distribution of Table 19.

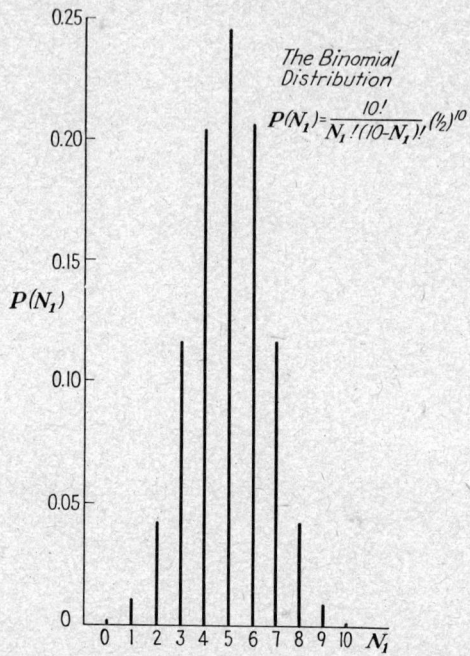

Fig. 95.—Graph of a symmetrical binomial distribution.

The mean of a distribution of probability, it will be recalled, is equal to the sum of the attributes times their probabilities.[1] The mean of the distribution of Table 19 is thus

$$\frac{1}{1,024}(0) + \frac{10}{1,024}(1) + \frac{45}{1,024}(2) + \frac{120}{1,024}(3) + \frac{210}{1,024}(4)$$

$$+ \frac{252}{1,024}(5) + \frac{210}{1,024}(6) + \frac{120}{1,024}(7) + \frac{45}{1,024}(8) + \frac{10}{1,024}(9)$$

$$+ \frac{1}{1,024}(10) = 5$$

According to the formula, the mean equals $N/2 = \frac{10}{2} = 5$, which is the same value as that derived above by direct calculation.

Similarly, the variance of a distribution of probability is equal to the sum of the deviations from the mean squared and multi-

[1] See p. 169.

plied by their probabilities. Hence, the variance of the distribution of Table 19 is

$$\frac{1}{1,024}(-5)^2 + \frac{10}{1,024}(-4)^2 + \frac{45}{1,024}(-3)^2 + \frac{120}{1,024}(-2)^2$$

$$+ \frac{210}{1,024}(-1)^2 + \frac{252}{1,024}(0)^2 + \frac{210}{1,024}(1)^2 + \frac{120}{1,024}(2)^2$$

$$+ \frac{45}{1,024}(3)^2 + \frac{10}{1,024}(4)^2 + \frac{1}{1,024}(5)^2 = 2.5$$

This again checks with the formula, which gives $\sigma^2 = N/4 = 2.5$.

Likewise, the third moment about the mean of a probability distribution is the sum of the deviations from the mean cubed and multiplied by their probabilities, and the fourth moment is the sum of the deviations from the mean raised to the fourth power and multiplied by their probabilities. Thus, for the distribution of Table 19,

$$\mu_3 = \frac{1}{1,024}(-5)^3 + \frac{10}{1,024}(-4)^3 + \frac{45}{1,024}(-3)^3$$

$$+ \frac{120}{1,024}(-2)^3 + \frac{210}{1,024}(-1)^3 + \frac{252}{1,024}(0)^3 + \frac{210}{1,024}(1)^3$$

$$+ \frac{120}{1,024}(2)^3 + \frac{45}{1,024}(3)^3 + \frac{10}{1,024}(4)^3 + \frac{1}{1,024}(5)^3 = 0$$

and

$$\mu_4 = \frac{1}{1,024}(-5)^4 + \frac{10}{1,024}(-4)^4 + \frac{45}{1,024}(-3)^4$$

$$+ \frac{120}{1,024}(-2)^4 + \frac{210}{1,024}(-1)^4 + \frac{252}{1,024}(0)^4 + \frac{210}{1,024}(1)^4$$

$$+ \frac{120}{1,024}(2)^4 + \frac{45}{1,024}(3)^4 + \frac{10}{1,024}(4)^4 + \frac{1}{1,024}(5)^4 = 17.5$$

Since, by definition, $\beta_1 = \mu_3^2/\mu_2^3$ and $\beta_2 = \mu_4/\mu_2^2$, it follows that for this distribution β_1 is zero and $\beta_2 = \dfrac{17.5}{(2.5)^2} = 2.8$, which are the values again given by the general formulas. These formulas are valid for all symmetrical binomial distributions.

The Normal Curve. If 40 instead of 10 coins were involved, the distribution of probability would be considerably more spread out than that of Table 19. This is readily seen from

Fig. 96.   In general, the formula $\sigma = \sqrt{N/4}$ indicates that the dispersion of the distribution increases in proportion to $\sqrt{N}$. If the horizontal scale is reduced, however, and the vertical scale enlarged, in the same proportion that the dispersion of the distribution is increased, then the effect of increasing N is to bring the ordinates of the distribution closer together and to raise them

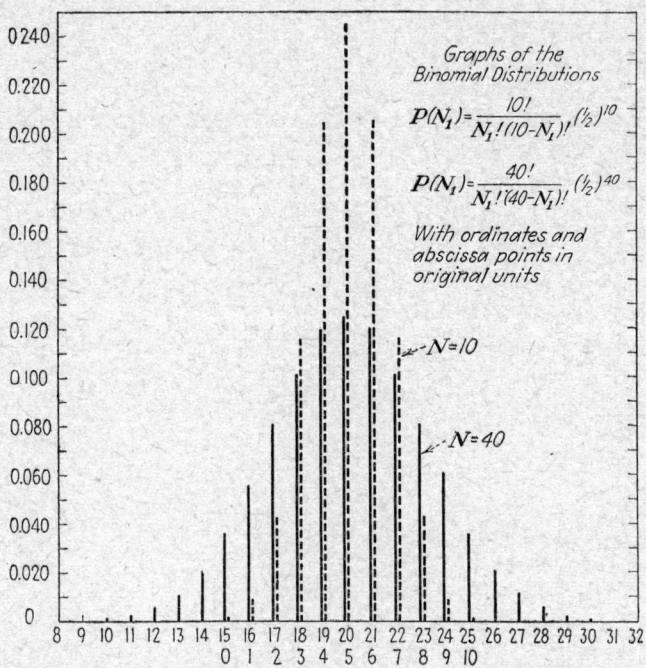

Graphs of the Binomial Distributions

$$P(N_1) = \frac{10!}{N_1!(10-N_1)!}(\tfrac{1}{2})^{10}$$

$$P(N_1) = \frac{40!}{N_1!(40-N_1)!}(\tfrac{1}{2})^{40}$$

With ordinates and abscissa points in original units

FIG. 96.—Graphs of two symmetrical binomial distributions, one for $N = 10$, the other for $N = 40$.

to the height of the original distribution.   Under these conditions the tops of the ordinates tend to sketch out a smooth curve as N is increased.   This is indicated in Fig. 97.   It can be shown that the limit that the symmetrical binomial distribution approaches as N is increased, while at the same time the scales are adjusted in proportion to $\sqrt{N}$, is the normal curve

$$y = \frac{1}{\sigma\sqrt{2\pi}} e^{\frac{-x^2}{2\sigma^2}}$$

That the symmetrical binomial distribution approaches the normal curve as a limit can be definitely proved by rigorous mathematical analysis.[1]   Certain general considerations, however, suggest this same conclusion.

1. The distributions of Figs. 95 to 97 have a shape similar to that of the normal curve; and if a normal curve with the same

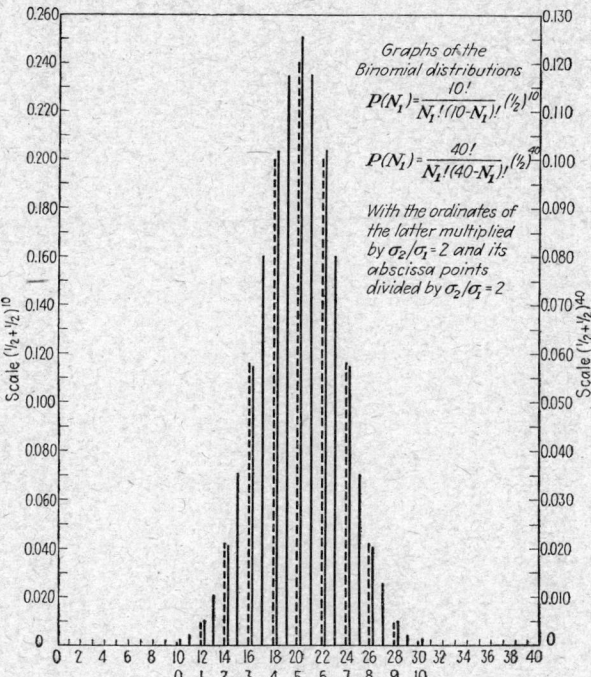

Fig. 97.—Illustration of effect of scale adjustments on a symmetrical binomial distribution.

mean as any one of these distributions and the same standard deviation is graphed together with that distribution, the curve is seen to be a good "fit."   This is shown[2] in Fig. 98.

---

[1] This is demonstrated in Smith and Duncan, *Sampling Statistics*, pp. 68–74.

[2] The binomial distribution is a discrete distribution, and its probabilities are correctly represented by a series of ordinates as in Figs. 96 and 97.   It is the ordinates of the normal curve of Fig. 98 at $1/\sigma$, $2/\sigma$, etc., and not sections of the curve area that approximate the binomial ordinates at these points.   As pointed out, however, in Smith and Duncan, *Sampling Statistics*, p. 74, it is possible to represent any symmetrical binomial distribution by a histogram whose area is approximated by that of a normal curve.   In this way the area tables of the normal curve can be used to approximate a series of binomial probabilities.

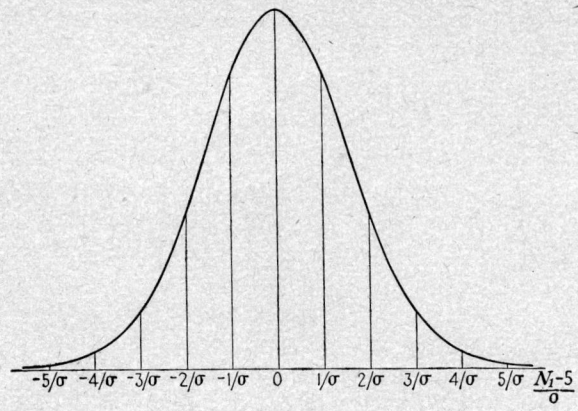

FIG. 98.—Comparison of a symmetrical binomial distribution with the normal curve.

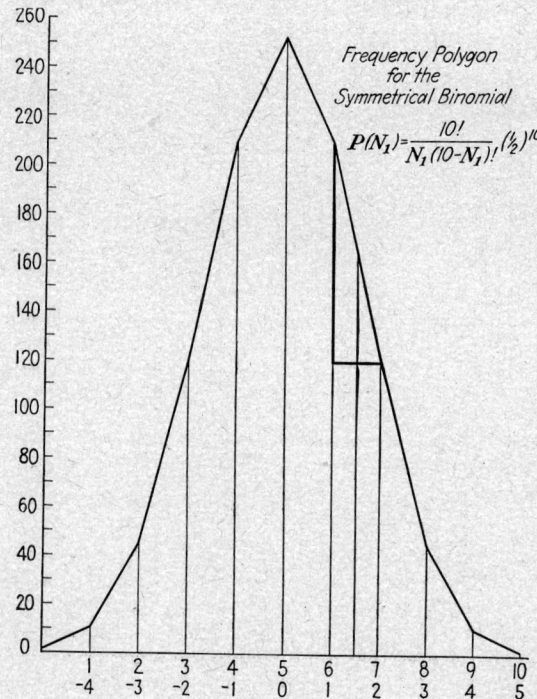

FIG. 99.—Graph illustrating computation of relative slope of frequency polygon at a given point.

2. Equations (2)* show that $\beta_1 = 0$ for the symmetrical binomial distribution and that β_2 approaches the value 3 as N is increased. These are also the values of β_1 and β_2 for the normal curve.

3. If a graph is made of the symmetrical binomial distribution in the form of a frequency polygon, the relative slope of any side of this polygon at its mid-point is the same as the relative slope of a normal curve at that point. Figure 99 shows, for example, that for $N = 10$ the ordinate of the symmetrical binomial at $N_1 = 6$ is equal to $210/1{,}024$ and the ordinate at $N_1 = 7$ is $120/1{,}024$. The mid-point between 6 and 7 is 6.5, and the ordinate of the polygon at that point is

$$\frac{1}{2}\left(\frac{210}{1{,}024} + \frac{120}{1{,}024}\right) = \frac{165}{1{,}024}$$

The absolute slope of the polygon at this mid-point is given by the ratio of the difference between the ordinates at 7 and 6 (that is $\dfrac{120}{1{,}024} - \dfrac{210}{1{,}024} = -\dfrac{90}{1{,}024}$) to the distance between the abscissa points 6 and 7 (that is, $7 - 6 = 1$); and the relative slope at the mid-point is given by the ratio of the absolute slope to the ordinate at that point. Thus, the relative slope of the polygon of Fig. 99 at the mid-point 6.5 is

$$\left(\frac{-\dfrac{90}{1{,}024}}{\dfrac{165}{1{,}024}}\right) = -\frac{90}{165} = -0.545$$

In general, the relative slope of a symmetrical binomial distribution at any mid-point $N_1 + \dfrac{1}{2}$ is equal[1] to $\dfrac{-2\left(N_1 + \dfrac{1}{2} - \dfrac{N}{2}\right)}{\dfrac{N+1}{2}}$.

If x is set equal to $N_1 + \dfrac{1}{2} - \dfrac{N}{2}$, that is, the deviation of the mid-point from the mean $\dfrac{N}{2}$, and if $2k^2$ is set equal to $\dfrac{N+1}{2}$,

---

* Page 283.

[1] See SMITH and DUNCAN, *Sampling Statistics*, pp. 74–76.

this expression for the relative slope at point x becomes $-\dfrac{2x}{2k^2}$ or

$-\dfrac{x}{k^2}$. But it can be shown[1] by the differential calculus that the relative slope of the normal curve at any point x is $-x/\sigma^2$, where $x = X - \bar{X}$. Hence the relative slope of the symmetrical binomial distribution at any mid-point is the same as that of a normal curve whose standard deviation is equal to $k = \sqrt{\dfrac{N+1}{4}}$, which, if N is large, is practically the same as the standard deviation of the symmetrical binomial distribution.[2]

CONDITIONS PRODUCING THE SYMMETRICAL BINOMIAL AND THE NORMAL CURVE IN REAL LIFE

The foregoing sections have been devoted to the derivation and description of a particular frequency distribution known as the binomial distribution. The analysis has consisted entirely of an application of the probability calculus, and the result is an abstract distribution of probability. Since the ultimate purpose of the analysis is an explanation of some of the frequency distributions of real life, it is desirable at this point to consider the question: What is the relationship between the symmetrical binomial distribution and a frequency distribution of real life?

Consider first the following hypothetical experiment: Suppose that the 10 coins referred to in the theoretical discussion are tossed a large number of times and the relative frequencies with which they come up 0, 1, 2, . . . , 10 heads are computed. What will be the results? Actually, no precise prediction can be made. Intuition suggests, however, that, if the coins are symmetrical and are tossed in an unbiased fashion, the relative frequencies with which the combinations 0, 1, 2, . . . , 10 heads will appear will be close to the probabilities of these combinations among the whole set of combinations that could be made from 10 coins. For if coins are tossed at random, it is to be expected that a head will appear on any one coin as often as a tail. The randomness also ensures that the appearance of a head on one coin will be independent of the appearance of a head or a tail on any other coin. Under these conditions it would seem likely

---

[1] *Ibid.*

[2] See Eqs. (2), p. 283.

that any particular arrangement of heads and tails would occur just as often as any other arrangement. Therefore, the relative number of times 3 heads and 7 tails would appear, for example, would be equal to the relative number of arrangements that would yield 3 heads and 7 tails out of the set of all possible arrangements. This is the relative frequency of the binomial distribution. Intuition thus suggests the results of random coin tossing will be closely approximated by the binomial frequencies. Actual experiments lend support to this argument, so that it would seem possible to predict the results of a large number of tossings by the use of the probability calculus. This is merely an application of the law of large numbers.

The relationship between the results of coin tossing and the binomial probabilities suggests even more important inferences. For there may be conditions in real life that are similar to those involved in the tossing of coins, and statistical variables produced by these conditions may be expected to follow the symmetrical binomial distribution and in special instances the normal curve. To illustrate the conditions that might give rise to such results consider the following examples:

Example 1. Suppose that the sex of the offspring of a certain animal is determined by the type of the egg cell in the female that unites with the sperm cell of the male, and suppose that the number of egg cells in the female that will produce male offspring is on the average equal to the number of egg cells that will produce female offspring. If sperm cells unite with egg cells in a random manner, the chance is $\frac{1}{2}$ of an offspring being a male and $\frac{1}{2}$ of its being a female. These are essentially the same conditions that determine whether a symmetrical coin should turn up heads or tails when tossed at random. Under such conditions the frequency distribution of the number of males in families of a given size should theoretically follow the symmetrical binomial distribution. Thus families of size 5 should be expected to vary in sex combination as follows:

Number of Males	Percentage of Families Having Specified Number of Males
0	$\frac{1}{32} = 0.03$
1	$\frac{5}{32} = 0.16$
2	$\frac{10}{32} = 0.31$
3	$\frac{10}{32} = 0.31$
4	$\frac{5}{32} = 0.16$
5	$\frac{1}{32} = 0.03$

A study of the sex of pigs in 116 litters of 5 pigs each showed the following:

Number of Males	Percentage of Litters Having Specified Number of Males
0	0.02
1	0.17
2	0.35
3	0.30
4	0.12
5	0.03

The closeness of these figures to those above suggests that the theory of sex determination outlined above might very well be valid for pigs.

Example 2.   In Example 1, conditions were such as to produce a variable (number of males) that was discrete and integral.   The present hypothetical example will suggest conditions which might produce a variable that was discrete but not integral and that was distributed in the form of a symmetrical binomial.   It also suggests conditions under which the variable might be practically continuous and distributed like a normal curve.

Suppose that there are a large number of bags of flour, say 10,000, each weighing exactly 5 pounds.   Suppose that an experimenter opens each bag in succession and adds or subtracts a certain quantity of flour to each bag in accordance with the following rule: Whenever he opens a bag, he also tosses 10 coins.   For each head that appears he adds an ounce of flour to the bag; for each tail, he subtracts an ounce.   The result of this procedure will be 10,000 bags of flour varying in weight from 5 pounds − 10 ounces to 5 pounds + 10 ounces, the unit difference being 2 ounces.   In accordance with the foregoing analysis, the distribution of the weights of these bags of flour would be approximately as follows:

Weight of Bag	Relative Frequency of Occurrence
4 lb. 6 oz.	1/1,024
4 lb. 8 oz.	10/1,024
4 lb. 10 oz.	45/1,024
4 lb. 12 oz.	120/1,024
4 lb. 14 oz.	210/1,024
5 lb. 0 oz.	252/1,024
5 lb. 2 oz.	210/1,024
5 lb. 4 oz.	120/1,024
5 lb. 6 oz.	45/1,024
5 lb. 8 oz.	10/1,024
5 lb. 10 oz.	1/1,024

In other words, the distribution of weights would approximately conform to a symmetrical binomial distribution with a mean weight of 5 pounds and a standard deviation of $2.5 \times 2 = 5$ ounces.

This shows how a variable may be produced that is discrete but not integral and that is distributed in the form of a symmetrical binomial distribution.   To produce a variable that is practically continuous, it is necessary to increase the number of coins from 10 to 100, say, and to reduce the amount of flour added or subtracted to 0.01 ounce.   Differences as small as 0.02 ounce would thus be possible, and for all practical purposes the weight of a bag of flour could be said to be continuous. Under these conditions a graph of the distributions of weights would be practically continuous and as indicated in the theoretical discussion would have the form of a normal frequency curve.

Example 3. Example 2 was entirely hypothetical. An apparatus has been constructed, however (see Fig. 100), that reproduces in somewhat different form the conditions of Example 2. By its use the results predicted in Example 2 can be concretely illustrated.

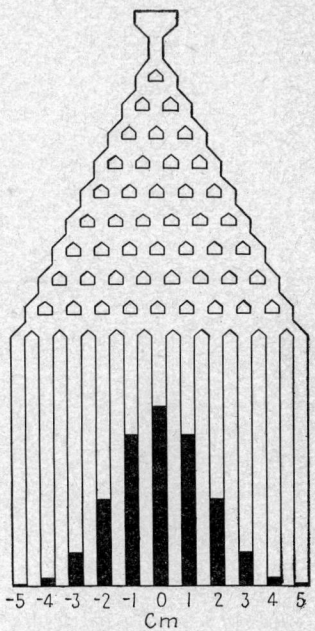

The apparatus of Fig. 100 was devised many years ago by Sir Francis Galton and subsequently elaborated by Karl Pearson.[1] As represented in Fig. 100 it consists of a series of rows of wedges, each row containing an additional wedge and so arranged that its wedges come halfway between the wedges of the row above. If the wedges are placed 1 centimeter apart, then a small ball dropped into the top of the machine will have an equal chance in each row of being deflected 0.5 centimeter either to the left or the right. The apparatus of Fig. 100 has 10 rows. The final deviation of the ball from the central point O will thus be the algebraic sum of the left (minus) and right (plus) deflections as it falls through the 10 rows. The possible range

Fig. 100.—The Pearson-Galton apparatus for physical derivation of a binomial distribution.

of this final deviation is from -5 to $+5$ centimeters. Since the probability of a plus and minus deviation of 0.5 centimeter is in each row equal to $\frac{1}{2}$ (similar to the probability of a head and a tail for a coin) and since there are 10 rows (as there were 10 coins in the previous case), the probabilities of final deviations of -5, -4, -3, -2, -1, 0, $+1$, $+2$, $+3$, $+4$, $+5$ centimeters will be the same as those of the binomial distribution,

$$P(N_1) = \frac{10!}{N_1!(10 - N_1)!}\left(\frac{1}{2}\right)^{10}$$

which are given in Table 19, page 282.

[1] GALTON, FRANCIS, *Natural Inheritance* (Macmillan & Company, Ltd., London, 1889), p. 63; PEARSON, KARL, "Skew Variation in Homogeneous Material," *Philosophical Transactions of the Royal Society of London*, Series A, Vol. 186 (1895), p. 343. Pearson's contribution was to replace the set of nails used by Galton by a set of sliding wedges that could be so adjusted that the chances of deflection to the left and right were not equal. Figure 100 follows the pattern of Galton's apparatus.

These are the theoretical probabilities of the apparatus. If a large number of balls are actually dropped into the machine, the exact result cannot be predicted. Intuition suggests, however, that the relative frequencies with which the balls will pile up in the different slots will tend to approximate the theoretical probabilities and this is demonstrated by actual experiments. Such a result is pictured in Fig. 100 by the shading of the slots in proportion to the binomial probabilities.

It will be noted that in this case the variable, that is, the final deviation of a ball from the central point O is again discrete. Deviations of integral centimeters only are possible. If, however, the number of rows were increased from 10 to 1,000, say, and if at the same time the wedges were reduced to 0.01 centimeter in size and placed so that they were only 0.01 centimeter apart (the balls would, of course, have to be correspondingly reduced in size), then the final deviations would vary by 0.01 centimeter and might be practically considered a continuous variable. The distribution of relative frequencies would in this case closely approximate a smooth frequency curve, which would once again be the normal curve.

Theory of Errors. Errors in physical measurements may be broken up into several components. (1) The "instrumental error" may be attributed to the particular instrument with which the measurement is made; every measurement by it will contain a certain error that may be assigned to that instrument. (2) The "personal error" may be attributed to the particular person undertaking the measurement; every observation by him will be influenced by his "personal equation." (3) Another component error may be attributed to particular external conditions, such as the temperature, sunlight, and wind. These errors due to the instrument, the observer, and specific external conditions are all "systematic errors" that can be allowed for. (4) A final component error is the "incidental error," or "residual error," to which no definite cause can be assigned. Such errors are the result of the whole host of chance forces, the same sort of forces that determine whether an unbiased coin comes up heads or tails. The total accidental error in any individual measurement may be taken to be the sum of a number of small accidental errors arising from different causes.[1] Slight irregular changes in external conditions, such as the vibration on account of air currents or irregular changes in the personal equation of the observer, are examples of causes for accidental error of measurement. If it is possible to discover the law of action of any error, it is thereby removed from the class of accidental errors to the class of systematic errors.

If the number of forces affecting the residual errors in any series of measurements is large, if each causes a very small plus or minus deviation from the true value, and if the probability of a plus and a minus deviation is for each force equal to $\frac{1}{2}$, then, as in the case of the flour-bag experiment and the Pearson-Galton apparatus, the final residual errors of the series of measurements will tend to be distributed in accordance with the normal curve. The mean of this curve will be the true value (after allowance has

---

[1] See BRUNT, DAVID, *The Combinations of Observations*, pp. 3–4.

been made, of course, for the systematic errors mentioned above), and the standard deviation of the curve will be an index of the precision of measurement. This is the theory of errors.[1] It is supported by the close agreement between the normal curve and distributions of actual measurements. In fact, the normal curve is often spoken of as the "error curve" or the "Gaussian error curve," after the man who was among the first to recognize the possibility of applying the theory of probability to the investigation of the errors of measurement.[2]

Summary of Conditions Leading to the Symmetrical Binomial Distribution and the Normal Curve. The foregoing examples suggest that whenever the following conditions exist in real life, the data generated by these conditions will tend to be distributed in the form of a symmetrical binomial distribution and, if certain other conditions are also present, in the form of a normal curve. The conditions giving rise to the symmetrical binomial distribution may be stated as follows:

1. In the absence of certain "causes" of variation or in the event of a perfect balancing of their effects, the data assume a fixed central value. (The 5 pounds of the flour illustration, the "true value" in a series of measurements.)

2. Deviations from this central value result from certain "causes" of variation, the effect of any "cause" being either to add a fixed quantity to the data or to subtract the same quantity. (To add or subtract 1 ounce of flour or to add or subtract an "error" of 0.5 centimeter.)

3. A "cause" of variation tends to produce positive effects and negative effects in equal proportion, that is, $P(+) = P(-) = \frac{1}{2}$. (The probability of a head equals the probability of a tail; the probability of a positive error equals the probability of a negative error.)

4. The effects of all contributory causes of variation are of equal magnitude. (Each adds or subtracts 1 ounce of flour or 0.5 centimeter.)

---

[1] Actually this is a special case of a more general statement of the theory. As pointed out in Smith and Duncan, *Sampling Statistics*, p. 97, each force may cause deviations of varying size with varying probabilities and the final residual errors will still tend to be normally distributed provided that the number of forces is very large and the relative importance of each is about the same.

[2] For Gauss's fundamental works see *Abhandlungen zur Methode der kleinsten Quadrate* (A. Borsch and P. Simon, Berlin, 1887).

5. The contributory causes are independent in their action. In other words, the contribution of a positive or negative effect by any causal factor is independent of the previous contributions of other causal factors.

6. The total deviation of any element from its central value is the algebraic sum of the positive and negative contributions of the individual causal factors.　(The total amount of flour added or subtracted from a bag is the sum of the ounces added for each head tossed minus the ounces subtracted for each tail tossed.)

If in addition to these conditions, the following also exist, then the resulting distribution will tend to conform to the normal curve:

7. The number of contributory causes is very large. (A large number of coins are tossed; the binomial machine contains a large number of rows.)

8. The positive and negative contributions of each cause are very small. (If 0.01 ounce is added or subtracted instead of 1 ounce; if 0.005 centimeter, instead of 0.5 centimeter.)

It is to be noted that, so far as the normal curve is concerned, not all these conditions are necessary for its generation. The above conditions will produce it, but the normal curve may also occur when some of these conditions are absent.[1] It may be stated here that the normal curve will still be produced if conditions 2 and 3 are relaxed so that a causal factor may affect the data in varying degree and with varying probabilities and also if condition 4 is only approximately and not exactly true.[2] The most important conditions are 6 to 8 and condition 4 in an approximate form. For example, in the case of the flour illustration, the resulting weights of the bags of flours would still tend to be normally distributed even if biased dice instead of unbiased coins were used and if the amount of flour added or subtracted varied with the result of the throw (say 0.001 ounce for the occurrence of a one, −0.002 ounce for the occurrence of a two, 0.003 ounce for the occurrence of a three, −0.004 for the occurrence of a four, etc.) provided that the number of dice thrown was very large and the amount added or subtracted per die was very small and of about the same order of magnitude from die to

---

[1] See SMITH and DUNCAN, *Sampling Statistics*, pp. 97–100.

[2] Under certain conditions the requirement of independence (condition 5) may also be relaxed. See SMITH and DUNCAN, *Sampling Statistics*, pp. 63–65.

die.   The normal curve is thus a more general phenomenon than the symmetrical binomial distribution.[1]

Examples of Normal Frequency Distributions.   Natural forces appear to generate normal frequency distributions in many fields. Physical measurements have already been mentioned.   Figure 101 shows the distribution of heights of 300 eighteen-year-old Princeton freshmen.   The grades of students on examinations, hourly earnings of workers, the length of life of electric-light bulbs, the distance of baseball throws of first-year high-school girls are all normally distributed variables.   In these fields and in many others, it would seem that the conditions of variation are those which theoretically give rise to the normal curve.

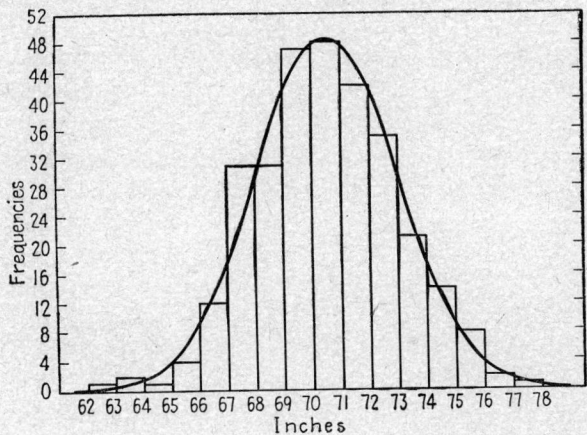

Fig. 101.—Normal curve fitted to heights of 300 Princeton freshmen.

DETERMINATION OF NORMALITY

Several procedures are available for determining whether the population from which a given set of sample data has been taken might reasonably be considered to conform to the normal curve. In general, these consist of comparing the histogram constructed from the sample data with a normal curve "fitted" to this histogram.   The difference in the various procedures lies in the bases

[1] Mathematically the normal curve can be derived from a great variety of different assumptions.   See, for example, Czuber, Emanuel, *Theorie der Biobachtungsfeller* (B. G. Teubner, Leipzig, 1891).

of comparison. Several of the more important procedures will now be discussed.

Graphic Comparison. The simplest method of determining whether the assumption of normality is or is not reasonable is to graph the histogram and normal curve together and see how well the curve fits. The test here is purely a subjective one, but in many cases when the fit is exceptionally good or exceptionally bad this is probably sufficient for acceptance or rejection of the hypothesis.

In making a graphic comparison of a sample histogram and a normal curve, it is necessary to determine what mean and what standard deviation should be assigned to the curve. Offhand the simplest procedure would appear to be the assignment to the curve of the mean and standard deviation of the histogram, for presumably these are the best estimates that may be made of the mean and standard deviation of the population from which the sample was taken.[1] It will be recalled, however, that in the calculation of the mean and standard deviation of the histogram the data were distributed among various classes or groups and all the cases in any class interval were assumed to be concentrated at the mid-point of the interval. But the population is presumably distributed in the form of a smooth curve, so that, in estimating its mean and standard deviation from that of the histogram, allowance must be made for the grouping of the data in the construction of the histogram. In any interval a smooth bell-shaped curve, such as the normal curve, will have more cases that are on the side toward the mean than on the side away from the mean. The assumption that all cases are concentrated at the mid-point of an interval will not cause any appreciable error in the mean calculated from grouped data, for plus and minus deviations will offset each other; but it will cause the standard deviation of the grouped data to be greater than the standard deviation of the smooth curve that represents the true distribution of the data. Some adjustment should therefore be made in the standard deviation of the histogram before it is taken as an estimate of the standard deviation of the population.

The adjustment that must be made for grouping has been determined by W. F. Sheppard. He has shown that under conditions that are true for a normal distribution the variance

[1] *Cf.* pp. 318 and 319.

σ^2 of the smooth curve is approximately equal to the variance of the grouped data minus one-twelfth the square of the class interval.[1] In other words, if μ_2 (uncorrected) is the second moment ($= \sigma^2$) of the grouped data about its mean and μ_2 is the second moment of the smooth curve about its mean, then

$$\mu_2 = \mu_2 \text{ (uncorrected)} - \tfrac{1}{12}(i)^2$$

The quantity $\tfrac{1}{12}(i)^2$ is *Sheppard's correction* for grouping that is required for estimating the standard deviation of the fitted normal curve.

In fitting a normal curve to a sample histogram, therefore, the mean of the curve is taken equal to the mean of the histogram and the variance of the curve is taken equal to the variance of the histogram minus $\tfrac{1}{12}(i)^2$. In plotting the curve a table of the ordinates of the standard normal curve may conveniently be used. If the histogram to which the curve is to be fitted is of the usual type, that is, if it consists of a series of rectangles of which the heights measure aggregate frequencies and if the intervals on which these rectangles are erected are laid off in terms of original X units, then ordinates of the standard normal curve can be taken to represent the particular normal curve desired by making certain simple adjustments. The ordinates of the standard normal curve, it will be recalled, are given for values of X that are measured from the mean of the distribution and are expressed in terms of standard deviation units. It will also be recalled that the area of the curve over any given interval measures the relative frequency of cases falling in this interval. To make these ordinates represent a normal curve with a given mean and a given standard deviation, they need only be plotted so that the ordinate for $X = 0$ comes at the specified mean value and ordinates for other values of X come at $X = \bar{X} \pm x$. To put them on the same basis as the histogram, however, they must also all be multiplied by Ni/σ. This is because the total area of the histogram[2] is Ni and that of the standard normal curve is 1 (that is, 100 per cent), whereas the abscissa scale on which the histogram is plotted is σ times the abscissa scale of the standard curve. This use of the ordinates of the standard normal curve

---

[1] *Cf. Proceedings of the London Mathematical Society*, Vol. 29, 353–380.

[2] The area of any one rectangle is Fi, and the total area is therefore $\Sigma Fi = Ni$.

may be illustrated by fitting a normal curve to the heights of 300 Princeton freshmen.

In Table 20 the mid-points of the various class intervals into which the 300 heights were distributed are set down in column (1). In column (2) the difference between these mid-points and the mean of the distribution ($\bar{X} = 70.47$) is computed, and in column (3) this is divided by the adjusted standard deviation. The results are the various values of x/σ that correspond to the mid-points of the various class intervals. The ordinates of the standard normal curve at these values of x/σ are then computed from Table VII (see Appendix, page 694) and entered in column (4). Finally, in column (5), these standard ordinates are multiplied by $\dfrac{Ni}{\sigma} = \dfrac{(300)(1)}{2.47} = 121.46$ to put them on a par with the sample histogram.

χ^2 *Test of Goodness of Fit.* Another method of comparing a sample histogram with a normal curve is to compare the frequencies given by the two, interval by interval. Whereas the previous method was primarily subjective in that a conclusion had to be reached from a mere inspection of the two graphs, comparison of the histogram and the curve, interval by interval, yields a numerical criterion of "goodness of fit." A procedure that has found favor because it permits a comparison with chance results is to take the difference between the absolute frequencies[1] given by the curve and by the histogram for each interval, square these differences, divide each by the frequency of the curve for that interval, and finally sum the results. The quantity so calculated may be represented by $\sum \dfrac{(F - f)^2}{f}$, where F represents for each class interval the frequency given by the histogram and f the frequency given by the curve.

Sampling theory shows[2] that, if this quantity is calculated for a large number (theoretically, an infinite number) of sample histograms from the same normal population, then the distribution of these various sample values of $\sum \dfrac{(F - f)^2}{f}$ will be adequately represented by a probability curve known as the "χ^2 curve" and this can be used to determine the probability of a larger value of

---

[1] For the curve, this means the relative frequencies times N, the total number of cases in the sample.

[2] On the χ^2 distribution see Smith and Duncan, *Sampling Statistics*, pp. 111–112 and Chap. XIII.

TABLE 20.—CALCULATION OF THE ORDINATES OF THE NORMAL CURVE THAT FITS THE DISTRIBUTION OF HEIGHTS OF 300 PRINCETON FRESHMEN

(1)	(2)	(3)	(4)	(5)
X	$X - \bar{X} = x$	$\dfrac{X - \bar{X}}{\sigma}$	Ordinate of standard curve	Col. (4) $\times \dfrac{Ni}{\sigma}$
62.5	−7.97	−3.22	0.00224	0.27
63.5	−6.97	−2.82	0.00748	0.91
64.5	−5.97	−2.42	0.02134	2.59
65.5	−4.97	−2.01	0.05292	6.43
66.5	−3.97	−1.59	0.11270	13.69
67.5	−2.97	−1.19	0.19652	23.87
68.5	−1.97	−0.80	0.28969	35.19
69.5	−0.97	−0.39	0.36973	44.91
70.5	0.03	−0.01	0.39892	48.45
71.5	1.03	0.42	0.36526	44.36
72.5	2.03	0.82	0.28504	34.62
73.5	3.03	1.22	0.18954	23.02
74.5	4.03	1.63	0.10567	12.83
75.5	5.03	2.04	0.04980	6.05
76.5	6.03	2.44	0.02033	2.47
77.5	7.03	2.84	0.00707	0.86

$$\bar{X} = 70.47 \qquad \sigma \text{ (corrected)} = 2.47$$

$\sum \dfrac{(F - f)^2}{f}$ by chance. If the probability is a large one, then the difference between the given sample histogram and the normal curve, as measured by $\sum \dfrac{(F - f)^2}{f}$, may reasonably be attributed to chance; the curve may be deemed a good fit, and the population from which the sample was drawn may tentatively be taken as normal. If the probability is very small, however, say less than 0.05, then the difference between the histogram and the curve is to be attributed to something else than chance, presumably to the nonnormality of the population from which the sample was drawn. In this case, the normal curve is not deemed a good fit, and the hypothesis of a normal population is rejected. Owing to its use of the χ^2 curve, this second method of comparison is called the "χ^2 test of goodness of fit."

The χ^2 test may be illustrated, as in the previous case, by the distribution of heights of 300 Princeton freshmen. The numerical calculations involved are set forth in Table 21. In column (1) are put the upper limits (not the mid-points in this case) of the various class intervals of the histogram of heights, the first and last intervals being considered to run to $-\infty$ and $+\infty$, respectively. The deviations of these class-interval limits from the mean of the distribution are calculated in column (2), and their ratio to the "corrected" standard deviation is computed in column (3). In column (4) are written the areas under the standard normal curve from its lower limit $(-\infty)$ to each of these class-interval limits, now measured in standard-deviation units. These areas are obtained from Table VI, page 693, of the Appendix. The figure in column (4) already gives the area for the first interval $(-\infty$ to 63), and the areas for the other intervals can be computed by taking the difference between the area under the curve up to one class limit and the area up to the next higher class limit. These differences are written in column (5). In order to avoid very small areas in the extreme intervals (and hence a distortion of the test[1]), several groups at each end are amalgamated so that the areas for the first and last interval are at least equal to $5/N$.

The new arrangement is indicated in columns (1′) and (5′). Now it will be noted that the figures of column (5′) represent the relative frequencies given by the curve. To convert them to aggregate frequencies that are comparable with the aggregate frequencies of the histogram, it is necessary to multiply them by N $(= 300)$, the total number of cases. This is done in column (6). In column (7) are written the histogram frequencies for the intervals of column (1′), and in the remaining columns the differences between the histogram and curve frequencies are computed, squared, and divided by the curve frequencies. The sum of the last column is the value of $\sum \frac{(F - f)^2}{f}$ desired. In the present instance this is found to be 3.867.

To determine whether the value of $\sum \frac{(F - f)^2}{f} = 3.867$ represents a good fit or not, turn to Table 22. Here are given certain critical values for the statistic $\sum \frac{(F - f)^2}{f}$. The n of

[1] See *ibid.*, p. 140.

Table 21.—Calculation of $\sum \frac{(F-f)^2}{f}$ for the Heights of 300 Princeton Freshmen

(1) X	(2) $X - \bar{X}$	(3) $\frac{X - \bar{X}}{\sigma}$	(4)* Area from $-\infty$	(5) Area for each interval	(1')	(5')	(6) Aggregate curve frequencies $(5')N = f$	(7) Histogram frequencies F	(8) $F - f$	(9) $(F - f)^2$	(10) $\frac{(F - f)^2}{f}$
—63	−7.47	−3.02	0.00130	0.00130							
—64	−6.47	−2.62	0.00440	0.00310							
—65	−5.47	−2.22	0.01321	0.00881							
—66	−4.47	−1.81	0.03515	0.02194	$-\infty$ to 66	0.03515	10.55	8	−2.55	6.5025	0.616
—67	−3.47	−1.41	0.07927	0.04412	66 to 67	0.04412	13.24	12	−1.24	1.5376	0.116
—68	−2.47	−1.00	0.15866	0.07939	67 to 68	0.07939	23.82	31	7.18	51.5524	2.164
—69	−1.47	−0.60	0.27425	0.11559	68 to 69	0.11559	34.68	31	−3.68	13.5424	0.391
—70	−0.47	−0.19	0.42465	0.15040	69 to 70	0.15040	45.12	47	1.88	3.5344	0.078
—71	0.53	0.22	0.58706	0.16241	70 to 71	0.16241	48.72	48	−0.72	0.5184	0.011
—72	1.53	0.62	0.73237	0.14531	71 to 72	0.14531	43.59	42	−1.59	2.5281	0.058
—73	2.53	1.02	0.84614	0.11377	72 to 73	0.11377	34.13	35	0.87	0.7569	0.022
—74	3.53	1.43	0.92364	0.07750	73 to 74	0.07750	23.25	21	−2.25	5.0625	0.218
—75	4.53	1.83	0.96638	0.04274	74 to 75	0.04274	12.82	14	1.18	1.3924	0.109
—76	5.53	2.24	0.98745	0.02107	75 to ∞	0.03362	10.08	11	0.92	0.8464	0.084
—77	6.53	2.64	0.99585	0.00840							
			1.00000	0.00415							

$$\sum \frac{(F - f)^2}{f} = 3.867$$

*The items in this column are obtained by subtracting from 0.50000 the figures found for each $-(X - \bar{X})/\sigma$ and by adding to 0.50000 the figures found for each $+(X - \bar{X})/\sigma$ in Table VI of the Appendix, p. 693.

the first column is equal to the number of class intervals minus 3.[1]
The figures in the second column represent values of $\sum \dfrac{(F - f)^2}{f}$
for which there is a probability of 0.05 that an equal or greater
value would be obtained by mere chance. For example, in the
present instance, $n = 11 - 3 = 8$, and Table 22 shows that, if
the data were truly normal, sample values for $\sum \dfrac{(F - f)^2}{f}$ that
were equal to or greater than 15.51 would be obtained only
5 times out of 100 for such a value of n. Since the computed
value of $\sum \dfrac{(F - f)^2}{f} = 3.867$, the chances of an equal or greater

TABLE 22.—CRITICAL VALUES FOR $\sum \dfrac{(F - f)^2}{f}$[*]

n	Values of $\sum \dfrac{(F - f)^2}{f}$ for Which the Probability of an Equal or Greater Value Is Just 0.05
1	3.84
2	5.99
3	7.81
4	9.49
5	11.07
6	12.59
7	14.07
8	15.51
9	16.92
10	18.31
11	19.67
12	21.03
13	22.36
14	23.68
15	25.00
16	26.30
17	27.59
18	28.87
19	30.14
20	31.41

[*] Abridged from Table III, Table of χ^2, in R. A. Fisher, *Statistical Methods for Research Workers*, Oliver & Boyd, Ltd., Edinburgh, by the kind permission of the publishers and author.

[1] See Smith and Duncan, *Sampling Statistics*, pp. 327–328, for an explanation of the significance of n in this case.

value is much more than 0.05.   Hence the curve is deemed a
good fit, and the distribution of heights may be said to be normal.

Comparison of Special Statistics.   Although the test just outlined is very commonly used, it has certain weaknesses as a test
of normality.   (1) It should be noted that the squaring of the
differences between the group frequencies removes any significance that might be attributed to the signs of the differences.
For example, it might happen in a given case that all the histogram frequencies to the left of the center were larger than the
normal curve frequencies and that all the histogram frequencies
to the right of the center were less than the normal curve frequencies, indicating a well-marked positive skewness; nevertheless, if the absolute values of these differences were all small, the
χ^2 test might not indicate any departure from normality.   (2)
The necessity of combining the extreme intervals into larger
groups causes a loss of information and reduces the number of
points of comparison.[1]   For these reasons, other methods of testing for normality have been proposed.

If a set of sample data actually has come from a normal population, it is to be expected that its skewness will be slight and its
kurtosis close to the normal kurtosis of 3.   It would also be
expected that the ratio of its average deviation to its standard
deviation would be somewhere in the neighborhood of the value of
this ratio for the normal curve (*i.e.*, 0.7979).   The departure of
the actual values of these sample statistics from the theoretical
values for the normal curve can thus be used as a test for normality.

For the 300 Princeton freshmen, β_1, β_2, and the ratio of average
deviation to standard deviation (indicated by the symbol a) had
the values[2] $\beta_1 = 0.023$, $\beta_2 = 3.021$, and $a = 0.805$.   These are

---

[1] Its practical effect is to reduce the value of n to be used in the χ^2 table.

[2] No account was taken of Sheppard's correction in computing these
values.   The average deviation used in making this test was computed from
the mean by the formula

$$\text{A.D.} = \frac{1}{N} \left[\sum \left| F\left(\frac{d}{i}\right) \right| + c(N_l - N_u) + N_0 \left(\frac{1}{4} + c^2\right) \right] i$$

where $c = \dfrac{\bar{X} - A}{i}$, N_l = number of cases in intervals below the arbitrary
origin, N_u = number of cases in intervals above the arbitrary origin, and
N_0 = number of cases in interval containing arbitrary origin.   (A must be
in the same interval as $\bar{X}$.)   *Cf.* GEARY, R. C., and E. S. PEARSON, *Tests of
Normality*, p. 4.

all very close to the values 0, 3, and 0.7979 of a truly normal distribution. Hence this last, as well as the other tests, suggests that heights are normally distributed.

Sometimes the sample values of β_1, β_2, and a are not so close to the normal values as in the foregoing illustration. In such instances, use may be made of tables published in *Tests of Normality*,[1] by R. C. Geary and E. S. Pearson. These tables give, for various-sized samples, the sample values of β_1, β_2, and a, for which the probability of a greater value is 0.05, and 0.01, respectively. For β_2 and a they also give values of these statistics for which the probability of a smaller value is 0.05 and 0.01, respectively. If, in any given instance, the sample value of β_1, β_2, or a falls outside the limits given for a probability of 0.05, say, then it may be concluded that the population from which the sample was drawn was not strictly normal. For the weights of the 300 Princeton freshmen, for example, the sample values of β_1 and β_2 were 0.378 and 4.606. Both these are beyond the 0.01 probability point given by Geary and Pearson's tables for a sample of 300 (these were 0.329 and 3.79, respectively), and it may therefore be concluded that the distribution of weights is definitely not normal.

[1] Issued by the Biometrika Office, University College, London, and printed at the University Press, Cambridge, England.

CHAPTER XII

USE OF THE NORMAL FREQUENCY CURVE IN SAMPLING ANALYSIS

The normal frequency curve has its greatest usefulness in the theory of random sampling.[1] While the full exposition of the theory of random sampling is beyond the scope of this book, some of the simpler aspects that relate to the use of the normal curve in sampling analysis are presented in the ensuing pages of this chapter.

SAMPLING FROM A TWOFOLD POPULATION

The Problem. An elementary problem in the theory of sampling is concerned with sampling from a twofold population. Consider the following problem: Suppose a large city is undergoing a fiercely contested election. The Radicals on the one hand and the Conservatives on the other are contending hotly for the mayoralty, and everyone in the city takes a stand on one side or the other. The voting population of the city thus forms a group in which a certain percentage are Radicals and a complementary percentage are Conservatives. Prior to the election these percentages will not be known. They may, however, be estimated by taking a random sample. The inferences that may be made from such a random sample constitute the statistical problem that will now be analyzed.

Sampling Distribution. For the sake of argument suppose that some omniscient being knew how each individual in the city stood politically. Suppose that he noted their positions on slips of paper—one for each individual—and put the slips into a large urn. Suppose, further, that there are actually an equal number of Radicals and Conservatives. Let the omniscient being mix the slips of paper thoroughly and then draw out a sample of 100 slips.[2]

---

[1] For more elaborate exposition than is contained in this chapter, see Smith and Duncan, *Sampling Statistics*, Parts II and III.

[2] Mundane methods of obtaining random samples are discussed in *ibid*.

Let him note the division of opinion for this sample, put the slips back, and thoroughly mix them again.   Finally, let him repeat this process many times, taking a sample of 100 each time, so that he eventually accumulates a large number of sample percentage divisions of opinion.   Many, but by no means all, of these sample percentages will be the actual population percentage of 50; the others will be distributed above and below the 50 per cent level. This will be the sampling distribution of the sample percentages.

It is one of the important conclusions of the probability theory, based upon the analysis of the preceding chapters,* that the outcome of this process of random sampling will be a set of samples in which the relative frequency of samples in which the division of opinion is 0 per cent Radical, 10 per cent Radical, 20 per cent Radical, 30 per cent Radical, . . . , 100 per cent Radical will be approximately the same as the probabilities of a binomial distribution in which $p_1 = 0.50$ and $p_2 = 0.50$ and $N = 100$.† In other words, relative frequencies of the sample percentages may be estimated a priori by means of the probability calculus. Furthermore, since the size of the sample is large ($N = 100$), the calculation of the probabilities can be simplified by using the normal curve as an approximation to the binomial distribution.‡ In this problem, the curve will have a mean of 50 per cent, because the population is equally divided between Radicals and Conservatives by hypothesis, and a standard deviation equal to 5 per cent.§   The normal curve, with a mean of 50 per cent and a standard deviation of 5 per cent, thus gives approximately the "sampling distribution" for sample percentages taken from a population in which the division of opinion is exactly 50 per cent; and this is the sampling distribution of sample percentages conceived in the preceding paragraph.

The foregoing result is not limited, however, to cases in which the actual division of opinion in the entire population is exactly

---

* See also *ibid.*

† When the symbol for a sample statistic is in boldface type, it refers to the corresponding population parameter; thus here p_1 and p_2 refer to the population values for which p_1 and p_2 are corresponding sample statistics.

‡ See pp. 283–290.

§ When the variable is expressed as a percentage instead of as an absolute deviation from an integral mean value, the formula for the standard deviation is $\sigma_{\text{per cent}} = \sqrt{(0.5)(0.5)/N}$.   *Cf.* p. 283.

fifty-fifty but may be shown to be valid for any division of opinion in the population.[1] Thus if the percentage of Radicals in the population is p_1 and the percentage of Conservatives is p_2 (where $p_1 + p_2 = 1$) and samples of size N are drawn at random from this population, with replacements as above, then the relative frequencies of various sample percentages of Radical opinion will be given approximately by the probabilities of a normal frequency curve whose mean is Np_1 and whose standard deviation is $\sqrt{p_1 p_2 / N}$.

This conclusion is of capital importance in making inferences about a population from which a single random sample has been drawn, as will now be demonstrated.

Statistical Inferences from Samples. *Types of Inference.* In a real instance, no omniscient being is available to record everyone's opinion. Prior to the actual election, the only practical way of determining the division of opinion is to take a random sample from the population. This may be done by stopping people on the street, ringing doorbells, sending out letters, or the like. When the results of the sample poll are counted, they may be used to draw inferences about the true division of opinion in the population in three ways—that is to say, three types of inference may be drawn. (1) A certain hypothesis regarding the true division of opinion may be tested as to its reasonableness in the light of the sample results and either rejected or accepted. (2) So-called "confidence limits" may be set up for which it may be said that there is a given probability that these limits include the true value. (3) A best single estimate may be made of the population percentage; this is called an "optimum estimate." Each of these three types of inference will now be studied.

Testing a Hypothesis as to the Population Percentage. Let the hypothesis be set up that the population is evenly divided between Radical and Conservatives. Suppose the sample poll of 100 voters shows 57 Radicals and 43 Conservatives. Although the sample shows a percentage in favor of the Radicals, it is possible, of course, that it may be misleading. Almost any result might be yielded by a single sample, whatever the population. If the population consisted even of 999,900 Conservatives and 100 Radicals, it would still be possible for a random sample of 100 to

[1] For proof of this, see Smith and Duncan, *Sampling Statistics*, pp. 186–190.

consist of all Radicals. Such a result would not be very probable, however, and the reasonableness of any hypothesis must be
judged by the probability of the sample result on the assumption
that the hypothesis is valid.

The general procedure for testing the hypothesis is as follows:
First, the risk that is to be allowed in rejecting a given hypothesis
when it is in fact true must be decided upon. The "coefficient of
risk," as it is called, is commonly, but not necessarily, set at 0.05.
In other words, it is the common practice to run the risk of rejecting a hypothesis 5 times out of 100 when it is in fact true. When a
sampling distribution is normal, this is often done by saying that a

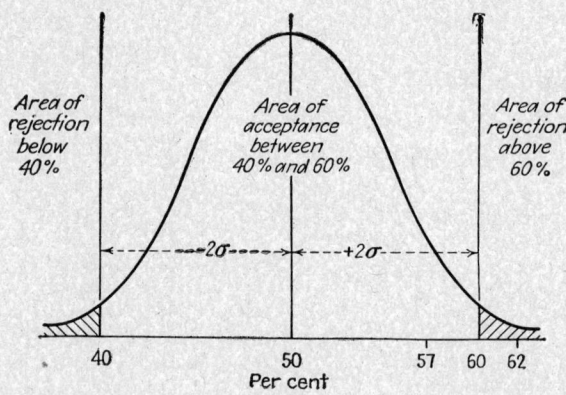

Fig. 102.—Sampling distribution of sample percentages of 100 votes.

given hypothesis will be rejected if the sample result falls beyond
$\pm 2\sigma$ from the mean value given by the hypothesis.[1] In the
present instance, the hypothesis that the true division of opinion
is fifty-fifty suggests that random samples of 100 taken from such
a population will have a mean percentage of Radical votes equal to
$p_1 = 50$ per cent and a standard deviation of sample percentages
equal to $\sqrt{p_1 p_2 / N} = \sqrt{(0.5)(0.5)/100} = 5$ per cent.

Accordingly, 95 per cent of the sample percentages would fall
between 50 per cent $\pm 2 \times 5$ per cent, or between 40 and 60 per
cent; 5 per cent of sample percentages would fall below 40 and
above 60 per cent. Hence, if this hypothesis is rejected when a

[1] The desirability in some cases of using regions of rejection that fall all
above or all below the mean are discussed in *ibid.*, pp. 196–201.

single sample return yields a percentage of Radical vote below 40 or above 60 per cent, then the hypothesis would in many sample polls be rejected only 5 per cent of the time when it was actually true. In other words, the rejector would be wrong only 1 out of 20 times in a large number of tries.

For the given problem, suppose the coefficient of risk is put at 0.05. Since the sample return is 57 Radical votes out of a total of 100, the hypothesis of an equal division of opinion is not to be rejected, for the sample result does not fall in the region of rejection below 40 or above 60 per cent. In this instance, the sample result does not deviate sufficiently from the hypothetical percentage to cause its rejection. If the sample return had been 62 Radicals and 38 Conservatives, however, the hypothesis of an equal division of opinion would have been rejected and it would have been concluded that the Radicals were in the majority. This argument and these conclusions are illustrated graphically in Fig. 102.

From the figure it is seen that with a sample result of 57 per cent the hypothesis that $p_1 = 0.5$ is accepted while with a sample result of 62 per cent the hypothesis that $p_1 = 0.5$ is rejected.

Determining Confidence Limits for Population Percentage. Before confidence limits can be established for a population percentage it is first necessary to decide upon the degree of confidence that is to be placed in the computed limits. This is usually determined by so choosing the limits that the probability of their including the true percentage equals an agreed-upon figure, called the "confidence coefficient." For example, if the confidence coefficient is set at 0.95, as is the common practice, then the limits will be so chosen that the probability of their embracing the true value is just 0.95.

In the case of a normal sampling distribution, confidence limits with a confidence coefficient of 0.95 may be set up as follows: Choose as the upper confidence limit a value for the population percentage that, if it were the true value, would make the probability of getting the given sample value or a lower sample value just equal to 0.025. Since the sampling distribution is normal, this upper limit may be obtained by choosing p_1 so that the sample value of 57 per cent falls at -2σ from the mean value of the sample percentage, *i.e.*, at -2σ from p_1. The mathematical equation becomes

$$0.57 - p_1 = -2 \sqrt{\frac{p_1 p_2}{N}}$$

or, since $p_2 = 1 - p_1$,

$$0.57 - p_1 = -2 \sqrt{\frac{p_1(1 - p_1)}{N}}$$

When solved for p_1, this becomes

$$p_1 = \frac{0.57 + \dfrac{2}{N} + 2 \sqrt{\dfrac{(0.57)(0.43)}{N} + \dfrac{1}{N^2}}}{1 + \dfrac{4}{N}}$$

When N is large, as it must be if the normal distribution is to be used as an approximation to the binomial distribution, the terms $2/N$, $4/N$, and $1/N^2$ can be dropped from the above equation without materially affecting the result. In this approximate form it becomes

$$p_1 = 0.57 + 2 \sqrt{\frac{(0.57)(0.43)}{100}} = 0.67$$

In effect, this indicates that the upper confidence limit can be found approximately by adding to the sample percentage twice the standard deviation of the sampling distribution, computed with the sample percentage in place of the hypothetical population percentage. In general, if p_1 is taken as the sample percentage (note that sample statistics are printed in text type and the corresponding population parameters in boldface type), the upper confidence limit of the population percentage is given by

$$p_1 = p_1 + 2 \sqrt{\frac{p_1(1 - p_1)}{N}} \tag{1}$$

This is shown graphically in Fig. 103a.

In a similar manner, the lower confidence limit is given approximately by the formula

$$p_1 = p_1 - 2 \sqrt{\frac{p_1(1 - p_1)}{N}} \tag{2}$$

For the given instance, in which $p_1 = 0.57$, this lower limit is

$$p_1 = 0.57 - 2\sqrt{\frac{(0.57)(0.43)}{100}} = 0.47$$

This is shown graphically in Fig. 103b.

How the upper limit is determined, how the lower limit is determined, and the resulting range or total interval between the confidence limits are pictured graphically in Figs. 103a, b, and c.

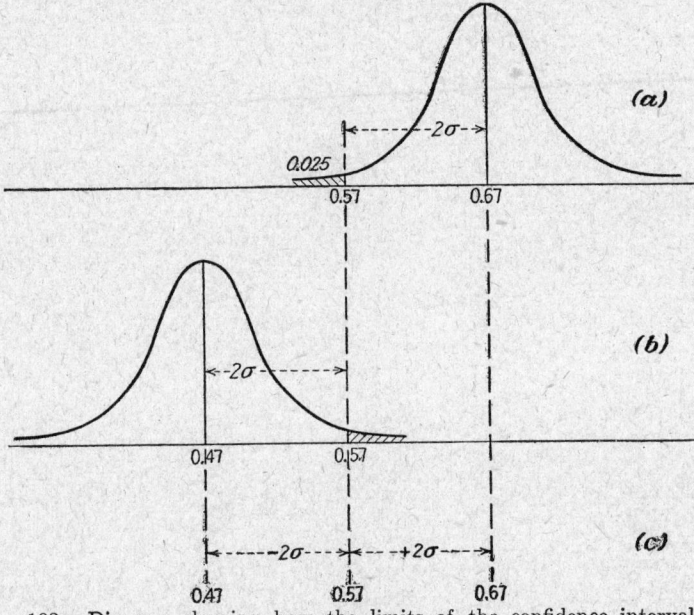

Fig. 103.—Diagram showing how the limits of the confidence interval are determined.

The limits of the range are 0.47 to 0.67. This is known technically as the "confidence interval" and is shown in Fig. 103c. Owing to the manner in which the confidence limits were derived, it may be said that there is a probability of 0.95 that this confidence interval includes the true population percentage. By this is meant that, if confidence intervals were set up like this from many samples, 95 per cent of them would include the true population percentage.

An Optimum Estimate of the Population Percentage. Up to this point in the argument, a particular hypothesis regarding the population has been tested and a method of setting up confidence intervals has been devised. A final problem of statistical inference is to indicate a method of making a single best estimate of the population percentage from the given sample. Various

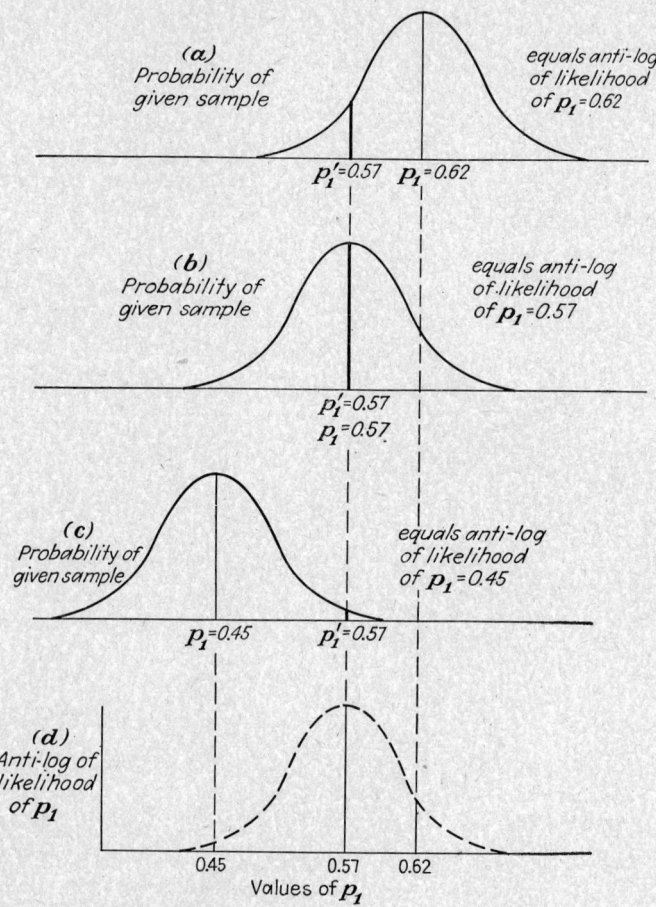

FIG. 104.—Diagram showing relationship between probability of sample and likelihood of population percentage.

methods are employed, but the one that has received considerable prominence in recent years and that will be employed here is the method of maximum likelihood.

When a population percentage is given, the probabilities of various sample results may be determined from the sampling distribution of sample percentages, in this case, approximately from the normal frequency curve. The analysis here runs from a given population percentage to probabilities of various sample results. When a particular sample result is given, however, it is possible to determine the probabilities of obtaining this sample result from various hypothetical values for the population percentage. Here the analysis runs from a given sample percentage to the probabilities of obtaining the particular sample from various hypothetical population percentages. In the latter analysis, the logarithm of the probability of the given sample result for a particular value of the population percentage is called the "likelihood" of the population percentage.

As shown in Figs. 104*a* to 104*c*, these likelihoods will vary for different hypothetical values of the population percentage. The value of the population percentage that has the maximum likelihood is considered the best, or optimum, estimate of the population percentage; this is shown in Fig. 104*d*. Figures 104*a* to 104*c* show graphically how the likelihoods of various population percentages (or, more exactly, their antilogs) vary with changes in the hypothetical values for these percentages. These various results are summarized in Fig. 104*d*, which, if completed for a large number of hypothetical values of the population percentage, would become a smooth curve showing the variation in the antilogs of the likelihoods of p_1 with changes in p_1. It is to be noted that the maximum point of this curve is also the point of maximum likelihood, since a logarithm is a maximum when its antilog is a maximum.

Without undertaking the mathematical analysis involved,[1] it may be pointed out that the value of p_1 which has the maximum likelihood is the value for which $p_1 = p_1$. In other words, the maximum likelihood estimate of a population percentage is the percentage yielded by a given sample. This then becomes the best estimate of the population figure; that is to say, the sample percentage is the optimum, or best, estimate of the population percentage.

SAMPLING OF MEANS AND VARIANCES

Sampling Distribution of Means and Variances. *The Mean.* Most of the preceding analysis applying to sample percentages

[1] For such analysis, see *ibid.*, pp. 208–209.

applies equally well to means of samples from a continuously distributed population. If the population is normal in form, it can readily be demonstrated that means of samples from such a population will form a frequency distribution which is also normal in form, the mean of which is the mean of the population and the variance of which is the variance of the population divided by the size of the sample.

If the population is not normal, the sampling distribution of sample means nevertheless tends to be normal, with a mean equal to the mean of the population and a variance equal to the variance of the population divided by the size of the sample.[1]

Accordingly, the equation for the standard deviation of the sampling distribution of sample means is as follows:

$$\sigma_{\bar{x}} = \frac{\sigma}{\sqrt{N}} \tag{3}$$

This is conventionally called the "standard error" of the mean.[2]

The Variance. If samples are taken from a normal population, the sampling distribution of sample variances is not normal for small samples but approaches the normal form as the samples become larger, say larger than 30 cases. The mean of this normal distribution is the variance of the population, and the standard deviation of the sampling distribution is the variance of the population multiplied by $\sqrt{2/N}$.

It is to be noted that, if the population is not normal, the sampling distribution of sample variances may not become normal, even for relatively large samples. Hence the use of the normal curve for making inferences about a population variance when the population is not normal may be an unwise procedure, even when the sample is large.

But for variances of large samples taken from normal populations, the standard error of the variance is given by

$$\sigma_{\sigma^2}^2 = \sigma^4 \frac{2}{N} \qquad \text{or} \qquad \sigma_{\sigma^2} = \sigma^2 \sqrt{\frac{2}{N}} \tag{4}$$

[1] *Ibid.*, p. 164.

[2] Standard errors are printed in boldface type because they represent the standard deviations of the populations of all possible sample statistics of the type in question. Thus $\sigma_{\bar{x}}$ is the standard deviation of all possible sample $\bar{X}$'s.

The Standard Deviation. For standard deviations of large samples taken from normal populations, the standard error of the standard deviation is given by

$$\delta_\sigma = \frac{\delta}{\sqrt{2N}} \tag{5}$$

Inferences about Population Means and Variances. Since the sampling distribution of sample means tends to be normal in form and the same is true of the sampling distribution of variances and standard deviations, if the population is normal, it follows that the normal curve can be used to make inferences about the population values of these parameters from corresponding sample statistics.

Testing a Hypothesis about the Population Mean. To illustrate how a hypothesis about a population mean may be tested, consider the following example. Suppose it is claimed that the mean length of life of a certain make of shoe (with constant wear) is 11.5 months. A random sample of 100 shoes is tested, and it is found that the average length of life of this sample is 10.8 months. The standard deviation of the sample is 1.2 months. Do these sample results warrant the rejection of the claim of a true mean value of 11.5 months?

To answer this question, proceed as follows: Let the risk of rejecting a hypothesis when it is true be set at 0.05. Then calculate the standard deviation of the sampling distribution of the mean (the "standard error" of the mean, as it is called) from Eq. (3). Since the standard deviation of the population is not known in this instance, the standard deviation of the sample must be used in its stead.[1]

The value of $\delta_{\bar{x}}$ for the given problem is accordingly

$$\delta_{\bar{x}} = \frac{1.2}{\sqrt{100}} = 0.12 \text{ month}$$

Next, calculate the difference between the hypothetical value of the mean and the sample value of the mean. This is

$$10.8 - 11.5 = 0.7 \text{ month}$$

Finally, compare this difference with the standard error of the mean. If the difference is more than twice the standard error,

---

[1] This substitution does not materially affect the analysis when the sample is large. For further discussion, see *ibid.*, pp. 273–284.

the hypothesis will not be accepted.   In the present instance 0.7 is over five times greater than 0.12; so the claim that the true mean is 11.5 is rejected.   The sample mean deviates too greatly from the hypothetical mean for the latter to be accepted as reasonable.

Confidence Limits for the Population Mean.   Confidence limits for the true mean with a confidence coefficient of 0.95 will be obtained by laying off $2\sigma_{\bar{x}}$ plus and minus from the sample value.   Thus, in the present problem these limits will be $10.8 \pm 2(0.12) = 11.04$ and 10.56.   Accordingly it can be said that there is a probability of 0.95 that the interval from 10.56 to 11.04 includes the true population mean within its range.

Optimum Estimate of the Population Mean.   If the method of maximum likelihood is used to give the best estimate of the population mean, it is found that the sample mean is the maximum likelihood estimate of the population mean.   Hence, in the present instance the best estimate of the population mean is 10.8 months.

Testing a Hypothesis about the Population Variance.   The same analysis can be applied to inferences regarding population variances from sample variances.   Suppose it is claimed that the true variability in the life of the given make of shoes is 1.0 month.   As in the case of the mean, this hypothesis may be tested by comparing the hypothetical value with the standard deviation of the sample of 100 shoes, which it will be assumed is 1.2 months.

The variances, or squares of the standard deviations, are 1.0 and 1.44 square months, respectively.   Their difference is $1.44 - 1.00 = 0.44$ square month.   The standard deviation of the sampling distribution of sample variances, *i.e.*, the standard error of the sample variance, is

$$\sigma^2 \sqrt{\frac{2}{N}} = 1.00 \sqrt{\frac{2}{100}} = 0.141$$

Since the difference between the hypothetical value and the sample value is more than three times $(0.44/0.14 = 3+)$ the standard error of the sample variance, the hypothesis must again be rejected.[1]

[1] For more exact methods especially applicable to small samples, see *ibid.*, pp. 284–287.

If it were desired to test a hypothesis about the standard deviation, rather than about the variance, Eq. (5) would be used. In the present instance, the population standard deviation is hypothetically set at 1.0 month and the standard deviation in the sample is 1.2 months; the difference is 0.2 month. Using Eq. (5), the standard error of the standard deviation in this problem is found to be

$$\delta_\sigma = \frac{1.00}{\sqrt{200}} = 0.07$$

Since the difference is almost three times the standard error, the hypothesis is rejected as unreasonable.

Confidence Limits for the Population Variance. Confidence limits for the population variance with a confidence coefficient of 0.95 are given by

$$\delta^2 = \sigma^2 \pm 2\delta_{\sigma^2}$$
$$= 1.44 \pm 2(0.14) = 1.72 \text{ and } 1.16$$

It can thus be said that there is a probability of 0.95 that the interval from 1.16 to 1.72 includes the true variance. The corresponding interval for the population standard deviation is from 1.06 to 1.34, obtained by making use of Eq. (5).

Optimum Estimate of the Population Variance. Finally, the maximum likelihood estimate of the population variance is (for large samples) approximately the variance of the sample.[1] Hence the best estimate of the population variance in this instance is 1.44, which gives a population standard deviation of 1.2.

CONCLUSION

From the few illustrations in this chapter, it should be clear that the normal curve is very useful in making inferences about populations from random samples. It can be used to measure sampling fluctuations in sample percentages, sample means, and, in certain instances, sample variances, as well as in a number of

---

[1] For small samples the multiplier $\frac{N}{N-1}$ should be applied to the sample variance to give a better estimate of the population variance. Thus the optimum estimate, if N is small, say less than 30, is as follows:

$$\breve{\sigma}^2 = \sigma^2 \left(\frac{N}{N-1} \right)$$

Cf. ibid., pp. 290–294.

other statistics. It also has many uses in more advanced sampling analyses and is probably the most important sampling distribution that occurs in statistical theory.

Table 23 contains not only the standard errors discussed in this chapter but also the standard errors for a number of other statistics. The method of applying these formulas to test hypotheses, to set up confidence intervals, or to obtain optimum estimates is similar for all statistics obtained from large samples.

TABLE 23.—SAMPLING ERRORS IN ELEMENTARY STATISTICS FOR WHICH THE SAMPLING DISTRIBUTION APPROXIMATES THE NORMAL CURVE
(Ordinarily these formulas for standard error cannot be used for $N < 30$)

Statistics	Standard errors
$\bar{X}$	$\sigma_{\bar{x}} = \dfrac{\sigma}{\sqrt{N}}$
σ^2	$\sigma_{\sigma^2} = \sigma^2 \sqrt{\dfrac{2}{N}}$
σ	$\sigma_{\sigma} = \dfrac{\sigma}{\sqrt{2N}}$
$\mathrm{Sk} = \dfrac{\sqrt{\beta_1}(\beta_2 + 3)}{2(5\beta_2 - 6\beta_1 - 9)}$	$\sigma_{Sk} = \dfrac{1.225}{\sqrt{N}}$ [*]
β_2	$\sigma_{\beta_2} = \sqrt{\dfrac{24}{N}}$ [*]
Mi	$\sigma_{Mi} = 1.25331 \dfrac{\sigma}{\sqrt{N}}$ [*]
$\mathrm{A.D.}_{Mi}$	$\sigma_{\mathrm{A.D.}} = 0.605 \sigma_{\bar{x}}$ [*]
$z(r = \tanh z)$	$\sigma_z = \dfrac{1}{\sqrt{N - 3}}$
Q_1 Q_3	$\sigma_{Q_1} = \sigma_{Q_3} = 1.36263 \dfrac{\sigma}{\sqrt{N}}$ [*]
p_1	$\sigma_{p_1} = \sqrt{\dfrac{p_1(1 - p_1)}{N}}$
$a_{i \cdot jk \ldots n}$	$\sigma_{a_{i \cdot jk \ldots n}} = \dfrac{\sigma_{i \cdot jk \ldots n}}{\sqrt{N}}$
$b_{ij \cdot k \ldots n}$	$\sigma_{b_{ij \cdot k \ldots n}} = \dfrac{\sigma_{i \cdot jk \ldots n}}{\sigma_{i \cdot jk \ldots n} \sqrt{N}}$

[*] *Cf.* WAUGH, ALBERT E., *Elements of Statistical Method* (1938), pp. 142–147.

PART IV

Study of Bivariates and Multivariates

CHAPTER XIII

SIMPLE CORRELATION

CORRELATION FUNDAMENTAL TO KNOWLEDGE

Progressive development in the methods of science and philosophy has been characterized by increase in the knowledge of relationships, or correlations. Nature has been found to be a multiplicity of interrelated forces. The phenomena of the physical world outside man seem to be well adapted to this concept of interrelationship. The same is true with respect to phenomena having to do with human beings and their environment.

Progress in the Discovery of Correlation. In the physical sciences, where the laws of nature are, within certain limits, determinate, experimental method has sufficed to disclose innumerable relationships. Many of these physical correlations have become definitely known as "cause and effect relationships." To some degree, too, this is true of biology, anthropology, geology, and the like. In these fields of study, great progress was made possible by the use of observation of "cases," by tracing correlations previously known or suspected, and by laboratory experiments. In the social sciences, however, the establishment of certain knowledge, or knowledge of a high degree of probability regarding relationships, is a more difficult problem; and little scientific progress, comparatively speaking, has been made through the speculative method. This is particularly true so far as cause and effect relationships are concerned.

For example, philosophical speculation, based upon qualitative or semiquantitative observation of experience seemed to many economists of the eighteenth, nineteenth, and twentieth centuries to have codified the relationship between money and credit on the one hand and prices and many social problems on the other hand. But no such certainty among these social scientists now exists as to the nature of the cause and effect order of events. In its earlier conception, the principle of the quantity theory of money seemed to be one of extraordinary simplicity and determinateness; but the more it is studied in its quantitative aspects the more complicated it is found to be in reality. By the 1930's and 1940's, the world of scientific monetary theorists came to be characterized by confused controversy. The practical world still awaits their solution of the theoretical problem in order to make possible a world-wide solution of the problem of monetary reform. Some say that increases or decreases in the quantity of money cause rising and falling prices, respectively; but others, with convincing argument, maintain that rising prices cause an increase in the quantity of money, and vice versa. It is a moot question as to whether or not statistics can come to the rescue in the matter of deciding the direction of the cause and effect relationship; but at least the technique has been developed to disclose the facts of relationship more precisely than was ever before possible.

By the latter half of the nineteenth century, in many fields of study, a point had been reached where speculation concerning relationships could advance no farther with the existing techniques. More exact measurement of relationship was needed. Many questions in biology, anthropology, and the social sciences generally awaited a scientific answer to the question: How can relationship be measured? Two interesting attempts were made by American scholars to devise a method of measuring relationship, one in 1877 and the other in 1892.[1] Credit for the discovery of a method, and for its subsequent mathematical development, however, belongs largely to the scholars of England.

Origin and Development of the Measurement of Correlation. In the nineteenth century pre-Darwinian and Darwinian doctrines of

[1] Bowditch, H. P., "The Growth of Children," Eighth Annual Report of the State Board of Health of Massachusetts (1877), pp. 275–324; Bryan, W. L., "On the Development of Voluntary Motor Ability," *American Journal of Psychology*, Vol. 5 (1892), pp. 123–204. These are both described in Helen M. Walker, *Studies in the History of Statistical Method* (1929), pp. 100–102, 109–110.

evolution were taking root, and the question of the influence of heredity vs. environment upon human characteristics was in a state of rarefied speculation and controversy. The experimental data appeared chaotic and amenable to as many interpretations as there were interpreters.

One of the great nineteenth-century students of the problem of heredity was Sir Francis Galton. He had been profoundly impressed by Darwin's *Origin of Species* (1859), concerning which he said,[1] "Its effect was to demolish a multitude of dogmatic barriers by a single stroke, and to arouse a spirit of rebellion against all ancient authorities whose positive and unauthenticated statements were contradicted by modern science." Galton made numerous studies on the subject of heredity. The question that was motivating his studies was: How is it possible for a whole population to remain alike in its features, as a whole, during many successive generations, if the average produce of each couple resemble their parents? He attacked the question by studying sweet peas, moths, hounds, and finally the records of human families, which he obtained by offering prizes.

Between the years 1877 and 1889, Galton worked out a mathematical method by which he could give an exact measure of the relationship between, for example, heights of children and the average heights of their parents. By statistical measurement he found that, if the stature of a group of parents is found to be, say y inches above or below the general average of the race, the average stature of their children will be only $\frac{2}{3}y$ inches above or below the average of the race; and he induced the law that the mean heights of offspring tend to "regress back toward the mean of the race" in spite of the strong hereditary influence of the parents. This is the famous law of regression to type, although the exact figure $\frac{2}{3}$ is not to be taken as final.

The method Galton used was based upon the median and quartiles and has not been generally followed in subsequent work. In the 1890's another method, based on the arithmetic mean and the standard deviation, was devised by Karl Pearson. His

[1] "Hereditary Talent and Character," *Macmillan's Magazine*, Vol. 12 (May, 1865–October, 1865), pp. 157–166, 318–327; *Hereditary Genius* (1869, 2d ed. 1892); *English Men of Science* (1874); *Human Faculty* (1883); *Record of Family Faculties* (1884); *Life History Album* (1884); *Natural Inheritance* (1889). *Cf.* WALKER, *op. cit.*, pp. 102–103.

method has been widely adopted and is known as the "Pearsonian coefficient of correlation."[1]

It should be pointed out that in the fields of meteorology and astronomy mathematicians had previously worked out a formula for a joint or bivariate normal frequency distribution. This gave the probability of the simultaneous occurrence of two errors of observation but did not directly indicate a measure of correlation between them. Work in this field was more concerned with the simultaneous occurrence of independent errors than of correlated errors.[2] Galton, as already indicated, was primarily concerned with the problem of correlation, and it remained for Karl Pearson and others to combine the work of Galton and the work of the mathematicians into a unified theory of correlation. Pearson's development of the theory of correlation will be explained on page 338 to 349.

Applications of the Method by Social Scientists. As early as 1901, R. H. Hooker, using the Pearsonian coefficient, studied correlation between marriage rates and trade. He correlated marriage rates with per capita exports of England, with per capita imports, and with other trade events.[3] In 1906, G. Udny Yule likewise made a study of correlation between marriage rates and trade. He also correlated trade activity with birth rates and death rates but found little correlation between them.[4]

---

[1] *Cf.* WALKER, *op. cit.*, pp. 110–115; PEARSON, KARL, "Notes on the History of Correlation," *Biometrika*, Vol. 13 (1920–1921), pp. 25–45, where he cites W. F. R. Weldon, "Variations Occurring in certain Decapod Crustacea—*I. Crangon vulgaris*," *Proceedings of the Royal Society of London*, Vol. 47 (1890), pp. 445–453; WELDON, W. F. R., "Certain Correlated Variations in *Crangon vulgaris*," *Proceedings of the Royal Society of London*, Vol. 51 (1892), pp. 2–21; YULE, G. U., "On the Theory of Correlation," *Journal of the Royal Statistical Society*, Vol. 60 (1897), pp. 812–850.

[2] PRETORIUS, S. J., "Skew Bivariate Frequency Surface, Examined in the Light of Numerical Illustrations," *Biometrika*, Vol. 22 (1930–1931), pp. 109–223; PEARSON, KARL, "The Contribution of Giovanni Plana to the Normal Bivariate Frequency Surface," *Biometrika*, Vol. 20A (1928), pp. 295–298; WALKER, HELEN M., "The Relation of Plana and Bravais to the Theory of Correlation," *Isis*, Vol. 10, No. 34 (1938), pp. 466–484.

[3] "Correlation of the Marriage-rate with Trade," *Journal of the Royal Statistical Society*, Vol. 64 (September, 1901), pp. 485–492.

[4] YULE, G. UDNY, "On Changes in the Marriage- and Birth-rates in England and Wales, Etc.," *Journal of the Royal Statistical Society*, Vol. 69

The entire science of biometrics has been built up by the development of correlation methods; Karl Pearson is one of the founders of *Biometrika*, the scientific organ in that field of study. Correlation measurement has been intensively applied in psychological and educational research.[1] In recent years, the correlation method has played an important role in the analysis of economic problems and in economic theory, a trend particularly evident in the field of agricultural economics.

THE BIVARIATE FREQUENCY DISTRIBUTION

The statistical basis for the study of correlation is the bivariate or multivariate frequency distribution. In the univariate frequency distributions studied in the previous chapters, the data were classified according to a single characteristic. In bivariate or multivariate distributions, data are classified according to two or more characteristics. This chapter will be concerned with the analysis of bivariate distributions. Chapter XVI will deal with multivariate distributions.

An Illustration of a Bivariate Distribution. Table 24 shows the distribution of grades of 81 freshmen in a second-semester English course at Mount Holyoke. For each of these 81 students

TABLE 24.—GRADES OF 81 MOUNT HOLYOKE FRESHMEN IN A SECOND-SEMESTER ENGLISH COURSE

Grades X_1	Frequencies F
60–	1
80–	0
100–	3
120–	0
140–	2
160–	9
180–	8
200–	16
220–	17
240–	13
260–	9
280–	1
300–	2
	81

(1906), pp. 88–132; "The Applications of the Method of Correlation to Social and Economic Statistics," *Journal of the Royal Statistical Society*, Vol. 72 (1909), pp. 721–730.

[1] RUGG, HAROLD O., *Statistical Methods Applied to Education*,

there is also available the grade in first-semester English. Hence they may be cross-classified according to both their first- and second-semester grades. This has been done in Table 25.

TABLE 25.—A BIVARIATE FREQUENCY DISTRIBUTION OF 81 MOUNT HOLYOKE FRESHMEN ACCORDING TO THEIR GRADES IN FIRST- (X_2) AND SECOND- (X_1) SEMESTER ENGLISH

X_1 \ X_2	60–	80–	100–	120–	140–	160–	180–	200–	220–	240–	260–	280–	F
60–				1									1
80–													0
100–	2		1										3
120–													0
140–				1			1						2
160–				5	3	1							9
180–					2	4	2						8
200–						3	4	7	2				16
220–							2	4	7	4			17
240–								2	7	3	1		13
260–									1	4	4		9
280–										1			1
300–												2	2
F	2	0	1	7	5	8	9	13	18	11	5	2	81

The bivariate frequency distribution represented by Table 25 gives more complete information than is contained in the univariate frequency distribution of Table 24. Of the 8 students having second-semester grades between 180 and 200, the seventh row of Table 25 shows that 2 had first-semester grades between 140 and 160, 4 had first-semester grades between 160 and 180, and 2 had first-semester grades between 180 and 200. This is a small univariate frequency distribution of the group of students who had grades between 180 and 200 in their second-semester course. In Table 25 there are 11 rows and 11 columns each of which contains a univariate frequency distribution. Since there are 11 subgroups of 11 groups, there are altogether 121 classes, represented in the table by 121 squares, or cells, of which 28 cells contain frequencies.

The totals of the columns of Table 25 gives the univariate frequency distribution of all the students classified according to their first-semester English grade. The totals of the rows gives the univariate frequency distribution of all the students classified according to their second-semester English grades.

For each of the columns an arithmetic mean could be calculated and the question could be answered: Did girls who earned high grades in their first-semester English average higher grades in second-semester English than did the girls who attained only low grades in their first-semester English? An arithmetic mean could similarly be calculated for each of the row frequency distributions. For all the 11 column frequency distributions and all the 11 row frequency distributions the standard deviations also could be calculated. In other words, in this bivariate frequency distribution there are 22 univariate frequency distributions in addition to the 2 univariate frequency distributions represented by the totals for the respective variables. Each of these 22 frequency distributions might be analyzed in the same way as any frequency distribution.

METHODS OF SUMMARIZATION AND COMPARISON IN BIVARIATE DISTRIBUTIONS

The characteristics of a bivariate frequency distribution can be described by various statistics. Many of these are the same as the statistics employed in the description of a univariate frequency distribution, but some are new. Thus, the central tendency of one of the two variables may be measured by its mean, its mode, or its median. The dispersion of this variable may be measured by its range, standard deviation, average deviation, or quartile deviation; and its skewness and kurtosis may be measured by β_1 and β_2, respectively. The same is true for the other variable and for the numerous univariate frequency distributions that make up the details of a single bivariate distribution, as explained in the preceding paragraph. New statistics are required, however, to describe the tendency of the variables to vary in unison. A bivariate frequency distribution thus presents the new problem of measuring correlation and the discovery of statistics for measuring it.

Progressions of Means. If the data are grouped in the form of a bivariate scatter diagram such as Table 25, one way to measure the association between the two variables is to compute the mean values of one variable for various values of the other

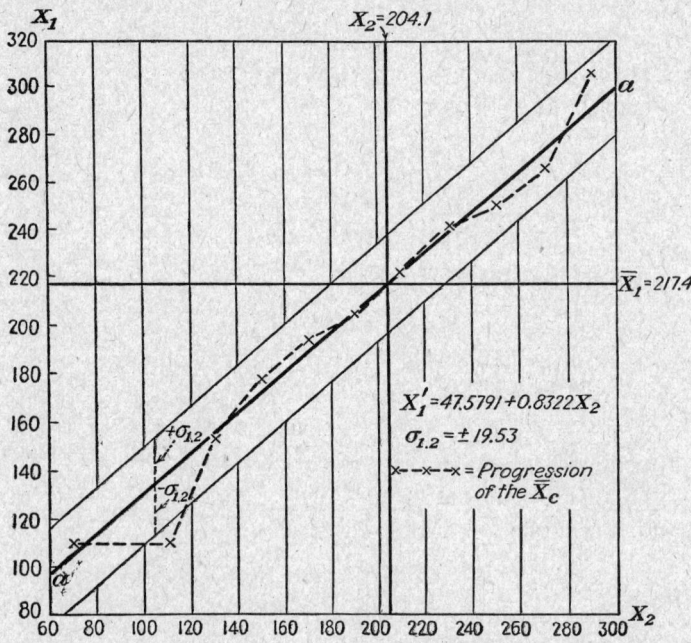

$$X_1' = 47.5791 + 0.8322X_2$$
$$\sigma_{1.2} = \pm 19.53$$

×‑‑×‑‑× = Progression of the $\overline{X}_c$

Fig. 105.—Progression of the means of X_1 with changes in X_2.

variable. In Table 26, for example, the means of the columns would show how the X_1 variable tends to change on the average with changes in X_2, and the means of the rows show how the X_2 variable tends to change on the average with changes in X_1. The values of these column and row means are given in Table 26 and graphed in Figs. 105 and 106.

The nature of the association between the variables is evident from these graphs. Consider, for example, the progression of the means of X_1 shown in Table 26 and Fig. 105. These show that the mean value of X_1 tends to increase with increases in X_2.

Thus, when X_2 is between 100 and 120, the mean value of X_1 is 110; when X_2 is between 200 and 220, the mean value of X_1 is 222.31; and when X_2 is between 260 and 280, the mean value of X_1 is 266.0. Although the increase in the average value of X_1 with a given increase in X_2 does not appear to be uniform, the progression of the means of X_1 with a change in X_2 does appear to follow

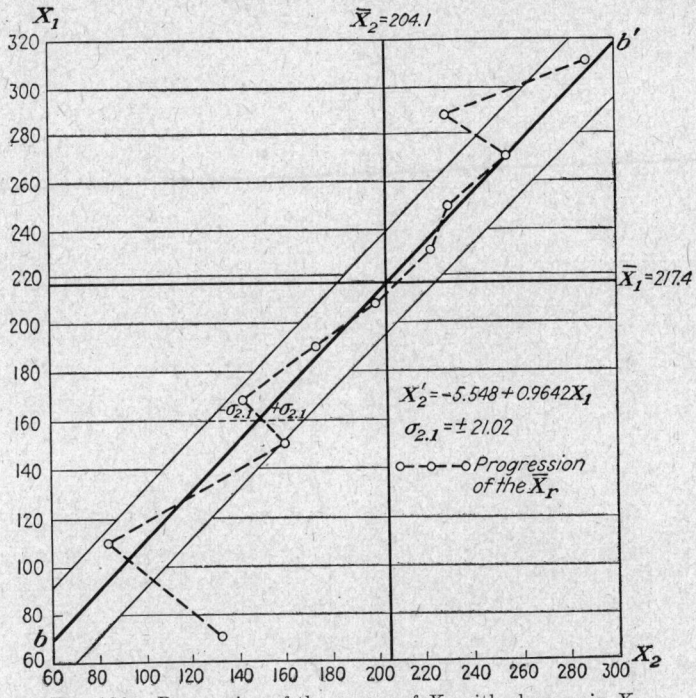

Fig. 106.—Progression of the means of X_2 with changes in X_1.

a straight line. The same can be said of the progression of the means of X_2 with changes in X_1.

Lines of Regression. The tendency of the progressions of means to follow straight lines suggests the following hypothesis: Consider first the progression of the means of X_1 with changes in X_2. Suppose that X_1 is related to X_2 in such a way that an increase in X_2 of one unit always produces an increase in X_1 of, say b units, b being a constant. If X_2 were the only factor affecting X_1, all the values of X_1, when plotted, would fall exactly on a straight line and the progression of all means would be perfectly linear. If there were other forces affecting X_1, however, causing

it to be higher or lower than the value expected from its association with X_2, then the actual values would not fall on a straight
line but would be scattered about that line.   If this view of the
variation between X_1 and X_2 is adopted, a straight line fitted to
the data should give the law of relationship between X_1 and X_2
and the scatter about it should give the deviation from this line
caused by the other factors affecting X_1.

TABLE 26.—MEANS OF ROWS AND MEANS OF COLUMNS
*From correlation table showing the relationship between second- and first-
semester grades of 81 Mount Holyoke freshmen*

Progression of means of second-semester English grade (X_1) with successive values of first-semester English grade (X_2) Regression of X_1 on X_2 (Vertical frequency distributions in Table 25)		Progression of means of first-semester English grade (X_2) with successive values of second-semester English grade (X_1) Regression of X_2 on X_1 (Horizontal frequency distributions in Table 25)	
Values of X_2	Means of X_1 $\bar{X}_c$	Values of X_1	Means of X_2 $\bar{X}_r$
60–	110.00	60–	130.00
80–	. . . . . .	80–	
100–	110.00	100–	83.33
120–	152.86	120–	
140–	178.00	140–	160.00
160–	195.00	160–	141.11
180–	203.33	180–	170.00
200–	222.31	200–	200.00
220–	241.11	220–	225.29
240–	250.00	240–	234.62
260–	266.00	260–	256.67
280–	310.00	280–	230.00
		300–	290.00

A similar view could be taken of the variation in the mean
value of X_2 with changes in X_1 and would justify drawing a
straight line to show the law of relationship between X_2 and X_1.
The lines that are derived to show the relationship between the
mean value of one variable and changes in value of another are
called "lines of regression," following Galton, who used this term
in his original study of the relationship between the heights of
children and the heights of their parents.

The Line of Regression of X_1 on X_2.   Suppose the above hypothesis is adopted, namely, that X_1 is linearly related to X_2 and

that deviations from this relationship are the result of forces independent of X_2. The statistical problem then becomes how to draw the line that is supposed to show this linear relationship.

One of the simplest ways of finding the line of regression of X_1 on X_2 is to plot the progression of the means of X_1 for various values of X_2 and to draw a line freehand through the means so that it seems to fit the progression of means. The great difficulty with this method is that it involves considerable personal discretion and that no two persons will necessarily draw the same line.

An impersonal method of fitting a line to a given set of data is the so-called "method of least squares." This fits a line to the data so that the sum of the deviations of the dependent variable from the line is zero and the sum of the squares of the deviations is a minimum (hence the name "method of least squares"). Mathematically, the first of these two conditions follows from the second, so that there is really only one condition, *viz.*, that of least squares.

The use of the method of least squares to fit lines to a set of data goes back to the beginning of the nineteenth century. It first came into prominence in 1806, when Adrien Marie Legendre (1752–1833) published a book on new methods of determining orbits of comets. After the publication of this book, Karl Friedrich Gauss (1777–1855), a German mathematician, claimed that he had been applying this principle since 1795.

Later it was shown that, if the method is used to fit a line to a sample set of data, then, under particular circumstances, the line so determined is the best, or optimum, estimate of the population line. For example, if data are available as to the orbit of a comet or planet and if a line or curve is fitted to these data by the method of least squares, then the line or curve so obtained would be the most probable estimate of the true orbit.[1]

The line of regression of X_1 on X_2 may be derived by the method of least squares as follows: Consider the point P, Fig. 107. This, according to hypothesis, would fall at P' if there were no forces associated with X_1 other than X_2. Supposedly, however, there are other forces that are independent of X_2 and make X_1 smaller than this average value so as to cause the point to be located actually at P. Since these other forces affect only X_1, the point is deflected in a vertical direction. The line of regression of X_1 on

---

[1] See SMITH and DUNCAN, *Sampling Statistics*, pp. 372–375.

X_2 is therefore to be obtained by minimizing the vertical deviations from the line.

Let the equation of this line of regression of X_1 on X_2 be

$$X_1' = a_{1.2} + b_{12}X_2$$

The deviations would then be

$$d_{1.2} = X_1 - X_1' = X_1 - a_{1.2} - b_{12}X_2$$

and the problem is to determine $a_{1.2}$ and b_{12} so as to minimize the

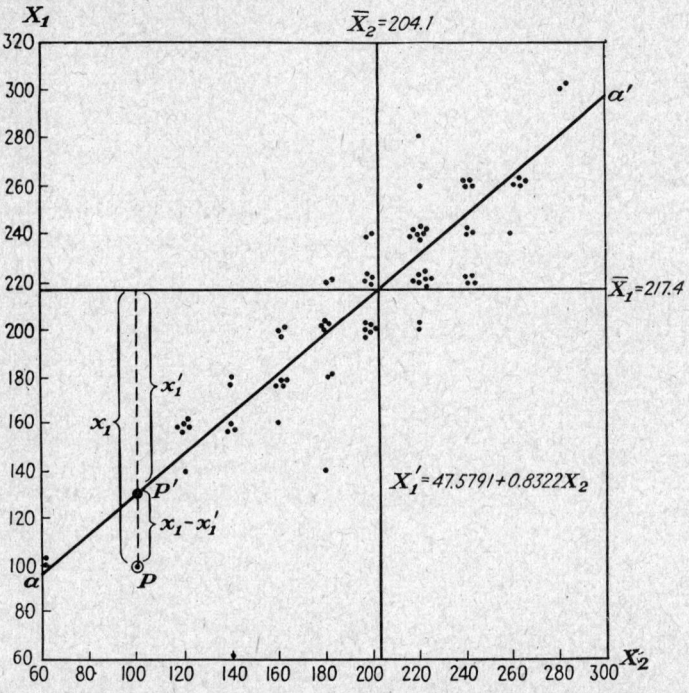

Fig. 107.—Diagram illustrating the fitting of the line of regression of X_1 on X_2
by the method of least squares (vertical deviations minimized).

sum of the squares of deviations like $x_1 - x_1'$ shown in Fig. 107, i.e.
$(X_1 - X_1' = x_1 - x_1'$ because $x_1 = X_1 - \bar{X}_1$ and $x_1' = X_1' - \bar{X}_1$),

$$\Sigma(X_1 - X_1')^2 = \Sigma(X_1 - a_{1.2} - b_{12}X_2)^2 = \text{minimum}$$

According to the differential calculus, the conditions for minimizing $\Sigma(X_1 - a_{1.2} - b_{12}X_2)^2$ are that the partial derivative
with respect to $a_{1.2}$ and the partial derivative with respect to b_{12}

should both be zero. These conditions are

$$\frac{\partial \Sigma(X_1 - a_{1.2} - b_{12}X_2)^2}{\partial a_{1.2}} = -2\Sigma(X_1 - a_{1.2} - b_{12}X_2)$$

$$= 0 = \Sigma d_{1.2} \quad (1)$$

$$\frac{\partial \Sigma(X_1 - a_{1.2} - b_{12}X_2)^2}{\partial b_{12}} = -2\Sigma(X_1 - a_{1.2} - b_{12}X_2)X_2$$

$$= 0 = \Sigma d_{1.2}X_2 \quad (2)$$

If the parentheses are removed, these equations may be written

$$Na_{1.2} + b_{12}\Sigma X_2 = \Sigma X_1$$
$$a_{1.2}\Sigma X_2 + b_{12}\Sigma X_2^2 = \Sigma X_1 X_2$$

($\Sigma a_{1.2} = Na_{1.2}$ because $a_{1.2}$ is a constant.)

The first gives $a_{1.2}$ in terms of b_{12} as follows:

$$a_{1.2} = \bar{X}_1 - b_{12}\bar{X}_2 \quad (3)$$

($\Sigma X_1/N = \bar{X}_1$, and $\Sigma X_2/N = \bar{X}_2$.)

If this is substituted in the second, the value of b_{12} is found to be

$$b_{12} = \frac{\Sigma X_1 X_2 - N\bar{X}_1\bar{X}_2}{\Sigma X_2^2 - N\bar{X}_2^2} \quad (4)$$

Equations (3) and (4) thus give the values of $a_{1.2}$ and b_{12} in terms of the sample values of X_1 and X_2. If these values are grouped into class intervals and deviations are measured from an arbitrary origin, the last equation may be put in the form

$$b_{12} = \frac{\Sigma F\left(\frac{d_1}{i_1}\right)\left(\frac{d_2}{i_2}\right) - N\left(\frac{C_1}{i_1}\right)\left(\frac{C_2}{i_2}\right)}{\Sigma F\left(\frac{d_2}{i_2}\right)^2 - N\left(\frac{C_2}{i_2}\right)^2} \left(\frac{i_1 i_2}{i_2^2}\right) \quad (5)$$

where

$$\frac{C_1}{i_1} = \frac{\Sigma F\left(\frac{d_1}{i_1}\right)}{N} \quad \text{and} \quad \frac{C_2}{i_2} = \frac{\Sigma F\left(\frac{d_2}{i_2}\right)}{N}$$

If deviations are measured from the means of X_1 and X_2, then

$$\left. \begin{array}{l} a_{1.2} = 0 \\[4pt] b_{12} = \dfrac{\Sigma x_1 x_2}{\Sigma x_2^2} \end{array} \right\} \quad (6)$$

In the next chapter in which the work of measuring correlation is illustrated by numerical calculations, it is found that for the

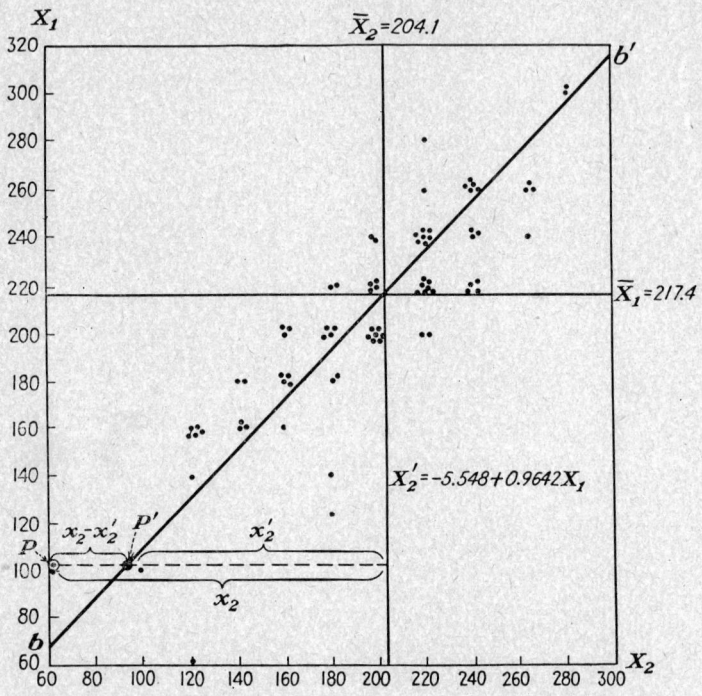

$X_2' = -5.548 + 0.9642X_1$

FIG. 108.—Diagram illustrating the fitting of the line of regression of X_2 on X_1 by the method of least squares (horizontal deviations minimized).

bivariate frequency distribution of Table 25,

$$\Sigma F \left(\frac{d_1}{i_1}\right)\left(\frac{d_2}{i_2}\right) = 455 \qquad \Sigma F \left(\frac{d_2}{i_2}\right)^2 = 493$$

$$\frac{C_1}{i_1} = \frac{111}{81} \qquad \frac{C_2}{i_2} = \frac{57}{81}$$

$$b_{12} = \frac{455 - \dfrac{(81)(111)(57)}{(81)(81)}}{493 - 81\dfrac{(57)^2}{(81)^2}}$$

$$= 0.8322$$

For these same data, $\bar{X}_1 = 217.4$ and $\bar{X}_2 = 204.1$ so that $a_{1.2} = 217.4 - 0.832(204.1) = 47.58$. The line of regression of X_1 on X_2 is thus $X_1' = 47.58 + 0.8322X_2$.

Line of Regression of X_2 on X_1. The line of regression of X_2 on X_1 may also be obtained by either freehand or mathematical methods. A freehand line could be obtained by drawing a line through the progression of the means of X_2 on X_1. A mathematical line could be obtained by the method of least squares.

The preceding section determined a mathematical formula for the line of regression of X_1 on X_2 by minimizing the sum of the squares of the vertical deviations. Now X_2 is assumed to be the dependent variable, and the line of regression of X_2 on X_1 is determined by minimizing the sum of the squares of the horizontal deviations (see Fig. 108). Except for this difference, the process is precisely the same as that described for fitting the other line and will not be repeated here. If the line of regression of X_2 on X_1 is represented by the equation

$$X_2' = a_{2.1} + b_{21}X_1$$

then minimizing $\Sigma(X_2 - X_2')^2 = \Sigma(X_2 - a_{2.1} - b_{21}X_1)^2$ gives the following values for $a_{2.1}$ and b_{21}:

$$a_{2.1} = \bar{X}_2 - b_{21}\bar{X}_1 \tag{7}$$

$$b_{21} = \frac{\Sigma X_1 X_2 - N\bar{X}_1\bar{X}_2}{\Sigma X_1^2 - N\bar{X}_1^2} \tag{8}$$

or

$$b_{21} = \frac{\Sigma F\left(\dfrac{d_1}{i_1}\right)\left(\dfrac{d_2}{i_2}\right) - N\left(\dfrac{C_1}{i_1}\right)\left(\dfrac{C_2}{i_2}\right)}{\Sigma F\left(\dfrac{d_1}{i_1}\right)^2 - N\left(\dfrac{C_1}{i_1}\right)^2}\left(\dfrac{i_1 i_2}{i_1^2}\right) \tag{9}$$

If deviations are measured from the means of X_1 and X_2, then

$$\left.\begin{aligned} a_{2.1} &= 0 \\ b_{21} &= \frac{\Sigma x_1 x_2}{\Sigma x_1^2} \end{aligned}\right\} \tag{10}$$

For the data of Table 25 the line of regression of X_2 on X_1 is thus found to be

$$X_2' = -5.548 + 0.9642X_1$$

This is shown in Fig. 108.

Interpretation of a Line of Regression.   A line of regression of one variable on another is to be interpreted as indicating the values of the first (the dependent variable) that would be obtained for various values of the second (the independent variable) if no other forces were affecting the dependent variable. If knowledge of the independent variable is all that is to be had, then the line of regression gives the best estimate that may be made of the dependent variable.

The regression statistic a (that is, $a_{1.2}$ or $a_{2.1}$) gives the value of the dependent variable when the independent variable is zero. It is of only arbitrary significance, since its value is affected by the origin selected for measuring the independent variable as well as the units of measurement.   The regression statistic b (that is, b_{12} or b_{21}) is independent of the origin selected and indicates the change that would occur in the dependent variable per unit change in the independent variable.   In the line of regression of X_1 on X_2, for example, when X_2 increases by one unit, X_1 increases or decreases by b_{12} units depending on the sign of b_{12}. The value of b_{12} will not be affected by proportional changes in the units of X_1 and X_2.   Similar statements hold for b_{21} in the case of the line of regression of X_2 on X_1.

Standard Deviation about Means or Line of Regression.   If the progressions of the means or the lines of regression are used to measure the average relationship between two variables, some additional measure is desirable to determine the degree of representativeness of these measures.   In the case of a monovariate distribution, it will be recalled, the representativeness of the mean depended upon how closely the cases were scattered around this mean value.   This dispersion was measured by the standard deviation or some other measure.   Similarly, in the present instance, the representativeness of the means of X_1, say, for various values of X_2 will be shown by the dispersion of the cases around each mean.   The standard deviation of the cases in each column around the mean of that column may thus be taken to show how well the mean represents the cases in the column. The same is true for any row.

In Table 27 are given the standard deviations of the columns of Table 25.   The zero values refer to the columns in which there is only one case.   The other values center around 16, their average being 16.9.

It is to be noted that the average standard deviation from the means of the columns, as well as the individual standard deviations from which this average is calculated, are considerably less than the total standard deviation of X_1, namely, $\sigma_1 = 43.9$. The column means are thus much more representative of the column values of X_1 than the grand mean is of all the X_1's.

TABLE 27.—STANDARD DEVIATIONS FOR COLUMNS OF TABLE 25

Column	N_c	$\Sigma F x_c^2$	$\dfrac{\Sigma F x_c^2}{N_c}$	$\sigma_c = \sqrt{\dfrac{\Sigma F x_c^2}{N_c}}$
(1)	2	0	0	0
(2)	0			
(3)	1	0	0	0
(4)	7	8,342.86	1,191.8	34.5
(5)	5	480.00	96.0	9.8
(6)	8	1,400.00	175.0	13.2
(7)	9	4,800.00	533.3	23.1
(8)	13	2,830.77	217.8	14.8
(9)	18	6,577.78	365.4	19.1
(10)	11	3,200.00	290.9	17.1
(11)	5	320.00	64.0	8.0
(12)	2	0	0	0
	81			

This may be explained by the fact that much of the total variation in X_1 is due to the variation from column to column, a variation that is presumably due to association with X_2. When this variation is eliminated, the remaining variation is considerably reduced. A similar analysis would show the same results with respect to variation around the means of the rows.

If the association between X_1 and X_2 is measured by a straight line, the representativeness of this line may be measured by the dispersion of cases around it. Such a measure would be the standard deviation of the deviations from the line. The standard deviation of the vertical deviations from the line of regression of X_1 on X_2 will measure the representativeness of that line, and the standard deviation of the horizontal deviations from the line of regression of X_2 on X_1 will measure its representativeness. In either case, σ^2 equals the sum of the squared deviations from the line divided by N. If the line is fitted by the method of least squares, the sum of the squared deviations from the line may be computed from the equations[1]

$$N\sigma_{1.2}^2 = \Sigma d_{1.2}^2 = \Sigma X_1^2 - a_{1.2}\Sigma X_1 - b_{12}\Sigma X_1 X_2 \qquad (11)$$

and

$$N\sigma_{2.1}^2 = \Sigma d_{2.1}^2 = \Sigma X_2^2 - a_{2.1}\Sigma X_2 - b_{21}\Sigma X_2 X_1 \qquad (12)$$

or

$$\sigma_{1.2}^2 = \frac{\Sigma d_{1.2}^2}{N} \quad \text{and} \quad \sigma_{2.1}^2 = \frac{\Sigma d_{2.1}^2}{N}$$

These standard deviations from the lines of regression will always be less than the total standard deviation, because the variation represented by the line of regression has been eliminated by taking deviations from the line.

The average standard deviations around the means of columns or rows and the standard deviations around the lines of regression may be called "first-order standard deviations," in contrast to the total standard deviations, which may be called "zero-order standard deviations." Sometimes the first-order standard deviations are called "standard errors of estimate" since they indicate the error involved in using a column or row mean or a line of regression as an estimate of the dependent variable.

If the association between X_1 and X_2, say, is assumed to be measured by the means of X_1 for given values of X_2 or by the line of regression of X_1 on X_2, then the smallness of the first-order standard deviations relative to the zero-order standard deviations will give some measure of the degree of representativeness of these measures of association. As will be seen in the next section, this measure of the degree of representativeness of a line of regression is closely related to the so-called "Pearsonian coefficient of correlation." As a measure of the degree of representativeness of a progression of means, it is closely related to the "correlation ratio," which is discussed in Chap. XV, Nonlinear Correlation.

The Pearsonian Coefficient of Correlation. The progressions of means and lines of regression described above were concerned with describing the "law of relationship" between the two variables. They gave the average value of one variable associ-

---

[1] The proof of this is as follows:

$$\Sigma d_{1.2}^2 = \Sigma d_{1.2}(X_1 - a_{1.2} - b_{12}X_2) = \Sigma d_{1.2}X_1 - a_{1.2}\Sigma d_{1.2} - b_{12}\Sigma d_{1.2}X_2$$

But by the least-squares equations (1) and (2) $\Sigma d_{1.2} = 0$ and $\Sigma d_{1.2}X_2 = 0$. Hence $\Sigma d_{1.2}^2 = \Sigma d_{1.2}X_1 = \Sigma X_1^2 - a_{1.2}\Sigma X_1 - b_{12}\Sigma X_1 X_2$.

ated with given values of the other variable and showed how these average values tended to change in unison with the other variable. In this section, a measure of the degree of association between the two variables will be described. This measure is known as the Pearsonian coefficient of correlation after the man who devised it.

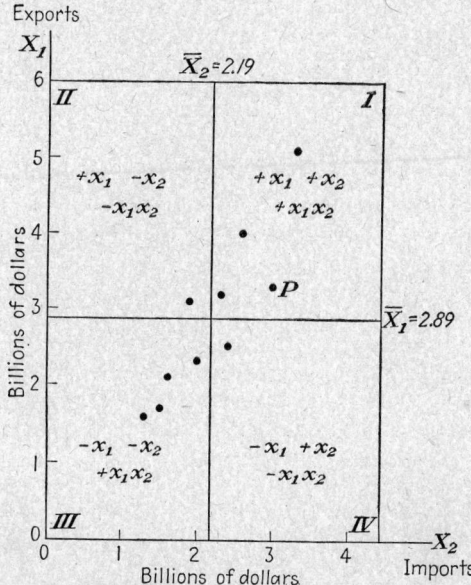

Fig. 109.—A bivariate scatter diagram showing the joint variation in imports into and exports from the United States. [*United States Department of Commerce, Monthly Summary of Foreign and Domestic Commerce of the United States, Vol.* 20 (*March*, 1940), *p.* 37; *Survey of Current Business, Vol.* 21 (*March*, 1941), *p.* 37; *Vol.* 22 (*March*, 1942), *pp.* 5–19.]

The coefficient of correlation suggested by Karl Pearson in 1890 is

$$r_{12} = \frac{\Sigma x_1 x_2}{N \sigma_1 \sigma_2} \qquad (13)$$

In this equation, x_1 and x_2 refer to deviations from the mean and N to the number of pairs of cases. For the sake of simplicity, this coefficient will now be explained by reference to a bivariate distribution in which the cases are not grouped into class intervals.

Arithmetic View of r. Table 28 and Fig. 109 show the joint variation of two variables. They indicate that the large values of X_1 representing total exports from the United States, 1932–1941, are associated, for the most part, with the large values of X_2, which represent total imports for consumption into the United States during the same period of years.

The average of X_1, designated $\bar{X}_1$, is found to be 2.89; and the average of X_2, designated $\bar{X}_2$, is 2.19. The deviations of each

TABLE 28.—EXPORTS AND IMPORTS OF MERCHANDISE, UNITED STATES, 1932–1941
(In billions of dollars)

Year	Total exports X_1 (1)	Total imports X_2 (2)	Deviations from respective $\bar{X}$		Product deviations $x_1 x_2$ (5)	
			x_1 (3)	x_2 (4)	+	−
1932	1.6	1.3	−1.29	−0.89	1.1481	
1933	1.7	1.5	−1.19	−0.69	0.8211	
1934	2.1	1.6	−0.79	−0.59	0.4661	
1935	2.3	2.0	−0.59	−0.19	0.1121	
1936	2.5	2.4	−0.39	0.21	. . . . .	−0.0819
1937	3.3	3.0	0.41	0.81	0.3321	
1938	3.1	1.9	0.21	−0.29	. . . . .	−0.0609
1939	3.2	2.3	0.31	0.11	0.0341	
1940	4.0	2.6	1.11	0.41	0.4551	
1941	5.1	3.3	2.21	1.11	2.4531	
$\Sigma =$	28.9	21.9	0	0	5.8218	−0.1428
	$\bar{X}_1 = 2.89$	$\bar{X}_2 = 2.19$			$\Sigma x_1 x_2 = 5.6790$	

variable from its respective mean are calculated and entered in the third and fourth columns of the table. The products of x_1 and x_2, the product deviations, are calculated, and the results entered in the appropriate division of the last column. The sum of column (5), that is, $\Sigma x_1 x_2$ (the sum of the product deviations), is 5.679.

In Fig. 109, an X_1 and an X_2 scale are set up in such a way as to accommodate the range of these variables as shown in columns (1) and (2) of Table 28. Lines perpendicular to the respective scales at the points $\bar{X}_1 = 2.89$ and $\bar{X}_2 = 2.19$ are drawn so that the figure is divided into four quadrants, quadrant

I containing values of X_1 and X_2 that are both higher than average (hence both x_1 and x_2 are positive); quadrant II containing values of X_2 that are smaller than average and values of X_1 that are larger than average (hence x_2 is negative and x_1 is positive); quadrant III containing values of X_1 and X_2 that are both smaller than average (hence both x_1 and x_2 are negative); and quadrant IV containing values of X_2 that are larger than average and values of X_1 that are smaller than average (hence x_2 is positive and x_1 is negative). The origin of the coordinates x_1, x_2, is at the intersection of the perpendicular lines at the $\bar{X}_1$ and $\bar{X}_2$ of the scales. For example, measured from the original origin, the point P has coordinates $X_1 = 3.3$, $X_2 = 3.0$; but measured from the intersection of the means the coordinates of point P are $x_2 = 0.41$, $x_1 = 0.81$ [see columns (1), (2), (3), and (4) for 1937, Table 28]. It should be noted that only one point is plotted in the fourth quadrant; this is the 1936 pair of variables from Table 28. The 1938 pair of variables from Table 28 appears as the sole point in the second quadrant. These two pairs of variables, 1936 and 1938, are the only ones in the set that have negative product deviations. The rest of the pairs of observations appear either in the first or third quadrant because their product deviations are positive quantities.

If the fluctuations of two variables are so associated that their plottings appear predominantly in quadrants I and III, the $\Sigma x_1 x_2$ will be positive. This will be so when larger than average values of X_1 are associated with larger than average values of X_2 (quadrant I) and smaller than average values of X_1 are associated with smaller than average values of X_2 (quadrant III). Also, if the two variables are so associated that their plottings appear predominantly in quadrants II and IV, the sum of the product deviations will be negative. This will be so when smaller than average values of X_2 are associated with larger than average values of X_1 (quadrant II) and when larger than average values of X_2 are associated with smaller than average values of X_1 (quadrant IV). Furthermore, if the plottings are equally distributed throughout the four quadrants, the sum of the product deviations will approach zero because of the canceling of plus and minus product deviations. This will be so when there is no tendency for association of the variables in any manner, that is, when smaller than average values of X_1 are associated about as often with larger values of X_2 as with smaller values of X_2, etc.

A similar procedure is followed in Table 29 and Fig. 110, in which X_3 is the price of United States government bonds and X_4 is the yield on such bonds. Casual inspection of the data reveals that, when the price of bonds is high, yield is low, and vice versa.

TABLE 29.—PRICES AND YIELDS ON UNITED STATES GOVERNMENT BONDS, 1932–1941

Averages on bonds outstanding due or callable after 12 years

Year	Average price ($100 par) X_3	Average yield, per cent X_4	Deviations from respective means		Product deviations x_3x_4	
			x_3	x_4		
	(1)	(2)	(3)	(4)	(5)	
					+	−
1932	98.8	3.68	−5.62	0.949	.....	−5.333
1933	102.3	3.31	−2.12	0.579	.....	−1.227
1934	104.6	3.12	0.18	0.389	0.070	
1935	105.5	2.79	1.08	0.059	0.064	
1936	103.7	2.65	−0.72	−0.081	0.583	
1937	101.7	2.68	−2.72	−0.051	0.139	
1938	103.4	2.56	−1.02	−0.171	0.174	
1939	106.0	2.36	1.58	−0.371	.....	−0.586
1940	107.2	2.21	2.78	−0.521	.....	−1.448
1941	111.0	1.95	6.58	−0.781	.....	−5.139
Σ =	1,044.2	27.31	0	0	1.030	−13.733
	$\bar{X}_3 = 104.42$	$\bar{X}_4 = 2.731$			or net	
					$\Sigma x_3x_4 = -12.703$	

The sum of the product deviations in Table 29 is a negative amount, namely, −12.703. Comparison of Figs. 109 and 110 will at once bring out the contrast in the location of pairs of plotted points. Whereas in Fig. 109 the points are mainly in quadrants I and III, the points in Fig. 110 appear principally in quadrants II and IV.

Again, the same procedure is followed in Table 30 and Fig. 111, in which X_5 is the height of Princeton freshmen and X_6 is the grade of these freshmen in their examination in economics.

In Table 30 the negative and positive product deviations so nearly offset each other that the sum of product deviations is only 1.33.   The tendency for the scatter of points throughout all four quadrants is depicted in Fig. 111 on page 345.

These three arithmetic illustrations appear to show that the sum of the product deviations from the arithmetic means of variables, $\Sigma x_1 x_2$, can be used to measure the extent to which

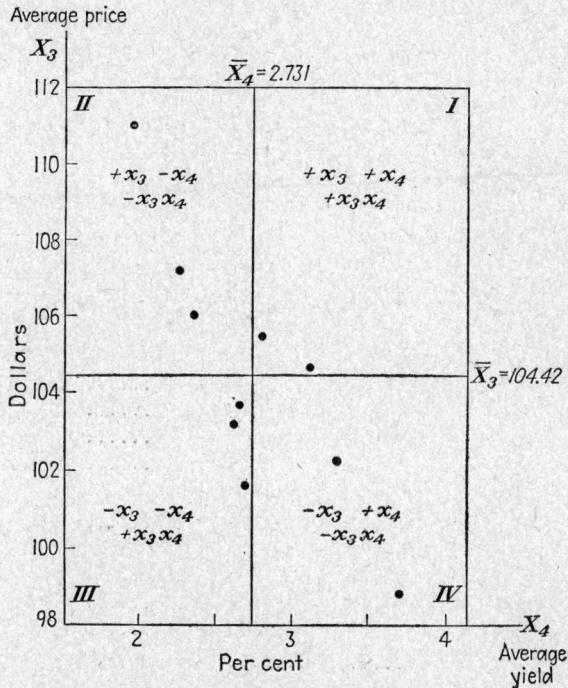

Fig. 110.—A bivariate scatter diagram showing the joint variation in the price and yield of United States government bonds.   [*Federal Reserve Bulletin, December,* 1938, *p.* 1045; *July,* 1940, *pp.* 701–702, *and Survey of Current Business, Vol.* 21 (*March,* 1941), *p.* 36; *Vol.* 22 (*March,* 1942), *p.* 18.]

the variables are associated or related.   Following are the reasons for this:

1. When smaller than average values of X_1 are associated with smaller than average values of X_2, the $x_1 x_2$ products, being $-x_1$ and $-x_2$, are positive, as shown in Tables 28 to 30.

2. When larger than average values of X_1 are associated with larger than average values of X_2, the $x_1 x_2$ products, being $+x_1$ and $+x_2$, are also positive, as shown in Tables 28 to 30.

3. On the other hand, when smaller than average values of X_1 are associated with larger than average values of X_2, the x_1x_2 products, being $-x_1$ and $+x_2$, are negative, as shown for 1932 and 1933 in Table 29.

4. When larger than average values of X_1 are associated with smaller than average values of X_2, the x_1x_2 products, being $+x_1$ and $-x_2$, are also negative, as shown for 1935, 1936, and 1939 in Table 29.

TABLE 30.—HEIGHTS OF FRESHMEN, PRINCETON CLASS OF 1941, AND GRADES ON EXAMINATION IN ECONOMICS

Heights of freshmen, in. X_5	Grades of freshmen, percentage of 100 X_6	Deviations from respective $\bar{X}$		Product deviations x_5x_6	
		x_5	x_6		
(1)	(2)	(3)	(4)	(5)	
				+	−
66.00	70	−3.96	+3.8	......	15.048
69.00	67	−0.96	+0.8	......	0.768
70.50	66	+0.54	−0.2	......	0.108
69.50	85	−0.46	+18.8	......	8.648
68.00	55	−1.96	−11.2	21.952	
70.50	60	+0.54	−6.2	......	3.348
70.50	67	+0.54	+0.8	0.432	
71.60	81	+1.64	+14.8	24.272	
73.25	66	+3.29	−0.2	......	0.658
70.75	45	+0.79	−21.2	......	16.748
$\Sigma = 699.60$	662	......	......	+46.656	−45.326
$\bar{X}_5 = 69.96$	$\bar{X}_6 = 66.2$			or net	
				$\Sigma x_5x_6 = +1.330$	

5. When no consistent association prevails between the pairs of variables observed, the $+x_1x_2$ products will balance or very nearly balance the $-x_1x_2$ products, as shown in Table 30.

The sum of the products of the deviations from the means indicates correspondence or lack of correspondence of variations in two sets of variables; but the simple sum of products cannot be taken as the measure of correlation between the two variables for the following reasons:

1. The sum of product deviations for one set of paired variables is not comparable with a similar sum of product deviations

for another set of paired variables. A small sum of product deviations may result from the fact that a small number of cases is included, and a large sum of product deviations may indicate merely that a large number of cases is involved; and yet the actual degree of correlation might be the same in the two sets. In the

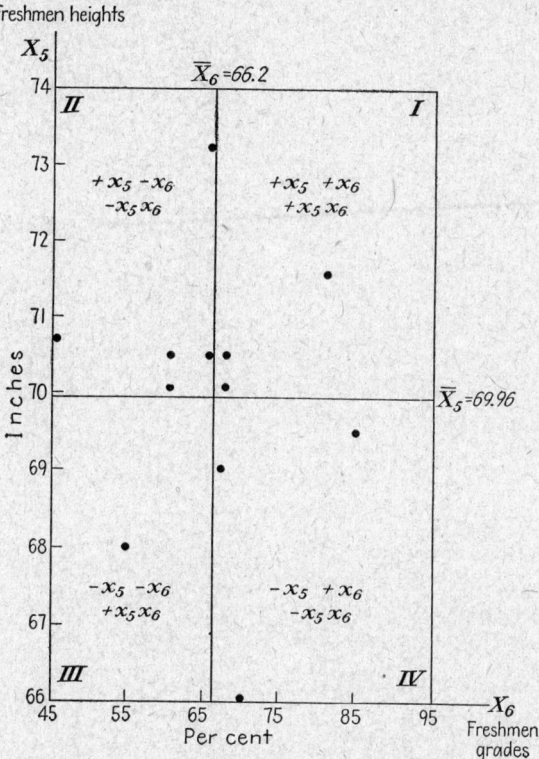

Fig. 111.—A bivariate scatter diagram showing the joint variation (or lack of it) between the heights of Princeton freshmen and their grades on an examination in economics.

second instance the larger sum of product deviations is due solely to the fact that it resulted from a larger number of cases. It seems obvious that an average of the product deviations is required. Such an average can be obtained by dividing the sum of product deviations by N. Thus the average product deviation is $\Sigma x_1 x_2 / N$.

2. The product deviations in terms of original units of the data are without meaning because of nonhomogeneity of units.

Suppose the X_1 variable is the price of wheat per bushel, which would be expressed in dollars and cents; and the X_2 variable is the birth rate. Or, again, suppose the X_1 variable is the height of men expressed in inches and the X_2 variable is the weight of men expressed in pounds. Or suppose the X_1 variable is the marriage rate and the X_2 variable is the volume of trade, or prices, etc. In all such pairs of variables, the product deviations in terms of original units are meaningless; they are products of nonhomogeneous things. What meaning can be ascribed to the product of inches and pounds or to the product of marriage rates and volume of trade? It is necessary to perceive in the situation a general common denominator.

The comparable thing being compared is the purely abstract thing, deviation above or below average; accordingly, the standard deviation σ may be used as a general common denominator. Whatever the original unit of measurement, if normally distributed the standard deviation represents approximately one-sixth the range of that variable. The standard deviation is a unit of deviation from the mean measuring a common characteristic among all variables and is, therefore, a homogeneous unit among all variables. Consequently, the standard deviation is used to reduce these product deviations to terms of comparability with each other. When this is done, the average product deviation becomes a measure of correlation known as the Pearsonian coefficient, namely,

$$r_{12} = \frac{\sum \frac{x_1}{\sigma_1} \frac{x_2}{\sigma_2}}{N}$$

Since σ_1 and σ_2 are constants in each particular problem, this equation may be written as follows:

$$r_{12} = \frac{\Sigma x_1 x_2}{N \sigma_1 \sigma_2}$$

This is the usual form in which the formula for the Pearsonian coefficient of correlation is given. The value of this average expression fluctuates between the limits $+1$ and -1. Any value greater than $+1$ or less than -1 is a mistake, not an error in the statistical sense. If $r = +1$, this means perfect positive correlation (large values of X_1 are associated with large values of X_2, and vice versa); if $r = -1$, this means perfect negative correlation (large values of X_1 are associated with small values of X_2, and vice versa); if $r_{12} = 0$, this means no linear correlation.

Calculation of the Coefficient of Correlation. The data in Table 28 may be taken to illustrate the detailed calculation

TABLE 31.—CALCULATION OF COEFFICIENT OF CORRELATION BETWEEN UNITED STATES EXPORTS AND IMPORTS, 1932–1941

Deviations from respective means, billions of dollars		Squares of deviations from respective means		Deviations from respective means in standard deviation units		Product deviations in standard-deviation units	
x_1	x_2	x_1^2	x_2^2	$\dfrac{x_1}{\sigma_1}$	$\dfrac{x_2}{\sigma_2}$	$\dfrac{x_1}{\sigma_1} \cdot \dfrac{x_2}{\sigma_2}$	
(1)	(2)	(3)	(4)	(5)	(6)	(7)	
						+	−
−1.29	−0.89	1.6641	0.7921	−1.251	−1.435	1.795	
−1.19	−0.69	1.4161	0.4761	−1.154	−1.112	1.283	
−0.79	−0.59	0.6241	0.3481	−0.766	−0.951	0.728	
−0.59	−0.19	0.3481	0.0361	−0.572	−0.306	0.175	
−0.39	0.21	0.1521	0.0441	−0.378	0.338	.....	−0.128
0.41	0.81	0.1681	0.6561	0.398	1.306	0.520	
0.21	−0.29	0.0441	0.0841	0.204	−0.467	.....	−0.C95
0.31	0.11	0.0961	0.0121	0.301	0.177	0.053	
1.11	0.41	1.2321	0.1681	1.077	0.661	0.712	
2.21	1.11	4.8841	1.2321	2.144	1.789	3.836	
		10.6290	3.8490	....	....	$\Sigma = 9.102$	−0.223
						or net	
		$\sigma_1 = 1.031$	$\sigma_2 = 0.6204$			$\sum \dfrac{x_1}{\sigma_1} \cdot \dfrac{x_2}{\sigma_2} = 8.879$	

The standard deviations were calculated from the sum of columns (3) and (4).

of the coefficient of correlation, by first making all product deviations in terms of respective standard-deviation units.

The Pearsonian coefficient of correlation may now be quickly calculated from the sum of product deviations in standard-deviation units [the foot of column (7) of Table 31]. This sum divided by N is the coefficient of correlation. In other words,

$$r = \frac{\sum \dfrac{x_1}{\sigma_1} \dfrac{x_2}{\sigma_2}}{N} = \frac{8.879}{10}$$
$$= 0.8879$$

It is not necessary, however, to divide each deviation by its standard deviation because the two standard deviations are constants. Table 28 having been constructed, if the standard deviations are calculated, as in columns (3) and (4), Table 31, it is then necessary only to use Eq. (3), as follows:

$$r = \frac{\Sigma x_1 x_2}{N \sigma_1 \sigma_2} = \frac{5.6790}{10(1.031)(0.6204)} = \frac{0.5679}{0.6396}$$
$$= 0.8879$$

Accordingly columns (5) to (7) of Table 31 need not be computed. For example, to calculate the coefficients of correlation for the data in Tables 29 and 30, the standard deviations are calculated and the respective coefficients of correlation are then obtained as follows:

Correlation between prices and yields on United States government bonds, 1932–1941:

$$r_{34} = \frac{\Sigma x_3 x_4}{N \sigma_3 \sigma_4} = \frac{-12.703}{10(3.16)(0.51)}$$
$$= \frac{-1.2703}{1.6116} \qquad \sigma_3 = 3.16$$
$$\qquad\qquad\qquad \sigma_4 = 0.51$$
$$= -0.7882$$

Correlation between heights and grades of freshmen:

$$r_{56} = \frac{\Sigma x_5 x_6}{N \sigma_5 \sigma_6} = \frac{1.33}{10(1.89)(10.96)}$$
$$= \frac{0.133}{(1.89)(10.96)} = \frac{0.133}{20.7} \qquad \sigma_5 = 1.889$$
$$\qquad\qquad\qquad\qquad\qquad \sigma_6 = 10.96$$
$$= 0.0064$$

For a small number of cases it is possible to calculate a coefficient of correlation according to the procedure illustrated in the tables and calculations immediately preceding. For a large number of pairs of values it is desirable to group the pairs into class intervals. The value of X_1 for each pair then becomes the mid-point of the interval to which the X_1 value belongs; the value of X_2 for the pair will be the mid-point to the interval to which the X_2 value belongs. If more than one pair of cases belongs to the same X_1 and X_2 intervals, the frequency of such pairs is determined. This procedure was illustrated by the analysis of Tables 24 and 25 in discussing the bivariate frequency distribution of 81 Mount Holyoke freshmen.[1] When the bivariates are arranged in a bivariate frequency distribution, r_{12} is measured by $\Sigma F x_1 x_2 / N \sigma_1 \sigma_2$ where F represents the frequency of pairs of values belonging to the same X_1 and X_2 intervals.   For example, in Table 25 (for $X_1 = 160-$, $X_2 = 120-$), $F = 5$, $x_1 = 47.4$, and $x_2 = 74.1$.   Accordingly, this $F x_1 x_2$ (for $X_1 = 160-$, $X_2 = 140-$) is equal to $5(47.4)(74.1) = 17,561.7$.   When this procedure is followed for the entire table, the $\Sigma F x_1 x_2$ is obtained. Special methods for calculating r from grouped data are described in detail in Chap. XIV, in which advantage is taken of certain short-cut procedures.

Relationship between Lines of Regression and r. If a line of regression is fitted by the method of least squares, the values of b_{12} and b_{21} are given by Eqs. 6 and 10.   It will now be shown that these reduce to formulas involving r_{12}.   From the definition of $r = \Sigma x_1 x_2 / N \sigma_1 \sigma_2$,

$$\Sigma x_1 x_2 = N \sigma_1 \sigma_2 r_{12}$$

Secondly, note that, from the definition of $\sigma_2^2 = \Sigma x_2^2 / N$,

$$\Sigma x_2^2 = N \sigma_2^2$$

Hence,

$$b_{12} = \frac{\Sigma x_1 x_2}{\Sigma x_2^2} = \frac{N \sigma_1 \sigma_2 r_{12}}{N \sigma_2^2} = r_{12} \frac{\sigma_1}{\sigma_2}$$

In the same manner it can be shown that

$$b_{21} = r_{12} \frac{\sigma_2}{\sigma_1}$$

Hence, if deviations of the variables are measured from their mean values, the lines of regression may be written (in this case the $a_{1.2}$ and $a_{2.1}$ are both zero)

$$x_1' = r_{12} \frac{\sigma_1}{\sigma_2} x_2 \tag{14}$$

$$x_2' = r_{12} \frac{\sigma_2}{\sigma_1} x_1 \tag{15}$$

If the first of these equations is divided by σ_1 and the second by

[1] See pp. 325–326.

σ_2, they become

$$\frac{x_1'}{\sigma_1} = r_{12} \frac{x_2}{\sigma_2}$$

$$\frac{x_2'}{\sigma_2} = r_{12} \frac{x_1}{\sigma_1}$$

Thus it may be concluded that if the variables are measured in standard-deviation units, the slopes of the lines of regression are the Pearsonian coefficient of correlation. In this light, r_{12} is the change in the average value of X_1 expressed in σ units when

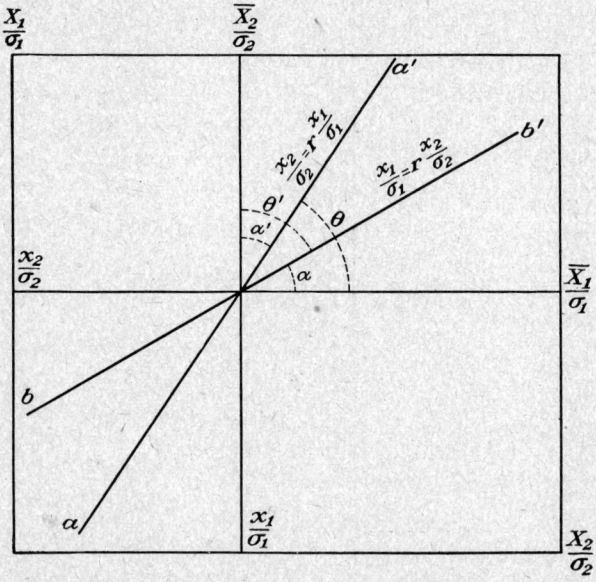

Fig. 112.—Diagram showing relationship between lines of regression and the Pearsonian coefficient of correlation r.

X_2 changes by one σ_2 unit. It is also the change in the average value of X_2 expressed in σ_2 units when X_1 changes by one σ_1 unit.

This property of r is shown geometrically in Fig. 112. This shows that the slope of the regression of X_1 on X_2 is r, with reference to the X_2-axis, and $1/r$ with reference to the X_1-axis; that is to say, the line of regression of X_1 on X_2 makes an angle with the X_2-axis equal to r and an angle with the X_1-axis equal to $1/r$. The slope of the regression of X_2 on X_1 is likewise r, but with reference to the X_1-axis, and $1/r$ with reference to the X_2-axis; that is to say, the line of regression of X_2 on X_1 makes an angle with the X_1-axis equal to r and an angle with the X_2-axis equal to $1/r$. In other words, in Fig. 112, angle α equals α', and angle θ equals angle θ'. All this is on the assumption that the variables are expressed in standard-deviation units as indicated in the equations above.

Thus, in Fig. 112, the tangent of the angle α is r, and that of the angle θ is $1/r$. When $|\alpha| \leqq \pi/4$, $r = \tan \alpha \leqq 1$. Geometrically, within the limits $|\alpha| \leqq \pi/4$, $\tan \alpha$ varies between $+1$ and -1, passing through zero, and $\tan \theta$ between $+1$ and -1, passing through infinity. The two lines of regression merge into one line when $r = 1$ (for $\tan \alpha = 1$ when the angle is a 45-degree angle).

Relationship between r and the First-order Standard Deviation. It will be recalled that the standard deviation of the deviations from the line of regression of X_1 on X_2 is equal to

$$N\sigma_{1.2}^2 = \Sigma X_1^2 - a_{1.2}\Sigma X_1 - b_{12}\Sigma X_1 X_2$$

If the variables are measured from their mean values, this becomes

$$N\sigma_{1.2}^2 = \Sigma x_1^2 - b_{12}\Sigma x_1 x_2$$

But

$$\Sigma x_1^2 = N\sigma_1^2 \qquad b_{12} = \frac{r_{12}\sigma_1}{\sigma_2} \qquad \text{and} \qquad \Sigma x_1 x_2 = N\sigma_1\sigma_2 r_{12}$$

Hence,

$$N\sigma_{1.2}^2 = N\sigma_1^2 - N\sigma_1^2 r_{12}^2$$

and

$$\sigma_{1.2}^2 = \sigma_1^2(1 - r_{12}^2)$$

Finally,

$$\sigma_{1.2} = \sigma_1 \sqrt{1 - r_{12}^2} \qquad (16)$$

In the same manner,

$$\sigma_{2.1} = \sigma_2 \sqrt{1 - r_{12}^2} \qquad (17)$$

These formulas may also be put in the form

$$r_{12}^2 = 1 - \frac{\sigma_{1.2}^2}{\sigma_1^2} \qquad (18)$$

$$r_{12}^2 = 1 - \frac{\sigma_{2.1}^2}{\sigma_2^2} \qquad (19)$$

It will thus be seen that r is closely related to the scatter about the lines of regression. If this scatter is a small percentage of the total scatter, indicating a high degree of representativeness of a line of regression, then r is high. If the scatter is a large percentage of the total variation in the dependent variable, indicating a low degree of representativeness of a line of regression, then the value of r is small. In other words, the better a line of regression fits the data, the higher the value of r, and vice versa. The Pearsonian coefficient of correlation is thus a measure of the goodness of fit of the lines of regression.

The Pearsonian Coefficient of Correlation and the Analysis of Variance. For every point on a bivariate scatter diagram such as Fig. 107, there is a corresponding point on the line of regression of X_1 on X_2. Geometrically this is obtained by projecting the point vertically onto the line of regression (see Fig. 107). Algebraically, the x_1 coordinate of a point on the line of regression is found by substituting the given value of x_2 in the regression equation $x_1' = r_{12} \dfrac{\sigma_1}{\sigma_2} x_2$.

When the variables are measured from their mean values, the mean of the various values of x_2 is zero. Hence the mean of the corresponding values of x_1' is zero also. The standard deviation of these x_1' values is thus

$$\sigma_{x_1'}^2 = \frac{\Sigma (x_1')^2}{N} = r_{12}^2 \frac{\sigma_1^2}{\sigma_2^2} \frac{\Sigma x_2^2}{N} = r_{12}^2 \sigma_1^2$$

Equation (16) may thus be written

$$\sigma_{1.2}^2 = \sigma_1^2 - \sigma_{x_1'}^2$$

or

$$\sigma_1^2 = \sigma_{x_1'}^2 + \sigma_{1.2}^2 \tag{20}$$

This says that the total variance of the x_1 values is equal to the variance of the corresponding points on the line of regression plus the variance of the deviations from these points. Another way of looking at this is to regard the total variation in X_1 as made up of two parts, one consisting of the variation $(\sigma_{x_1'}^2)$ due to its association with X_2 as represented by the line of regression, the other representing the variation in X_1 due to its association with factors independent of X_2 (that is, $\sigma_{1.2}^2$).

Similar analysis shows that

$$\sigma_2^2 = \sigma_{x_2'}^2 + \sigma_{2.1}^2 \tag{21}$$

in other words, that the total variance in X_2 is made up of a part $(\sigma_{x_2'}^2)$ due to its association with X_1 as represented by the line of regression of X_2 on X_1 and a part $(\sigma_{2.1}^2)$ due to its association with factors independent of X_2 as measured by the deviations from this line of regression.

The formula $\sigma_{x_1'}^2 = r_{12}^2 \sigma_1^2$, which may also be written $r_{12}^2 = \sigma_{x_1'}^2 / \sigma_1^2$, sheds further light on the meaning of r. It shows that r_{12}^2 measures the proportion of the total variance in X_1 that is due to its association with X_2. It also measures the proportion of the total variance in X_2 that is due to its association with X_1.

CHAPTER XIV

COMPUTATION OF r AND OTHER MEASURES OF CORRELATION

The previous chapter was concerned with an explanation of the various devices used to measure the association between two variables. This chapter will illustrate their use by carrying out a numerical analysis. Only linear correlation will be considered here. Measures of nonlinear correlation will be discussed in Chap. XV.

The order of analysis will be first to calculate the correlation coefficient. This will be done for both ungrouped and grouped data, and use will be made of short-cut methods of calculation. For the grouped data, lines of regression will be computed, and first-order variances and standard deviations. Reference will again be made to the progressions of means, but the analysis will be continued no further than in the previous chapter.

Computation of r from Ungrouped Data. Since $x = X - \bar{X}$, it follows that

$$\Sigma x_1 x_2 = \Sigma(X_1 - \bar{X}_1)(X_2 - \bar{X}_2) = \Sigma X_1 X_2 - N\bar{X}_1\bar{X}_2$$

Likewise, σ_1 and σ_2 are equal to

$$\sqrt{\frac{\Sigma X_1^2}{N} - \bar{X}_1^2} \quad \text{and} \quad \sqrt{\frac{\Sigma X_2^2}{N} - \bar{X}_2^2}$$

Hence the correlation coefficient can be computed from the equation

$$r_{12} = \frac{\Sigma X_1 X_2 - N\bar{X}_1\bar{X}_2}{\sqrt{\Sigma X_1^2 - N\bar{X}_1^2}\sqrt{\Sigma X_2^2 - N\bar{X}_2^2}} \tag{1}$$

To illustrate the use of this formula consider again the data on exports and imports of Table 28.[1] These are reproduced in Table 32, together with the calculations of $\Sigma X_1 X_2$, $\bar{X}_1$, $\bar{X}_2$, ΣX_1^2, and ΣX_2^2. Three check columns are also employed. The checks are column (1) + column (2) = column (6);

column (3) + column (4) = column (7);

and   column (3) + column (5) = column (8).

[1] See p. 340.

In the preliminary calculations of Table 32, the last check failed. This showed that a mistake had been made in either column (5) or column (8), for column (3) checked with columns (4) and (7). After some investigation the mistake was found in column (8). By dividing the checks up in this way, an error can be easily located. This sort of check is called a "Charlier check."

TABLE 32.—WORK SHEET FOR COMPUTING r FROM UNGROUPED DATA

(1)	(2)	(3)	(4)	(5)	(6)	(7)	(8)
X_1	X_2	$X_1 X_2$	$X_1{}^2$	$X_2{}^2$	$X_1 + X_2$	$X_1(X_1 + X_2)$	$X_2(X_1 + X_2)$
1.6	1.3	2.08	2.56	1.69	2.9	4.64	3.77
1.7	1.5	2.55	2.89	2.25	3.2	5.44	4.80
2.1	1.6	3.36	4.41	2.56	3.7	7.77	5.92
2.3	2.0	4.60	5.29	4.00	4.3	9.89	8.60
2.5	2.4	6.00	6.25	5.76	4.9	12.25	11.76
3.3	3.0	9.90	10.89	9.00	6.3	20.79	18.90
3.1	1.9	5.89	9.61	3.61	5.0	15.50	9.50
3.2	2.3	7.36	10.24	5.29	5.5	17.60	12.65
4.0	2.6	10.40	16.00	6.76	6.6	26.40	17.16
5.1	3.3	16.83	26.01	10.89	8.4	42.84	27.72
$\Sigma = 28.9$ $\bar{X}_1 = 2.89$	21.9 $\bar{X}_2 = 2.19$	68.97	94.15	51.81	50.8	163.12	120.78

Checks:
$$\Sigma(1) + \Sigma(2) = \Sigma(6)$$
$$28.9 + 21.9 = 50.8$$
$$\Sigma(3) + \Sigma(4) = \Sigma(7)$$
$$68.97 + 94.15 = 163.12$$
$$\Sigma(3) + \Sigma(5) = \Sigma(8)$$
$$68.97 + 51.81 = 120.78$$

From Table 32, r is found according to Eq. (1) to be equal to

$$r_{12} = \frac{68.97 - 10(2.89)(2.19)}{\sqrt{(94.15 - 10 \times \overline{2.89^2})} \sqrt{(51.81 - 10 \times \overline{2.19^2})}}$$
$$= \frac{68.97 - 63.291}{\sqrt{(94.15 - 83.521)} \sqrt{(51.81 - 47.961)}}$$
$$= \frac{5.679}{\sqrt{(10.629)} \sqrt{(3.849)}} = \frac{5.679}{(3.26)(1.962)} \quad \begin{matrix} \sigma_1 = \sqrt{1.0629} \\ \sigma_2 = \sqrt{0.3849} \end{matrix}$$
$$= \frac{5.679}{6.396} = 0.8879$$

TABLE 33.—GRADES IN SECOND- AND FIRST-SEMESTER ENGLISH, 81 FRESH-
MEN AT MOUNT HOLYOKE

(A, B, C, and D grades have been converted to a numerical scale)

Student number	Second-semester grade X_1	First-semester grade X_2	Student number	Second-semester grade X_1	First-semester grade X_2
1	240	220	41	260	260
2	200	180	42	180	160
3	260	240	43	100	60
4	260	260	44	200	220
5	160	160	45	200	200
6	240	220	46	160	120
7	220	200	47	180	160
8	60	120	48	280	220
9	220	240	49	200	200
10	200	180	50	220	220
11	220	220	51	220	200
12	140	180	52	240	220
13	160	120	53	100	60
14	240	260	54	220	220
15	260	240	55	240	200
16	200	160	56	200	220
17	200	160	57	220	220
18	240	240	58	220	200
19	240	220	59	240	200
20	240	220	60	180	140
21	160	140	61	160	140
22	220	240	62	240	220
23	200	200	63	260	260
24	100	100	64	160	120
25	160	140	65	260	240
26	200	160	66	220	180
27	180	180	67	220	240
28	180	160	68	260	260
29	240	240	69	240	220
30	200	200	70	200	200
31	200	200	71	140	120
32	180	160	72	260	240
33	260	220	73	200	180
34	160	120	74	300	280
35	240	240	75	180	140
36	220	220	76	220	180
37	220	240	77	180	180
38	160	120	78	300	280
39	200	200	79	220	220
40	220	220	80	220	200
			81	200	180

This agrees to two decimal places with the previous calculations of this coefficient made in Chap. XIII. The difference is due to the different ways of rounding off decimals in making the calculations.

Computation of r from Grouped Data. *The Data.* The data to be used to illustrate the computation of *r* for grouped data are given in Table 33. They may be explained as follows:

First pair X_1, X_2. The first pair of observations are the second-semester and the first-semester English grades, respectively, of student 1, *viz.*, 240,220.

Second pair X_1, X_2. The second pair of observations are the second-semester and the first-semester English grades, respectively, of student 2, *viz.*, 200,180.

Third pair X_1, X_2. The third pair of observations are the second-semester and the first-semester English grades, respectively, of student 3, *viz.* 260,240.

The Correlation, or Bivariate Frequency, Table. After the data have been tabulated as in Table 33, a correlation table, which is in effect a bivariate frequency distribution, is constructed. The table is set up with class-interval scales suitable for each variable,[1] and additional columns and rows are arranged for the required calculations. In the center of each cell of the correlation table, frequencies are shown; for example, in the first column opposite the X_1 scale of Table 34, 2 is the frequency of occurrence of X_1 between 100 and 120 and X_2 between 60 and 80. Two students, in other words, have grades in second-semester English between 100 and 120 and grades in first-semester English between 60 and 80. When all the frequencies are recorded in the correlation table, it may be used as a work sheet for the calculation of the coefficient of correlation.

Short Method for Calculating r. Like the standard deviation and the mean, it is possible to find *r* by a short method making use of arbitrary origins.

In the formula for *r*,

$$r_{12} = \frac{\Sigma F x_1 x_2}{N \sigma_1 \sigma_2} \tag{2}$$

σ_1 and σ_2 may be calculated by the short method that has already been presented.[2] It remains only to evaluate $\Sigma F x_1 x_2$ in terms

[1] On the question of proper selection of class intervals, see pp. 199–206.
[2] See pp. 214–215.

TABLE 34.—CORRELATION TABLE

Showing the relationship between second-semester (X_1) and first-semester (X_2) grades of 81 Mount Holyoke freshmen

$X_1 \backslash X_2$	60-	80-	100-	120-	140-	160-	180-	200-	220-	240-	260-	280-	300-	320-	340-	Σ	$\dfrac{d_1}{i_1}$	$F\,\dfrac{d_1}{i_1}$	$F\left(\dfrac{d_1}{i_1}\right)^2$	$F\left(\dfrac{d_1}{i_1}\right)\left(\dfrac{d_2}{i_2}\right)$	$\bar{X}_r$
60-				1 18/18												1	-6	-6	36	18	130.00
80-																0	-5	0	0	0	
100-	2 48/24		1 16/16													3	-4	-12	48	64	83.33
120-																0	-3	0	0	0	
140-				1 6/6			1 0/0									2	-2	-4	8	6	160.00
160-				5 15/3	3 6/2	1 1/1										9	-1	-9	9	22	141.11
180-					2 0/0	4 0/0	2 0/0									8	0	0	0	0	170.00
200-						3 -3/-1	4 0/0	7 7/1	2 4/2							16	1	16	16	8	200.00
220-							2 0/0	4 8/2	7 28/4	4 24/6						17	2	34	68	60	225.29
240-								2 6/3	7 42/6	3 27/9	1 12/12					13	3	39	117	87	234.62
260-									1 8/8	4 48/12	4 64/16					9	4	36	144	120	256.67
280-									1 10/10							1	5	5	25	10	230.00
300-												2 60/30				2	6	12	72	60	290.00
$\Sigma =$	2	0	1	7	5	8	9	13	18	11	5	2				81	×	111	543	455	81
$\dfrac{d_2}{i_2}$	-6	-5	-4	-3	-2	-1	0	1	2	3	4	5								$A_1 = 190$	
$F\,\dfrac{d_2}{i_2}$	-12	0	-4	-21	-10	-8	0	13	36	33	20	10				57				$i_1 = 20$	
$F\left(\dfrac{d_2}{i_2}\right)^2$	72	0	16	63	20	8	0	13	72	99	80	50				493					
$F\left(\dfrac{d_1}{i_1}\right)\left(\dfrac{d_2}{i_2}\right)$	48	0	16	39	6	-2	0	21	92	99	76	60				455			$A_2 = 190$		
$\bar{Y}_c$	110.00		110.00	152.86	178.00	195.00	203.33	222.31	241.11	250.00	266.00	310.00							$i_2 = 20$		

of deviations from the arbitrary origins, A_1 and A_2, selected for the respective variables and in terms of the two correction factors C_1 and C_2. To do this, note that[1]

$$x_1 = d_1 - C_1$$

where

$$C_1 = \frac{\Sigma F d_1}{N}$$

and

$$x_2 = d_2 - C_2$$

where

$$C_2 = \frac{\Sigma F d_2}{N}$$

Therefore,

$$\Sigma F x_1 x_2 = \Sigma F(d_1 - C_1)(d_2 - C_2) \tag{3}$$

which expanded is as follows:

$$\Sigma F x_1 x_2 = \Sigma F d_1 d_2 - C_1 \Sigma F d_2 - C_2 \Sigma F d_1 + N C_1 C_2 \tag{4}$$

But $\Sigma F d_1 = N C_1$ and $\Sigma F d_2 = N C_2$, and hence

$$\Sigma F x_1 x_2 = \Sigma F d_1 d_2 - N C_1 C_2 \tag{5}$$

and accordingly the formula for calculating r by the use of an arbitrary origin for X_1 and an arbitrary origin for X_2 is

$$r_{12} = \frac{\Sigma F d_1 d_2 - N C_1 C_2}{N \sigma_1 \sigma_2} \tag{6}$$

Further saving in calculation results, however, if this formula is put in terms of class-interval units. In other words, the following form is more conveniently used:[2]

$$r_{12} = \frac{\sum F \dfrac{d_1}{i_1} \dfrac{d_2}{i_2} - N \dfrac{C_1}{i_1} \dfrac{C_2}{i_2}}{N \dfrac{\sigma_1}{i_1} \dfrac{\sigma_2}{i_2}} \tag{7}$$

The correlation table serves as a work sheet for the calculation of the coefficient of correlation, as follows:

[1] When $C_1 = \dfrac{\Sigma F d_1}{N}$, $\bar{X}_1 = A_1 + C_1$. By definition $x_1 = X_1 - \bar{X}_1$ and $d_1 = X_1 - A$; so that $x_1 = d_1 + A_1 - A_1 - C_1 = d_1 - C_1$.

[2] The value of the numerator alone is $\Sigma F x_1 x_2$; if the problem is one in multiple correlation, it will be convenient to have a record of this value as well as the value of r_{12}.

1. An arbitrary origin is chosen for each variable; thus, in Table 34, $A_1 = 190$ and $A_2 = 190$. The arbitrary origins are taken at the mid-points of a class interval about midway in the range of the distribution in order to reduce to a minimum the necessary computations.

2. A column at the side and a row at the bottom of the correlation table are used to indicate, in class-interval units, the deviations of each variable from the respective arbitrary origins. This supplies entries for the rows under the caption d_1/i_1 and entries in the columns opposite the stub headings d_2/i_2. In Table 34, $i_1 = i_2 = 20$.

3. The next column at the side and row at the bottom of Table 34 are for the purpose of entering the frequencies multiplied by the class-interval deviations. The sums of this column and row, respectively, are used in the calculation of the correction figures C_1/i_1 and C_2/i_2 and in the computation of the means of the separate frequency distributions. The sums of the columns give the separate frequency distribution of X_2, and the sums of the rows give the separate frequency distribution of X_1.

4. The next column and the next row are for the frequencies multiplied by the class-interval deviations squared, in order to obtain sums from which to calculate the standard deviations of the respective variables.

5. The means and standard deviations of the two variables are calculated as follows:[1]

Calculation of the means:

$$\bar{X}_1 = 190 + \tfrac{111}{81}(20) = 190 + 27.40740$$
$$= 217.4$$
$$\bar{X}_2 = 190 + \tfrac{57}{81}(20) = 190 + 14.074$$
$$= 204.1$$

Calculation of the standard deviations:[2]

$$\left(\frac{\sigma_1}{i_1}\right)^2 = \frac{543}{81} - \left(\frac{111}{81}\right)^2 = 6.70370 - 1.87791$$
$$= 4.82579$$

$$\frac{\sigma_1}{i_1} = 2.1968$$

$$\sigma_1 = 43.94$$

[1] Using Eq. (3), p. 213.
[2] Using Eq. (5), p. 215.

$$\left(\frac{\sigma_2}{i_2}\right)^2 = \frac{493}{81} - \left(\frac{57}{81}\right)^2 = 6.08642 - 0.49519$$

$$= 5.59123$$

$$\frac{\sigma_2}{i_2} = 2.3646$$

$$\sigma_2 = 47.29$$

6. The product of the deviations from the chosen arbitrary origins is obtained for each cell in the correlation table. This is obtained by multiplying the d_1/i_1 by the d_2/i_2 corresponding to the position of that cell. For example, for $X_1 = 100-$ and $X_2 = 60-$, the cell in the first column and third row of Table 34 there is a frequency of 2. According to the chosen arbitrary origins, this cell has a product deviation (in terms of class-interval units) of -6 multiplied by -4, or $+24$. Symbolically, this is $(d_1/i_1)(d_2/i_2)$. The table is divided into four quadrants by lines through the A_1 and A_2.

Two of these quadrants will have positive product deviations, and two will have negative product deviations. A product deviation is entered in each cell that contains frequencies and appears in the lower right corner of the cell. None are entered in the first quadrant because no frequencies occur in that quadrant. Frequencies occur in only one cell in the third quadrant, that is, in the $X_1 = 200-$, $X_2 = 160-$ cell, for which the deviation product is -1 multiplied by $+1$, or -1.

7. The product deviation in each cell is multiplied by the frequency occurring in that cell, in order to obtain the proper number of product deviations of that particular cell. The product deviation occurs once in some cases and several times in others. Obviously, when it occurs several times the sum of the product deviations is obtained by multiplying by the frequencies. These figures are entered in each cell in the upper right corner. Symbolically, they are $F(d_1/i_1)(d_2/i_2)$, for each cell.

8. The sum of the figures calculated in item 7 is obtained, that is, the sum of the product deviations multiplied by their respective frequencies. This is accomplished by adding the figures occurring in the upper right corner of each cell by rows and by columns and adding the sums of the rows or the sums of the columns to obtain the final sum. If both the latter are com-

puted, there will be a cross check on addition.   Symbolically, the
final aggregate is $\sum F\left(\dfrac{d_1}{i_1}\right)\left(\dfrac{d_2}{i_2}\right)$.

9. The coefficient of correlation is calculated by the use of
Eq. (7) shown above, as follows:

Calculation of r:

$$r_{12} = \frac{455 - 81\frac{57}{81}\frac{111}{81}}{81(2.19677)(2.36458)}$$

$$= \frac{455 - 78.11111}{420.74964} = \frac{376.88889}{420.74964} = +0.89576$$

Lines of Regression and First-order Variances.   All the values
that are needed to find the lines of regression of Table 34 have
now been calculated.   There are two lines of regression for each
correlation table—the first one represents the regression of X_1
on X_2 and the second the regression of X_2 on X_1.   Since r has
been computed, the easiest formulas for calculating these two
lines (in original units measured from the intersection of the
means of the two variables as an origin and not in class-interval
units) are as follows:

$$x_1' = r\,\frac{\sigma_1}{\sigma_2}\,x_2 \qquad x_2' = r\,\frac{\sigma_2}{\sigma_1}\,x_1$$

These equations can be expressed in the units of the original
data, that is, the scale as originally formed rather than in deviations from the means, as follows:

$$X_1' - \bar{X}_1 = r\,\frac{\sigma_1}{\sigma_2}\,(X_2 - \bar{X}_2) \qquad X_2' - \bar{X}_2 = r\,\frac{\sigma_2}{\sigma_1}\,(X_1 - \bar{X}_1)$$

Calculation.   For the problem illustrated, the lines of regression are calculated as

$$x_1' = 0.89576\,\frac{43.9354}{47.2915}\,x_2 \qquad x_2' = 0.89576\,\frac{47.2915}{43.9354}\,x_1$$

$$= 0.8322x_2 \qquad\qquad\qquad = 0.9642x_1$$

By substituting $X_1' - \bar{X}_1$ for x_1' and $X_2' - \bar{X}_2$ for x_2', these
equations may be written as follows:

$$X_1' - 217.4 = 0.8322(X_2 - 204.1)$$
$$X_1' = 0.832X_2 + 47.58$$
$$X_2' - 204.1 = 0.9642(X_1 - 217.4)$$
$$X_2' = 0.964X_1 - 5.55$$

In this form the equations are more easily interpreted as
prediction equations.   The first equation says that when a

student has a grade of 100 in first-semester English the predicted grade in second-semester English is $83.2 + 47.6 = 130.8$. The second equation says that when a student has a grade of 100 in second-semester English the predicted grade in first-semester English is $96.4 - 5.55 = 90.8$.

The two lines of regression are shown in Figs. 105 and 106.[1] In Fig. 105 line aa' represents the first line of regression,

$$X_1' = 0.832X_2 + 47.58$$

The small crosses show the location of the means of the columns (calculated and shown in Table 34). It is to be noted that the line of regression follows the progression of the means of the columns.

In Fig. 106, line bb' represents the second line of regression $X_2' = 0.964X_1 - 5.55$. The small circles show the location of the means of the rows (calculated and shown in Table 34). It is to be noted that the line of regression follows the progression of the means of the rows.

The scatter about each of the lines of regression, the first-order σ, is calculated by using the following formulas:[2]

$$\sigma_{1.2} = \sigma_1 \sqrt{1 - r_{12}^2} \qquad \sigma_{2.1} = \sigma_2 \sqrt{1 - r_{12}^2}$$

In the problem illustrated, the first-order variances are calculated as follows:

$$\sigma_{1.2} = 43.94(0.44453) \qquad \sigma_{2.1} = 47.29(0.44453)$$
$$= 19.53 \qquad\qquad\qquad = 21.02$$

(When $r = 0.89576$, $\sqrt{1 - r^2} = 0.44453$.)

In Figs. 105 and 106, which show the lines of regression, there are also shown the limits indicated by the first-order standard deviations. Between these limits, that is, the line of regression $\pm\sigma_{1.2}$ for Fig. 105 and the line of regression $\pm\sigma_{2.1}$ for Fig. 106, lie roughly two thirds of the frequencies, if it can be assumed that the population from which the sample is derived is normally distributed. This gives some idea of how accurate estimates based upon the lines of regression are likely to be. It is to be

---

[1] See pp. 328, 329.

[2] Calculation of $\sqrt{1 - r^2}$ and $1 - r^2$ is avoided by the use of J. R. Miner, *Tables of $\sqrt{1 - r^2}$ and $1 - r^2$ for Use in Partial Correlation and in Trigonometry* or an ordinary table of sines and cosines, since $\sin x = \sqrt{1 - \cos^2 x}$.

noted that all the means of the columns lie within the limits described by the first-order standard deviations and that all but two of the means of the rows lie within these limits.   Each of the latter two means of rows, lying outside these limits (the first row and the next to the last row) is based upon only one student's record.

Progressions of Means.   For these data the progressions of means have already been discussed in Chap. XIII.   Figures 105 and 106 show the means of the columns and the means of the rows plotted from the values computed in Table 34 and reproduced in Table 26.[1]   Figure 105 represents the means of the vertical frequency distributions of Tables 25 and 34; it gives the progression of the means of X_1 with changing values of X_2.   Figure 106 gives a similar analysis for the means of the rows.

[1] See pp. 330 and 358.

CHAPTER XV

NONLINEAR CORRELATION

All the foregoing discussion has been concerned with those cases in which the progression of the means is linear. In such cases it was found that $r = \Sigma x_1 x_2 / N \sigma_1 \sigma_2$ was an appropriate measure of correlation. If the progression of means and the distribution of cases around the means is as pictured in Fig. 113, however, r may show little correlation, especially in such cases as A and C, although there may be a high degree of association between the variables. It is the purpose of this chapter to indicate ways of describing and measuring such nonlinear correlation.

As indicated in an earlier chapter, the best way of studying any correlation is to make a bivariate scatter diagram of the data. If the data are numerous enough to be grouped into class intervals, then the means of the rows and columns may be computed and the variation in the means of each variable with changes in the other variable may be studied.

In the linear case in which a line of regression was used to measure the association it was found that, the smaller the scatter, the higher the degree of correlation, the equation being

$$r_{12}^2 = 1 - \frac{\sigma_{1.2}^2}{\sigma_1^2}$$

The same sort of formula may be used to measure the degree of relationship indicated by the progression in the means. To distinguish them from the correlation coefficient these measures are called "correlation ratios" and are defined by the formulas

$$\left. \begin{aligned} \eta_{12}^2 &= 1 - \frac{\sigma_{X - \bar{X}_c}^2}{\sigma_1^2} \\ \eta_{21}^2 &= 1 - \frac{\sigma_{X - \bar{X}_r}^2}{\sigma_2^2} \end{aligned} \right\} \quad (1)$$

where $\bar{X}_c$ represents the means of X_1 for various values of X_2,

$\bar{X}_r$ represents the means of X_2 for various values of X_1, and $\sigma^2_{X-\bar{X}_c}$ and $\sigma^2_{X-\bar{X}_r}$ represent the sum of the squared deviations around the means pooled for all the column or row means and

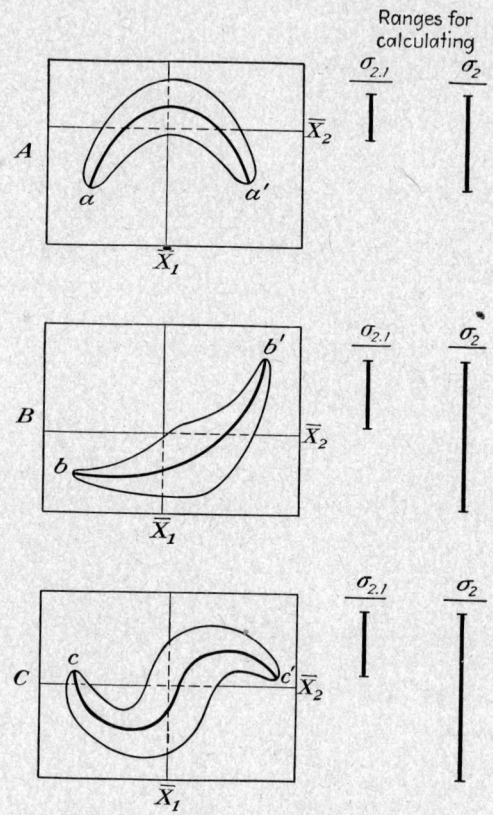

Fig. 113.—Illustrations of various kinds of nonlinear correlation.

divided by N.   Thus,

$$\sigma^2_{X-\bar{X}_c} = \frac{\sum_c \sum_i (X_{ic} - \bar{X}_c)^2}{N}$$

$$\sigma^2_{X-\bar{X}_r} = \frac{\sum_r \sum_i (X_{ir} - \bar{X}_r)^2}{N}$$

The correlation ratios η^2_{12} and η^2_{21} give some indication of the degree to which the means of one variable are successful in measuring the variation in the other variable. They may be used to measure either linear or nonlinear correlation.

If the means of one variable seem to mark off a definite curve or if in the case of ungrouped data a bivariate chart indicates a fairly definite form of nonlinear variation, then the average variation in one variable with changes in the other variable may be indicated by drawing a smooth curve or fitting one by some mathematical process, such as the method of least squares. Such a curve might be called a "curve of regression." A line of regression on the one hand indicates the average change in one variable with a unit change of the other variable; this average change is the same for all values of the independent variable, since the slope of a straight line is constant. A curve of regression on the other hand gives the average change in one variable with a unit change in the other variable; but this average change varies from one value of the independent variable to another, since the slope of a curve changes at each point. The technique of fitting a curve of regression will be discussed in a subsequent section.

To measure the degree with which a curve of regression measures the association between two variables, an index of correlation is defined in a manner similar to the definitions of r and η. It depends on the closeness with which the various cases are scattered about the curve and is defined by the formula

$$\left.\begin{aligned} I_{12}^2 &= 1 - \frac{\sigma_{X_1 - C_{12}}^2}{\sigma_1^2} \\[2mm] I_{21}^2 &= 1 - \frac{\sigma_{X_2 - C_{21}}^2}{\sigma_2^2} \end{aligned}\right\} \quad (2)$$

where C_{12} and C_{21} refer to the regression curves, $\sigma_{X_1 - C_{12}}^2$ refers to the variance of the deviations from the curve of regression of X_1 on X_2, and $\sigma_{X_2 - C_{21}}^2$ refers to the variance of the deviations from the curve of regression of X_2 on X_1.

Although $r_{12} = r_{21}$, the two correlation ratios and the two indexes of correlation are not necessarily equal. That is, $\eta_{12} \neq \eta_{21}$ and $I_{12} \neq I_{21}$. In addition, $\eta \geq I \geq r$.

Since the variance about the means or about a curve is never greater than the total variance, these formulas always give a positive value and their square roots are indeterminate as to sign.   The square roots of η^2 and I^2 give an index of correlation and the question as to whether it is a positive or negative relationship must be answered by reference to a correlation table or a figure showing the polygon or curve of regression.   In the case of curvilinear correlation, the question of positive or negative relationship often is irrelevant because two variables may be positively correlated up to a certain point and then negatively correlated beyond that point.   Consequently, it becomes necessary to describe the entire relationship.   For example, the death rate due to puerperal septicemia is correlated with ages of the female population in a nonlinear manner.   The relationship between the two is best described by a curve or polygon of regression, which would have to be seen in its entirety if the relationship is to be completely understood.   This is illustrated in Fig. 55 (page 151).   If r merely were calculated, it might conceivably be zero when there is in fact a close relationship.   An index of such a relationship is found by the calculation of the η's or the I's.

Calculation of the Correlation Ratio.   The calculation of the correlation ratio will be illustrated by reference to the Mount Holyoke data in Table 34 (page 358).   Although the relationship appears to be linear, it is worth while to compute the correlation ratio to see how close it comes to r.   If the difference is not very great, the linearity will be numerically demonstrated.

Equation (1) for the correlation ratios may be put in the form

$$\left.\begin{aligned}
\eta_{12}^2 &= \frac{\sigma_1^2 - \sigma_{\eta 1.2}^2}{\sigma_1^2} \\[2mm]
\eta_{21}^2 &= \frac{\sigma_2^2 - \sigma_{\eta 2.1}^2}{\sigma_2^2}
\end{aligned}\right\} \quad (3)$$

where $\sigma_{\eta 1.2}$ and $\sigma_{\eta 2.1}$ are abbreviated expressions for $\sigma_{x-\bar{x}_c}$ and $\sigma_{x-\bar{x}_r}$ and thus represent the average standard deviations around the means of the columns and the means of the rows, respectively, as explained above.   In order to apply these equations for finding the correlation ratios it is necessary to find the values of $\sigma_{\eta 1.2}^2$ and $\sigma_{\eta 2.1}^2$.   This can be most conveniently done with the help of a work sheet that makes use of arbitrary origins (A_1 and A_2) and class-interval deviations $\left(\dfrac{d_1}{i_1}\text{ and }\dfrac{d_2}{i_2}\right)$.   Such a work sheet is Table 35 in which the computations are carried out for the data of Table 34. The algebraic foundation for these computations is as follows:

It is assumed that the same A_1 is used for every column as for the total frequency distribution of X_1. Then for each column the sum of the squares of the deviation from the column mean would be[1]

$$\frac{\sum_{1}^{N_c} (X_{ic} - \bar{X}_c)^2}{i_1^2} = \sum_{1}^{N_c} F\left(\frac{d_1}{i_1}\right)^2 - \frac{\left(\sum_{1}^{N_c} F\frac{d_1}{i_1}\right)^2}{N_c}$$

For the sum of all "m" columns this would be

$$\frac{\sum_{1}^{m} \sum_{1}^{N_c} (X_{ic} - \bar{X}_c)}{i_1^2} = \sum_{1}^{m} \left[\sum_{1}^{N_c} F\left(\frac{d_1}{i_1}\right)^2 - \frac{\left(\sum_{1}^{N_c} F\frac{d_1}{i_1}\right)^2}{N_c} \right]$$

But

$$\sum_{1}^{m} \sum_{1}^{N_c} F\left(\frac{d_1}{i_1}\right)^2 \equiv \sum_{1}^{N} F\left(\frac{d_1}{i_1}\right)^2$$

and by definition $\sum_{1}^{m} \sum_{1}^{N_c} (X_{ic} - \bar{X}_c)^2 = N\sigma_{\eta 1.2}^2.$

Therefore,

$$\frac{N\sigma_{\eta.2}^2}{i_1^2} = \sum_{1}^{N} F\left(\frac{d_1}{i_1}\right)^2 - \sum_{1}^{m} \frac{\left(\sum_{1}^{N_c} F\frac{d_1}{i_1}\right)^2}{N_c} \tag{4}$$

It has been determined already that[2]

$$\frac{N\sigma_1^2}{i_1^2} = \frac{\sum F x_1^2}{i_1^2} = \sum F\left(\frac{d_1}{i_1}\right)^2 - \frac{\left(\sum F\frac{d_1}{i_1}\right)^2}{N} \tag{5}$$

[1] This follows from Eqs. (1) and (2) of Chap. VII. For it will be noted $\nu_2' = \Sigma F\left(\frac{d}{i}\right)^2 \Big/ N$

and $\qquad \nu_1' = \Sigma F\left(\frac{d}{i}\right) \Big/ N \quad$ and $\quad \mu_2' = \Sigma F x^2/N.$

[2] See Eqs. (1) and (2) of Chap. VII and previous footnote.

Each of the variances in Eq. (3) may be expressed in class-interval units so that its numerator is the arithmetic difference between Eqs. (5) and (4) and its denominator is Eq. (5). Thus,

$$\eta_{12}^2 = \frac{\sum\limits_{1}^{m} \dfrac{\left(\sum\limits_{1}^{N_c} F \dfrac{d_1}{i_1}\right)^2}{N_c} - \dfrac{\left(\sum F \dfrac{d_1}{i_1}\right)^2}{N}}{\sum F \left(\dfrac{d_1}{i_1}\right)^2 - \dfrac{\left(\sum F \dfrac{d_1}{i_1}\right)^2}{N}} \tag{6}$$

Similarly it can be shown that for a table with "l" rows

$$\eta_{21}^2 = \frac{\sum\limits_{1}^{l} \dfrac{\left(\sum\limits_{1}^{N_r} F \dfrac{d_2}{i_2}\right)^2}{N_r} - \dfrac{\left(\sum F \dfrac{d_2}{i_2}\right)^2}{N}}{\sum F \left(\dfrac{d_2}{i_2}\right)^2 - \dfrac{\left(\sum F \dfrac{d_2}{i_2}\right)^2}{N}} \tag{7}$$

All the items in these two formulas (6) and (7) are to be found on the work sheet in Table 34 with the exception of

$$\sum\limits_{1}^{m} \frac{\left(\sum\limits_{1}^{N_c} F \dfrac{d_1}{i_1}\right)^2}{N_c} \quad \text{and} \quad \sum\limits_{1}^{l} \frac{\left(\sum\limits_{1}^{N_r} F \dfrac{d_2}{i_2}\right)^2}{N_r}$$

These two figures are obtained from the correlation-ratio work sheet (Table 35).

In Table 35, the frequency is placed in large type in the center of a cell. Each column is now regarded as a separate frequency distribution whose total number of cases N_c is shown in the row headed N_c. For each column the same arbitrary origin ($A_1 = 190$) as that used in Table 34 is used; hence the same d_1/i_1 can be used for each column.

For all 11 columns in the upper right corner of each interval that contains a frequency is a number in small type representing

TABLE 35.—CORRELATION-RATIO WORK SHEET

Calculation of η_{12} and η_{21} between second-semester (X_1) and first-semester (X_2) grades of 81 Mount Holyoke freshmen

X_1 \ X_2	60-	80-	100-	120-	140-	160-	180-	200-	220-	240-	260-	280-	300-	320-	340-	N_r	$\sum_1^{N_r} F \dfrac{d_2}{i_2}$	(2) $\dfrac{(1)\times i_2}{N_r}$	(3) $\bar{X}_r$	(4) $\dfrac{(1)^2}{N_r}$	$\dfrac{d_1}{i_1}$
60-				1 / -6 / -3												1	-3	-60.00	130.00	9.0000	-6
80-																0	0				-5
100-	2 / -8 / -12		1 / -4 / -4													3	-16	-106.67	83.33	85.3333	-4
120-																0	0				-3
140-				1 / -2 / -3			1 / -2 / 0									2	-3	-30.00	160.00	4.5000	-2
160-				5 / -5 / -15	3 / -3 / -6	1 / -1 / -1										9	-22	-48.89	141.11	53.7777	-1
180-					2 / 0 / -4	4 / 0 / -4	4 / 0 / 0	2 / 0 / 2	2 / 0 / 4							8	-8	-20.00	170.00	8.0000	0
200-							4 / 4 / 0	7 / 7 / 7	4 / 4 / 8	4 / 4 / 12						16	8	10.00	200.00	4.0000	1
220-								2 / 2 / 2	7 / 14 / 14	3 / 6 / 9	1 / 2 / 3					17	30	35.29	225.29	52.9412	2
240-									7 / 21 / 14	3 / 9 / 9	4 / 12 / 16					13	29	44.62	234.62	64.6923	3
260-									1 / 4 / 2	4 / 16 / 12	4 / 16 / 16					9	30	66.67	256.67	100.0000	4
280-									1 / 5 / 2							1	2	40.00	230.00	4.0000	5
300-												2 / 12 / 10				2	10	100.00	290.00	50.0000	6
N_c	2	0	1	7	5	8	9	13	18	11	5	2				**81**				**436.2445**	$A_1 = 190$
(1) $\sum_1^{N_c} F \dfrac{d_1}{i_1}$	-8	0	-4	-13	-3	2	6	21	46	33	19	12									$i_1 = 20$
(2) $\dfrac{(1)\times i_1}{N_c}$	-80.00	0	-80.00	-37.14	-12.00	5.00	13.33	32.31	51.11	60.00	76.00	120.00									
(3) $\bar{X}_c$	110.00	0	110.00	152.86	178.00	195.00	203.33	222.31	241.11	250.00	266.00	310.00								$A_2 = 190$	
(4) $\dfrac{(1)^2}{N_c}$	32.0000		16.0000	24.1428	1.8000	0.5000	4.0000	33.9231	117.5556	99.0000	72.2000	72.0000				**473.1215**					$i_2 = 20$
$\dfrac{d_2}{i_2}$	-6	-5	-4	-3	-2	-1	0	1	2	3	4	5									

the $F\dfrac{d_1}{i_1}$ for that interval of the column.   These are then summed,

giving for each column a $\displaystyle\sum_1^{N_c} F\dfrac{d_1}{i_1}$; each of these sums is shown

in the row with the stub title $\displaystyle\sum_1^{N_c} F\dfrac{d_1}{i_1}$. If each sum is divided

by the number of cases in the column N_c and multiplied by i, the resulting number is the correction factor C_c for that column. Accordingly, the mean for that column $(\bar{X}_c)$ can be found by using the formula $\bar{X}_c = A_1 + C_c$. The results of this calculation are shown in the row with the stub title $\dfrac{(1) \times i_1}{N_c}$; and the column means are shown in the row with the stub heading $\bar{X}_c$.

In order to obtain the figure to be used in the formula for the correlation ratio—that is, for the square root of η_{12}^2—another row of figures is now added to Table 35; this set of figures consists of the $\left(\displaystyle\sum_1^{N_c} F\dfrac{d_1}{i_1}\right)^2 \Big/ N_c$ for each column; and when these

are summed for all columns (say for "m" columns), the resulting figure is as follows:

$$\sum_1^m \frac{\left(\displaystyle\sum_1^{N_c} F\dfrac{d_1}{i_1}\right)^2}{N_c} = 473.1215$$

Using Eq. (6), the correlation ratio of X_1 on X_2 is thus[1]

$$\eta_{12}^2 = \frac{473.1215 - \dfrac{(111)^2}{81}}{543 - \dfrac{(111)^2}{81}}$$

$$= \frac{473.1215 - 152.1111}{543.0000 - 152.1111} = \frac{321.0104}{390.8889}$$

$$= 0.82123$$

$$\eta_{12} = 0.9062$$

[1] The values of $\displaystyle\sum F\dfrac{d_1}{i_1} = 111$ and $\displaystyle\sum F\left(\dfrac{d_1}{i_1}\right)^2 = 543$ are found in Table 34. In that table the same A_1 was used for the frequency distribution of X_1.

To calculate the means of the rows and the correlation ratio of X_2 on X_1, every row of Table 35 is treated as a separate frequency distribution. The same A_2 is used for each row as the A_2 in Table 34 for the entire X_2 distribution. Accordingly, the same set of d_2/i_2 may be used for each row. The $F\dfrac{d_2}{i_2}$ for each interval of each row is placed in small type in the lower right corner of the interval. These summed for each row give the $\displaystyle\sum_1^{N_r} F\dfrac{d_2}{i_2}$, shown in the column with that title heading. From these are obtained the C_r for each row, by the same procedure as that used for finding the column means. For each row, the $\left(\displaystyle\sum_1^{N_r} F\dfrac{d_2}{i_2}\right)^2 \Big/ N_r$ is then computed and entered in the column with the title $(1)^2/N_r$. The sum of these for all row frequency distributions (say l rows) constitutes the aggregate

$$\sum_1^{l} \frac{\left(\displaystyle\sum_1^{N_r} F\dfrac{d_2}{i_2}\right)^2}{N_r} = 436.2445$$

This is the value required by Eq. (7) for finding η_{21}. Thus,[1]

$$\eta_{21}^2 = \frac{436.2445 - \dfrac{(57)^2}{81}}{493 - \dfrac{(57)^2}{81}}$$

$$= \frac{436.2445 - 40.1111}{493.000 - 40.1111} = \frac{396.1334}{452.8889}$$

$$= 0.87467$$

$$\eta_{21} = 0.9352$$

The Correlation Ratio and Analysis of Variance. The square of the correlation ratio is a measure of the proportion of variance due to correlation, in the same manner as it was indicated that

---

[1] The values for $\displaystyle\sum F\dfrac{d_2}{i_2} = 57$ and $\displaystyle\sum F\left(\dfrac{d_2}{i_2}\right)^2 = 493$ are found in Table 34. In that table the A_2 is the same as the A_2 used in the present table.

the square of the coefficient of correlation is a measure of pro-portion of variance due to correlation.

As has been explained, when expressed in the form $r^2\sigma_1^2 = \sigma_{x'_1}^2$ the square of the coefficient of correlation reveals itself as the proportion of the total variance that is due to correlation or association with X_2 as measured by the line of regression of X_1 on X_2. In a similar manner, $\eta_{12}^2\sigma_1^2 = \sigma_{\bar{X}_c}^2$, and likewise $\eta_{21}^2\sigma_2^2 = \sigma_{\bar{X}_r}^2$. The square of the correlation ratio thus describes the proportion of the total variance that is due to correlation as measured by the fluctuations in the means of the columns and rows. The standard deviation of the means of the columns squared is the variance that is due to correlation of X_1 with X_2 and similarly for the correlation of X_2 with X_1.

To demonstrate algebraically that $\eta_{12}^2\sigma_1^2 = \sigma_{\bar{X}_c}^2 = \sigma_1^2 - \sigma_{\eta 1.2}^2$, it is necessary first to note that by definition the mean of the weighted means of the columns equal $\bar{X}_1$. By definition,

$$\bar{X}_c = \frac{\sum\limits_1^{N_c} X_1}{N_c}$$

and thus

$$N_c\bar{X}_c = \sum\limits_1^{N_c} X_1$$

which, if summed for all columns, becomes

$$\sum\limits_1^m N_c\bar{X}_c = \sum\limits_1^m \sum\limits_1^{N_c} X_1 \tag{8}$$

But

$$\sum\limits_1^m \sum\limits_1^{N_c} X_1 = \sum X_1$$

and hence, if Eq. (8) is divided by N, it is equivalent to

$$\frac{\sum\limits_1^m N_c\bar{X}_c}{N} = \frac{\Sigma X_1}{N} \tag{9}$$

which was to be proved.

If $\bar{X}_1$, the mean of the entire X_1 distribution, is now selected as the arbitrary origin,

$$\bar{X}_c = \bar{X}_1 + C_c \quad \text{or} \quad C_c = \bar{X}_c - \bar{X}_1$$

Also, when the mean of the entire distribution is selected as the arbitrary origin for each column, the standard deviation of the column is found by

$$\sigma_c^2 = \frac{\sum\limits_1^{N_c} x_1^2}{N_c} - C_c^2 \quad [x_1^2 = (X_1 - \bar{X}_1)^2]$$

On substituting $C_c = \bar{X}_c - \bar{X}_1$ and transposing, an expression for each column similar to the following will result:

(a)
$$\frac{\sum\limits_1^{N_c} x_1^2}{N_c} = \sigma_c^2 + (\bar{X}_c - \bar{X}_1)^2$$

Multiplying the equation for each column by its N_c, respectively, will result for each column in

(b)
$$\sum\limits_1^{N_c} x_1^2 = N_c \sigma_c^2 + N_c(\bar{X}_c - \bar{X}_1)^2$$

When the whole series, one for each column, of equations such as (b) are totaled, the following result is obtained:

(c)
$$\sum\limits_1^m \sum\limits_1^{N_c} x_1^2 = \sum\limits_1^m N_c \sigma_c^2 + \sum\limits_1^m N_c(\bar{X}_c - \bar{X}_1)^2$$

But, in this equation,

$$\sum\limits_1^m \sum\limits_1^{N_c} x_1^2 = \sum\limits_1^N x_1^2 = N\sigma_1^2$$

and

$$\sum\limits_1^m N_c \sigma_c^2 = N\sigma_{\eta_{1.2}}^2$$

Moreover, by definition, the explained variance, that is to say, the variance of the means of the columns about the weighted mean of these means, is as follows:

$$N\sigma_{\bar{X}_c}^2 = \Sigma N_c(\bar{X}_c - \bar{X}_1)^2 = \sum\limits_1^m N_c(\bar{X}_c - \bar{X}_1)^2$$

Consequently, (c) may be written

$$N\sigma_1^2 = N\sigma_{\eta_{1.2}}^2 + N\sigma_{\bar{X}_c}^2$$

or

$$\sigma_1^2 = \sigma_{\eta_{1.2}}^2 + \sigma_{\bar{X}_c}^2$$

Substituting the value of $\sigma_{\eta_{1.2}}^2 = \sigma_1^2 - \sigma_{\bar{X}_c}^2$ in Eq. (3) for the correlation ratio gives the following:

$$\left. \begin{array}{c} \eta_{12}^2 = \dfrac{\sigma_{\bar{X}_c}^2}{\sigma_1^2} \\[2mm] \sigma_{\bar{X}_c}^2 = \eta_{12}^2 \sigma_1^2 \end{array} \right\} \quad (10)$$

Similarly, it can be shown that

$$\left. \begin{array}{c} \eta_{21}^2 = \dfrac{\sigma_{\bar{X}_r}^2}{\sigma_2^2} \\[2mm] \sigma_{\bar{X}_r}^2 = \eta_{21}^2 \sigma_2^2 \end{array} \right\} \quad (11)$$

Calculation of Curvilinear Regression. To illustrate the statistical problem involved in curvilinear regression and the calcula-

TABLE 36.—STOCKS, PRODUCTION, AND IMPORTS OF COTTON AND PRICE OF COTTON RECEIVED BY PRODUCERS IN THE UNITED STATES
Stocks at beginning of crop year plus year's production plus net imports. Prices are deflated by United States index of wholesale prices for crop years.

Year beginning Aug. 1	Deflated average price, cents per pound X_1	Stocks, production, and imports, ten billion bales X_2
1920–1921	13.47	1.726
1921–1922	18.06	1.480
1922–1923	22.63	1.306
1923–1924	29.30	1.274
1924–1925	22.63	1.550
1925–1926	19.19	1.805
1926–1927	12.92	2.195
1927–1928	20.95	1.711
1928–1929	18.71	1.749
1929–1930	18.34	1.755
1930–1931	12.13	1.862
1931–1932	8.38	2.378
1932–1933	10.30	2.307
1933–1934	14.04	2.162
1934–1935	15.76	1.765
1935–1936	13.83	1.815
1936–1937	14.48	1.821
1937–1938	10.29	2.382
1938–1939	11.17	2.383

tion of the correlation index I, data on cotton stocks, production, and imports compared with cotton prices, 1920–1939, have been selected. They are shown in Table 36 and plotted in Fig. 114.

The position of plotted bivariates in Fig. 114 suggests that a curve such as aa' might fit the data. The question of the type of curve fitted is of particular importance in curvilinear regression and accordingly three types will be discussed for illustrative purposes.

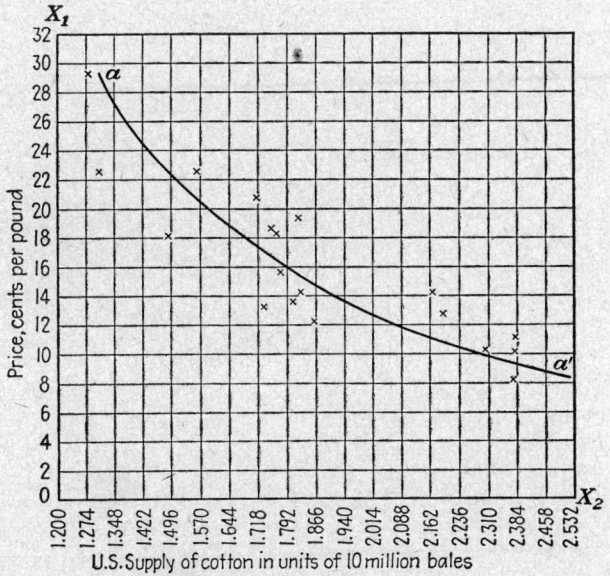

Fig. 114.—Bivariate scatter diagram and fitted curve showing relationship between the price of cotton and the supply of cotton.

Logarithmic Regression. The constant slope of a straight line depicts the fact that the change in X_1 is constant for a given quantity of change in X_2, and vice versa. The changing slope of a curve depicts the fact that change in X_1 varies for different values of X_2, and vice versa. One such curvilinear relationship between X_1 and X_2 is as follows:

$$X_1 X_2^b = k \tag{12}$$

In Eq. (12) the varying manner in which X_1 fluctuates with respect to X_2 depends on the exponent b. If b is larger than 1, a small change in X_2 must produce a large change in X_1 because, as the equation indicates, their product (when X_2 is raised to the b power) is constant. If b is equal to 1, the changes in X_1 must be just proportionate (in an inverse manner) to the changes in X_2. If b is less than 1, the changes in X_1 must be proportionately less than the changes in X_2. If such an equation is used to describe the line of regression of price of cotton on stocks and production of cotton, a very flexible price of cotton will

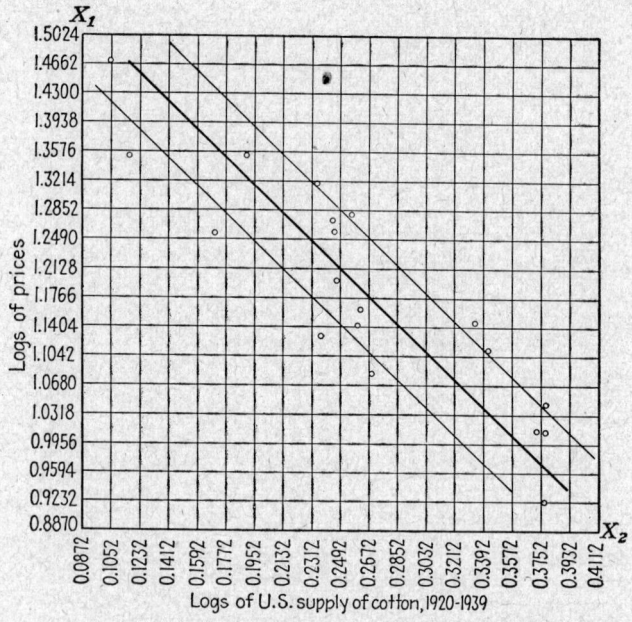

FIG. 115.—The relationship of Fig. 114 in logarithmic form.

result in a value of b larger than 1; a very inflexible price of cotton will result in a value of b less than 1. The nature of Eq. (12) assumes that the flexibility in the price of cotton remains the same regardless of stocks and production, because it sets up the hypothesis that the product equals a constant.

If such an equation is assumed to be suitable for the problem in hand, the fitting of the curve of regression may be simplified by first transforming the equation to its logarithmic form, namely,

$$\log X_1 + b \log X_2 = \log k$$
$$= a \qquad \text{if } \log k = a \quad (13)$$

Figure 115 shows the effect of transforming the bivariate frequency distribution from original units to logarithmic units. The data plotted are the same as the data plotted in Fig. 114, except that, in Fig. 115, the X_1 and X_2 scales refer to the logarithms of X_1 and X_2. When the bivariate logarithms shown in the first two columns of Table 37 are plotted in Fig. 115, a straight

TABLE 37.—LOGARITHMS OF UNITED STATES PRODUCTION, STOCKS, AND IMPORTS OF COTTON AND OF THE PRICE OF COTTON RECEIVED BY PRODUCERS
With columns for the squares of the logarithms and their cross products
X_1 = price of cotton
X_2 = stocks, production, and imports of cotton

log X_1	log X_2	log X_1 log X_2	log^2 X_1	log^2 X_2
1.1294	0.2370	0.2677	1.2755	0.0562
1.2567	0.1703	0.2140	1.5793	0.0290
1.3547	0.1159	0.1570	1.8352	0.0134
1.4669	0.1052	0.1543	2.1518	0.0111
1.3547	0.1903	0.2578	1.8352	0.0362
1.2831	0.2565	0.3291	1.6464	0.0658
1.1113	0.3414	0.3794	1.2350	0.1166
1.3212	0.2333	0.3082	1.7456	0.0544
1.2721	0.2428	0.3089	1.6182	0.0590
1.2634	0.2443	0.3086	1.5962	0.0597
1.0839	0.2700	0.2927	1.1748	0.0729
0.9232	0.3762	0.3473	0.8523	0.1415
1.0128	0.3631	0.3677	1.0258	0.1318
1.1474	0.3349	0.3843	1.3165	0.1122
1.1976	0.2467	0.2954	1.4343	0.0609
1.1408	0.2589	0.2954	1.3014	0.0670
1.1608	0.2603	0.3022	1.3475	0.0678
1.0124	0.3769	0.3816	1.0250	0.1421
1.0481	0.3771	0.3952	1.0985	0.1422
$\Sigma = 22.5405$	5.0011	5.7468	27.0945	1.4398

line fits the points. Thus the logarithmic transformation has converted a curvilinear correlation problem into a simple linear correlation problem in which the Pearsonian coefficient of correlation is $r_{\log X_1 \log X_2}$ and the line of regression of log X_1 on log X_2 is as follows:

$$\log X_1 - \text{mean of } \log X_1 = r_{\log X_1 \log X_2} \frac{\sigma_{\log X_1}}{\sigma_{\log X_2}} (\log X_2 - \text{mean of } \log X_2)$$

The equations of regression could be obtained in the above form and then transformed into their antilogarithmic form; but in this problem it is more convenient to find the regression equation directly from the least-squares equations. Accordingly, the regression statistics a and b of Eq. (13) may be calculated by using the following least-squares equations:[1]

$$\Sigma \log X_1 = Na + b\Sigma \log X_2$$
$$\Sigma \log X_1 \log X_2 = a\Sigma \log X_2 + b\Sigma \log^2 X_2$$

Table 37 is a work sheet providing columns to calculate $\Sigma \log X_1$, $\Sigma \log X_2$, $\Sigma \log X_1 \log X_2$, $\Sigma \log^2 X_1$, and $\Sigma \log^2 X_2$, using the data of the cotton problem for which the raw data are found in Table 36. The first two columns of Table 37 show the logarithms of the price of cotton in the United States and of the stocks, production, and imports of cotton. The third column contains the cross products of the logarithms. The fourth and fifth columns contain the squares of the logarithms in the first two columns. The sums of the columns provide the values that are required to find the regression statistics a and b, for Eq. (13).

Calculation of the regression of $\log X_1$ on $\log X_2$:

$$22.5405 = 19a + 5.0011b$$
$$5.7468 = 5.0011a + 1.4398b$$

In order to solve, eliminate a by multiplying the second equation by 3.7992 and subtract it from the first, as follows:

$$22.5405 = 19a + 5.0011b$$
$$\underline{22.8332 = 19a + 5.4701b}$$
$$0.7073 = -0.4690b$$
$$b = -1.5081$$

Substituting this value of b in either of the equations will show that

$$a = 1.5833$$

Accordingly, the equation of logarithmic regression of $\log X_1$ on $\log X_2$ is as follows:

$$\log X_1 = 1.5833 - 1.5081 \log X_2$$

which may be transformed into antilogarithmic form as follows:

$$X_1 X_2^{-1.5081} = 38.31$$

[1] See p. 333.

Reciprocal Regression. Reciprocal regression is a special form of the type of regression indicated by Eq. (12); for if $b = 1$, changes in X_1 are related reciprocally to changes in X_2. In

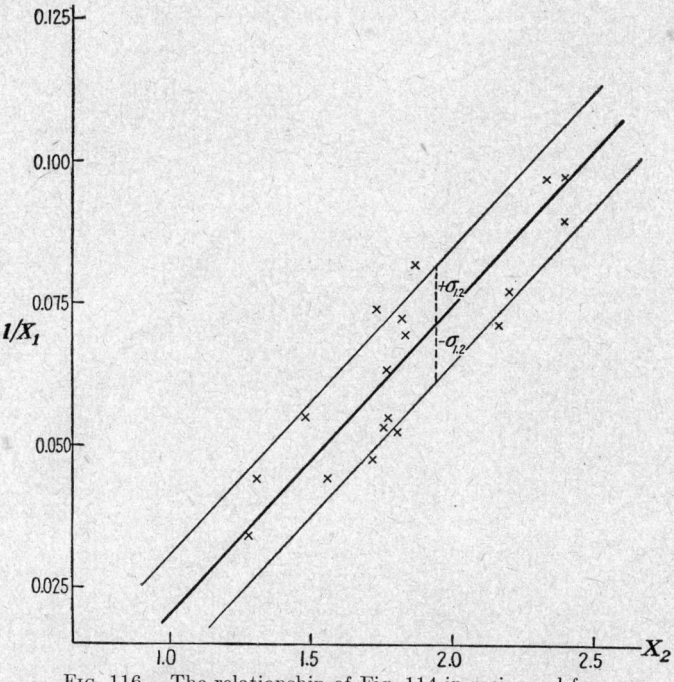

Fig. 116.—The relationship of Fig. 114 in reciprocal form.

other words, the equation becomes

$$X_1 X_2 = k' \qquad \text{or} \qquad \frac{1}{X_1} = k' X_2 \qquad (14)$$

which, placed in a more general form, is as follows:

$$\frac{1}{X_1} = a + b X_2 \qquad (15)$$

If the reciprocal of each X_1 is found, it is possible to find the equation for the reciprocal regression by fitting a straight line to X_2 and the reciprocal of X_1, that is to say, by fitting an equation such as (15). Figure 116 shows the effect of transforming one of the variables of the bivariate frequency distribution from original units to reciprocal units. In the figure the vertical scale is $1/X_1$ while the horizontal scale remains X_2. When the bivariates shown in Table 38 are plotted in Fig. 116, a straight line fits the points. Thus the reciprocal transformation has converted a problem in curvilinear correlation into a problem in simple linear correlation in which the Pearsonian coefficient of correlation is $r_{\frac{1}{x_1}x_2}$ and the line of regression is as follows:

$$\frac{1}{X_1} - \bar{X}_{\frac{1}{X_1}} = r_{\frac{1}{x_1}x_2} \frac{\sigma_{\frac{1}{x_1}}}{\sigma_2} (X_2 - \bar{X}_2)$$

TABLE 38.—UNITED STATES SUPPLY OF COTTON AND THE RECIPROCAL OF THE PRICE OF COTTON RECEIVED BY PRODUCERS
With columns for the squares and the cross products
X_1 = price of cotton
X_2 = supply of cotton

X_2	$\frac{1}{X_1}$	$X_2\frac{1}{X_1}$	$X_2{}^2$	$\frac{1}{X_1{}^2}$
1.726	0.07424	0.12814	2.97908	0.00551
1.480	0.05537	0.08195	2.19040	0.00307
1.306	0.04419	0.05771	1.70564	0.00195
1.274	0.03413	0.04348	1.62308	0.00116
1.550	0.04419	0.06849	2.40250	0.00195
1.805	0.05211	0.09406	3.25803	0.00272
2.195	0.07740	0.16989	4.81803	0.00599
1.711	0.04773	0.08167	2.92752	0.00228
1.749	0.05345	0.09348	3.05900	0.00286
1.755	0.05453	0.09570	3.08003	0.00297
1.862	0.08244	0.15350	3.46704	0.00680
2.378	0.11933	0.28377	5.65488	0.01424
2.307	0.09709	0.22399	5.32225	0.00943
2.162	0.07123	0.15400	4.67424	0.00507
1.765	0.06345	0.11199	3.11523	0.00403
1.815	0.07231	0.13124	3.29423	0.00523
1.821	0.06906	0.12576	3.31604	0.00477
2.382	0.09718	0.23148	5.67392	0.00944
2.383	0.08953	0.21335	5.67869	0.00802
$\Sigma = 35.426$	1.29896	2.54365	68.23983	0.09749

The equations of regression could be obtained in the above form and then transformed into their original units, but in this problem it is more convenient to find the regression equation directly from the least-squares equations. The normal least-squares equations are as follows:

$$\sum \frac{1}{X_1} = Na + b \sum X_2$$

$$\sum \frac{X_2}{X_1} = a \sum X_2 + b \sum X_2^2$$

Table 38 is a work sheet with columns in which the required sums are obtained. Entering these sums in the above least-squares equations makes it possible to evaluate the regression statistics a and b for Eq. (15).

Calculation of the regression of $1/X_1$ on X_2:

$$1.29896 = 19a + 35.4260b$$
$$2.54365 = 35.4260a + 68.23983b$$

Multiplying the first equation by 1.8645263 and subtracting the result from the second equation eliminates a and gives a solution for b as follows:

$$b = 0.05564$$

Substituting this value in either equation gives the solution of a as follows:

$$a = -0.03538$$

The equation of regression is therefore as follows:

$$\frac{1}{X_1} = -0.03538 + .05564X_2$$

This equation describes the straight line plotted in Fig. 116. Plotted on scales of X_1 and X_2, the equation is a curve.

Parabolic Regression. The curvilinear relationships so far considered have been relationships that could readily be transformed to a linear form, by taking logarithms or reciprocals. Such transformations reduced the problem to one of simple linear correlation between the transformed variables, and there was little in the analysis that was different from that of the previous chapters. A curve that cannot easily be transformed to a linear form is the parabolic relationship

$$X_1 = a + b_1X_2^2 + b_2X_2^2 \tag{16}$$

This must be fitted directly. Fortunately, the nature of the curve is such that the method of least squares can be used. According to this, to fit a parabolic regression the least-squares equations are obtained as follows:

The least-squares criterion is that

$$\Sigma d^2 = \Sigma(X_1 - X_1')^2 = \text{minimum}$$

or

$$\Sigma(X_1 - a - b_1X_2 - b_2X_2^2) = \text{minimum}$$

For this to be a minimum its total differential should be equal to zero; that is, differentiating with respect to a, b_1, and b_2 and setting equal to zero, the following normal equations are obtained:

$$\Sigma X_1 = Na + b_1\Sigma X_2 + b_2\Sigma X_2^2$$
$$\Sigma X_1X_2 = a\Sigma X_2 + b_1\Sigma X_2^2 + b_2\Sigma X_2^3$$
$$\Sigma X_1X_2^2 = a\Sigma X_2^2 + b_1\Sigma X_2^3 + b_2\Sigma X_2^4$$

Table 39 is a work sheet providing for the calculation and checking of the sums entering into the three parabolic equations of regression. Using the sums of the appropriate columns the following set of equations is obtained for the calculation of the regression statistics a, b_1, and b_2 for the regression of X_1 on X_2, shown in Eq. (16):

$$306.58 = 19a + 35.426b_1 + 68.2398b_2 \tag{I}$$
$$542.7359 = 35.426a + 68.2398b_1 + 135.4744b_2 \tag{II}$$
$$994.4092 = 68.2398a + 135.4744b_1 + 276.3974b_2 \tag{III}$$

The solution of three equations for three unknowns should be undertaken in an orderly manner; this is attempted in Table 40, which is a work sheet following the so-called Doolittle method. This work sheet provides a step-by-step check on the calculations as the solution of the equations proceeds. In order to avoid copying a, b_1, and b_2 each time an equation is written down, a, b_1, and b_2 are written as the titles of columns in which their coefficients are entered. In the table only the coefficients are entered in their respective columns with the proper sign before each figure. For example, row (1) of the table is presumed to read as follows:

$$19a + 35.4260b_1 + 68.2398b_2 - 306.58 = 0$$

which is the first equation above with slight rearrangement of terms.

TABLE 39.—UNITED STATES SUPPLY OF COTTON AND THE PRICE OF COTTON RECEIVED BY PRODUCERS

With columns for the second, third, and fourth powers and for the necessary cross products to fit parabolic regressions

X_1 = price of cotton
X_2 = supply of cotton

X_1	X_2	X_1^2	X_1^3	X_1^4	X_2^2	X_2^3	X_2^4	X_1X_2	$X_1^2X_2$	$X_1X_2^2$	Checking columns $(X_1^3 - X_1^2 - X_1 - X_2 - X_1X_2 - 1)X_1$	Checking columns $(X_2^3 - X_2^2 - X_2 + X_1X_2 - 1)X_2$
13.47	1.726	181.4409	2,444.0089	32,920.7999	2.979076	5.141885	8.874894	23.249220	313.166993	40.128154	29,945.4574	39.156086
18.06	1.480	326.1636	5,890.5146	106,382.6837	2.190400	3.241792	4.797852	26.728800	482.722128	39.558624	99,638.5045	37.444284
22.63	1.306	512.1169	11,589.2054	262,263.7092	1.705636	2.227561	2.909194	29.554780	668.824671	38.598343	249,441.3927	36.968541
29.30	1.274	858.4900	25,153.7570	737,005.0801	1.623076	2.067799	2.634376	37.328200	1,093.716260	47.556127	709,832.4945	45.225628
22.63	1.550	512.1169	11,589.2054	262,263.7092	2.402500	3.723875	5.772006	35.076500	793.781195	54.368575	249,310.9082	52.464206
19.19	1.805	368.2561	7,066.8346	135,612.5560	3.258025	5.880735	10.614727	34.637950	664.702260	62.521500	127,458.9341	62.192466
12.92	2.195	166.9264	2,156.6891	27,864.4232	4.818025	10.575565	23.213365	28.359400	366.403448	62.248883	25,133.1248	67.873658
20.95	1.711	438.9025	9,195.0074	192,635.4050	2.927521	5.008988	8.570378	35.845450	750.962178	61.331565	182,193.7386	60.254434
18.71	1.749	350.0641	6,549.6993	122,544.8739	3.059001	5.350193	9.357488	32.723790	612.262111	57.233909	114,981.4144	56.433202
18.34	1.755	336.3556	6,168.7617	113,135.0896	3.080025	5.405444	9.486554	32.186700	590.304078	56.487658	105,989.1415	55.733744
12.13	1.862	147.1369	1,784.7706	21,649.2674	3.467044	6.455636	12.020394	22.580060	273.968908	42.055244	19,408.6744	42.290058
8.38	2.378	70.2244	588.4805	4,931.4663	5.654884	13.447314	31.977713	19.927640	166.993623	47.387928	4,077.4602	57.885442
10.30	2.307	106.0900	1,092.7270	11,255.0851	5.322249	12.278428	28.326333	23.762100	244.749630	54.819165	9,777.4594	63.237821
14.04	2.162	197.1216	2,767.5873	38,856.9257	4.674244	10.105716	21.845558	30.354480	426.176899	65.626386	35,421.6452	70.532984
15.76	1.765	248.3776	3,914.4310	61,691.4326	3.115225	5.498372	9.704626	27.816400	438.386464	49.095946	57,046.6611	48.421975
13.38	1.815	191.2689	2,645.2489	36,563.7923	3.294225	5.979018	10.851918	25.101450	347.153054	45.559132	33,361.1907	45.322906
14.48	1.821	209.6704	3,036.0274	43,961.6708	3.316041	6.038511	10.996128	26.368080	381.809797	48.016274	40,293.3208	47.836850
10.29	2.382	105.8841	1,089.5474	11,211.4427	5.673924	13.515287	32.193414	24.510780	252.215926	58.384678	9,728.9945	69.006881
11.17	2.383	124.7689	1,393.6686	15,567.2783	5.678689	13.532336	32.247509	26.618110	297.324289	63.430956	13,713.7285	74.084460
$\Sigma = 306.58$	35.426	5,451.3758	106,116.1721	2,238,336.7103	68.2398	135.4744	276.3974	542.7359	9,165.6239	994.4092	2,116,754.2	1,031.666426

The last two columns serve for checking, as follows:

$$-(\Sigma X_1^3 + \Sigma X_1^2 + \Sigma X_1X_2 + \Sigma X_1^2X_2 + \Sigma X_1) \qquad \Sigma X_1^4 = 2{,}238{,}336.7103$$
$$= -121{,}582.5876$$
$$= 2{,}116{,}754.13$$

$$-(\Sigma X_2^3 + \Sigma X_2^2 + \Sigma X_2) \qquad \Sigma X_2^4 + \Sigma X_1X_2^2 = 1{,}270.806674$$
$$= -239.140195$$
$$= 1{,}031.666479$$

TABLE 40.—DOOLITTLE WORK SHEET FOR CALCULATING THREE REGRESSION STATISTICS FOR CURVILINEAR CORRELATION

Regression of X_1 on X_2

Row	Equation number	Multipliers	a	b_1	b_2	Constant	Σ	Checks	Remarks
(1)	(I)		19.0000	35.4260	68.2398	−306.5800	−183.9142		Equation (I)
(2)		$\frac{-1}{19}$	−1.0000	−1.864526	−3.59157	16.1358	9.6797	9.6797	Row (1) × $\frac{-1}{19}$
(3)	(II)		35.4260	68.2398	135.4744	−542.7359	−303.5957		Equation (II)
(4)		$\frac{-35.4260}{19}$	−35.4260	−66.0527	−127.23488	571.62638	342.9128	342.9128	Row (1) × $\frac{-35.4260}{19}$ = −1.864526
(5)			0	2.1871	8.23952	28.89048	39.3171	39.3171	Row (3) + row (4)
(6)		$\frac{-1}{2.1871}$	0	−1.0000	−3.76733	−13.2095	−17.9768	−17.9768	Row (5) × $\frac{-1}{2.1871}$
(7)	(III)		68.2398	135.4744	276.3974	−994.4092	−514.2976		Equation (III)
(8)		$\frac{-68.2398}{19}$	−68.2398	−127.23496	−245.08802	1101.1035	660.5407	660.5407	Row (1) × $\frac{-68.2398}{19}$ = −3.59157
(9)		8.2394*	0	−8.2394	−31.04099	−108.8400	−148.1205	−148.1205	Row (6) × (135.4744 − 127.23496)
(10)			0	0	0.2684	−2.1457	−1.8773	−1.8774	Σ rows (7), (8), and (9)
(11)		$\frac{-1}{0.2684}$	0	0	−1.0000	7.9944	6.9944	6.9944	Row 10 × $\frac{-1}{0.2684}$

* 8.2395 = 135.4744 − 127.23496.

Row (11) is used to find b_2; row (6) is used to find b_1 after b_2 is found; row (2) is used to find a after b_2 and b_1 are found, from the equations

Row (11), $-1.0000b_2 + 7.9944 = 0$

Row (6), $-1.0000b_1 - 3.76733b_2 - 13.2095 = 0$

Row (2), $-1.0000a - 1.864526b_1 - 3.59157b_2 + 16.1358 = 0$

Three steps are involved in solving three equations for three unknowns: (1) to get an equation in the three unknowns in which the coefficient of one of the unknowns is unity, (2) to get an equation in only two of the unknowns in which the coefficient of one of the two is unity, and (3) to get an equation in only one of the unknowns in which its coefficient is unity. When the third step is accomplished, the value of the third unknown is obtained. This value, applied in the equation obtained by the second step, makes it possible to evaluate the second unknown; and the third unknown is then obtained by applying these two values in the equation obtained by the first step. This is the same process as that used for finding two unknowns from two equations.

Table 40 provides an orderly procedure and also a check for these steps. The first step is accomplished in row (2) of the table, by multiplying Eq. (I), copied in row (1), by the negative reciprocal of the coefficient of a, that is, by $\frac{-1}{19}$; this will make the coefficient of a become -1. The second step, rows (3) to (6), eliminates a from two of the equations in order to obtain in line (5) an equation in b_1 and b_2. In order to eliminate a, the first equation must be divided by its own coefficient of a and multiplied by the coefficient of a of Eq. (II); in other words, Eq. (I) must be multiplied by $\frac{-35.4260}{19}$. The multiplier is given a negative sign so that, when added to Eq. (II), the a term will cancel. Row (6) divides row (5) by the negative reciprocal of the coefficient of b_1 in row (5). The third step, rows (7) to (11), accomplish the elimination of two of the variables, ending with an equation in only one of them, which of course gives its value. In order to do this, Eq. (III) is copied in row (7); Eq. (I) is multiplied by a number that will give it a coefficient of a equal to the coefficient of a of Eq. (III), that is, by $\frac{-68.2398}{19}$, and this is entered in row (8); then the equation obtained in row (6) (in terms of only b_1 and b_2, a having been eliminated) is multiplied by a number that, combined with the two coefficients of b_1 in rows (7) and (8), will give a sum of zero. The sum of rows (7) to (9) will then eliminate both a and b_1, giving in row (10) such an equation. When row (10) is multiplied by the negative reciprocal of its coefficient of b_2, the value of b_2 is obtained; this is shown in row (11).

A column for sums is provided in order to obtain a step-by-step check on all calculations. This is done by applying to the sums the same multipliers as those applied to the equations. For example, the sum of row (1) multiplied by $\dfrac{-1}{19}$ should equal the sum of row (2). In the column headed Checks are entered the products obtained by multiplying the sums as indicated under Remarks to visualize the checks.

From Table 40, the values of a, b_1, and b_2, are obtained from equations in rows (2), (6), and (11), as follows:

Row (2), $-a - 1.864526b_1 - 3.59157b_2 + 16.1358 = 0$
Row (6), $-b_1 - 3.76733b_2 - 13.2095 = 0$
Row (11), $-b_2 + 7.9944 = 0$

$$b_2 = 7.9944$$
$$b_1 = -3.76733(7.9944) - 13.2095$$
$$= -43.327$$
$$a = 43.327(1.864526) - 7.9944(3.59157) + 16.135789$$
$$= 68.2077$$

The equation of regression of X_1 on X_2 is therefore as follows:

$$X_1 = 68.2077 - 43.327X_2 + 7.9944X_2^2$$

Estimates Based on Regression Equations. Using the three equations of regression calculated above for the regression of X_1 on X_2, that is, for the regression of the price of cotton on production, stocks, and imports of cotton in the United States, estimates may be made of the price that will result from a given volume of stocks plus production plus imports. The three equations are as follows:

Logarithmic regression, $\log X_1' = 1.5833 - 1.5081 \log X_2$

Reciprocal regression, $\dfrac{1}{X_1'} = -0.03538 + 0.05564X_2$

Parabolic regression, $X_1' = 68.2077 - 43.327X_2 + 7.9944X_2^2$

To illustrate the method of estimation, suppose the questions are asked: What is the expected price of cotton if the cotton stocks plus the year's production and imports amount to 25 million bales? What is the expected price of cotton if the cotton stocks plus the year's production and imports amount to 22 million bales? 19 million bales? 16 million bales? 13 million bales? Only 10 million bales? How much higher will the price be in a year of shortage than in a year of large carry-over

TABLE 41.—ESTIMATES OF COTTON PRICES BASED ON THREE REGRESSION CURVES

Estimates based on logarithmic regression

Values of X_2	$\log X_2$	Equation of estimate $1.5833 - 1.5081 \log X_2 = \log X_1$	$\log X_1$	Estimate of X_1
2.5	0.39794	$1.5833 - 1.5081(0.39794) =$	0.98317	9.62
2.2	0.34242	$1.5833 - 1.5081(0.34242) =$	1.06690	11.67
1.9	0.27875	$1.5833 - 1.5081(0.27875) =$	1.16292	14.55
1.6	0.20412	$1.5833 - 1.5081(0.20412) =$	1.27547	18.86
1.3	0.11394	$1.5833 - 1.5081(0.11394) =$	1.46612	29.25
1.0	0.00000	$1.5833 - 1.5081(0.00000) =$	1.58330	38.31

Estimates based on reciprocal regression

Values of X_2	Equation of estimate $-0.03538 + 0.05564 X_2 = \frac{1}{X_1}$	$\frac{1}{X_1}$	Estimate of X_1
2.5	$-0.3538 + 0.05564(2.5) =$	0.10372	9.64
2.2	$-0.3538 + 0.05564(2.2) =$	0.08703	11.49
1.9	$-0.3538 + 0.05564(1.9) =$	0.07034	14.22
1.6	$-0.3538 + 0.05564(1.6) =$	0.05364	18.64
1.3	$-0.3538 + 0.05564(1.3) =$	0.03695	27.06
1.0	$-0.3538 + 0.05564(1.0) =$	0.02026	49.36

Estimates based on parabolic regression

Values of X_2	Equation of estimate $68.2077 - 43.327 X_2 + 7.9944 X_2{}^2 = X_1$	Estimates of X_1
2.5	$68.2077 - 43.327(2.5) + 7.9944(6.25) =$	9.85
2.2	$68.2077 - 43.327(2.2) + 7.9944(4.84) =$	11.58
1.9	$68.2077 - 43.327(1.9) + 7.9944(3.61) =$	14.75
1.6	$68.2077 - 43.327(1.6) + 7.9944(2.56) =$	19.35
1.3	$68.2077 - 43.327(1.3) + 7.9944(1.69) =$	25.39
1.0	$68.2077 - 43.327(1.0) + 7.9944(1.00) =$	32.87

and large production and imports of cotton? Table 41 shows how these estimates are made by using the above three equations of regression. When the year's cotton stocks, production, and imports are large, the three regression equations give results that are approximately equal to each other; but when the year's cotton stocks, production, and imports are small, the estimates based upon the three regression equations differ sharply from each other.

First-order Standard Deviation Used as Standard Error of Estimate. The dispersion about a curve of regression can be measured in the same manner as the dispersion of cases about a progression of means or a line of regression. The measure generally used is the standard deviation and is called a "first-order standard deviation" or a "standard error of estimate," because it is the standard deviation of the residuals about the curves of regression by means of which estimates such as those illustrated in Table 41 are made.

For the illustration in which cotton stocks, production, and imports are correlated with cotton prices compared with cotton-price correlation, three types of regression lines have been fitted, as follows:

$$\log X_1' = a + b \log X_2 \tag{A}$$

$$\frac{1}{X_1'} = a + bX_2 \tag{B}$$

$$X_1' = a + b_1 X_2 + b_2 X_2^2 \tag{C}$$

The standard error of estimate, being a standard deviation, is defined as follows:

$$N\sigma_{1.2}^2 = \Sigma d^2 \tag{17}$$

where each d is defined, taking regression type (C), for example, as

$$d = X_1 - X_1' = X_1 - a - b_1 X_2 - b_2 X_2^2 \tag{18}$$

Hence, each d^2 will be as follows:

$$d^2 = d(a - b_1 X_2 - b_2 X_2) = dX_1 - ad - b_1 X_2 d - b_2 X_2^2 d \tag{19}$$

If all these d^2's are added, the following result is obtained:

$$\Sigma d^2 = \Sigma X_1 d - a\Sigma d - b_1 \Sigma X_2 d - b_2 \Sigma X_2^2 d \tag{20}$$

By the least-squares condition, however, the last three terms of Eq. (20) are equal to zero, for[1]

$$\Sigma d = \Sigma(X_1 - a - b_1 X_2 - b_1 X_2^2) = 0$$
$$\Sigma X_2 d = \Sigma X_2(X_1 - a - b_1 X_2 - b_2 X_2^2) = 0$$
$$\Sigma X_2^2 d = \Sigma X_2^2(X_1 - a - b_1 X_2 - b_2 X_2^2) = 0$$

[1] See p. 384.

Therefore, Eq. (20) reduces to the following:

$$\Sigma d^2 = \Sigma X_1 d = \Sigma X_1(X_1 - a - b_1 X_2 - b_2 X_2^2)$$
$$= \Sigma X_1^2 - a\Sigma X_1 - b_1\Sigma X_1 X_2 - b_2\Sigma X_1 X_2^2 \qquad (21)$$

Accordingly, the formula for the square of the standard error of estimate is as follows:

$$\sigma_{1.2}^2 = \frac{\Sigma X_1^2 - a\Sigma X_1 - b_1\Sigma X_1 X_2 - b_2\Sigma X_1 X_2^2}{N} \qquad (22)$$

If regression type (B) were taken, it can be shown similarly that

$$\sigma_{1.2}^2 = \frac{\sum \dfrac{1}{X_1^2} - a\sum \dfrac{1}{X_1} - b\sum \dfrac{X_2}{X_1}}{N} \qquad (23)$$

If the logarithmic regression equation is chosen, the standard error of estimate is found by a similar procedure to be as follows:

$$\sigma_{1.2}^2 = \frac{\Sigma \log^2 X_1 - a\Sigma \log X_1 - b\Sigma \log X_1 \log X_2}{N} \qquad (24)$$

The values necessary to calculate these standard errors of estimate are available, respectively, in Tables 40, 39, and 38.

Calculation of standard error of estimate: For the logarithmic regression:[1]

$$\sigma_{1.2}^2 = \frac{27.0945 - (1.5833)(22.5405) - (-1.5081)(5.7468)}{19}$$

$$= \frac{27.0945 - 35.6884 + 8.6668}{19} = \frac{0.0729}{19}$$

$$= 0.0038$$
$$\sigma_{1.2} = 0.06164$$

By using the ordinary formula for the standard deviation,

$$\sigma^2 = \frac{\Sigma X^2}{N} - \left(\frac{\Sigma X}{N}\right)^2$$

(when the arbitrary origin is taken as zero), the necessary figures are found in totals of the appropriate columns of Table 37, and

[1] The scatter formula for the logarithmic regression could be calculated by using the formula employed in the linear case, as follows:

$$\sigma_{1.2}^2 = \sigma_1^2(1 - r_{\log X_1 \log X_2}^2)$$

Since, however, the logarithmic r has not been calculated, it is simpler to use the formula based on the least squares equations.

it is found that

$$\sigma_1^2 = 0.0187$$
$$\sigma_1 = 0.1368$$

For the reciprocal regression:[1]

$$\sigma_{1.2}^2 = \frac{0.09749 - (-0.03538)(1.29896) - (0.05564)(2.54365)}{19}$$

$$= \frac{0.09749 + 0.04596 - 0.14153}{19} = \frac{0.00192}{19}$$

$$= 0.000101$$
$$\sigma_{1.2} = 0.01$$

The standard deviation of $1/X_1$ is found by using the following formula

$$\sigma_{\frac{1}{X_1}}^2 = \frac{\sum \left(\frac{1}{X_1}\right)^2}{N} - \left(\frac{\sum \frac{1}{X_1}}{N}\right)^2$$

The necessary values are found in the sums of the appropriate columns of Table 38.

$$\sigma_{\frac{1}{X_1}}^2 = 0.00869$$

$$\sigma_{\frac{1}{X_1}} = 0.0932$$

For the parabolic regression:

$$\sigma_{1.2}^2 = \frac{\begin{aligned}5,451.3758 - 68.2077(306.58) - (-43.327)(542.7359)\\ - (7.9944)(994.4092)\end{aligned}}{19}$$

$$= \frac{5,451.3758 - 20,911.1167 + 23,515.1183 - 7,949.7049}{19}$$

$$= \frac{105.6725}{19}$$

$$= 5.5617$$
$$\sigma_{1.2} = 2.3583$$

Using the ordinary formula for calculating the standard deviation when zero is taken as the arbitrary origin,

$$\sigma_1^2 = 26.5508 \qquad \sigma_1 = 5.1528$$

---

[1] The scatter formula for the reciprocal regression could be calculated by using the formula for the linear case, as follows:

$$\sigma_{1.2}^2 = \sigma_1^2 [1 - r^2_{\left(\frac{1}{X_1}\right) X_2}]$$

Since, however, the reciprocal r has not been calculated, it is simpler to use the formula based on the least-squares equations.

Table 42 is a summary of the estimates of cotton prices made above, together with ranges of plus and minus one standard

TABLE 42.—ESTIMATES AND RANGES OF TWICE THE STANDARD ERROR OF ESTIMATE FOR COTTON PRICES BASED ON THREE REGRESSION CURVES

Estimates and ranges, logarithmic regression

Estimated log of price log X_1	Range logarithms		Estimated price X_1	Range of price, antilogarithms	
	$\log X_1 + \sigma_{1.2}$	$\log X_1 - \sigma_{1.2}$			
0.98317	1.04481	0.92153	9.62	11.19	8.35
1.06690	1.12854	1.00526	11.67	13.45	11.29
1.16292	1.22456	1.10128	14.55	16.77	12.63
1.27547	1.33711	1.21383	18.86	21.73	13.23
1.46612	1.52776	1.40448	29.25	33.71	25.38
1.58330	1.64494	1.52166	38.31	44.15	33.24

Estimates and ranges, reciprocal regression

Estimated reciprocal of price $\frac{1}{X_1}$	Range reciprocals		Estimated price X_1	Range of estimated price, converted from reciprocals	
	$\frac{1}{X_1} + \sigma_{1.2}$	$\frac{1}{X_1} - \sigma_{1.2}$			
0.10372	0.11372	0.09372	9.64	8.79	10.67
0.08703	0.09703	0.07703	11.49	10.31	12.98
0.07034	0.08034	0.06034	14.22	12.45	16.57
0.05364	0.06364	0.04364	18.64	15.71	22.91
0.03695	0.04695	0.02695	27.06	21.30	37.11
0.02026	0.03026	0.01026	49.36	33.05	97.96

Estimates and ranges, parabolic regression

Estimated price X_1	Standard error of estimate	
	$X_1 + \sigma_{1.2}$	$X_1 - \sigma_{1.2}$
9.85	12.21	7.49
11.58	13.94	9.22
14.75	17.11	12.39
19.35	21.71	16.99
25.39	27.75	23.03
32.87	35.23	30.51

error of estimate. In the cases of the logarithmic and reciprocal regressions these ranges are converted into original units of

the data in order to show their significance.   The differences
are notable. For the lower levels of price, the reciprocal
regression gives estimates with small standard errors of estimate,
but for the higher price levels the standard error of estimate is
smallest with the parabolic regression.   Each of these methods of
calculating regression curves assumes that the variance in X_1
is the same for all subgroups of X_1 associated with varying
values of X_2. The logarithmic regression assumes that, when
converted into logarithms, the variance about the logarithmic
regression is equal at all points but that, when converted into
antilogarithms, it will be larger for the higher prices. The
reciprocal regression assumes equal variance about the curve in
terms of reciprocals but, when converted, the variance about the
higher prices is larger than the variance about the lower prices.

The question suggests itself: Which one of these three assumptions about the character of variance about the curves of regression best suits the data of the particular problem?   This question
is answered by determining which of the regression curves is the
best fit for the data in question.

Correlation Index. For each of the curves of regression
calculated in the previous section, a corresponding index of
correlation will help to determine which of the regression curves
is the best fit for the data. The standard error of estimate
measures the divergence of the bivariates from the curve of
regression; the correlation index measures the goodness of fit
of the curve of regression. The indexes of correlation may be
calculated by using Eq. (2).

Calculation of Indexes of Correlation: For the logarithmic
regression:

$$I_{12}^2 = \frac{\sigma_1^2 - \sigma_{1.2}^2}{\sigma_1^2} = \frac{0.0187 - 0.0038}{0.0187} = \frac{0.0149}{0.0187}$$
$$= 0.7968$$
$$I_{12} = 0.8926$$

For the reciprocal regression:

$$I_{12}^2 = \frac{0.00869 - 0.00010}{0.00869} = \frac{0.00859}{0.00869}$$
$$= 0.9885$$
$$I_{12} = 0.9942$$

For the parabolic regression:

$$I_{12}^2 = \frac{26.5508 - 5.5617}{26.5508} = \frac{20.9891}{26.5508}$$
$$= 0.7905$$
$$I_{12} = 0.8891$$

The high correlation index obtained for the reciprocal regression appears to indicate that the cotton supply and price data for the period 1900 to 1940 are correlated in a reciprocal manner. It indicates that the sample data are fitted by the reciprocal curve of regression better than by either the logarithmic curve or the parabolic curve.

It is to be noted that, in general, the use of the index of correlation to show which curve is the best fit is valid only when all curves have the same number of regression statistics. Here two curves had two regression statistics and one had three. A curve with a larger number of regression statistics will always give a better fit than a similar curve with a smaller number of regression statistics. Here, however, the parabola that had three regression statictics gives a worse fit than either the logarithmic or the reciprocal curve, each of which has only two regression statistics.

The Index of Correlation and Analysis Variance. As already pointed out, in the cases of the logarithmic and reciprocal curves of regression, the Pearsonian coefficient of correlation may be calculated. When transformed into original units, this coefficient of correlation becomes the index of correlation. In the problems above illustrated, however, the correlation index was calculated instead by using the general formula based upon the scatter because the arithmetic involved in the latter method is simpler. In logarithmic and reciprocal units, respectively, the coefficient of correlation squared is, for these curves of regression, a coefficient of proportional variance just as is the r^2 for simple linear correlation problems.

For the parabolic curve of regression, the deviations from the curve of regression may be described as

$$X_1 - X_1' = d \quad \text{and} \quad X_1' = X_1 - d$$

If these are added for the entire data, the result is

$$\Sigma X_1' = \Sigma X_1 - \Sigma d$$

and since $\Sigma d = 0$ it follows that

$$\Sigma X_1' = \Sigma X_1 = N\bar{X}_1$$

and hence the mean of X_1' equals the mean of X_1.

Consequently, the sum of squares of X_1' may be obtained as follows:

$$N\sigma_{X'_1}^2 = \Sigma X_1'^2 - N\bar{X}_1^2 \qquad (25)$$

In Eq. (25), $\Sigma X_1'^2$ may be evaluated as follows:

$$\Sigma X_1'^2 = \Sigma(X_1 - d)^2 = \Sigma X_1^2 - 2\Sigma X_1 d + \Sigma d^2$$

As shown above on page 391, $\Sigma X_1 d = \Sigma d^2$. Therefore,

$$\Sigma X_1'^2 = \Sigma X_1^2 - \Sigma d^2$$

and

$$N\sigma_{X'_1}^2 = \Sigma X_1^2 - \Sigma d^2 - N\bar{X}_1^2 \qquad (26)$$

However, it is true by definition that

$$\Sigma X_1^2 - N\bar{X}_1^2 = N\sigma_1^2 \qquad \text{and} \qquad \Sigma d^2 = N\sigma_{1.2}^2$$

Therefore, Eq. (26) reduces to the following:

$$N\sigma_{X'_1}^2 = N\sigma_1^2 - N\sigma_{1.2}^2 \qquad (27)$$

From Eq. (27), by dividing by N and then by σ_1^2 and transposing terms, it follows that

$$\frac{\sigma_{X'_1}^2}{\sigma_1^2} = 1 - \frac{\sigma_{1.2}^2}{\sigma_1^2} \qquad (28)$$

and from Eq. (28) it follows by definition of I_{12}^2 that

$$I_{12}^2 = \frac{\sigma_{X'_1}^2}{\sigma_1^2} \qquad (29)$$

Hence the square of the correlation index has the same significance as the square of the linear coefficient of correlation; it measures the proportion of the total variance accounted for by the assumed type of curvilinear correlation.

CHAPTER XVI

MULTIPLE AND PARTIAL CORRELATION

To deal with the relationship between only two variables the method of correlation so far discussed is useful, but in the nonexperimental sciences it is frequently and indeed usually more important to be able to deal with the association between three or more variables. In the social sciences in particular, variations in practically every factor are related to variations in several other rather than in a single other factor. For example, variations in the price of cotton are related not only to changes in the production and consumption of cotton but also to changes in the prices of substitutes for cotton such as rayon and, in addition, to changes in the value of money. Again, the consumption of a commodity such as gasoline may depend more upon the number of automobiles in existence and upon the number of miles of hard-surfaced roads available for use than upon the price of gasoline. As a matter of fact, it is dependent on all these factors and others too. In such cases it is essential to have some method of "multiple correlation" and "partial correlation."

Definitions of Terms. *Multiple Correlation.* Multiple correlation is an extension to more than two variables of the methods of simple correlation. Simple linear correlation provides a line of regression from which an average value for the dependent variable may be estimated if the value of the independent variable is given. Multiple linear correlation provides a "plane" of regression by means of which an average value for the dependent variable may be estimated if the values of two or more independent variables are given. The plane of regression of the price of cotton on the price of rayon and on the wholesale price level, for example, would permit the estimation of the former from joint knowledge of the latter, instead of from the price of rayon alone. Similarly, the plane of regression of the second-semester English grade on the first-semester English grade and on the verbal scholastic-aptitude test grade would permit the estimation of the former from joint knowledge of the latter, instead of from only the first-semester English grade. The regression equation, accordingly, has two or more terms to the right instead of one; its general form is as follows:

$$X_1' = a_{1.23} \ldots + b_{12.3} \ldots X_2 + b_{13.2} \ldots X_3 + \cdots$$

where X_1 is the dependent variable, X_2, X_3, etc., are the independent variables, and a and the b's are estimated parameters, or regression statistics, whose numerical values are determined in any particular case by the method of least squares. The numerical subscripts will be explained later. For the moment it only need be noted that a plane of regression is but the extension to more than two variables of the idea of a line of regression.

In simple linear correlation, dispersion about the line of regression of X_1 on X_2 serves as a measure of the accuracy of any estimate of X_1 made from the line of regression. In multiple correlation, dispersion about the plane of regression serves as a measure of the accuracy of any estimate of the dependent variable made by reference to the plane of regression. One of the essential problems of multiple correlation is to calculate dispersion about the plane of regression.

In simple correlation, a line of regression is merely a law of relationship between one variable taken as a dependent variable and another taken as an independent variable; it does not of itself describe the degree of relationship or association that exists. To measure the degree of linear association is the function of the coefficient of correlation. Since the coefficient of correlation measures the amount of linear association, it also serves as a measure of the goodness of fit of the linear-regression equation to the bivariate distribution and yields a measure of the general degree of accuracy of estimates made by reference to the regression equation. In multiple correlation, the coefficient of multiple correlation serves the same general function. First, it serves as a measure of the degree of association between one variable taken as the dependent variable and a group of other variables taken as the independent variables. Hence, it also serves as a measure of the goodness of fit of the calculated plane of regression and consequently as a measure of the general degree of accuracy of estimates made by reference to the equation for the plane of regression.

In simple linear correlation, relationships are completely described by two lines of regression, one in which X_1 is taken as the dependent variable and the other in which X_2 is the dependent variable. In multiple correlation involving three variables, there are three planes of regression. If four variables are involved, there are four planes of regression, and so forth. In general, there are as many planes of regression as there are variables that may be taken as dependent variables, in short, as many planes of regression as variables. In particular cases, the intuitive sense of cause and effect may lead to the rejection of some of these possible planes of regression as being without any practical significance. They must always, however, be considered as theoretical possibilities.

Where only two variables are considered, the coefficient of correlation between X_2, taken as dependent, and X_1, taken as independent, is the same as the coefficient of correlation between X_1, taken as dependent, and X_2, taken as independent. The measure of goodness of fit of the line of regression of X_2 on X_1 is the same as the measure of the goodness of fit of the line of regression of X_1 on X_2. This cannot be said of the various multiple-correlation coefficients. The multiple-correlation coefficient that measures the degree of association between X_1, dependent, and X_2 and X_3, independent, as a group and that also serves as a measure of the goodness of fit of the plane of regression of X_1 on X_2 and X_3 is not the same as the coefficient of multiple correlation that measures the degree of association of X_2, dependent, with X_1 and X_3, independent, taken as a group and that also measures the goodness of fit of the plane of regression of X_2 on X_1 and X_3. Furthermore, neither of these two coefficients is equal, except by mere chance, to the coefficient of multiple correlation that measures the degree of association of X_3, dependent, with X_1 and X_2, independent, taken together and that also measures the goodness of fit of the plane of regression of X_3 on X_1 and X_2. In multiple correlation, there are as many different coefficients of multiple correlation as there are planes of regression.

Linear vs. Nonlinear Relationships. The simplest form of correlation analysis rests on the assumption that the association between the variables is of a linear type. In some cases, this assumption does violence to the facts, the association being clearly of a nonlinear form. Where a simple form of nonlinear relationship exists between two variables, it has been found possible to fit a curve of regression instead of a line of regression and to calculate a correlation coefficient that measures the goodness of fit of this curve. Whether such a simple curve can be fitted or not, it is possible to calculate a measure of nonlinear relationship, called the "correlation ratio," that depends on a comparison of the variation about the means of the columns (or rows) of the grouped data with the total variation in the data.[1]

Such devices as these can also be used when nonlinear relationships exist among three or more variables. When the nonlinear relationship takes a simple form, it is possible to fit a curved plane or a surface of regression. A multiple-correlation index $I_{1.23}$ can also be calculated to serve as a measure of the goodness of fit of this surface of regression. Whether a simple form of a curved surface can be fitted or not, it is always possible to calculate a multiple-correlation ratio of the same sort as the correlation ratio for only two variables. Similar nonlinear relationships can also be carried over into the analysis of partial correlation.

Partial Correlation. Partial correlation is concerned with a concept resulting from the fact that more than two variables are correlated; if only two variables are considered, there is no place for partial correlation. Where there are three or more variables, however, the question of the interrelationships between the variables becomes a part of the analysis. How much of the apparent association between two variables (X_1 and X_2) is due to their common association with a third variable (X_3) and how much to their direct connection or to some connection through other variables independent of X_3? Would X_1 and X_2 continue to vary together if X_3 were held constant? This is the new problem that partial correlation attempts to solve. Fortunately, the methods employed in its solution are the same fundamentally as those involved in simple linear correlation.

This chapter is primarily concerned with linear multiple and partial correlation involving three variables. The notation involved in multiple and partial correlation will first be sum-

[1] See Chap. XV.

marized. A brief discussion of a multivariate frequency distribution, upon the basis of which any form of multiple or partial analysis must be based, will follow. Ensuing sections of the chapter will explain the fitting of planes of regression and will derive formulas for finding the numerical values of the regression statistics of any given plane fitted by the method of least squares. Formulas for measuring dispersion and for calculating multiple-correlation coefficients will also be derived. Partial correlation will be explained in more detail, and methods of calculating partial-correlation coefficients will be indicated. In the next chapter the entire subject will be illustrated by an example.

Notation. It is the practice in multiple- and partial-correlation analysis to let a symbol indicate the class to which a given quantity belongs and to denote by subscripts the particular number of the designated class. For example, if X stands for any variable measured in original units, X_1 indicates a particular member of this group and its subscript distinguishes it from X_2, X_3, etc., which are members of other groups. In a designated problem, X_1 may be the price of cotton, X_2 the price of rayon, and X_3 the general price level. Following is a summary of the various symbols used in the subsequent analysis, in which special attention should be directed to the subscripts:

X_1, X_2, X_3	Variables measured in original units
X_1', X_2', X_3'	The estimated value of these variables given by the three regression equations in which the variables are taken as dependent. The primes distinguish them from the actual values of X_1, X_2, and X_3
x_1, x_2, x_3	Variables measured from their means as origins ($x_1 = X_1 - \bar{X}_1$, etc.)
x_1', x_2', x_3'	The estimated values of x_1, x_2, and x_3 given by their regression equations and measured from the means of X_1, X_2, X_3 ($x_1' = X_1' - \bar{X}_1$, etc.)
$\bar{X}_1$, $\bar{X}_2$, $\bar{X}_3$	Means of X_1, X_2, X_3
σ_1, σ_2, σ_3	Standard deviations of X_1, X_2, X_3
$\dfrac{x_1}{\sigma_1}$, $\dfrac{x_2}{\sigma_2}$, $\dfrac{x_3}{\sigma_3}$	Variables measured from their means as origins and expressed in terms of standard-deviation units
$\dfrac{x_1'}{\sigma_1}$, $\dfrac{x_2'}{\sigma_2}$, $\dfrac{x_3'}{\sigma_3}$	x_1', x_2', x_3' expressed in terms of the standard-deviation units of X_1, X_2, X_3

$$\left. \begin{aligned} X_1' &= a_{1.23} + b_{12.3}X_2 + b_{13.2}X_3 \\ X_2' &= a_{2.13} + b_{21.3}X_1 + b_{23.1}X_3 \\ X_3' &= a_{3.12} + b_{31.2}X_1 + b_{32.1}X_2 \end{aligned} \right\} \quad (1)$$

These are the equations for the three planes of regression in which the variables are measured in terms of original units. The a's and b's are the regression statistics of the equations, of which the explanation follows:

$a_{1.23}$ The constant term in the regression equation in which X_1 is taken as the dependent variable and X_2 and X_3 as the independent variables

$a_{2.13}$ and $a_{3.12}$ These are the constant terms, when X_2 and X_3, respectively, are the dependent variables. The subscript before the point refers to the dependent-variable number; the subscripts after the point refer to the independent variables. The order of subscripts after the point is immaterial; that is, $a_{2.13} = a_{2.31}$

$b_{12.3}$ The coefficient of X_2 in the regression equation in which X_1 is taken as the dependent variable and X_3 is the other independent variable. The first number in the subscript indicates the dependent variable; the second number in the subscript indicates the variable of which the b is a coefficient; the point followed by the other subscript indicates that a third variable is considered. Similarly, $b_{13.2}$ is the coefficient of X_3 in the same regression equation. It is to be noted that $b_{12.3} \neq b_{21.3}$

$b_{21.3}$ The coefficient of X_1 in the regression equation in which X_2 is taken as the dependent variable and X_3 is the other independent variable; $b_{23.1}$ is the coefficient of X_3 in the same regression equation

$b_{32.1}$ and $b_{31.2}$ These have a similar meaning for the third regression equation

$$\left. \begin{aligned} x_1' &= b_{12.3}x_2 + b_{13.2}x_3 \\ x_2' &= b_{21.3}x_1 + b_{23.1}x_3 \\ x_3' &= b_{31.2}x_1 + b_{32.1}x_2 \end{aligned} \right\} \quad (2)$$

Equations (2) are another form of the three regression equations. Here the variables are expressed in terms of deviations from their respective means. In these equations there are no a's, or constant terms, because the planes of regression all pass through the point given by the means of the three variables. The b's are the same as those in Eqs. (1)

$$\left.\begin{array}{l} \dfrac{x_1'}{\sigma_1} = \beta_{12.3}\,\dfrac{x_2}{\sigma_2} + \beta_{13.2}\,\dfrac{x_3}{\sigma_3} \\[2ex] \dfrac{x_2'}{\sigma_2} = \beta_{21.3}\,\dfrac{x_1}{\sigma_1} + \beta_{23.1}\,\dfrac{x_3}{\sigma_3} \\[2ex] \dfrac{x_3'}{\sigma_3} = \beta_{31.2}\,\dfrac{x_1}{\sigma_1} + \beta_{32.1}\,\dfrac{x_2}{\sigma_2} \end{array}\right\} \quad (3)$$

Equations (3) give a third form in which the three regression equations may be written. Here the variables represent deviations from their respective means expressed in standard-deviation units [the x''s are expressed in terms of the standard deviations of the x's (σ_1, σ_2, σ_3) instead of the standard deviations of the x''s themselves]. The form is similar to $\dfrac{x_1'}{\sigma_1} = r\,\dfrac{x_2}{\sigma_2}$ for two variables[1]

In Eqs. (3), the β's correspond to the b's in the Eqs. (1) and (2). As may be seen by comparing Eqs. (2) and (3), the β's are related to the b's in the following way:

$$\left.\begin{array}{l} b_{12.3} = \beta_{12.3}\,\dfrac{\sigma_1}{\sigma_2} \\[2.5ex] b_{21.3} = \beta_{21.3}\,\dfrac{\sigma_2}{\sigma_1} \\[2.5ex] b_{31.2} = \beta_{31.2}\,\dfrac{\sigma_3}{\sigma_1} \\[2.5ex] b_{13.2} = \beta_{13.2}\,\dfrac{\sigma_1}{\sigma_3} \\[2.5ex] b_{23.1} = \beta_{23.1}\,\dfrac{\sigma_2}{\sigma_3} \\[2.5ex] b_{32.1} = \beta_{32.1}\,\dfrac{\sigma_3}{\sigma_2} \end{array}\right\} \quad (4)$$

[1] See pp. 349–351.

If the symmetry of these equations is noted, they are easily remembered; for example, the subscripts of the b's are the same as the subscripts of the β's, and the order of the first two subscript numbers describes the subscript for sigma in numerator and denominator, respectively. It is to be noted that the $\beta_{12.3}$ does not equal $\beta_{21.3}$, etc.

$\sigma_{1.23}$ The scatter about the plane of regression of X_1 on X_2 and X_3

$\sigma_{2.13}$ The scatter about the plane of regression of X_2 on X_1 and X_3

$\sigma_{3.12}$ The scatter about the plane of regression of X_3 on X_1 and X_2

$R_{1.23}$ The multiple-correlation coefficient between X_1 on the one hand and X_2 and X_3 on the other

$R_{2.13}$ The multiple-correlation coefficient between X_2 on the one hand and X_1 and X_3 on the other

$R_{3.12}$ The multiple-correlation coefficient between X_3 on the one hand and X_1 and X_2 on the other

$r_{12.3}$ The partial-correlation coefficient between X_1 and X_2 when X_3 is held constant. The position of the subscripts is more important than the noncapitalization of the r in distinguishing it from the multiple-correlation coefficients. The subscript after the point indicates which variable is held constant. $r_{21.3} = r_{12.3}$

$r_{13.2}$ The partial-correlation coefficient between X_1 and X_3 when X_2 is held constant

$r_{23.1}$ The partial-correlation coefficient between X_2 and X_3 when X_1 is held constant

Study of the symmetry in the above system of notation will make it easy to remember. With the exception of the notation for partial-correlation coefficients, the order of subscripts before the point is always significant; following the point it is always immaterial.

MULTIVARIATE FREQUENCY DISTRIBUTION

The monovariate frequency distribution, it will be recalled, is the basis for the determination of various measures describing the central tendency and variation about the central tendency of a single variable. The bivariate frequency distribution (Chap. XIII) is the basis for the calculation of the lines of regression and the simple correlation r as well as for the calculation of correlation ratios. In fact, the bivariate frequency distribution contained all the information regarding the joint variation or covariance of X_1 and X_2 and hence formed the basis for the calculation of any measure or law of relationship between these two variables, linear or otherwise. Similarly, the multivariate frequency distribution contains all the information about

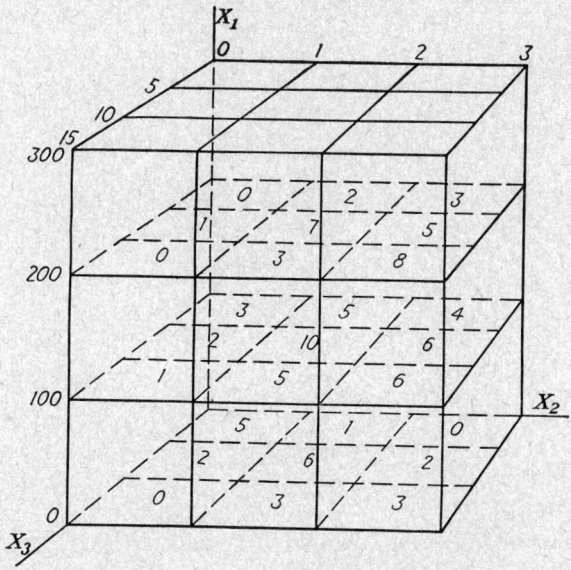

Fig. 117.—A trivariate frequency distribution.

the covariance of X_1, X_2, X_3, etc., and it thus forms the basis for the calculation of any measure or law of relationship between the different variables, individually or in groups.

Figure 117 shows a trivariate frequency distribution in which each variable is grouped into three class intervals. A small number of class intervals is taken in order to simplify the diagram; in any actual problem, the number of class intervals would, of course, be larger.

The figure shows the frequency (the number written on the floor of each cubical cell) with which X_1 falls within a given class interval at the same time that X_2 falls within another given class interval and X_3 falls within a third given class interval.   Accordingly, in Fig. 117, the frequency with which X_1 takes on values between 100 and 200 at the same time that X_2 takes on values between 1 and 2 and X_3 takes on values between 5 and 10 is 10. This is the frequency of the joint occurrence of the specified X_1, X_2, and X_3 values.   The frequencies in other cells represent the frequency of joint occurrence of other X_1, X_2, and X_3 combinations.

If the frequencies of this trivariate frequency distribution are projected upon any one of the three reference planes, that is, if the frequencies are added from top to bottom, from left to right, or from front to rear, a bivariate frequency distribution is obtained for two of the three variables.   For example, if the frequencies are projected upon the X_2X_3 plane, the bivariate frequency distribution for these two variables shown in Table 43 is obtained.   In Table 43 the frequencies of the trivariate fre-

TABLE 43

	0	1	2	3 X_2
5	8	8	7	
10	5	23	13	
15	1	11	17	
X_3				

quency distribution in Fig. 117 are added from top to bottom.

If the frequencies are projected upon the X_1X_2 plane, the bivariate frequency distribution of X_1 and X_2 shown in Table 44

TABLE 44

X_1			
300	1	12	16
200	6	20	16
100	7	10	5
0			
	0 1 2 3 X_2		

is found.   To obtain the frequencies in Table 44, the frequencies in the trivariate frequency distribution (Fig. 117), are added from front to rear.

Finally, if the frequencies are projected onto the X_1X_3 plane, the bivariate frequency distribution of X_1 and X_3 shown in Table 45 is obtained. The frequencies shown in Table 45 are the sum from left to right of the frequencies in the trivariate frequency distribution shown in Fig. 117.

TABLE 45

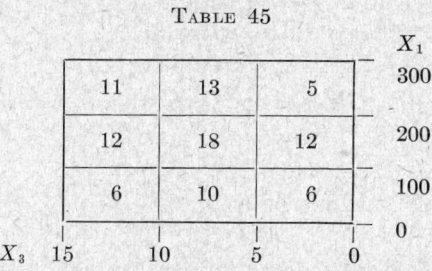

In the three bivariate frequency distributions shown in Tables 43 to 45, it is to be noted that X_2 and X_3 are positively correlated, as are also X_1 and X_2 and X_1 and X_3. The given trivariate frequency distribution (Fig. 117) is one in which all the variables are positively correlated with each other. In this case, as the values of X_2 and X_3 both increase, the mean value of X_1 also tends to increase; in other words, the plane of regression of X_1 on X_2 and X_3 would slope upward from the origin in both the X_2 and the X_3 direction. Because of the all-round positive correlation between the variables, the other planes of regression would also slope upward from the origin in both directions.

The net regression between two variables in a multivariate distribution is measured by the b statistic, and it is possible to have a negative net regression $b_{12.3}$ although the Pearsonian coefficient of correlation r_{12} is positive, and vice versa. If r_{12} is small compared with r_{13} and r_{23}, the latter being either both negative or both positive, the plane of regression of X_1 on X_2 and X_3 may slope downward in the X_2 direction even if r_{12} is positive. The statistic $b_{12.3}$ is of the same sign as r_{12} so long as $r_{12} - r_{13}r_{23}$ is of the same sign as r_{12}. If this condition is not fulfilled, that is, if $r_{12} - r_{13}r_{23}$ and r_{12} are of opposite sign, $b_{12.3}$ will be opposite in sign to r_{12} and the plane will slope in the opposite direction from that indicated by the sign of r_{12}, which, when multiplied by the ratio σ_1/σ_2, describes the slope of the line of regression in the bivariate distribution of X_1 and X_2.* In

* See pp. 349–351.

the case where r_{12} is positive but $b_{12.3}$ is negative, the coefficient of partial correlation $r_{12.3}$ is negative, agreeing with the sign of the b statistic.   For this reason, the partial-correlation coefficient may be said to measure the net correlation between the two variables.

If the net correlations between X_1 and X_2 and between X_1 and X_3 are both negative, the plane of regression of X_1 on X_2 and X_3 slopes downward in both directions.   In this instance, the $b_{12.3}$ and the $b_{13.2}$ of the regression equation are both negative. In other words, the mean value of X_1 would tend to decrease with increases in the values of both X_2 and X_3.   This particular plane of regression would have an all-round negative slope.   If the net correlation between X_1 and X_3 is negative, however, and that between X_1 and X_2 is positive, the plane of regression of X_1 on X_2 and X_3 slopes upward in the X_2 direction, that is, the mean value of X_1 increases as X_2 increases; and the plane slopes downward in the X_3 direction, that is, the mean value of X_1 declines as X_3 increases.   In this instance, $b_{12.3}$ is positive, and $b_{13.2}$ is negative.   The plane of regression shows a positive relationship in one direction and a negative relationship in the other direction.

These are a few of the possible forms that a trivariate frequency distribution might take.   Others include nonlinear relationships.   For example, the mean value of X_1 might first increase as X_2 increases and also as X_3 increases and then later decrease as both these variables continued to increase, or X_1 might decline in the X_2 direction after a certain point but continue to rise in the X_3 direction.   For either of these combinations, a curved plane or surface of regression would give a better fit than a straight plane.

In order that there be all-round independence, that is to say, absolutely no correlation whatsoever, either linear or nonlinear, between any of the variables, the following conditions must exist:

1. The distribution of X_1 for any given X_2 and X_3 class intervals, that is, the distribution of X_1 values for any given vertical shaft, must be of the same form, it must have the same mean, the same standard deviation, etc., even though it does not have the same number of cases, as the distribution of X_1 values for every other vertical shaft of the trivariate frequency distribution (see Fig. 117).

2. The distribution of X_2 values for any given X_1 and X_3 class interval, that is, the distribution of X_2 values in any given horizontal shaft parallel to the X_2-axis and perpendicular to the X_1X_3 plane, must be of the same form as the distribution of X_2 values in every other horizontal shaft parallel to the X_2-axis (see Fig. 117).

3. The distribution of X_3 values for any given X_1 and X_2 class interval, that is, the distribution of X_3 values in any given horizontal shaft parallel to the X_3-axis and perpendicular to the X_1X_2 plane, must be of the same form as the distribution of X_3 values in every other shaft parallel to the X_3-axis and perpendicular to the X_1X_2 plane (see Fig. 117).

A close study of a multivariate frequency distribution is therefore always desirable before attempting to calculate any measure of relationship. Since in some instances the net correlation may be of opposite sign from simple linear correlation, as illustrated above, the examination of separate bivariate distributions for each pair of variables is not always a reliable method. It is better to undertake a study of the multivariate distribution. In a trivariate problem a diagram similar to Fig. 117 could be set up, but for a large number of class intervals it would be extremely difficult, if not impossible, to draw. The multivariate distribution can be studied, however, by selecting all the X_1 and X_2 variates associated with a given range of X_3 variates, for example, in Fig. 117, all the X_1 and X_2 variates associated with values of X_3 from 5 to 10. In this manner, a series of frequency distributions of X_1 for varying values of X_2 is obtained.

TABLE 46.—VALUES OF X_1 AND X_2 ASSOCIATED WITH VALUES OF X_3 BETWEEN 5 AND 10

	0	1	2	3	X_2
200	1	7	5		
100	2	10	6		
X_1 0	2	6	2		

Similar tables could be constructed showing the values of X_1 and X_2 associated with values of X_3 between 0 and 5 and with values of X_3 between 10 and 15. In this manner, the net correlation between X_1 and X_2 can be studied; and, by a similar procedure, the net correlations between X_1 and X_3 and between X_2 and X_3 can be examined. If such a study should reveal that linear relationships prevail, the methods to be discussed in the ensuing sections could be applied. If simple curvilinear relationships are apparent, some curved plane might better be fitted instead of a straight plane. In some instances, the latter could be accomplished by using logarithms, reciprocals, or some other transformation of the variables, to which linear functions could be fitted; in other instances, it might be necessary to fit parabolic functions to the original units.

MULTIPLE LINEAR REGRESSION

The a's, b's, and β's of a linear plane of regression are calculated in terms of given data or of quantities easily calculated from the data. The β's can be evaluated in terms of the simple correlation coefficients, the r's; knowledge of these therefore permits the immediate calculation of the former. The b's can be computed readily from the β's by multiplying by the proper ratio of standard deviations [see Eqs. (4)]. Finally, the a's can be computed from the b's and the means of the different variables.

The common method of evaluating the β's is the method of least squares. It was pointed out that for three variables there are three planes of regression. Values for the regression statistics in the regression equation of X_1 on X_2 and X_3 are derived by minimizing the sum of the squares of the deviations of the actual values of X_1 from those (X_1') given by the plane of regression, that is, by minimizing $\Sigma(X_1 - X_1')^2$. Similarly, values for the regression statistics in the regression equation of X_2 on X_1 and X_3 are derived by minimizing the sum of the squares of the deviations of X_2 from those (X_2') given by the second plane of regression, that is, by minimizing $\Sigma(X_2 - X_2')^2$. Finally, the values of the regression statistics in the regression equation of X_3 on X_1 and X_2 are derived by minimizing $\Sigma(X_3 - X_3')^2$. All three planes of regression are thus fitted by the method of least squares, but in each case the sum of the squares of a different set of deviations is minimized.

Using the third form of regression equation, the values of the statistics for the plane of regression of X_1 on X_2 and X_3 are derived as follows:

In the equation for the plane of regression,

$$\frac{x_1'}{\sigma_1} = \beta_{12.3}\frac{x_2}{\sigma_2} + \beta_{13.2}\frac{x_3}{\sigma_3}$$

the problem is to determine $\beta_{12.3}$ and $\beta_{13.2}$ such that

$$\sum\left(\frac{x_1}{\sigma_1} - \frac{x_1'}{\sigma_1}\right)^2 = \sum\left(\frac{x_1}{\sigma_1} - \beta_{12.3}\frac{x_2}{\sigma_2} - \beta_{13.2}\frac{x_3}{\sigma_3}\right)^2 = \text{minimum} \quad (5)$$

Since $\sum\left(\dfrac{x_1}{\sigma_1} - \dfrac{x_1'}{\sigma_1}\right)^2$ is merely

$$\frac{1}{\sigma_1^2}\sum\left[(X_1 - \bar{X}_1) - (X_1' - \bar{X}_1)\right]^2 = \frac{1}{\sigma_1^2}\sum(X_1 - X_1')^2$$

it follows that $\Sigma(X_1 - X_1')^2$ will be a minimum when

$$\sum\left(\frac{x_1}{\sigma_1} - \frac{x_1'}{\sigma_1}\right)^2$$

is a minimum, and hence the plane of regression derived by minimizing the latter is the same as that derived by minimizing the former.

If $\sum\left(\dfrac{x_1}{\sigma_1} - \beta_{12.3}\dfrac{x_2}{\sigma_2} - \beta_{13.2}\dfrac{x_3}{\sigma_3}\right)^2$ is to be a minimum, the derivative of this sum with respect to $\beta_{12.3}$ must equal zero and also its derivative with respect to $\beta_{13.2}$ must equal zero. These conditions are expressed in the following equations:

$$\left.\begin{array}{l}\displaystyle\sum\frac{x_2}{\sigma_2}\left(\frac{x_1}{\sigma_1} - \beta_{12.3}\frac{x_2}{\sigma_2} - \beta_{13.2}\frac{x_3}{\sigma_3}\right) = 0 \\[4mm] \displaystyle\sum\frac{x_3}{\sigma_3}\left(\frac{x_1}{\sigma_1} - \beta_{12.3}\frac{x_2}{\sigma_2} - \beta_{13.2}\frac{x_3}{\sigma_3}\right) = 0\end{array}\right\} \quad (6)$$

If in these equations the indicated multiplication is carried out and if each equation is divided by N, they become

$$\left.\begin{array}{l}\displaystyle\frac{\Sigma x_1 x_2}{N\sigma_1\sigma_2} - \beta_{12.3}\frac{\Sigma x_2^2}{\sigma_2^2 N} - \beta_{13.2}\frac{\Sigma x_3 x_2}{N\sigma_3\sigma_2} = 0 \\[4mm] \displaystyle\frac{\Sigma x_1 x_3}{N\sigma_1\sigma_3} - \beta_{12.3}\frac{\Sigma x_2 x_3}{N\sigma_2\sigma_3} - \beta_{13.2}\frac{\Sigma x_3^2}{\sigma_3^2 N} = 0\end{array}\right\} \quad (7)$$

But it will be noted that $\dfrac{\Sigma x_1 x_2}{N\sigma_1\sigma_2} = r_{12}$, $\dfrac{\Sigma x_1 x_3}{N\sigma_1\sigma_3} = r_{13}$, $\dfrac{\Sigma x_3 x_2}{N\sigma_3\sigma_2} = r_{23}$,

$\dfrac{\Sigma x_2^2}{N} = \sigma_2^2$ and $\dfrac{\Sigma x_3^2}{N} = \sigma_3^2$. Hence Eqs. (7) reduce to the following:

$$\left.\begin{array}{l} r_{12} - \beta_{12.3} - \beta_{13.2} r_{23} = 0 \\ r_{13} - \beta_{12.3} r_{23} - \beta_{13.2} = 0 \end{array}\right\} \quad (8)$$

When solved by the ordinary method of simultaneous equations,

$$\left.\begin{array}{l} \beta_{12.3} = \dfrac{r_{12} - r_{13} r_{23}}{1 - r_{23}^2} \\[2ex] \beta_{13.2} = \dfrac{r_{13} - r_{12} r_{23}}{1 - r_{23}^2} \end{array}\right\} \quad (9)$$

From Eqs. (9) it will be noted that, when $r_{23} = 0$, $\beta_{12.3} = r_{12}$ and $\beta_{13.2} = r_{13}$.*

If the other planes of regression are put in the form

$$\frac{x_2'}{\sigma_2} = \beta_{21.3}\,\frac{x_1}{\sigma_1} + \beta_{23.1}\,\frac{x_3}{\sigma_3}$$

$$\frac{x_3'}{\sigma_3} = \beta_{31.2}\,\frac{x_1}{\sigma_1} + \beta_{32.1}\,\frac{x_2}{\sigma_2}$$

and the values of the β's are determined in the same manner as the values of $\beta_{12.3}$ and $\beta_{13.2}$ were determined, the following results are obtained:

$$\left.\begin{array}{l} \beta_{21.3} = \dfrac{r_{12} - r_{13} r_{23}}{1 - r_{13}^2} \\[2ex] \beta_{23.1} = \dfrac{r_{23} - r_{12} r_{13}}{1 - r_{13}^2} \end{array}\right\} \quad (9')$$

$$\left.\begin{array}{l} \beta_{31.2} = \dfrac{r_{13} - r_{12} r_{23}}{1 - r_{12}^2} \\[2ex] \beta_{32.1} = \dfrac{r_{23} - r_{12} r_{13}}{1 - r_{12}^2} \end{array}\right\} \quad (9'')$$

If the simple linear-correlation coefficients are known, therefore, it is possible to obtain all the β's that enter into the three multiple-regression equations; and the regression equations in the β form are thus determined. The other forms of the regression

* See pp. 417 and 421.

equations can be derived from the β form by calculating the b's from the β's, and the a's from the b's and the means. For example, Eqs. (4), such as $b_{12.3} = \beta_{12.3}\dfrac{\sigma_1}{\sigma_2}$, will give the values of the b's. The regression equations in the form

$$x_1' = b_{12.3}x_2 + b_{13.2}x_3$$

are then determined. If, in this latter form, $X_1 - \bar{X}_1$ is substituted for x_1', $X_2 - \bar{X}_2$ for x_2, and $X_3 - \bar{X}_3$ for x_3, the equation becomes

$$X_1' = \bar{X}_1 - b_{12.3}\bar{X}_2 - b_{13.2}\bar{X}_3 + b_{12.3}X_2 + b_{13.2}X_3$$

from which it may be seen that the value of $a_{1.23}$ is as follows:

$$a_{1.23} = \bar{X}_1 - b_{12.3}\bar{X}_2 - b_{13.2}\bar{X}_3 \qquad (10)$$

Similarly, the value of a for the other regression equations is found to be as follows:

$$a_{2.13} = \bar{X}_2 - b_{21.3}\bar{X}_1 - b_{23.1}\bar{X}_3 \qquad (10')$$
$$a_{3.12} = \bar{X}_3 - b_{31.2}\bar{X}_1 - b_{32.1}\bar{X}_2 \qquad (10'')$$

It is helpful in the use of these equations to remember the symmetry in the notation, that is, the symmetry in the position of the subscripts.

Second-order Variances for Linear Plane of Regression. The formulas derived below measure the dispersion of the individual items about the plane of regression fitted by the method of least squares. As in the simpler case of the line of regression, so also for the plane of regression, the mathematical procedure consists in finding the standard deviation of the deviations of actual X values from the estimated values (X') given by the planes of regression. For example, by definition, $\sigma_{1.23}^2 = \Sigma(X_1 - X_1')^2/N$. The task reduces to one of evaluating such expressions in terms of quantities already known, that is, the r's and the β's. This can be done as follows:

Since it has been found easier to work with the variables when they are converted into deviations from their respective means and expressed in terms of their standard deviations, the formula for $\sigma_{1.23}^2$ will first be put in that form. This can be done by subtracting $\bar{X}_1$ from X_1 and adding it to X_1' and by multiplying both numerator and denominator by σ_1^2, neither of which will affect the value of the expression.   Thus,

$$\sigma_{1.23}^2 = \frac{\Sigma(X_1 - X_1')^2}{N} = \frac{\sigma_1^2 \Sigma[(X_1 - \bar{X}_1) - (X_1' - \bar{X}_1)]^2}{\sigma_1^2 N}$$

$$= \frac{\sigma_1^2 \Sigma \left(\dfrac{x_1}{\sigma_1} - \dfrac{x_1'}{\sigma_1} \right)^2}{N} = \sigma_1^2 \frac{\Sigma d^2}{N} \quad (11)$$

where

$$d = \frac{x_1}{\sigma_1} - \frac{x_1'}{\sigma_1}$$

The problem is to evaluate Σd^2.

By Eqs. (3), the third form of the regression equation of X_1 on X_2 and X_3, it follows that

$$d = \frac{x_1}{\sigma_1} - \frac{x_1'}{\sigma_1} = \frac{x_1}{\sigma_1} - \beta_{12.3} \frac{x_2}{\sigma_2} - \beta_{13.2} \frac{x_3}{\sigma_3} \quad (12)$$

Accordingly, for any given set of values of x_1, x_2, and x_3, there corresponds a particular value for d, which is the deviation of the actual value of x_1 from the value of x_1' obtained by putting the given values of x_2 and x_3 in the regression equation.   There are just as many d's, therefore, as there are different sets of values of x_1, x_2, and x_3. If any one of these d's is squared, Eq. (12) gives

$$d^2 = \frac{x_1}{\sigma_1} d - \beta_{12.3} \frac{x_2}{\sigma_2} d - \beta_{13.2} \frac{x_3}{\sigma_3} d \quad (13)$$

If all values of d are squared and summed, the following equation results:

$$\Sigma d^2 = \frac{\Sigma x_1 d}{\sigma_1} - \beta_{12.3} \frac{\Sigma x_2 d}{\sigma_2} - \beta_{13.2} \frac{\Sigma x_3 d}{\sigma_3} \quad (14)$$

But from Eqs. (6) and (12), it will be noted that

$$\frac{\Sigma x_2 d}{\sigma_2} = \frac{\Sigma x_2}{\sigma_2} \left(\frac{x_1}{\sigma_1} - \beta_{12.3} \frac{x_2}{\sigma_2} - \beta_{13.2} \frac{x_3}{\sigma_3} \right) = 0$$

and

$$\frac{\Sigma x_3 d}{\sigma_3} = \frac{\Sigma x_3}{\sigma_3} \left(\frac{x_1}{\sigma_1} - \beta_{12.3} \frac{x_2}{\sigma_2} - \beta_{13.2} \frac{x_3}{\sigma_3} \right) = 0$$

Therefore,

$$\Sigma d^2 = \frac{\Sigma x_1 d}{\sigma_1} \tag{15}$$

The evaluation, therefore, of $\displaystyle\sum \frac{x_1 d}{\sigma_1}$ will solve the problem. This can be done as follows:

If each d, as shown in Eq. (12), is multiplied by the x_1/σ_1 to which that d belongs, the following result is obtained:

$$\frac{x_1 d}{\sigma_1} = \frac{x_1^2}{\sigma_1^2} - \beta_{12.3} \frac{x_1 x_2}{\sigma_1 \sigma_2} - \beta_{13.2} \frac{x_1 x_3}{\sigma_1 \sigma_3} \tag{16}$$

Values of $\dfrac{x_1 d}{\sigma_1}$ for all values of d and x_1 sum up as follows:

$$\sum \frac{x_1 d}{\sigma_1} = \frac{\Sigma x_1^2}{\sigma_1^2} - \beta_{12.3} \frac{\Sigma x_1 x_2}{\sigma_1 \sigma_2} - \beta_{13.2} \frac{\Sigma x_1 x_3}{\sigma_1 \sigma_3} \tag{17}$$

Hence, dividing by N,

$$\frac{\Sigma d^2}{N} = \sum \frac{x_1 d}{N \sigma_1} = \frac{\Sigma x_1^2}{N \sigma_1^2} - \beta_{12.3} \frac{\Sigma x_1 x_2}{N \sigma_1 \sigma_2} - \beta_{13.2} \frac{\Sigma x_1 x_3}{N \sigma_1 \sigma_3}$$

But since

$$\frac{\Sigma x_1^2}{N} = \sigma_1^2 \qquad \frac{\Sigma x_1 x_2}{N \sigma_1 \sigma_2} = r_{12} \qquad \frac{\Sigma x_1 x_3}{N \sigma_1 \sigma_3} = r_{13}$$

it follows that

$$\frac{\Sigma d^2}{N} = 1 - \beta_{12.3} r_{12} - \beta_{13.2} r_{13} \tag{18}$$

and, finally, from Eqs. (11) and (18),

$$\sigma_{1.23}^2 = \frac{\sigma_1^2 \Sigma d^2}{N} = \sigma_1^2 (1 - \beta_{12.3} r_{12} - \beta_{13.2} r_{13}) \tag{19}$$

This gives an easy method for evaluating $\sigma_{1.23}^2$ when the r's and β's have been calculated. Similar formulas for evaluating

$\sigma_{2.13}^2$ and $\sigma_{3.12}^2$, the scatters about the other planes of regression, are found to be as follows:[1]

$$\sigma_{2.13}^2 = \sigma_2^2(1 - \beta_{21.3}r_{12} - \beta_{23.1}r_{23}) \qquad (19')$$

$$\sigma_{3.12}^2 = \sigma_3^2(1 - \beta_{31.2}r_{13} - \beta_{32.1}r_{23}) \qquad (19'')$$

Note the symmetry of these three equations.

COEFFICIENT OF MULTIPLE CORRELATION

The multiple-correlation coefficient measures the correlation between the dependent variable and the two independent variables taken together. For reasons previously indicated,[2]

[1] The dispersion $\sigma_{1.23}^2$ may also be calculated from the formulas:

$$\sigma_{1.23}^2 = \sigma_{1.2}^2(1 - r_{13.2}^2) \qquad \text{and} \qquad \sigma_{1.23}^2 = \sigma_1^2(1 - r_{12}^2)(1 - r_{13.2}^2)$$

This may be demonstrated as follows: From Eq. (23'),

$$r_{13.2}^2 = \frac{r_{13}^2 + r_{12}^2 r_{23}^2 - 2r_{13}r_{12}r_{23}}{(1 - r_{12}^2)(1 - r_{23}^2)}$$

and

$$1 - r_{13.2}^2 = \frac{1 - r_{12}^2 - r_{23}^2 + r_{12}^2 r_{23}^2 - r_{13}^2 - r_{12}^2 r_{23}^2 + 2r_{13}r_{12}r_{23}}{(1 - r_{12}^2)(1 - r_{23}^2)}$$

This gives

$$(1 - r_{12}^2)(1 - r_{13.2}^2) = \frac{(1 - r_{23}^2) - (r_{12}^2 + r_{13}^2 - 2r_{13}r_{12}r_{23})}{(1 - r_{23}^2)}$$

$$= 1 - r_{12}\frac{(r_{12} - r_{13}r_{23})}{(1 - r_{23}^2)} - r_{13}\frac{(r_{13} - r_{12}r_{23})}{(1 - r_{23}^2)}$$

Equation (9), however, shows that the two fractions on the right are equal respectively to $\beta_{12.3}$ and $\beta_{13.2}$. Hence

$$(1 - r_{12}^2)(1 - r_{13.2}^2) = 1 - r_{12}\beta_{12.3} - r_{13}\beta_{13.}$$

or on making use of Eq. (19),

$$\sigma_{1.23}^2 = \sigma_1^2(1 - r_{12}^2)(1 - r_{13.2}^2)$$

In Chap. XIII (p. 321) it was shown that $\sigma_{1.2}^2 = \sigma_1^2(1 - r_{12}^2)$. Hence the last equation may be written

$$\sigma_{1.23}^2 = \sigma_{1.2}^2(1 - r_{13.2}^2)$$

Thus both of the original formulas are derived from previously demonstrated relationships. Similar formulas hold for $\sigma_{2.13}^2$ and $\sigma_{3.12}^2$. These are

$$\sigma_{2.13}^2 = \sigma_{2.3}^2(1 - r_{12.3}^2)$$
$$= \sigma_2^2(1 - r_{23}^2)(1 - r_{12.3}^2)$$

and

$$\sigma_{3.12}^2 = \sigma_{3.2}^2(1 - r_{13.2}^2)$$
$$= \sigma_3^2(1 - r_{23}^2)(1 - r_{13.2}^2)$$

[2] See pp. 351–353 and 365–368.

$$R_{1.23}^2 = 1 - \frac{\sigma_{1.23}^2}{\sigma_1^2}$$

may be taken as a good measure of multiple correlation.

$R_{1.23}$ measures the degree of association between the X_1 variable and X_2 and X_3 taken jointly. It can also be looked upon as a measure of the goodness of fit of the plane of regression of X_1 on X_2 and X_3 to the set of X_1 values. For if the fit is perfect, $\sigma_{1.23}^2$ will be zero and hence $R_{1.23}$ will equal 1. Similarly, $R_{2.13}$ measures the degree of association between the X_2 variable and X_1 and X_3 taken jointly, and $R_{3.12}$ measures the association between the X_3 variable and X_1 and X_2 taken jointly. They also can be looked upon as measures of goodness of fit of their respective planes of regression. It will be recalled that all three of these multiple-correlation coefficients may have different values.

The multiple coefficient of correlation $R_{1.23}$ is always larger than or at least equal to r_{12} and r_{13}; for it stands to reason that X_1 can be estimated better (or at least no more poorly) from two variables X_2 and X_3 than from X_2 alone or X_3 alone. Similarly, $R_{2.13}$ is greater than, or at least equal to, r_{12} and r_{23}; and $R_{3.12}$ is greater than, or at least equal to, r_{13} and r_{23}. Furthermore, $R_{1.23}^2$ is equal to the sum of r_{12}^2 and r_{13}^2 if X_2 and X_3 are independent of each other; for, by Eq. (19), it follows that

$$R_{1.23}^2 = 1 - \frac{\sigma_{1.23}^2}{\sigma_1^2} = 1 - \frac{\sigma_1^2(1 - \beta_{12.3}r_{12} - \beta_{13.2}r_{13})}{\sigma_1^2} \qquad (20)$$

$$= \beta_{12.3}r_{12} + \beta_{13.2}r_{13}$$

If X_2 and X_3 are independent of each other, $r_{23} = 0$; and, by Eqs. (9), $\beta_{12.3} = r_{12}$ and $\beta_{13.2} = r_{13}$. Accordingly, if $r_{23} = 0$,

$$R_{1.23}^2 = r_{12}^2 + r_{13}^2 \qquad (21)$$

Similarly, if $r_{13} = 0$,

$$R_{2.13}^2 = r_{12}^2 + r_{23}^2 \qquad (21')$$

and if $r_{12} = 0$,

$$R_{3.12}^2 = r_{13}^2 + r_{23}^2 \qquad (21'')$$

Consequently, by adding to the regression equation a second variable that is independent of the first, the accuracy with which the dependent variable can be estimated is increased by the amount of the correlation between that variable and the newly added variable.

It should be noted that only in special instances can a definite sign be given the multiple-correlation coefficient, although it is usually assumed to be inherently positive. For, as was indicated above, it may happen that the plane of regression to which a given multiple-correlation coefficient pertains may slope upward in one direction and downward in another direction, indicating a positive relationship between the dependent variable and one independent variable and a negative relationship between the dependent variable and the other independent variable. In such an instance, the correlation between the dependent variable and the two independent variables taken jointly, that is, the multiple correlation, cannot be said to be either positive or negative. For such a multiple-correlation coefficient, no sign is attached. It is only when the dependent variable is positively or negatively correlated with each and every one of the independent variables that the multiple-correlation coefficient can be given a positive or negative sign.

COEFFICIENT OF PARTIAL CORRELATION

In the preceding sections of this chapter the discussion has centered on the problem of estimating the value of one variable from one or more other variables by means of a regression equation. In connection with this problem, a coefficient measuring the degree of association between the dependent variable and the independent variables as a group was evaluated to show the accuracy with which such estimates can be made. This coefficient is a measure of the goodness of fit of the plane of regression.

When there are interrelationships among three or more variables, another problem appears. It often happens that an apparent relationship between two variables is in reality the result of their individual connection with a third variable that commonly affects them both. For example, it may be that the correlation between the price of cotton and the price of rayon is due largely to the correlation of each of them with the index of wholesale prices. In other words, the concomitant movements in the prices of cotton and rayon may be due, fundamentally not to any direct relationship between these two competing commodities, but primarily to their common tendency to rise and fall with the general price level; they may be joint effects of a common cause. Similarly, the concomitant variations in first- and second-semester English grades of freshmen in a woman's college may be basically accounted for by their respective relationships to the grades attained by the same freshmen in verbal scholastic-aptitude tests or to their school records.

The statistical device for discovering how much correlation there is between one variable and another variable when a third variable or a number of other variables are "held constant" is the method of "partial correlation." The correlation between the freshmen grades in second-semester English, X_1, and the freshmen grades in first-semester English, X_2, when the grades of the respective freshmen in verbal scholastic-aptitude tests, X_3, are held constant is the partial correlation between X_1 and X_2. Such a partial correlation coefficient will show how much connection there is between grades in first- and second-semester English independent of their common connection with grades in verbal scholastic-aptitude tests. The coefficient of partial correlation, indicated in this instance as $r_{12.3}$, will measure the degree of this independent association.[1]

A variable is, of course, not held constant in any physical sense. It is not possible in any way *ex post facto* to change the fact that a Mount Holyoke freshman, who had grades of 160 in first-semester English and 160 in second-semester English, had also a grade of 437 in her verbal scholastic-aptitude test; nor is it possible to change the fact that another Mount Holyoke freshman, who had grades of 120 in first-semester English and 160 in second-semester English, had also a grade of 384 in her verbal scholastic-aptitude test. The ideal of holding constant

---

[1] The position of the point in the subscripts of $r_{12.3}$, rather than the fact that it is a smaller letter, distinguishes it from $R_{1.23}$. In the latter, the point comes after the first digit, setting off the two independent variables X_3 and X_2, jointly associated with the dependent variable X_1. In the coefficient of partial correlation, the point sets off the variable that is held constant coming immediately after the pair that are correlated, X_1 and X_2. Thus, in $r_{12.3}$, X_3 is held constant while X_1 and X_2 are correlated; in $r_{12.345}$, X_3, X_4, and X_5 are held constant while X_1 and X_2 are correlated. The symbol $R_{1.2345}$, by the position of the point, indicates a multiple-correlation coefficient between X_1, dependent, and X_2, X_3, X_4, and X_5 taken jointly as the independent variables.

one of the three variables is wholly a statistical idea. It consists in eliminating from each of the two variables between which the partial correlation is sought the effect of the third variable. More specifically, the line of regression of X_1 on X_3 is found, and the deviations of the actual values of X_1 from those given by the line of regression $X_1' = a_{1.3} + b_{13}X_3$ are determined. These deviations from the line of regression represent the variation in X_1 that is left over after the linear effect of X_3 is eliminated. Similarly, the line of regression of X_2 on X_3 is computed, and the deviations of the actual values of X_2 from those given by the line of regression $X_2' = a_{2.3} + b_{23}X_3$ are determined. These deviations from the line of regression represent the variation in X_2 that is left over after the linear effect of X_3 is eliminated. When these residual deviations in X_1 and X_2 are correlated, the result is the partial-correlation coefficient between X_1 and X_2 when X_3 is held constant, because the effect of X_3 upon each of them has been eliminated.

To calculate a partial coefficient of correlation the extended calculations involved in computing two lines of regression and measuring the deviations of the actual values from them is not necessary. The coefficient of partial correlation can be algebraically evaluated in a formula that makes it possible to compute it from the coefficients of simple linear correlation, as follows:

The deviation of X_1 from the line of regression of X_1 on X_3 may be written as $x_1 - x_1'$ or $x_1 - r_{13}\dfrac{\sigma_1}{\sigma_3}x_3$ where the x's are measured from their respective means. Similarly, the deviation of X_2 from the line of regression of X_2 on X_3 may be written as $x_2 - x_2'$ or $x_2 - r_{23}\dfrac{\sigma_2}{\sigma_3}x_3$. The standard deviations of these deviations from the lines of regression have already been determined to be $\sigma_{1.3}$ and $\sigma_{2.3}$, respectively. In accordance with the ordinary formula for a simple correlation coefficient, that is, $r = \Sigma x_1 x_2 / N\sigma_1\sigma_2$, the partial-correlation coefficient between X_1 and X_2, when X_3 is held constant, is, by definition,

$$r_{12.3} = \frac{\Sigma(x_1 - x_1')(x_2 - x_2')}{N\sigma_{x_1-x_1'}\sigma_{x_2-x_2'}}$$

$$= \frac{\sum\left(x_1 - r_{13}\dfrac{\sigma_1}{\sigma_3}x_3\right)\left(x_2 - r_{23}\dfrac{\sigma_2}{\sigma_3}x_3\right)}{N\sigma_{1.3}\sigma_{2.3}} \tag{22}$$

If the numerator is expanded and the values for $\sigma_{1.3}$ and $\sigma_{2.3}$ are substituted in the denominator, this becomes

$$r_{12.3} = \frac{\sum x_1 x_2 - r_{23} \dfrac{\sigma_2}{\sigma_3} \sum x_1 x_3 - r_{13} \dfrac{\sigma_1}{\sigma_3} \sum x_2 x_3 + r_{13} r_{23} \dfrac{\sigma_1 \sigma_2}{\sigma_3^2} \sum x_3^2}{N \sigma_1 \sqrt{1 - r_{13}^2}\, \sigma_2 \sqrt{1 - r_{23}^2}}$$

Upon transferring the divisor $N\sigma_1\sigma_2$ from the denominator to each term of the numerator, this becomes

$$r_{12.3} = \frac{\dfrac{\Sigma x_1 x_2}{N\sigma_1\sigma_2} - r_{23} \dfrac{\sigma_2}{\sigma_2} \dfrac{\Sigma x_1 x_3}{N\sigma_1\sigma_3} - r_{13} \dfrac{\sigma_1}{\sigma_1} \dfrac{\Sigma x_2 x_3}{N\sigma_2\sigma_3} + r_{13} r_{23} \dfrac{\sigma_1\sigma_2}{\sigma_1\sigma_2} \dfrac{\Sigma x_3^2}{N\sigma_3^2}}{\sqrt{1 - r_{13}^2} \sqrt{1 - r_{23}^2}}$$

in which r_{12}, r_{13}, r_{23} can be substituted for their respective equivalent values, making the formula appear as follows:

$$r_{12.3} = \frac{r_{12} - r_{23} r_{13} - r_{13} r_{23} + r_{13} r_{23}}{\sqrt{1 - r_{13}^2} \sqrt{1 - r_{23}^2}}$$

which reduces to

$$r_{12.3} = \frac{r_{12} - r_{13} r_{23}}{\sqrt{1 - r_{13}^2} \sqrt{1 - r_{23}^2}} \tag{23}$$

Similar formulas for the partial correlation between X_1 and X_3 when X_2 is held constant and the partial correlation between X_2 and X_3 when X_1 is held constant are as follows:[1]

$$r_{13.2} = \frac{r_{13} - r_{12} r_{23}}{\sqrt{1 - r_{12}^2} \sqrt{1 - r_{23}^2}} \tag{23'}$$

$$r_{23.1} = \frac{r_{23} - r_{12} r_{13}}{\sqrt{1 - r_{12}^2} \sqrt{1 - r_{13}^2}} \tag{23''}$$

From Eq. (23) it can be seen that if X_1 and X_2 are both uncorrelated with X_3, that is, if r_{13} and r_{23} are zero, then $r_{12.3} = r_{12}$. Similarly, if r_{12} and r_{23} are zero, $r_{13.2} = r_{13}$; and if r_{12} and r_{13} are zero, $r_{23.1} = r_{23}$.

---

[1] For the coefficient of partial correlation, the order of the numbers in the subscripts either before or after the point is a matter of indifference; that is, $r_{12.3} = r_{21.3}$ and $r_{12.345} = r_{21.435}$, etc. It will be remembered that this is not true with respect to the order of the numbers in the subscripts before the decimal in the b's and the β's; that is, $b_{12.3} \neq b_{21.3}$, $\beta_{12.3} \neq \beta_{21.3}$.

Any one of the following formulas, which can be readily derived algebraically [see Eq. (9)] may be used in place of, or as a check on, Eq. (23):

$$r_{12.3} = \sqrt{\beta_{12.3}\beta_{21.3}} \tag{24}$$

$$r_{12.3} = \beta_{12.3}\left(\frac{\sqrt{1 - r_{23}^2}}{\sqrt{1 - r_{13}^2}}\right) \tag{25}$$

$$r_{12.3} = \beta_{12.3}\frac{\sigma_1}{\sigma_2}\frac{\sigma_{2.3}}{\sigma_{1.3}} \tag{26}$$

$$r_{12.3} = b_{12.3}\frac{\sigma_{2.3}}{\sigma_{1.3}} \tag{27}$$

Thus the partial-correlation coefficient can be calculated directly from the β's or from the b's and the dispersion formulas for the simple lines of regression, as well as from the simple r's. The equations for the other coefficients of partial correlation are symmetrical with Eqs. (24) to (27).

The partial coefficients of correlation illustrated above are called correlation coefficients of the "first order," while the simple coefficients r_{12}, r_{23}, etc., are called "zero-order" correlation coefficients. If there are more than three variables involved so that a partial coefficient of correlation, $r_{12.34}$, for example, is found, it is called a "second-order" coefficient of correlation; similarly, $r_{12.345}$ is a "third-order" coefficient of correlation, etc. This classification is helpful in distinguishing different sets of correlation coefficients. The same terminology may be conveniently carried over to the other statistics in a correlation problem. Thus, σ_1 is a zero-order standard deviation, $\sigma_{1.2}$ is a first-order standard deviation, etc.; $b_{12.3}$ is a first-order regression statistic, $b_{12.34}$ is a second-order regression statistic; etc.

ANALYSIS OF VARIANCE IN MULTIPLE CORRELATION

When a plane of regression, for example, X_1 on X_2 and X_3, is fitted to a trivariate frequency distribution by the method of least squares, variation in X_1 may be viewed as made up of a part that is due to its linear association with X_2, a second part that is due to its linear association with X_3, and a third part that is due to association with factors independent of both X_2 and X_3. For the least squares Equation (6) show that $\Sigma x_2 d = 0$ and $\Sigma x_3 d = 0$, which means that neither X_2 nor X_3 is linearly correlated with deviations from the plane of regression. In the case of a normal trivariate frequency distribution, the independent variables are not correlated in any way with the deviations from the plane of regression. Owing to the lack of correlation, the variance in the dependent variable is equal to the variance of the values given by the plane of regression plus the variance of the deviations from the plane. This may be shown as follows:

$$x_1 = x_1' - (x_1 - x_1')$$

and

$$x_1^2 = (x_1')^2 - 2(x_1 - x_1')x_1' + (x_1 - x_1')^2 \qquad (28)$$

If all the deviations squared, like x_1^2, described in Eq. (28) are added, the following result is obtained:

$$\Sigma x_1^2 = \Sigma(x_1')^2 + \Sigma(x_1 - x_1')^2 - 2\Sigma(x_1 - x_1')x_1'$$

or, by substituting $x_1' = \left(\beta_{12.3}\dfrac{x_2}{\sigma_2} + \beta_{13.2}\dfrac{x_3}{\sigma_3}\right)\sigma_1$ for the last x_1',

$$\sum x_1^2 = \sum (x_1')^2 + \sum (x_1 - x_1')^2 - 2\sigma_1\beta_{12.3} \sum (x_1 - x_1')\frac{x_2}{\sigma_2}$$
$$- 2\sigma_1\beta_{13.2} \sum (x_1 - x_1')\frac{x_3}{\sigma_3}$$

But, as just stated, the deviations $x_1 - x_1'$ are not linearly correlated with x_2 and x_3, so that the cross-product terms are zero. Therefore,

$$\Sigma x_1^2 = \Sigma(x_1')^2 + \Sigma(x_1 - x_1')^2$$

If each term is divided by N, it is found that

$$\sigma_1^2 = \sigma_{x_1'}^2 + \sigma_{1.23}^2 \qquad (29)$$

In Eq. (29), $\sigma_{x_1'}^2$ may be further evaluated, as follows:[1]

$$\sum (x_1')^2 = \sum \left(\beta_{12.3}\frac{x_2}{\sigma_2} + \beta_{13.2}\frac{x_3}{\sigma_3}\right)^2 \sigma_1^2$$
$$= \sigma_1^2 \left(\beta_{12.3}^2 \sum \frac{x_2^2}{\sigma_2^2} + \beta_{13.2}^2 \sum \frac{x_3^2}{\sigma_3^2} + 2\beta_{12.3}\beta_{13.2} \sum \frac{x_2 x_3}{\sigma_2 \sigma_3}\right)$$

[1] Since $x_1' = \left(\beta_{12.3}\dfrac{x_2}{\sigma_2} + \beta_{13.2}\dfrac{x_3}{\sigma_3}\right)\sigma_1.$ See p. 411.

If the above is divided by N and $\sigma_{x_1'}^2$, σ_2^2, σ_3^2, and r_{23} are substituted for equivalent values, the expression becomes

$$\sigma_{x_1'}^2 = \sigma_1^2(\beta_{12.3}^2 + \beta_{13.2}^2 + 2r_{23}\beta_{12.3}\beta_{13.2}) \qquad (30)$$

By substituting this value for $\sigma_{x_1'}^2$ in Eq. (29), it is found that

$$\sigma_1^2 = \sigma_1^2(\beta_{12.3}^2 + \beta_{13.2}^2 + 2r_{23}\beta_{12.3}\beta_{13.2}) + \sigma_{1.23}^2$$

or

$$1 = \beta_{12.3}^2 + \beta_{13.2}^2 + 2r_{23}\beta_{12.3}\beta_{13.2} + \frac{\sigma_{1.23}^2}{\sigma_1^2} \qquad (31)$$

From the manner in which Eq. (31) was derived, it is known that the terms on the right side each represent a percentage of

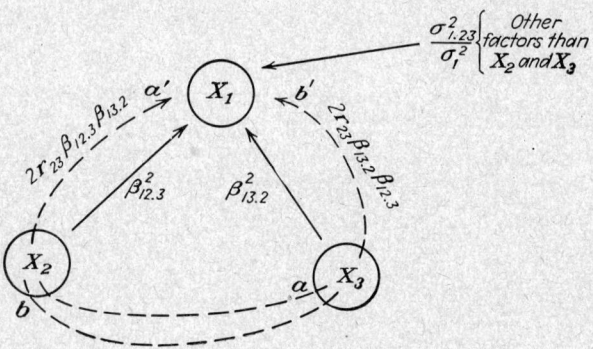

FIG. 118.—Illustration of coefficients of direct determination, meaning of $2r$-β cross-product term and the residual variance.

the total variance of X_1. This may be interpreted in the following manner:

Coefficients of Direct Determination. The first term of the right side of Eq. (31), $\beta_{12.3}^2$, may be interpreted as the percentage of the total variation in X_1 that is due to its direct association with X_2. It has consequently been called the "coefficient of direct determination" of X_1 by X_2. Similarly, $\beta_{13.2}^2$ may be interpreted as the percentage of the total variation in X_1 that is due to its direct association with X_3. Figure 118 depicts the coefficients of direct determination by arrows pointing from X_2 directly to X_1 and from X_3 directly to X_1.

Coefficients of Net Regression. The beta unsquared, $\beta_{12.3}$, describes the change in X_1 in standard-deviation units that accompanies a given change of X_2 in standard-deviation units, when X_3 is constant. Geometrically, $\beta_{12.3}$ is the slope of the line of intersection of a plane perpendicular to the $\dfrac{x_3}{\sigma_3}$ axis with the plane of regression,

$$\frac{x_1'}{\sigma_1} = \beta_{12.3}\,\frac{x_2}{\sigma_2} + \beta_{13.2}\,\frac{x_3}{\sigma_3}$$

The statistic $\beta_{12.3}$ has been called the "coefficient of net regression" of X_1 on X_2 in standard-deviation units. The coefficient of net regression in original units is $b_{12.3}$.

Coefficient of Joint Determination. The term $2r_{23}\beta_{12.3}\beta_{13.2}$ may be taken as representing the percentage of the total variation in X_1 that is due to the joint or combined effect of X_2 and X_3 resulting from the correlation between these two variables. In Fig. 118 the influence of X_3 on X_1 through its correlation with X_2 is depicted by the line aa'; the influence of X_2 on X_1 through its correlation with X_3 is depicted by the line bb'. Relationships along these lines indicate the significance of the r-β cross-product term of Eq. (31). While variation in X_2 may directly affect X_1, it may also, through its correlation with X_3, bring about a change in X_3 and hence cause further variation in X_1 resulting from the connection between X_3 and X_1. Similarly, variation in X_3 may affect X_1, not only directly, but also indirectly through the association of X_3 and X_2. The term $2r_{23}\beta_{12.3}\beta_{13.2}$ may be taken to represent the combined indirect variation in X_1 resulting from variations in X_2 and X_3.

Meaning of Residual Variance. The portion of variance in X_1 due directly to X_2 is $\beta_{12.3}^2$; the portion due directly to X_3 is $\beta_{13.2}^2$; the portion due to the joint influence of X_2 and X_3 is the $2r$-β cross-product term; the remainder of the variance is due to other factors not linearly correlated with X_2 and X_3. This is depicted in Fig. 118. The sum of all of these four terms is equal to the total variance, or, expressed as a proportion, to 1. The sum of the first three terms may be interpreted as the total portion of variance in X_1 that is due to its association with X_2 and X_3 jointly; the final term $\sigma_{1.23}^2/\sigma_1^2$ represents the portion of the variance in X_1 that is due to its association with other factors not linearly correlated with X_2 and X_3. The sum of all these portions of the total variance of X_1 is necessarily equal to 1.

The Coefficient of Multiple Correlation. From the previous discussion regarding the interpretation of the simple correlation coefficient and the correlation ratio, it is to be expected that a similar interpretation might be made of the multiple-correlation coefficient, that is, that $R_{1.23}^2$ represents the portion of the total variance in X_1 which is due to its joint association with X_2 and X_3. Equation (31) shows that this is actually the case; for it will be recalled that

$$R_{1.23}^2 = 1 - \frac{\sigma_{1.23}^2}{\sigma_1^2}$$

Therefore, it follows by Eqs. (29), (30), and (31) that

$$R_{1.23}^2 = \beta_{12.3}^2 + \beta_{13.2}^2 + 2r_{21}\beta_{12.3}\beta_{13.2} = \frac{\sigma_{x_1'}^2}{\sigma_1^2} \qquad (32)$$

This interpretation of $R_{1.23}^2$ is similar to that previously made of

$$r_{12}^2 = \frac{\sigma_{x_1'}^2}{\sigma_1^2} \qquad \text{and} \qquad \eta_{12}^2 = \frac{\sigma_e^2}{\sigma_1^2}$$

where $\sigma_{x_1'}$ is the standard deviation of the line of regression.

It has been noted that $R_{1.23}^2$ can be interpreted as the portion of the total variance of X_1 that may be attributed to its joint association with X_2 and X_3. It has also been shown that $R_{1.23}^2 = \beta_{12.3}r_{12} + \beta_{13.2}r_{13}$ [see Eq. (20)]. Consequently, it is possible to view $\beta_{12.3}r_{12}$ as the portion of the variance of X_1 that is due to its total association, both direct and indirect, with X_2 and also to view $\beta_{13.2}r_{13}$ as the portion of the variance of X_1 that is due to its total association, both direct and indirect, with X_3. Therefore, these two products have been called "coefficients of total determination" of X_1 by X_2 and X_3.

When either of the products is negative, however,[1] it is preferable to resolve the expression into its equal, namely,

$$\beta_{12.3}^2 + \beta_{13.2}^2 + 2r_{23}\beta_{12.3}\beta_{13.2}$$

---

[1] The interpretation of the products as coefficients of total determination runs into difficulties in any particular case if either of them is negative. Either $\beta_{12.3}r_{12}$ or $\beta_{13.2}r_{13}$ but not both may be negative, since their sum equals $R_{1.23}^2$, which, of course, is not negative. To say that a variable contributes a negative percentage to the total variance of X_1 has no meaning, and consequently when either term is negative the interpretation is imaginary.

because

$$R^2_{1.23} = \beta_{12.3}r_{12} + \beta_{13.2}r_{13} = \beta^2_{12.3} + \beta^2_{13.2} + 2r_{23}\beta_{12.3}\beta_{13.2}$$

Expressed in the β^2 and cross-product form, it is easier to understand why a negative value of $\beta_{12.3}r_{12}$ or of $\beta_{13.2}r_{13}$ (but not of both) may occur; for whenever either $\beta_{12.3}r_{12}$ or $\beta_{13.2}r_{13}$ is negative, it will be found that the joint contribution of X_2 and X_3 to the variance of X_1, represented by $2r_{23}\beta_{12.3}\beta_{13.2}$, is also negative. This follows because either r_{23} is negative or $\beta_{12.3}$ and $\beta_{13.2}$ are of opposite signs. In such a case, the direct effect of X_2, for example, on the variation of X_1 would be opposite in sign to its indirect effect, that is, through its correlation with X_3; and the existence of this indirect link to X_1 through X_3 would tend to diminish the total variation caused in X_1 by changes in X_2. This dampening effect of a negative value for the r-β cross-product term is what explains the existence of a negative value for either $\beta_{12.3}r_{12}$ or $\beta_{13.2}r_{13}$. The form where they are squared also shows the difficulty in trying to assign to the variables X_2 and X_3 an independent part in accounting for the variation in X_1. When there is a joint contribution by the two variables, it becomes misleading to attempt to break it up and assign part of it to one and part to the other, as the foregoing interpretation based upon the form $\beta_{12.3}r_{12} + \beta_{13.2}r_{13}$ appears to do.

As noted above, the part of the variance, σ^2_1, that is due to correlation between X_1 and X_2 and X_3 together is described as follows:[1]

$$\sigma^2_{x_{1'}} = R^2_{1.23}\sigma^2_1$$

The right side of this expression describes the variance of the plane of regression, just as $r^2_{12}\sigma^2_1$ describes the variance of the line of regression. This part of the variance in the X_1 variable is made up of two parts that may be analyzed as follows:[2]

$$\begin{aligned}
\sigma^2_{1.23} &= \sigma^2_1(1 - r^2_{12})(1 - r^2_{13.2}) \\
&= \sigma^2_1 - r^2_{13.2}\sigma^2_1 - r^2_{12}\sigma^2_1 + r^2_{12}r^2_{13.2}\sigma^2_1 \\
&= \sigma^2_1 - r^2_{12}\sigma^2_1 - \sigma^2_1(1 - r^2_{12})r^2_{13.2} \\
&= \sigma^2_1 - r^2_{12}\sigma^2_1 - \sigma^2_{1.2}r^2_{13.2}
\end{aligned}$$

[1] *Cf.* Eqs. (29) and (31).

[2] See footnote, p. 416.

Therefore, by transposing terms,

$$\sigma_1^2 = r_{12}^2\sigma_1^2 + \sigma_{1.2}^2 r_{13.2}^2 + \sigma_{1.23}^2 \tag{33}$$

It follows from Eqs. (33) and (29) that

$$\sigma_{x_1'}^2 = r_{12}^2\sigma_1^2 + \sigma_{1.2}^2 r_{13.2}^2$$

in which $\sigma_{1.2}^2$ is the scatter about the line of regression of X_1 on X_2.

It is thus seen that the variance $\sigma_{x_1'}^2$ of the plane of regression consists of two parts: (1) the variance due to the total linear association between X_1 and X_2, which is $r_{12}^2\sigma_1^2$; and (2) of the remaining variance about the line of regression ($\sigma_{1.2}^2$), the portion that is due to the influence of X_3 not already included in r_{12}, namely, $r_{13.2}^2\sigma_{1.2}^2$. The partial coefficient of correlation $r_{13.2}$ describes the relationship between X_1 and X_3 when X_2 is held constant; in other words, it is the net correlation between X_1 and X_3. The square of this partial coefficient of correlation is therefore the coefficient of proportional variance in X_1 due to net correlation with X_3. If to variance due to total association with X_2 is added the variance due to net correlation with X_3, the result is the variance due to total correlation with X_2 and X_3 jointly. The remainder of the variance, as Eq. (33) indicates, is due to other causes not linearly correlated with X_2 and X_3.

Analysis of Variance and Causal Relationships. Where other knowledge suggests that causal relationships run only in one direction, the preceding analysis takes on considerable significance. In biological investigations, for example, where the effect of heredity is being studied, it seems logical to assume that variations in parents cause variations in offspring and that the causal relationship does not run the other way. Again, in certain economic problems, it is to be assumed that fluctuations in weather conditions bring about changes in economic conditions, but that the latter have no effect upon the former. In one-directional setups of this kind, the β's take on the full significance of the connotation "coefficients of determination." The β^2's measure the amount of variation in the dependent variable caused by fluctuations in each of the independent variables separately, and in conjunction with the other variables in the $2r$-β cross-product expression. It is in this type of problem that correlation analysis attains its greatest significance.

Where there is no reason to believe that causal relationships are unilateral, the interpretation of the results of correlation analysis in terms of causal determination becomes unscientific. In most problems there is interaction between the variables rather than a strictly one-directional association. It is still possible to estimate what is called the dependent variable from knowledge of so-called independent variables, but the latter must not be looked upon as determining the former. With reference to a regression equation used for purposes of estimation and prediction, the β^2's and the $2r$-β cross-product terms are useful in showing how important certain factors are, separately and in conjunction with other factors, in making estimates or predictions of the dependent variable. They become coefficients of determination only in the sense of statistical determination or estimation and not in any sense of physical, biological, or economic causation.

Of incidental importance to method and theory but of considerable importance to practice, Eq. (31) provides a cross check on the arithmetical work for finding most of the statistics in the multiple-correlation problem.

EXTENSION OF MULTIPLE- AND PARTIAL-CORRELATION ANALYSIS TO FOUR VARIABLES

The foregoing analysis, which has pertained to only three variables, may be extended to cover a greater number of variables. In this section its extension to a four-variable problem will be discussed. In the next section its extension to any desired number of variables will be considered.

When there are more than two independent variables in a regression equation, the number of β coefficients to be determined is correspondingly increased. If there were four variables, for example, that is, three independent variables, the β form of the regression equation would become

$$\frac{x_1'}{\sigma_1} = \beta_{12.34} \frac{x_2}{\sigma_2} + \beta_{13.24} \frac{x_3}{\sigma_3} + \beta_{14.23} \frac{x_4}{\sigma_4} \qquad (34)$$

If this regression plane is fitted by the method of least squares, the β's can be determined in terms of the r's in the manner described for the three-variable problem; but, there being three equations to be solved for three β's, the solutions are not so simple as those given by Eqs. (8) and (9). Some special method of solution may be employed, such as the so-called "Doolittle method" of substitution or some determinant method.[1]

The chief advantage claimed for the Doolittle method is that it provides a check at each step in the problem; but experience for several years with its use for four-variable correlation problems has demonstrated its complexity and sensitivity. For a multivariate problem of more than four variables both the Doolittle work sheet and the determinant methods become increasingly cumbersome.

A saving in computation is obtained by using formulas based upon the algebraic evaluation of correlation statistics. This saving was demonstrated for the trivariate case in the first part of this chapter where it was found that the β's could be evaluated in terms of the zero-order r's [see Eq. (9)]. In addition, however, it is possible by symmetry to extend the algebraic results of some of the formulas to apply to a multivariate correlation of as many variables as desired, in effect to evaluate algebraically the correlation statistics for the general regression equation.

$$X_i = a_{i.jk...n} + b_{ij.k...} X_j + b_{ik.j...} X_k + \cdots + b_{in.jk...} X_n \quad (35)$$

First the correlation statistics will be algebraically evaluated for the four-variable case, which is done as follows:

The normal least-squares equations for fitting a plane of regression of X_1 on X_2, X_3, and X_4, when divided by N, are as follows:[2]

$$\frac{\Sigma x_1 x_2}{N\sigma_1\sigma_2} = \beta_{12.34} \frac{\Sigma x_2^2}{N\sigma_2^2} + \beta_{13.24} \frac{\Sigma x_2 x_3}{N\sigma_2\sigma_3} + \beta_{14.23} \frac{\Sigma x_2 x_4}{N\sigma_2\sigma_4}$$

$$\frac{\Sigma x_1 x_3}{N\sigma_1\sigma_3} = \beta_{12.34} \frac{\Sigma x_2 x_3}{N\sigma_2\sigma_3} + \beta_{13.24} \frac{\Sigma x_3^2}{N\sigma_3^2} + \beta_{14.23} \frac{\Sigma x_3 x_4}{N\sigma_3\sigma_4}$$

$$\frac{\Sigma x_1 x_4}{N\sigma_1\sigma_4} = \beta_{12.34} \frac{\Sigma x_2 x_4}{N\sigma_2\sigma_4} + \beta_{13.24} \frac{\Sigma x_3 x_4}{N\sigma_3\sigma_4} + \beta_{14.23} \frac{\Sigma x_4^2}{N\sigma_4^2}$$

These may be written, by substituting for their equivalent values, r_{12}, σ_2^2, r_{23}, r_{24}, r_{13}, σ_3^2, r_{34}, r_{14}, σ_4^2, as follows:

[1] In theoretical work the determinant method gives neat and easily remembered solutions. In practical work, however, many statisticians prefer the method of substitution.

[2] See pp. 411–412.

$$r_{12} = \beta_{12.34} + r_{23}\beta_{13.24} + r_{24}\beta_{14.23}$$
$$r_{13} = r_{23}\beta_{12.34} + \beta_{13.24} + r_{34}\beta_{14.23} \quad\left.\right\} \quad (36)$$
$$r_{14} = r_{24}\beta_{12.34} + r_{34}\beta_{13.24} + \beta_{14.23}$$

If the first of Eqs. (36) is multiplied by r_{23} and the result is subtracted from the second, $\beta_{12.34}$ is eliminated and it is found that

$$r_{13} - r_{12}r_{23} = (1 - r_{23}^2)\beta_{13.24} + (r_{34} - r_{23}r_{24})\beta_{14.23}$$

or

$$\frac{r_{13} - r_{12}r_{23}}{1 - r_{23}^2} = \beta_{13.24} + \frac{r_{34} - r_{23}r_{24}}{1 - r_{23}^2}\beta_{14.23}$$

which, by Eqs. (9), is equivalent to saying

$$\beta_{13.2} = \beta_{13.24} + \beta_{43.2}\beta_{14.23} \tag{37}$$

Similarly, if the first of Eqs. (36), multiplied by r_{24}, is subtracted from the third, $\beta_{12.34}$ is eliminated and it is found that

$$\beta_{14.2} = \beta_{14.23} + \beta_{34.2}\beta_{13.24} \tag{38}$$

Correlation Statistics in Terms of Lower-order Correlation Statistics of the Same Kind. From Eqs. (37) and (38), solved simultaneously, it is found that

$$\beta_{14.23} = \frac{\beta_{14.2} - \beta_{34.2}\beta_{13.2}}{1 - \beta_{34.2}\beta_{43.2}} \tag{39}$$

All the other second-order β's may be evaluated in a similar algebraic manner, or written by symmetry; for example, by symmetry with Eq. (39), the $\beta_{13.24}$ is as follows:

$$\beta_{13.24} = \frac{\beta_{13.2} - \beta_{43.2}\beta_{14.2}}{1 - \beta_{43.2}\beta_{34.2}} \tag{40}$$

Equations (39) and (40) are equivalent to the following expressions in terms of the b's, because, if $b_{14.2}\dfrac{\sigma_4}{\sigma_1}$, $b_{34.2}\dfrac{\sigma_4}{\sigma_3}$, and similar values of β's in terms of corresponding b's and standard-deviation ratios are substituted, the standard deviations cancel out.[1]

---

[1] Since the order of digits in the subscript after the point is immaterial in both the b and β statistics, the following formulas may be used as checks

$$b_{14.23} = \frac{b_{14.2} - b_{34.2}b_{13.2}}{1 - b_{34.2}b_{43.2}} \tag{39'}$$

$$b_{13.24} = \frac{b_{13.2} - b_{43.2}b_{14.2}}{1 - b_{43.2}b_{34.2}} \tag{40'}$$

Correlation Statistics in Terms of Lower-order r's and σ's.   It is possible to express the above formulas in terms of lower-order r's and σ's if this method of calculation is preferred.   It was noted in Eq. (26) that

$$r_{12.3} = \beta_{12.3}\frac{\sigma_1}{\sigma_2}\frac{\sigma_{2.3}}{\sigma_{1.3}}$$

and, by symmetry, it follows that

$$r_{14.2} = \beta_{14.2}\frac{\sigma_1}{\sigma_4}\frac{\sigma_{4.2}}{\sigma_{1.2}}$$

Also, by Eq. (27),

$$r_{14.2} = b_{14.2}\frac{\sigma_{4.2}}{\sigma_{1.2}}$$

Consequently,

$$\beta_{14.2} = r_{14.2}\frac{\sigma_4}{\sigma_1}\frac{\sigma_{1.2}}{\sigma_{4.2}}$$

$$b_{14.2} = r_{14.2}\frac{\sigma_{1.2}}{\sigma_{4.2}}$$

If these values of the β's in terms of r's and standard deviations are substituted in Eq. (39) and the values of the b's in terms of the r's and the scatter are substituted in Eq. (39'), the following results are obtained:

$$\beta_{12.34} = \frac{r_{12.3} - r_{42.3}r_{14.3}}{1 - r_{24.3}^2}\frac{\sigma_2}{\sigma_1}\frac{\sigma_{1.3}}{\sigma_{2.3}} \tag{41}$$

$$b_{12.34} = \frac{r_{12.3} - r_{24.3}r_{14.3}}{1 - r_{24.3}^2}\frac{\sigma_{1.3}}{\sigma_{2.3}} \tag{41'}$$

Correlation Statistics in Terms of Correlation Statistics of Same Order.   The preceding formulas may be transformed to still

---

on the ones given in the text:

$$\beta_{14.32} = \frac{\beta_{14.3} - \beta_{24.3}\beta_{12.3}}{1 - \beta_{24.3}\beta_{42.3}} \tag{39}$$

$$b_{14.32} = \frac{b_{14.3} - b_{24.3}b_{12.3}}{1 - b_{24.3}b_{42.3}} \tag{39'}$$

another form in which the correlation statistics are expressed in terms of other correlation statistics of the same order. Thus, since $\sigma_{1.34} = \sigma_{1.3} \sqrt{1 - r_{14.3}^2}$ and $\sigma_{2.34} = \sigma_{2.3} \sqrt{1 - r_{24.3}^2}$, it follows that

$$\sigma_{1.3} = \frac{\sigma_{1.34}}{\sqrt{1 - r_{14.3}^2}}$$

$$\sigma_{2.3} = \frac{\sigma_{2.34}}{\sqrt{1 - r_{24.3}^2}}$$

If these values are substituted in Eqs. (41) and (41'), the following results are obtained:

$$\beta_{12.34} = r_{12.34} \frac{\sigma_2}{\sigma_1} \frac{\sigma_{1.34}}{\sigma_{2.34}} \qquad (42)$$

$$b_{12.34} = r_{12.34} \frac{\sigma_{1.34}}{\sigma_{2.34}} \qquad (42')$$

Similar algebraic procedure will show that all the other β's and b's have formulas that are symmetrical with the above. For example,

$$\beta_{13.24} = r_{13.24} \frac{\sigma_3}{\sigma_1} \frac{\sigma_{1.24}}{\sigma_{3.24}}$$

$$b_{13.24} = r_{13.24} \frac{\sigma_{1.24}}{\sigma_{3.24}}$$

$$\beta_{14.23} = r_{14.23} \frac{\sigma_4}{\sigma_1} \frac{\sigma_{1.23}}{\sigma_{4.23}}$$

$$b_{14.23} = r_{14.23} \frac{\sigma_{1.23}}{\sigma_{4.23}}$$

Partial Correlation in the Four-variable Case. If there are four variables X_1, X_2, X_3, and X_4, the partial-correlation coefficient between X_1 and X_2 when X_3 and X_4 are held constant, that is, $r_{12.34}$, is defined as the simple correlation coefficient between the deviations of X_1 from the plane of regression of X_1 on X_3 and X_4 and the deviations of X_2 from the plane of regression of X_2 on X_3 and X_4. Accordingly, partial correlation, when four variables are involved, is no more complex algebraically than when three variables are involved; both are simple linear correlations between residuals. In the three-variable problem the partial coefficient of correlation is found by correlating the residuals about lines of regression; in the four-variable problem the partial coefficient of correlation is found by correlating the residuals about planes of regression. The formula for the second-order partial coefficient of correlation $r_{12.34}$ is obtained in the same algebraic manner as for the first-order partial coefficients of correlation [see Eqs. (22) and (23)]. The formula is

$$r_{13.24} = \frac{r_{13.2} - r_{14.2}r_{34.2}}{\sqrt{1 - r_{14.2}^2}\sqrt{1 - r_{34.2}^2}} \tag{43}$$

This is a partial coefficient of correlation of the second order. It will be noted that the formula runs in terms of the correlation coefficients of the first order. To make use of this formula in practice, therefore, it first becomes necessary to calculate the zero-order correlation coefficients and then the first-order coefficients before the second-order coefficients can be determined. The calculation of higher-order partial-correlation coefficients is thus similar to the calculation of those of lower order, but they require additional work.

Third-order Variance and Multiple-correlation Coefficient. The formula for third-order variance in the four-variable problem is obtained by adding a term to the formula for scatter in the three-variable problem, as follows:

$$\sigma_{1.234}^2 = \sigma_1^2(1 - \beta_{12.34}r_{12} - \beta_{13.24}r_{13} - \beta_{14.23}r_{14}) \tag{44}$$

The equation for the multiple-correlation coefficient is, by symmetry, as follows:

$$R_{1.234}^2 = 1 - \frac{\sigma_{1.234}^2}{\sigma_1^2} \tag{45}$$

or

$$R_{1.234}^2 = \beta_{12.34}r_{12} + \beta_{13.24}r_{13} + \beta_{14.23}r_{14}$$

EXTENSION OF MULTIPLE- AND PARTIAL-CORRELATION ANALYSIS TO ANY DESIRED NUMBER OF VARIABLES

For a three-variable and even for a four-variable correlation problem, it is probably desirable first to calculate the β's from the lower-order β's. In the three-variable correlation problem, this means calculating the β's from the zero-order r's, which at that level correspond to the β's.

For more than four variables it may be better first to calculate the higher-order r's from the lower-order r's and thereafter obtain the b and β statistics. Following is the extension to the general multivariate problem of the various formulas, showing the series of formulas in some cases from the simple correlation to the multivariate in order to depict how they are readily obtained by symmetry.

Extension of Formulas to General Multivariate Problem. *Statistics for the Regression Planes.* The b and β statistics are evaluated, in general, by the following formula:

(a)
$$b = r \frac{\sigma}{\sigma}$$

or

$$b_{ij.kt\ldots n} = r_{ij.kt\ldots n} \frac{\sigma_{i.kt\ldots n}}{\sigma_{ikt\ldots n}}$$

This formula can be used when the r's and σ's of the same order have already been obtained, but it does not provide for the calculation of the b's from lower-order statistics.

In the simple linear-regression equation, carrying out the instructions of the above formula gives $b_{12} = r_{12} \frac{\sigma_1}{\sigma_2}$. If there are three variables, it becomes $b_{12.3} = r_{12.3} \frac{\sigma_{1.3}}{\sigma_{2.3}}$, etc.

The relationship between the b's and the β's is not affected by the number of variables and may be summarized as follows:

(b)
$$\beta_{12.3} = b_{12.3} \frac{\sigma_2}{\sigma_1}$$

$$\beta_{12.34} = b_{12.34} \frac{\sigma_2}{\sigma_1}$$

$$\beta_{13.2} = b_{13.2} \frac{\sigma_3}{\sigma_1}$$

$$\beta_{13.24} = b_{13.24} \frac{\sigma_3}{\sigma_1}$$

$$\cdot \quad \cdot \quad \cdot \quad \cdot \quad \cdot \quad \cdot \quad \cdot$$

$$\beta_{ij.kt\ldots n} = b_{ij.kt\ldots n} \frac{\sigma_j}{\sigma_i}$$

The a's for the various planes of regression are found by formulas such as the following:

(c)
$$a_{1.234} = \bar{X}_1 - b_{12.34}\bar{X}_2 - b_{13.24}\bar{X}_3 - b_{14.23}\bar{X}_4$$
$$a_{2.134} = \bar{X}_2 - b_{21.34}\bar{X}_1 - b_{23.14}\bar{X}_3 - b_{24.13}\bar{X}_4$$

$$\cdots \cdots \cdots \cdots \cdots \cdots$$

$$a_{i.jk\ldots n} = \bar{X}_i - b_{ij.k\ldots n}\bar{X}_j - b_{ik.j\ldots n}\bar{X}_k \cdots - b_{in.kj\ldots m}\bar{X}_n$$

High-order Variances. The higher-order variances may be estimated by using either the β formulas or the partial r formulas:

(d) $$\sigma^2_{1.234} = \sigma^2_1(1 - \beta_{12.34}r_{12} - \beta_{13.24}r_{13} - \beta_{14.23}r_{14})$$

$$\cdots \cdots \cdots \cdots \cdots \cdots$$

$$\sigma^2_{i.jk\ldots n} = \sigma^2_i(1 - \beta_{ij.k\ldots n}r_{ij} - \beta_{ik.j\ldots n}r_{ik} \cdots - \beta_{in.k\ldots}r_{in})$$

and

$$\sigma^2_{1.2} = \sigma^2_1(1 - r^2_{12})$$
$$\sigma^2_{1.23} = \sigma^2_1(1 - r^2_{12})(1 - r^2_{13.2})$$
$$\sigma^2_{1.234} = \sigma^2_1(1 - r^2_{12})(1 - r^2_{13.2})(1 - r^2_{14.32})$$

$$\cdots \cdots \cdots \cdots \cdots \cdots$$

$$\sigma^2_{i.jkt\ldots pn} = \sigma^2_i(1 - r^2_{ij})(1 - r^2_{ik.j}) \cdots (1 - r^2_{in.jkt\ldots p})$$

The Multiple-correlation Formulas. As in the case of the relationship between the b's and the β's, the formula for the multiple-correlation coefficient is of the same form regardless of the number of variables; it is always a comparison of the residual scatter about a plane of regression with the total standard deviation. In the four-variable and the general multiple-variable cases it is as follows:

(e) $$R^2_{1.234} = 1 - \frac{\sigma^2_{1.234}}{\sigma^2_1}$$

$$R^2_{i.jkt\ldots n} = 1 - \frac{\sigma^2_{i.jkt\ldots n}}{\sigma^2_i}$$

The Partial-correlation Formulas. The forms of the formulas for the partial coefficients of correlation are also independent of the number of variables in the problem, because the partial correlation coefficient always pertains to a simple linear correlation. The formulas are therefore symmetrical, as follows:

Second-order partials:

$$r_{12.34} = \frac{r_{12.3} - r_{14.3}r_{24.3}}{\sqrt{1 - r^2_{14.3}}\sqrt{1 - r^2_{24.3}}}$$

And in general, the formula for calculating partials of a given order from the next lower order partials:

$$r_{ij.ko\ldots n} = \frac{r_{ij.ko\ldots n-1} - r_{in.ko\ldots n-1}r_{jn.ko\ldots n-1}}{\sqrt{1 - r^2_{in.ko\ldots n-1}}\sqrt{1 - r^2_{jn.ko\ldots n-1}}}$$

CHAPTER XVII

ANALYSIS OF A MULTIVARIATE FREQUENCY DISTRIBUTION ILLUSTRATED

To illustrate the analysis of a multivariate frequency distribution, data on grades of 81 freshmen in a woman's college were selected. These are arranged in Table 47 in such a way as to facilitate the construction of simple linear-correlation tables and to facilitate detailed study of the multivariate distribution. The first part of this chapter will illustrate trivariate-frequency-distribution analysis. The X_4 variable is included in the table so that later in the chapter the analysis can be extended to four variables. Beyond four variables, the method proceeds in a symmetrical fashion.

Examination of Multivariate Distribution. The first step in the analysis of a multivariate distribution is to determine how well the assumption of linearity of relationship is approximated. The scatter of cases in the correlation table for X_1 and X_2 appears to indicate simple linear regression between X_1 and X_2.* In Tables 48 and 49, correlation tables for X_1 and X_3 and for X_2 and X_3, respectively, the scatter of cases suggests that these regressions might be only slightly if at all nonlinear. As pointed out in the preceding chapter, however, the simple correlation charts cannot be expected to reveal how much net regression exists in a trivariate correlation problem; accordingly, further study of the trivariate distribution of X_1, X_2, and X_3, should be undertaken. In order to do this the multivariate distribution itself, shown in Table 47, must be studied.

For example, the net regression of X_2 on X_3 may be tested in a preliminary fashion by holding constant the X_1 variable. Accordingly, analysis may be made of the X_2 and X_3 grades of the 16 students whose X_1 grades are 200. Table 50 shows the X_2 and X_3 grades of these 16 freshmen, selected from Table 47.

---

* See Table 34 (p. 358).

TABLE 47.—GRADES OF 81 MOUNT HOLYOKE FRESHMEN IN VERBAL SCHO-
LASTIC-APTITUDE TEST, IN COLLEGE BOARD ENGLISH EXAMINATION, AND IN
FIRST- AND SECOND-SEMESTER ENGLISH
(A, B, C, and D grades converted to a numerical scale)

Student number	Second-semester English grade X_1	First-semester English grade X_2	Verbal S.A.T. X_3	College Board English examination X_4
1	240	220	573	407
2	200	180	473	456
3	260	240	680	615
4	260	260	568	671
5	160	160	437	546
6	240	220	567	615
7	220	200	671	449
8	60	120	415	428
9	220	240	434	726
10	200	180	437	504
11	220	220	443	601
12	140	180	583	449
13	160	120	384	553
14	240	260	634	546
15	260	240	477	671
16	200	160	594	553
17	200	160	495	449
18	240	240	592	532
19	240	220	598	574
20	240	220	536	650
21	160	140	408	532
22	220	240	569	518
23	200	200	443	477
24	100	100	421	518
25	160	140	356	366
26	200	160	535	449
27	180	180	415	671
28	180	160	502	539
29	240	240	477	532
30	200	200	504	546
31	200	200	431	518
32	180	160	442	518
33	260	220	509	518
34	160	120	449	560
35	240	240	416	539
36	220	220	531	587
37	220	240	518	622
38	160	120	472	532
39	200	200	619	643
40	220	220	456	463

TABLE 47.—GRADES OF 81 MOUNT HOLYOKE FRESHMEN IN VERBAL SCHO-
LASTIC-APTITUDE TEST, IN COLLEGE BOARD ENGLISH EXAMINATION, AND IN
FIRST- AND SECOND-SEMESTER ENGLISH.—(*Continued*)

Student number	Second-semester English grade X_1	First-semester English grade X_2	Verbal S.A.T. X_3	College Board English examination X_4
41	260	260	646	643
42	180	160	511	532
43	100	60	339	442
44	200	220	424	594
45	200	200	515	594
46	160	120	460	525
47	180	160	418	504
48	280	220	581	684
49	200	200	479	560
50	220	220	579	532
51	220	200	600	594
52	240	220	610	497
53	100	60	376	435
54	220	220	458	484
55	240	200	600	497
56	200	220	489	539
57	220	220	567	525
58	220	200	513	636
59	240	200	644	581
60	180	140	521	401
61	160	140	345	442
62	240	220	596	636
63	260	260	667	567
64	160	120	384	546
65	260	240	646	511
66	220	180	500	504
67	220	240	613	608
68	260	260	707	615
69	240	220	703	657
70	200	200	391	497
71	140	120	416	442
72	260	240	667	657
73	200	180	477	664
74	300	280	709	518
75	180	140	527	539
76	220	180	475	629
77	180	180	636	594
78	300	280	543	726
79	220	220	432	546
80	220	200	380	428
81	200	180	479	539

TABLE 48

$X_3 \backslash X_1$	60–	80–	100–	120–	140–	160–	180–	200–	220–	240–	260–	280–	300–	Σ	$\frac{d_3}{i_3}$	$F\frac{d_3}{i_3}$	$F\left(\frac{d_3}{i_3}\right)^2$	$F\frac{d_3}{i_3}\frac{d_1}{i_1}$	X_r
339–			24/24			2 12/6								3	−6	−18	108	36	150.0
369–			20/20			2 10/5								5	−5	−25	125	15	178.0
399–	1 24/24		16/16		1 8/8	1 4/4		1 4/4	1 4/4					8	−4	−32	128	36	167.5
429–						2 6/3		3 9/3	1 4/4					11	−3	−33	99	−33	210.0
459–						2 4/2		4 8/2	3 6/2		1 8/8			9	−2	−18	36	−22	214.44
480–							2 0/0	4 4/1	3 6/2	2 18/9	1 4/4			10	−1	−10	10	−14	218.00
519–							2 0/0	1 0/0	0 0				1 0/0	6	0	0	0	0	230.00
549–								1 2/2	2 4/2	2 6/3	1 4/4			5	1	5	5	14	246.00
579–					1 4/4				2 8/4	2 18/9	4 64/16	1 10/10		9	2	18	36	40	234.44
609–							1 0/0		1 6/6	1 12/12	1 20/20			5	3	15	45	27	226.00
630–										1 12/12	1 24/24		1 36/36	5	4	20	80	76	266.00
660–									1 10/10		1 24/24			2	5	10	50	30	250.00
699–									1 10/10	1 18/18	1 24/24		1 36/36	3	6	18	108	78	276.67
Σ														81		−50	830	283	
																$A_3 = 534$			
																$i_3 = 30$			
Σ	1	0	3	0	2	9	8	16	17	13	9	1	2	81			111		
$\frac{d_1}{i_1}$	−6	−5	−4	−3	−2	−1	0	1	2	3	4	5	6				$A_1 = 190$		
$F\frac{d_1}{i_1}$	−6	0	−12	0	−4	−9	0	16	34	39	36	5	12	111			$i_1 = 20$		
$F\left(\frac{d_1}{i_1}\right)^2$	36	0	48	0	8	9	0	16	68	117	144	25	72	543					
$F\frac{d_1}{i_1}\frac{d_3}{i_3}$	24	0	60	0	4	36	0	−25	−22	60	100	10	36	283					
X_c	414.0	414.0	384.0		504.0	414.0	496.5	487.13	514.59	580.15	617.33	594.00	624.00						

X_1 = second-semester English grade. X_3 = verbal scholastic-aptitude test.

TABLE 49

$A_2 = 190 \qquad i_2 = 20 \qquad A_3 = 534 \qquad i_3 = 30$

X_2 \ X_3	339–	369–	399–	429–	459–	489–	519–	549–	579–	609–	639–	669–	699–	Σ	$\frac{d_2}{i_2}$	$F\frac{d_2}{i_2}$	$F\left(\frac{d_2}{i_2}\right)^2$	$F\frac{d_2 d_3}{i_2 i_3}$	$\bar{X}_r$
60–	1 36/36	1 30/30												2	−6	−12	72	66	369.00
80–			1 16/16											0	−5	0	0	0	414.0
100–														1	−4	−4	16	16	426.86
120–	2 24/12	2 30/15	2 24/12	1 9/9	2 12/6									7	−3	−21	63	75	438.00
140–			1 8/8	1 9/19		3 3/1								5	−2	−10	20	32	492.75
160–			1 4/4	2 6/3	4 0/0	1 0/0	2 0/0							8	−1	−8	8	11	497.33
180–		2 −10/−5	1 0/0	1 0/0	4 0/0	3 −3/1	1 0/0			0 0/0				9	0	0	0	0	522.46
200–			1 −8/−8	2 −6/−3; 4 −24/−6	1 −2/−2	3 −3/−3; 1 −3/−3	2 0/0	3 6/2	1 −2/−2	1 3/1				13	1	13	13	−5	537.33
220–			1 −12/−12	1 −9/−9; 2 −12/−6	2 −12/−6	2 −3/−2		1 3/2	4 16/4	3 13/6	4 4/4	1 5/5	1 12/12	18	2	36	72	4	553.09
240–								1 3/3	1 6/6	1 9/9	2 24/12; 2 16/8	1 15/15	2 4/24; 1 24/24	11	3	33	99	21	642.00
260–								1 4/4	1 16/16	1 12/12; 1 12/12	3 32/16; 2 16/16	1 15/15	1 30/30	5	4	20	80	72	624.00
280–							1 0/0							2	5	10	50	30	
Σ	3	5	8	11	9	10	6	5	9	5	5	2	3	81		57	493	322	
$\frac{d_3}{i_3}$	−6	−5	−4	−3	−2	−1	0	1	2	3	4	5	6						
$F\frac{d_3}{i_3}$	−18	−25	−32	−33	−18	−10	0	5	18	15	20	10	18	−50					
$F\left(\frac{d_3}{i_3}\right)^2$	108	125	128	99	36	10	0	5	36	45	80	50	108	830					
$F\frac{d_2 d_3}{i_2 i_3}$	60	50	32	−24	−2	−7	0	5	24	60	60	20	66	322					
X_c	123.33	150.00	170.00	204.55	192.22	204.22	203.33	242.00	216.67	230.00	250.00	230.00	263.33						

X_2 = first-semester English grade. X_3 = verbal scholastic-aptitude test.

TABLE 50.—X_2 AND X_3 GRADES OF 16 STUDENTS WHOSE X_1 GRADE IS 200

Student number	X_2	X_3
2	180	473
10	180	437
16	160	594
17	160	495
23	200	443
26	160	535
30	200	504
31	200	431
39	200	619
44	220	424
45	200	515
49	200	479
56	220	489
70	200	391
73	180	477
81	180	479

Figure 119 shows the scatter of these 16 bivariates; it indicates that the regression may be linear although there appears to be little tendency for X_2 and X_3, unaffected by X_1, to be correlated

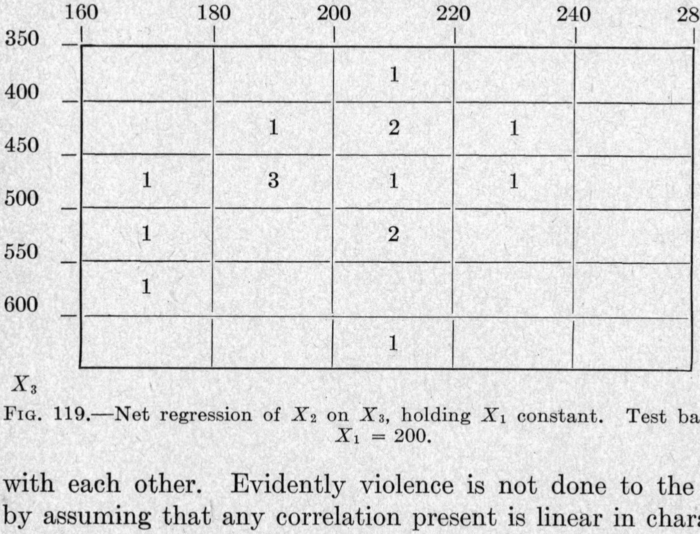

X_3	160	180	200	220	240	280
350–400			1			
400–450		1	2	1		
450–500	1	3	1	1		
500–550	1		2			
550–600	1					
600–			1			

FIG. 119.—Net regression of X_2 on X_3, holding X_1 constant. Test based on $X_1 = 200$.

with each other. Evidently violence is not done to the facts by assuming that any correlation present is linear in character. It must be remembered, of course, that this preliminary test of net regression between X_2 and X_3, holding X_1 constant, is based on a small sample of only 16 observations. Similar tests, holding X_1 constant at several other values, respectively, should be made, especially if nonlinearity is suspected.

Inasmuch as Table 34 (page 358) shows such a clear linear total regression between X_1 and X_2, it may be assumed that the net regression of X_1 on X_2, and vice versa, is linear. For further illustration of the method of examining the multivariate frequency distribution to test for linearity of regression, Table 51 presents the joint variation in X_1 and X_3 grades of those students whose X_2 grade is 220. This will make it possible to test the linearity of net regression between X_1 and X_3, holding X_2 constant.

TABLE 51.—X_1 AND X_3 GRADES OF 18 STUDENTS WHOSE X_2 GRADE IS 220

Student number	X_1	X_3
1	240	573
6	240	567
11	220	443
19	240	598
20	240	536
33	260	509
36	220	531
40	220	456
44	200	424
48	280	581
50	220	579
52	240	610
54	220	458
56	200	489
57	220	567
62	240	596
69	240	703
79	220	432

The bivariate frequency distribution of the eighteen cases in Table 51 is plotted in Fig. 120, which shows that their scatter, with the exception of one case, follows a linear path. It may be concluded that the net regression between X_1 and X_3 approximates the linear form. Here again, especially if nonlinearity is suspected, similar tests using several different values of X_2, respectively, should be made. Tables 50 and 51 serve only to illustrate the method, which would ordinarily need to be applied more completely than is done here.

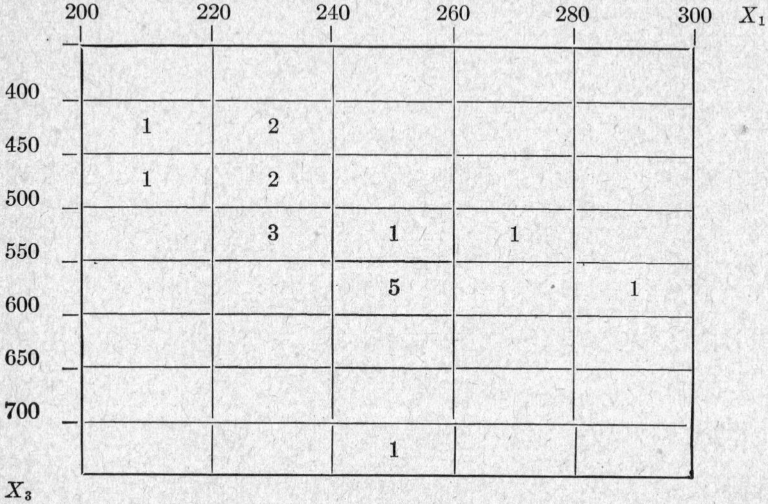

Fig. 120.—Net regression between X_1 and X_3, holding X_2 constant. Test based on $X_2 = 220$.

Statistics of the Trivariate Frequency Distribution. Study of the trivariate frequency distribution X_1, X_2, and X_3, shown in Table 47, appears to indicate that regressions are linear, and therefore it may be assumed that the methods of correlation outlined in Chap. XVI may appropriately be applied. In order to calculate the statistics for a trivariate frequency distribution, it is necessary to obtain first the statistics for the various monovariate distributions.

Calculation of Zero-order Statistics. Correlation tables 48 and 49 may be used as work sheets, as illustrated in Chap. XIV, to calculate the zero-order statistics. Since the problem is now one of analyzing a trivariate frequency distribution, it is well to set up a schedule for calculation of the respective statistics. Table 52 is a schedule of the means and variances for the three monovariate frequency distributions taken separately. In each case the mean was calculated by using the formula

$$\bar{X} = A + \frac{\sum F\left(\dfrac{d}{i}\right)}{N}\ (i)$$

TABLE 52.—MEANS AND VARIANCES

Means	Sums of squares	Variances	Standard deviations
$\bar{X}_1 = 217.4$	$N\sigma_1^2 = 156,355.56$	$\sigma_1^2 = 1,930.3155$	$\sigma_1 = 43.94$
$\bar{X}_2 = 204.1$	$N\sigma_2^2 = 181,155.56$	$\sigma_2^2 = 2,236.4883$	$\sigma_2 = 47.29$
$\bar{X}_3 = 515.5$	$N\sigma_3^2 = 719,222.22$	$\sigma_3^2 = 8,879.2866$	$\sigma_3 = 94.23$

The sum of squares of deviations from the mean in each case is calculated by using the formula

$$N\sigma^2 = i^2 \left[\sum F \left(\frac{d}{i} \right)^2 - \frac{\left(\sum F \frac{d}{i} \right)^2}{N} \right]$$

The required sums are all found in the correlation tables, for example,

$$N\sigma_1^2 = 400 \left[543 - \frac{(111)^2}{81} \right] = 400(543 - 152.11111)$$
$$= 156,355.56$$

Table 53 is a schedule for the calculation of zero-order Pearsonian coefficients of correlation, using the equation that was used in Chap. XIV. This equation is shown at the head of Table 53. The entries all come from Tables 48 and 49 and Table 34 (page 358).

TABLE 53.—CALCULATION OF SIMPLE r'S

$$r = \frac{\sum F \left(\frac{d}{i} \right) \left(\frac{d}{i} \right) - N \left(\frac{C}{i} \right) \left(\frac{C}{i} \right)}{N \left(\frac{\sigma}{i} \right) \left(\frac{\sigma}{i} \right)}$$

	(1) $\sum F \left(\frac{d}{i} \right) \left(\frac{d}{i} \right)$	(2) $N \left(\frac{C}{i} \right) \left(\frac{C}{i} \right)$	(3) $N \left(\frac{\sigma}{i} \right) \left(\frac{\sigma}{i} \right)$	(4) (1) − (2)	(5) (4) ÷ (3)
r_{12}	455.00	78.11111	420.74964	376.88889	+0.89576
r_{13}	283.00	−68.51852	558.90486	351.51852	+0.62894
r_{23}	322.00	−35.18519	601.59915	357.18519	+0.59373

Calculation of First-order Statistics. As suggested in Chap. XVI the first-order statistics of a trivariate frequency distribution may be calculated by several methods. The most efficient method appears to be to calculate the first-order β's and from the first-order β's to calculate the other first-order statistics. Table 54 is a work sheet for the orderly calculation of the first-

TABLE 54.—CALCULATION OF THE FIRST-ORDER β'S FROM THE ZERO-ORDER r'S[1]

$$\beta_{ij.k} = \frac{r_{ij} - r_{ik}r_{jk}}{1 - r_{jk}^2}$$

[See Chap. XVI, Eqs. (9)]

(1)		(2)	(3)	(4)	(5)	
Zero-order r (β)		Product term of numerator	Whole numerator	$1 - r^2$	First-order β	
Subscript	Regression statistic				Subscript	Regression statistic
12	0.89576	0.37342	0.52234	0.64748	12.3	0.80673
13	0.62894					
23	0.59373					
13	0.62894	0.53184	0.09710	0.64748	13.2	0.14997
12	0.89576					
23	0.59373					
12	0.89576	0.37342	0.52234	0.60444	21.3	0.86417
23	0.59373					
13	0.62894					
23	0.59373	0.56338	0.03035	0.60444	23.1	0.05021
12	0.89576					
13	0.62894					
13	0.62894	0.53184	0.09710	0.19762	31.2	0.49135
23	0.59373					
12	0.89576					
23	0.59373	0.56338	0.03035	0.19762	32.1	0.15358
13	0.62894					
12	0.89576					

[1] Note the internal checks in columns (2), (3), and (4), in which each of three values occurs twice; in column (2), the first and third, second and fifth, fourth and sixth figures check; in column (3), the same orders check; in column (4), the first and second, the third and fourth, and the fifth and sixth figures check. While not independent checks, they nevertheless give confidence in the accuracy of the work as it proceeds.

If preferred, the b's instead of the β's could first be calculated, by using a similar table and the general formula

$$b_{ij.k} = \frac{b_{ij} - b_{ik}b_{kj}}{1 - r^2_{jk}}$$

order β's in the illustrated trivariate frequency distribution. The entries in column (1) of the table are obtained from Table 53. Bearing in mind the symmetry in the formula shown at the head of Table 54, the zero-order r's, which are also the zero-order β's, are copied in the order in which they occur in the formula. Consequently, the entries in column (2) are the products of the r's in the second and third lines of each trio of r's in column (1). The entry in column (3) is the first r of each trio minus the entry in column (2). The $1 - r^2$ in column (4), which may be found by using a sine table, is for the third r in each trio of r's in column (1). Thus, if the trios of r's are properly arranged in column (1), which can be done by following the general formula at the head of the table, the symmetry of the work sheet facilitates all necessary calculations. In using this work sheet, the first step is to write in column (5) the subscript for the first-order β that is to be calculated; this subscript then determines the order of the zero-order r's in column (1). The value of the first-order β, entered in column (5), is found by dividing the entry in column (3) by the corresponding entry in column (4).

The coefficients of partial correlation are readily calculated from the β's, as follows:[1]

$$r_{ij.k}^2 = \beta_{ij.k}\beta_{ji.k}$$
$$r_{12.3}^2 = \beta_{12.3}\beta_{21.3}$$
$$= 0.80673(0.86417) = 0.69715$$
$$r_{12.3} = 0.83496$$
$$r_{13.2}^2 = \beta_{13.2}\beta_{31.2}$$
$$= 0.14997(0.49135) = 0.07369$$
$$r_{13.2} = 0.27146$$
$$r_{23.1}^2 = \beta_{23.1}\beta_{32.1}$$
$$= 0.05021(0.15358) = 0.007711$$
$$r_{23.1} = 0.08782$$

[1] The coefficients of partial correlation could be checked by using any one of several formulas, as follows:

$$r_{ij.k} = \frac{r_{ij} - r_{ik}r_{jk}}{\sqrt{1 - r_{ik}^2}\ \sqrt{1 - r_{jk}^2}}$$

$$r_{ij.k} = b_{ij.k}\frac{\sigma_{j.k}}{\sigma_{i.k}}$$

$$r_{ij.k} = \beta_{ij.k}\frac{\sqrt{1 - r_{jk}^2}}{\sqrt{1 - r_{ik}^2}}$$

These formulas all have the advantage that they determine the positive or negative sign of the partial r; but the partial r always has the same sign as its corresponding β. *Cf.* also p. 460.

Thus is determined the arithmetical value of the first-order coefficients of partial correlation. Each coefficient of partial correlation is positive if the β's from which it is derived are both positive, negative if the β's are negative. The respective pairs of β's involved are never of opposite sign.

The b statistics are calculated from the β's as follows:

$$b_{ij.k} = \beta_{ij.k} \frac{\sigma_i}{\sigma_j}$$

$$b_{12.3} = \beta_{12.3} \frac{\sigma_1}{\sigma_2}$$

$$= 0.80673 \frac{43.9354}{47.2915} = 0.80673(0.92903)$$

$$= 0.74948$$

$$b_{13.2} = 0.14997 \frac{43.9354}{94.2300} = 0.14997(0.46626)$$

$$= 0.06992$$

$$b_{21.3} = 0.86417 \frac{47.2915}{43.9354} = 0.86417(1.07639)$$

$$= 0.93020$$

$$b_{23.1} = 0.05021 \frac{47.2915}{94.2300} = 0.05021(0.50187)$$

$$= 0.02520$$

$$b_{31.2} = 0.49135 \frac{94.2300}{43.9354} = 0.49135(2.1447)$$

$$= 1.05380$$

$$b_{32.1} = 0.15358 \frac{94.2300}{47.2915} = 0.15358(1.9925)$$

$$= 0.30601$$

The first-order a statistics are calculated as follows:

$$a_{i.jk} = \bar{X}_i \quad - \quad b_{ij.k}\bar{X}_j \quad - \quad b_{ik.j}\bar{X}_k$$
$$a_{1.23} = 217.4074 - 0.74948(204.074) - 0.06992(515.4816) = 28.4156$$
$$a_{2.13} = 204.074 - 0.93020(217.40740) - 0.02520(515.4816) = -11.148$$
$$a_{3.12} = 515.4816 - 1.05380(217.4074) - 0.30601(204.074) = 223.929$$

The equations of the three planes of regression are, therefore, as follows:

$$X_1' = 28.42 + 0.75X_2 + 0.07X_3$$
$$X_2' = -11.15 + 0.93X_1 + 0.025X_3$$
$$X_3' = 223.93 + 1.05X_1 + 0.31X_2$$

If X_1 is considered the dependent variable, it can be estimated from the first equation; if X_2 is considered the dependent variable, it can be estimated from the second equation; if X_3 is considered the dependent variable, it can be estimated from the third equation. The second-order standard deviations, respectively, about the three planes of regression may also be calculated.[1]

$$\sigma_{i.jk}^2 = \sigma_i^2(1 - r_{ij}^2)(1 - r_{ik.j}^2)$$
$$\sigma_{1.23}^2 = \sigma_1^2(1 - r_{12}^2)(1 - r_{13.2}^2)$$
$$= 1{,}930.3155(0.19762)(0.92631) = 353.3585$$
$$\sigma_{1.23} = 18.7975$$
$$\sigma_{2.13}^2 = \sigma_2^2(1 - r_{12}^2)(1 - r_{23.1}^2)$$
$$= 2{,}236.4883(0.19762)(0.99229) = 438.5672$$
$$\sigma_{2.13} = 20.9416$$
$$\sigma_{3.12}^2 = \sigma_3^2(1 - r_{13}^2)(1 - r_{23.1}^2)$$
$$= 8{,}879.2866(0.60444)(0.99229) = 5{,}325.616$$
$$\sigma_{3.12} = 72.9767$$

The multiple-correlation coefficients, which also measure the goodness of fit of the planes of regression, may now be calculated as follows:[2]

$$R_{i.jk}^2 = 1 - \frac{\sigma_{i.jk}^2}{\sigma_i^2}$$
$$R_{1.23}^2 = 1 - \frac{\sigma_{1.23}^2}{\sigma_1^2}$$
$$= 1 - \frac{353.358}{1{,}930.3155} = 1 - 0.1830$$
$$= 0.8170$$
$$R_{1.23} = 0.9039$$
$$R_{2.13}^2 = 1 - \frac{438.567}{2{,}236.4883} = 1 - 0.1961$$
$$= 0.8039$$
$$R_{2.13} = 0.8966$$

[1] They could also be calculated by using Eq. (19), (p. 415). Thus the calculation of $\sigma_{1.23}^2$ could be checked not only by using

$$\sigma_{1.32}^2 = \sigma_1^2(1 - r_{13}^2)(1 - r_{12.3}^2)$$

but also by using the following formula:

$$\sigma_{1.23}^2 = \sigma_1^2(1 - \beta_{12.3}r_{12} - \beta_{13.2}r_{13})$$

[2] The calculation of R may be checked by using Eq. (20), p. 417.

$$R^2_{3.12} = 1 - \frac{5,325.616}{8,879.2866} = 1 - 0.5998$$
$$= 0.4002$$
$$R_{3.12} = 0.6326$$

An all-round check on the various calculations may be obtained by using Eq. (31), Chap. XVI, as follows:

TABLE 55

$$1 = \beta^2_{ik.j} + \beta^2_{ik.j} + 2r_{kj}\beta_{ij.k}\beta_{ik.j} + \frac{\sigma^2_{i.jk}}{\sigma^2_i}$$

$1 =$	$\beta^2_{12.3}$	$+$	$\beta^2_{13.2}$	$+$	$2r_{23}$	$\beta_{12.3}$	$\beta_{13.2}$	$+\dfrac{\sigma^2_{1.23}}{\sigma^2_1}$
	$(0.80673)^2$		$(0.14997)^2$		$2(0.59373)(0.80673)(0.14997)$			
$1.0000 =$	0.65081	$+$	0.02249	$+$	0.14367	$+$	0.18304	

$1 =$	$\beta^2_{23.1}$	$+$	$\beta^2_{21.3}$	$+$	$2r_{13}$	$\beta_{23.1}$	$\beta_{21.3}$	$+\dfrac{\sigma^2_{2.13}}{\sigma^2_2}$
	$(0.05021)^2$		$(0.86417)^2$		$2(0.62894)(0.05021)(0.86417)$			
$1.0000 =$	0.00252	$+$	0.74679	$+$	0.05458	$+$	0.19608	

$1 =$	$\beta^2_{32.1}$	$+$	$\beta^2_{31.2}$	$+$	$2r_{12}$	$\beta_{32.1}$	$\beta_{31.2}$	$+\dfrac{\sigma^2_{3.12}}{\sigma^2_3}$
	$(0.15358)^2$		$(0.49135)^2$		$2(0.89576)(0.15358)(0.49135)$			
$1.0000 =$	0.02359	$+$	0.24142	$+$	0.13519	$+$	0.59978	

Interpretation of Results Illustrated. The interpretation of the above statistics of a trivariate frequency distribution may be illustrated by assuming that it is desired to predict X_1, the second-semester grades of freshmen at the woman's college selected. From the equation for the plane of regression of X_1 on X_2 and X_3, namely, $X'_1 = 28.42 + 0.75X_2 + 0.07X_3$, estimates may be made of a freshman's grade in second-semester English if her grades in the verbal scholastic-aptitude test and in first-semester English are known.

Estimates Based on Regression Equation. If a freshman's grade in first-semester English were 300 and her grade in the verbal scholastic-aptitude test were 600, her second-term English grade would be estimated at

$$X'_1 = 28.42 + 0.75(300) + 0.07(600)$$
$$= 28.42 + 225 + 42$$
$$= 295$$

Since the second-term English grade will, of course, be affected by other factors, the student's actual grade in second-semester English will deviate from estimates based upon the regression equation. This raises the question as to how much, on the average, it can be expected that estimates based on the regression equation will deviate from the actual values. The answer is found by the determination of the value of $\sigma_{1.23}$, which has been found above to be 18.8, or approximately 19. The standard deviation of the differences between the actual grades and estimates based on the above regression equation is therefore about 19. If this regression equation and first-order standard deviation are typical of these college grades and if the differences between actual and estimated values are in general normally distributed, the chances are about $\frac{95}{100}$ that the actual value in any particular case will fall within limits ± 38 $(= 2\sigma_{1.23})$ from the estimated value.

The foregoing conclusion, which is based on the value of $\sigma_{1.23}$, can be summarized very succinctly by the calculation of $R_{1.23}$, which has been found to be equal to 0.9039. This is a fairly high coefficient of multiple correlation. It shows that the above plane of regression is a good fit, and therefore estimates based upon it can be expected to be fairly good.

Partial-correlation Coefficients. Since both b statistics in the equation of regression are positive, it is known that the net correlations between X_1 and X_2 and between X_1 and X_3 are positive. The amount of the net correlation is given by the coefficients of partial correlation $r_{12.3} = 0.83496$ and $r_{13.2} = 0.27146$. These show that second-semester English grades are much more closely related to first-semester English grades than they are to verbal scholastic-aptitude test grades.

Analysis of Variance in X_1. From the β^2's and the β cross products, analysis of the variance in second-semester English grades can be made. Thus, from the first set of β^2's and cross products in Table 55, it is seen that 65.1 per cent of the variance in second-semester English grades, X_1, is accounted for by direct association with first-semester English grades. Only 2.2 per cent is accounted for by direct association with verbal scholastic-aptitude test grades, although 14.4 per cent of the variance in second-semester English is accounted for by indirect association with both first-semester grades and verbal scholastic-

TABLE 56

X_4 \ X_1	60-	80-	100-	120-	140-	160-	180-	200-	220-	240-	260-	280-	300-	Σ	$\frac{d_4}{i_4}$	$F\frac{d_4}{i_4}$	$F\left(\frac{d_4}{i_4}\right)^2$	$F\frac{d_1 d_4}{i_1 i_4}$
366-						1 · 6/6								1	-6	-6	36	6
396-	1 · 24/24				2 · 16/8		1 · 0/0			1 · -15/-15				2	-5	-10	50	-15
426-			2 · 32/16		2 · 16/8			2 · -8/-4	2 · -16/-8					10	-4	-40	160	52
456-														4	-3	-12	36	-18
486-						4 · 4/1	1 · 0/0	2 · -4/-2	2 · -12/-6	2 · -12/-6	1 · -8/-8			7	-2	-14	28	-28
516-			1 · 4/4			4 · 4/1	4 · 0/0	2 · -4/-2	1 · -4/-4	2 · -6/-3	1 · -4/-4			19	-1	-19	19	-17
546-						3 · 0/0	3 · 0/0	3 · -3/-1	3 · -6/-2	2 · -6/-3	1 · 0/0			11	0	0	0	0
576-							1 · 0/0	3 · 0/0	1 · 0/0	3 · 0/0	1 · 0/0			7	1	7	7	11
606-								2 · 2/1	3 · 6/2	1 · 3/3	2 · 16/8			6	2	12	24	34
636-								2 · 6/3	3 · 12/4	1 · 6/6	2 · 24/12			8	3	24	72	63
666-									1 · 6/6	3 · 27/9	2 · 32/16	1 · 20/20		4	4	16	64	52
696-														0	5	0	0	0
726-									1 · 12/12				1 · 36/36	2	6	12	72	48
Σ	1	0	3	0	2	9	8	16	17	13	9	1	2	81 / 81		-30	568	188
$\frac{d_1}{i_1}$	-6	-5	-4	-3	-2	-1	0	1	2	3	4	5	6	111				
$F\frac{d_1}{i_1}$	-6	0	-12	0	-4	-9	0	16	34	39	36	5	12	111		$A_1 = 190$	$A_4 = 561$	
$F\left(\frac{d_1}{i_1}\right)^2$	36	0	48	0	8	9	0	16	68	117	144	25	72	543		$i_1 = 20$	$i_4 = 30$	
$F\frac{d_1 d_4}{i_1 i_4}$	24	0	36	0	16	14	0	-13	-2	3	60	20	30	188				

X_1 = second-semester English grade. X_4 = College Board English examination.

TABLE 57

X₂ \ X₄	60-	80-	100-	120-	140-	160-	180-	200-	220-	240-	260-	280-	Σ	d_4/i_4	$F\,d_4/i_4$	$F(d_4/i_4)^2$	$F\,d_2d_4/i_2i_4$
366-					1 (6/6)								1	−6	−6	36	6
396-				2 (16/8)	1 (15/15)	2 (0/0)	1 (4/4)						2	−5	−10	50	−10
426-	2 (40/20)			2 (16/8)	1 (4/4)		1 (3/3)	2 (16/8)					10	−4	−40	160	40
456-							2 (4/2)	1 (6/6)	2 (18/9)	1 (8/8)			4	−3	−12	36	−27
486-						1 (0/0)	1 (1/1)	2 (8/4)	1 (6/6)				7	−2	−14	28	−26
516-			1 (3/3)	2 (4/2)	2 (2/1)	3 (0/0)	1 (1/1)	1 (2/2)	4 (12/3)	4 (16/4)		1 (6/6)	19	−1	−19	19	−28
546-				3 (0/0)		2 (0/0)		2 (0/0)	2 (0/0)		2 (0/0)		11	0	0	0	0
576-							1 (1/1)	2 (0/0)	3 (3/3)?				7	1	7	7	16
606-							1 (2/2)	3 (6/2)	3 (9/3)	3 (24/8)	1 (10/10)		6	2	12	24	42
636-							1 (3/3)	2 (12/6)	3 (27/9)	1 (12/12)	1 (15/15)		8	3	24	72	69
666-							1 (4/4)		1 (12/12)	1 (16/16)	1 (20/20)		4	4	16	64	52
696-													0	5	0	0	0
726-										1 (24/24)		1 (36/36)	2	6	12	72	60
Σ	2	0	1	7	5	8	9	13	18	11	5	2	81 / 81		−30	568	194
d_2/i_2	−5	−4	−3	−2	−1	0	1	2	3	4	5	6				$A_4 = 561$	
$F\,d_2/i_2$	−10	0	−3	−14	−5	0	9	26	54	44	25	12	138				$i_4 = 30$
$F\left(\dfrac{d_2}{i_2}\right)^2$	50	0	9	28	5	0	9	52	162	176	125	72	688		$A_2 = 170$		
$F\,d_2d_4/i_2i_4$	40	0	3	20	17	0	−2	−14	3	52	45	30	194		$i_2 = 20$		

X_2 = first-semester English grade. X_4 = College Board English examination.

TABLE K

$X_4 \backslash X_3$	339-	369-	399-	429-	459-	489-	519-	549-	579-	609-	639-	669-	699-	Σ	$\dfrac{d_4}{i_4}$	$F\dfrac{d_4}{i_4}$	$F\left(\dfrac{d_4}{i_4}\right)^2$	$F\dfrac{d_3 d_4}{i_3 i_4}$
366-	$1\,\tfrac{36}{36}$													1	-6	-6	36	36
396-								$1\,\tfrac{-5}{-5}$						2	-5	-10	50	-5
426-	$2\,\tfrac{48}{24}$	$2\,\tfrac{40}{20}$	$2\,\tfrac{32}{16}$											10	-4	-40	160	96
456-			$1\,\tfrac{18}{4}$	$3\,\tfrac{27}{9}$	$1\,\tfrac{6}{6}$	$1\,\tfrac{4}{4}$								4	-3	-12	36	33
486-		$1\,\tfrac{10}{10}$	$3\,\tfrac{12}{4}$	$2\,\tfrac{16}{6}$	$4\,\tfrac{8}{2}$	$1\,\tfrac{2}{2}$	$1\,\tfrac{1}{1}$		$1\,\tfrac{8}{8}$					7	-2	-14	28	8
516-				$2\,\tfrac{3}{3}$	$4\,\tfrac{1}{1}$	$4\,\tfrac{1}{1}$	$1\,\tfrac{0}{0}$	$1\,\tfrac{2}{2}$	$1\,\tfrac{2}{2}$	$3\,\tfrac{3}{3}$			$1\,\tfrac{6}{6}$	19	-1	-19	19	18
546-		$2\,\tfrac{0}{0}$	$3\,\tfrac{0}{0}$		$1\,\tfrac{0}{0}$	$1\,\tfrac{0}{0}$	$1\,\tfrac{0}{0}$	$2\,\tfrac{0}{0}$						11	0	0	0	0
576-				$1\,\tfrac{-3}{-3}$		$1\,\tfrac{-1}{-1}$								7	1	7	7	1
606-					$1\,\tfrac{-4}{-4}$	$1\,\tfrac{-2}{-2}$		$1\,\tfrac{4}{4}$	$1\,\tfrac{6}{6}$	$1\,\tfrac{9}{9}$			$1\,\tfrac{12}{12}$	6	2	12	24	24
636-				$1\,\tfrac{-18}{-18}$	$1\,\tfrac{-8}{-8}$	$1\,\tfrac{-3}{-3}$		$1\,\tfrac{4}{4}$	$1\,\tfrac{8}{8}$	$1\,\tfrac{9}{9}$	$2\,\tfrac{24}{12}$		$1\,\tfrac{18}{18}$	8	3	24	72	48
666-				$1\,\tfrac{-16}{-16}$	$1\,\tfrac{-6}{-6}$	$1\,\tfrac{-3}{-3}$			$1\,\tfrac{0}{0}$	$1\,\tfrac{0}{0}$				4	4	16	64	-12
696-														0	5	0	0	0
726-						$1\,\tfrac{-2}{-2}$	$1\,\tfrac{0}{0}$				$1\,\tfrac{-18}{-18}$		2	6	12	72	-18
Σ	3	5	8	11	9	10	6	5	9	5	5	2	3	81		-30	568	229
$\dfrac{d_3}{i_3}$	-6	-5	-4	-3	-2	-1	0	1	2	3	4	5	6					
$F\dfrac{d_3}{i_3}$	-18	-25	-32	-33	-18	-10	0	5	18	15	20	10	18	-50		$A_3 = 534$		
$F\left(\dfrac{d_3}{i_3}\right)^2$	108	125	128	99	36	10	0	5	36	45	80	50	108	830			$A_4 = 561$	
$F\dfrac{d_3 d_4}{i_3 i_4}$	84	50	32	18	-4	4	0	-1	0	12	20	-10	24	229		$i_3 = 30$	$i_4 = 30$	

X_3 = verbal scholastic-aptitude test. X_4 = College Board English examination.

aptitude test grades. The variation in other influences accounts for 18.3 per cent of the variance in second-semester English grades.

Under conditions existing at the woman's college studied, it appears to be an inevitable conclusion that knowledge of grades in verbal scholastic-aptitude tests is not so helpful as might be supposed in predicting the subsequent performance of college freshmen students.

Extension of Analysis to Include Four Variables. *Additional Zero-order Statistics.* The extension of the trivariate frequency distribution to include a fourth variable X_4 requires first the calculation of the mean and standard deviation of the added variable. It requires also the calculation of the simple correlation coefficients between the new variable and each of the other three. For illustration, the fourth variable taken is the grade in the College Board English examination. Tables 56 to 58 are the usual work sheets for a correlation problem. From them the necessary data are obtained for calculating the additional zero-order statistics, as follows:

$$\bar{X}_4 = 549.8889 \qquad r_{14} = 0.49106$$
$$N\sigma_4^2 = 501,201.9828 \qquad r_{24} = 0.48807$$
$$\sigma_4^2 = 6,187.6788 \qquad r_{34} = 0.31551$$
$$\sigma_4 = 78.6618$$

Additional First-order Statistics. Among four variables it is possible to distinguish four different sets of trivariate frequency distributions, each of which will have three planes of regression. Accordingly, when four variables are involved the total number of first-order β statistics is 24, two for each plane of regression. Six of these twenty-four were calculated in Table 54; the remaining 18 may be obtained by a similar procedure. Table 59 shows the 24 β's for the illustrated four-variable problem, grouped according to the four possible trivariate frequency distributions.

Each of the four trivariate frequency distributions could be analyzed as illustrated in the preceding sections of this chapter. From the first-order β's shown in Table 59 all the other first-order statistics may be obtained, by methods already explained.

In few problems is it necessary or even desirable to calculate all 24 first-order β statistics of the four trivariate frequency distributions involved in a four-variable set. As may be seen from

Table 59.—The First-order β's in the Four Trivariate Frequency
Distributions for Four Variables

*Data on four kinds of grades of 81 college freshmen, at the Selected Woman's
College*

First plane	Second plane	Third plane
Trivariate Distribution X_1, X_2, X_3		
$\beta_{12.3} = 0.80673$	$\beta_{21.3} = 0.8641\ 7$	$\beta_{31.2} = 0.49135$
$\beta_{13.2} = 0.14997$	$\beta_{23.1} = 0.05021$	$\beta_{32.1} = 0.15358$
Trivariate Distribution X_1, X_2, X_4		
$\beta_{12.4} = 0.86124$	$\beta_{21.4} = 0.86457$	$\beta_{41.2} = 0.27260$
$\beta_{14.2} = 0.07071$	$\beta_{24.1} = 0.06352$	$\beta_{42.1} = 0.24392$
Trivariate Distribution X_1, X_3, X_4		
$\beta_{13.4} = 0.52642$	$\beta_{31.4} = 0.62463$	$\beta_{41.3} = 0.48413$
$\beta_{14.3} = 0.32498$	$\beta_{34.1} = 0.00877$	$\beta_{43.1} = 0.01101$
Trivariate Distribution X_2, X_3, X_4		
$\beta_{23.4} = 0.48837$	$\beta_{32.4} = 0.57724$	$\beta_{42.3} = 0.46447$
$\beta_{24.3} = 0.33400$	$\beta_{34.2} = 0.03378$	$\beta_{43.2} = 0.03974$

an examination of Table 60, it is possible to calculate all the
second-order β statistics if only 18 of the 24 first-order β statistics
are known.   If one only of the four planes of regression in the
four-variable correlation problem is significant or important, it is
necessary to calculate only 8 of the first-order β statistics.

Second-order Statistics in a Four-variable Problem. In the
four-variable correlation problem, statistics for four planes of
regression may be obtained.   Following are the four possible
regression equations:

$$X_1' = a_{1.234} + b_{12.34}X_2 + b_{13.24}X_3 + b_{14.23}X_4$$
$$X_2' = a_{2.134} + b_{21.34}X_1 + b_{23.14}X_3 + b_{24.13}X_4$$
$$X_3' = a_{3.124} + b_{31.24}X_1 + b_{32.14}X_2 + b_{34.12}X_4$$
$$X_4' = a_{4.123} + b_{41.23}X_1 + b_{42.13}X_2 + b_{43.12}X_3$$

Also, for each plane of regression a scatter and a coefficient of
multiple correlation may be calculated.   The procedure is
similar to that already illustrated; that is to say, the second-order

β's are first obtained, and from them all the other second-order statistics are calculated. Table 60 illustrates the procedure for making the necessary calculations to obtain the 12 possible second-order β statistics.

Calculation of Second-order Statistics. In a problem where the first-order partial coefficients of correlation are already calculated, it is advisable to modify the formula for finding second-order β statistics from first-order β statistics as follows:

According to Eq. (39), Chap. XVI, it was found that

$$\beta_{ij.kn} = \frac{\beta_{ij.k} - \beta_{in.k}\beta_{nj.k}}{1 - \beta_{nj.k}\beta_{jn.k}}$$

But from Eq. (24), Chap. XVI, it is known that

$$r_{jn.k}^2 = \beta_{nj.k}\beta_{jn.k}$$

Accordingly, the formula for finding the second-order β statistics can be modified as follows:

$$\beta_{ij.kn} = \frac{\beta_{ij.k} - \beta_{in.k}\beta_{nj.k}}{1 - r_{jn.k}^2}$$

In order to secure the greatest convenience in calculation, the arrangement of the items in the work sheet (Table 61) is according to the terms of this formula. First the desired subscript for the β statistic to be calculated is entered in column (5); then, following the formula, the order in which the required trio of first-order β's appear in column (1) is determined. If this order is followed, the entry in column (2) is the product of the second two β's of the trio in column (1); the entry in column (3) is found by subtracting the entry in column (2) from the first β of the trio in column (1); the subscript of the third β of the trio in column (1) is the subscript of the partial r for which $1 - r^2$ is to be found in appropriate tables or, if preferred, calculated. The desired second-order β's are then calculated, by dividing the entry in column (3) by the entry in column (4), and entered in column (5).

In problems for which it is not desired to calculate the first-order coefficients of partial correlation, the alternative method illustrated in Table 61 may be used. It is to be noted that the only differences are that an additional β must be entered in column (1) in each of the sets and that an additional column,

TABLE 60.—CALCULATION OF THE SECOND-ORDER β'S FROM THE FIRST-ORDER β'S

$$\beta_{ij.kn} = \frac{\beta_{ij.k} - \beta_{in.k}\beta_{nj.k}}{1 - r^2_{jn.k}}$$

in which

$$r^2_{jn.k} = \beta_{nj.k}\beta_{jn.k}$$

[See Chap. XVI, Eqs. (24 and 39)]

(1)		(2)	(3)	(4)	(5)	
First-order β		Product term of numerator	Whole numerator	$1 - r^2_{jn.k}$	Second-order β	
Subscript	Regression statistic				Subscript	Regression statistic
12.3	0.80673	0.15094	0.65579	0.84487	12.34	0.77620
14.3	0.32498					
42.3	0.46447					
13.2	0.14997	0.00281	0.14716	0.99866	13.24	0.14736
14.2	0.07071					
43.2	0.03974					
14.2	0.07071	0.00507	0.06564	0.99866	14.23	0.06573
13.2	0.14997					
34.2	0.03378					
21.3	0.86417	0.16170	0.70247	0.84267	21.34	0.83362
24.3	0.33400					
41.3	0.48413					
23.1	0.05021	0.00070	0.04951	0.99990	23.14	0.04951
24.1	0.06352					
43.1	0.01101					
24.1	0.06352	0.00044	0.06308	0.99990	24.13	0.06309
23.1	0.05021					
34.1	0.00877					
31.2	0.49135	0.00921	0.48214	0.98072	31.24	0.49162
34.2	0.03378					
41.2	0.27260					
32.1	0.15358	0.00214	0.15144	0.98451	32.14	0.15382
34.1	0.00877					
42.1	0.24392					
34.2	0.03378	0.03474	−0.00096	0.98072	34.21	−0.00098
31.2	0.49135					
14.2	0.07071					
41.2	0.27260	0.01953	0.25307	0.92631	41.23	0.27320
43.2	0.03974					
31.2	0.49135					
42.1	0.24392	0.00169	0.24223	0.99229	42.13	0.24411
43.1	0.01101					
32.1	0.15358					
43.1	0.01101	0.01225	−0.00124	0.99229	43.12	−0.00125
42.1	0.24392					
23.1	0.05021					

TABLE 61.—CALCULATION OF THE SECOND-ORDER β'S FROM THE FIRST-ORDER β'S

(Alternative method illustrated)

$$\beta_{ij \cdot kn} = \frac{\beta_{ij \cdot k} - \beta_{in \cdot k}\beta_{nj \cdot k}}{1 - \beta_{nj \cdot k}\beta_{jn \cdot k}}$$

(1)		(2)	(3)	(4)	(5)	(6)	
First-order β		Product term of numerator	Whole numerator	Product term of denominator	Whole denominator	Second-order β	
Subscript	Regression statistic					Subscript	Regression statistic
12.3	0.80673	0.15094	0.65579	0.155133	0.84487	12.34	0.77620
14.2	0.32498						
42.3	0.46447						
24.3	0.33400						
13.2	0.14997	0.00281	0.14716	0.001342	0.99866	13.24	0.14736
14.2	0.07071						
43.2	0.03974						
34.2	0.03378						
14.2	0.07071	0.00507	0.06564	0.001342	0.99866	14.23	0.06573
13.2	0.14997						
34.2	0.03378						
43.2	0.03974						

If this method is used, the b's instead of the β's could be first calculated, using a similar table and the general formula

$$b_{ij \cdot kn} = \frac{b_{ij \cdot k} - b_{in \cdot k}b_{nj \cdot k}}{1 - b_{nj \cdot k}b_{jn \cdot k}}$$

column (4), is required in which to enter the product term of the denominator. The item in column (5) is then obtained by taking the complement of the corresponding entry in column (4). The second-order β is found by dividing the entry in column (3) by the entry in column (5). For convenience of arrangement, the product term of the numerator is written in the order $\beta_{in \cdot k}\beta_{nj \cdot k}$ rather than $\beta_{nj \cdot k}\beta_{in \cdot k}$, and the product term of the denominator is arranged in the order $\beta_{nj \cdot k}\beta_{jn \cdot k}$ rather than $\beta_{jn \cdot k}\beta_{nj \cdot k}$. Except for the convenience in arrangement of the work sheet, the order in which such product terms occur is immaterial; but, when arranged as indicated, once the subscript of the desired second-order β is entered in column (6), the order in which the first-order β's occur in the equation may be followed in entering them in column (1). There are only four first-order

β's in each set, for the third (in the numerator) is repeated in the first part of the product term of the denominator. When this procedure as to arrangement in the work sheet is followed, the entry in column (2) is always the product of the two middle β's in the set of four in column (1), and the entry in column (4) is always the product of the last two β's entered in column (1).

The second-order coefficients of partial correlation are calculated from the second-order β's as follows:[1]

$$r^2_{ij.kn} = \beta_{ij.kn}\beta_{ji.kn}$$

or, for the four-variable case,

$$r^2_{ij.kn} = \beta_{ij.kn}\beta_{ji.kn}$$
$$r^2_{12.34} = 0.77620(0.83362) = 0.647056$$
$$r_{12.34} = 0.80440$$
$$r^2_{13.24} = 0.14736(0.49162) = 0.072445$$
$$r_{13.24} = 0.26916$$
$$r^2_{14.23} = 0.06573(0.27320) = 0.017957$$
$$r_{14.23} = 0.13400$$
$$r^2_{24.13} = 0.06309(0.24411) = 0.015401$$
$$r_{24.13} = 0.12410$$
$$r^2_{23.14} = 0.04951(0.15382) = 0.007616$$
$$r_{23.14} = 0.08728$$
$$r^2_{34.12} = -0.00098(-0.00125) = 0.000001225$$
$$r_{34.12} = -0.00111$$

(The negative sign of the partial r is determined by the negative sign of the corresponding β statistic.)

The b statistics of the second order are calculated from the second-order β's in the same way as the first-order b's from the first-order β's, by the formula

$$b_{ij.kn} = \beta_{ij.kn}\frac{\sigma_i}{\sigma_j}$$

or, for the four-variable problem,

$$b_{ij.kn} = \beta_{ij.kn}\frac{\sigma_i}{\sigma_j}$$

$$b_{12.34} = \beta_{12.34}\frac{\sigma_1}{\sigma_2}$$

[1] For checking or alternative formulas to find the partial coefficients of correlation, see p. 447.

$$= 0.77620(0.92903)$$
$$= 0.72111$$
$$b_{13.24} = 0.14736(0.46626)$$
$$= 0.06871$$

$$b_{14.23} = 0.06573 \left(\frac{43.9354}{78.6618} \right) = 0.06573(0.55854)$$

$$= 0.03671$$
$$b_{21.34} = 0.83362(1.07639)$$
$$= 0.89730$$
$$b_{23.14} = 0.04951(0.50187)$$
$$= 0.02485$$

$$b_{24.13} = 0.06309 \left(\frac{47.2915}{78.6618} \right) = 0.06309(0.60120)$$

$$= 0.03793$$

$$b_{34.12} = -0.00098 \left(\frac{94.2300}{78.6618} \right) = -0.00098(1.19791)$$

$$= -0.00117$$
$$b_{31.24} = 0.49162(2.1447)$$
$$= 1.05438$$
$$b_{32.14} = 0.15382(1.9925)$$
$$= 0.30650$$

$$b_{41.23} = 0.27320 \left(\frac{78.6618}{43.9354} \right) = 0.27320(1.79040)$$

$$= 0.48914$$

$$b_{42.13} = 0.24411 \left(\frac{78.6618}{47.2915} \right) = 0.24411(1.66334)$$

$$= 0.40604$$

$$b_{43.12} = -0.00125 \left(\frac{78.6618}{94.2300} \right) = -0.00125(0.83478)$$

$$= -0.00104$$

It will be noted that, with the exception of those involving σ_4, the standard-deviation ratios used in the above calculations have all been computed and may be copied from the preceding section, where the first-order b's were calculated from the first-order β's.

The second-order a statistics are calculated as follows:

$$a_{i.jkn} = \bar{X}_i - b_{ij.kn}\bar{X}_j - b_{ik.jn}\bar{X}_k - b_{in.jk}\bar{X}_n$$
$$a_{1.234} = 217.4074 - 0.72111(204.074) - 0.06871(515.4816)$$
$$\qquad - 0.03671(549.8889)$$
$$= 14.64244$$

$$a_{2.134} = 204.074 - 0.89730(217.4074) - 0.02485(515.4816)$$
$$- 0.03793(549.8889)$$
$$= -24.67266$$
$$a_{3.124} = 515.4816 - 1.05438(217.4074) - 0.30650(204.074)$$
$$+ 0.00117(549.8889)$$
$$= 224.34628$$
$$a_{4.231} = 549.8889 - 0.40604(204.074) + 0.00104(515.4816)$$
$$- 0.48914(217.4074)$$
$$= 361.22013$$

The equations for the four planes of regression may now be written as follows:

$$X'_1 = 14.64 + 0.721X_2 + 0.069X_3 + 0.037X_4$$
$$X'_2 = -24.67 + 0.897X_1 + 0.025X_3 + 0.038X_4$$
$$X'_3 = 224.35 + 1.05X_1 + 0.306X_2 - 0.0012X_4$$
$$X'_4 = 361.22 + 0.489X_1 + 0.406X_2 - 0.001X_3$$

If X_1 is considered the dependent variable, it can be estimated from the first equation; if X_2 is considered the dependent variable, it can be estimated from the second equation; if X_3 is considered the dependent variable, it can be estimated from the third equation; if X_4 is considered the dependent variable, it can be estimated from the fourth equation. The standard errors of estimate, that is, the scatters, respectively, about the four planes of regression may also be calculated.[1]

$$\sigma^2_{i.jkn} = \sigma^2_{i.jk}(1 - r^2_{in.jk})$$
$$\sigma^2_{1.234} = \sigma^2_{1.23}(1 - r^2_{14.23})$$
$$= 353.34(0.98204)$$
$$= 346.9940$$
$$\sigma_{1.234} = 18.628$$
$$\sigma^2_{2.134} = \sigma^2_{2.13}(1 - r^2_{24.13})$$
$$= 438.53(0.98460)$$
$$= 431.7766$$
$$\sigma_{2.134} = 20.779$$
$$\sigma^2_{3.124} = \sigma^2_{3.12}(1 - r^2_{34.12})$$
$$= 5,325.56(1.00000)$$
$$= 5,325.56$$
$$\sigma_{3.124} = 72.976$$

[1] For alternative methods, see p. 415 and Eq. (19), Chap. XVI.

$$\sigma_{4.123}^2 = \sigma_{4.12}^2(1 - r_{43.12}^2)$$
$$= 4{,}622.8210(1.00000)$$
$$= 4{,}622.8210$$
$$\sigma_{4.123} = 67.991$$

The multiple-correlation coefficients, which measure the goodness of fit of the planes of regression, are calculated in the same way as for the trivariate problem, namely,[1]

$$R_{i.jkn}^2 = 1 - \frac{\sigma_{i.jkn}^2}{\sigma_1^2}$$

$$R_{1.234}^2 = 1 - \frac{346.994}{1{,}930.3155} = 1 - 0.17976$$
$$= 0.8202$$
$$R_{1.234} = 0.9056$$

$$R_{2.134}^2 = 1 - \frac{431.7766}{2{,}236.4883} = 1 - 0.19306$$
$$= 0.8069$$
$$R_{2.134} = 0.8983$$

$$R_{3.124}^2 = 1 - \frac{5{,}325.56}{8{,}879.2866} = 1 - 0.5998$$
$$= 0.4002$$
$$R_{3.124} = 0.6326$$

$$R_{4.123}^2 = 1 - \frac{4{,}622.8210}{6{,}187.6788} = 1 - 0.74710$$
$$= 0.2529$$
$$R_{4.123} = 0.5029$$

For the four-variable problem, the equation for the β squares and β cross products is as follows:

$$\beta_{ij.kn}^2 + \beta_{ik.jn}^2 + \beta_{in.jk}^2 + 2r_{jk}\beta_{ij.kn}\beta_{ik.jn} + 2r_{jn}\beta_{ij.kn}\beta_{in.jk}$$
$$+ 2r_{kn}\beta_{ik.jn}\beta_{in.jk} + \frac{\sigma_{i.jkn}^2}{\sigma_i^2} = 1$$

In Table 62 some of these checks are illustrated.

Interpretation of Results Illustrated. The interpretation of the above statistics of a four-variable frequency distribution may be illustrated by assuming that it is desired to predict the second-semester English grades of freshmen at the woman's college selected; in other words, the X_1 is assumed to be the

---

[1] For an alternative method, see Eq. (20), Chap. XVI.

TABLE 62

$$\beta^2_{12,34} + \beta^2_{13,24} + \beta^2_{14,23} + 2r_{23}\beta_{12,34}\beta_{13,24} + 2r_{24}\beta_{12,34}\beta_{14,23} + 2r_{34}\beta_{13,24}\beta_{14,23} + \frac{\sigma^2_{1,234}}{\sigma^2_1} = 1.00000$$

$$0.60247 + 0.02171 + 0.00432 + 0.13582 + 0.04980 + 0.00611 + 0.17977 = 1.00000$$

$$\beta^2_{21,34} + \beta^2_{23,14} + \beta^2_{24,13} + 2r_{13}\beta_{21,34}\beta_{23,14} + 2r_{14}\beta_{21,34}\beta_{24,13} + 2r_{34}\beta_{23,14}\beta_{24,13} + \frac{\sigma^2_{2,134}}{\sigma^2_2} = 1.00000$$

$$0.69496 + 0.00245 + 0.00398 + 0.05193 + 0.05165 + 0.00197 + 0.19306 = 1.00000$$

$$\beta^2_{31,24} + \beta^2_{32,14} + \beta^2_{34,12} + 2r_{12}\beta_{32,14}\beta_{31,24} + 2r_{14}\beta_{31,24}\beta_{34,12} + 2r_{24}\beta_{32,14}\beta_{34,12} + \frac{\sigma^2_{3,124}}{\sigma^2_3} = 1.00000$$

$$0.24170 + 0.02366 + 0.000001 + 0.13549 + (-0.00048) + (-0.00015) + 0.59976 = 0.99998$$

$$\beta^2_{41,23} + \beta^2_{42,13} + \beta^2_{43,12} + 2r_{12}\beta_{41,23}\beta_{42,13} + 2r_{13}\beta_{41,23}\beta_{43,12} + 2r_{23}\beta_{42,13}\beta_{43,12} + \frac{\sigma^2_{4,123}}{\sigma^2_4} = 1.00000$$

$$0.07463 + 0.05960 + 0.000002 + 0.11948 + (-0.00043) + (-0.00036) + 0.74710 = 1.00002$$

dependent variable. From the equation for the plane of regression of X_1 on X_2, X_3, and X_4, namely,

$$X_1' = 14.64 + 0.721X_2 + 0.069X_3 + 0.037X_4$$

estimates may be made of a freshman's grade in second-semester English if her grades in the verbal scholastic-aptitude test, in College Board English, and in the first-semester freshman English course are known.

Estimates Based on Regression Equation. If a freshman's grade in first-semester English is 300, in the verbal scholastic-aptitude test 600, and in College Board English 500, her second-semester English grade is estimated as follows:

$$
\begin{aligned}
X_1' &= 14.64 + 0.721(300) + 0.069(600) + 0.037(500) \\
&= 14.64 + 216.3 + 41.4 + 18.5 \\
&= 291
\end{aligned}
$$

Since the second-semester English grade will, of course, be affected by other factors, the student's actual grade in second-semester English will deviate from estimates based upon the regression equation. This raises the question as to how much on the average it can be expected that estimates based on the regression equation will deviate from the actual values. The answer is found by the determination of the value of $\sigma_{1.234}$, which has been found above to be 18.6, or approximately 19. The standard deviation of the differences between the actual and the estimated grades in second-semester English is therefore about 19. If this regression equation and second-order standard deviation are typical of these college grades and if the differences between actual and estimated values are in general normally distributed, the chances are about $\frac{95}{100}$ that the actual value in a particular case will be within limits $\pm 38 (= 2\sigma_{1.234})$ from the estimated value.

The foregoing conclusion, which is based on the value of $\sigma_{1.234}$, can be summarized very succinctly by the calculation of $R_{1.234}$, which has been found to be equal to 0.9056.

If this result is compared with the estimate based on only two independent variables, it is found that the standard error of estimate is almost as large for the plane based on three independent variables as the standard error of estimate based on two

independent variables.[1] In other words, very little increase in
accuracy was obtained by including the fourth variable into
the correlation problem. This same conclusion is borne out
by comparing the coefficients of multiple correlation. Thus
$R_{1.234} = 0.9056$, while $R_{1.23} = 0.9039$, which is nearly as large,
indicating that the trivariate plane was nearly as good a fit as
the four-variable plane of regression.

Partial-correlation Coefficients. The unimportance of knowledge of grades in College Board English examinations in predicting the grades of freshmen in second-semester English is
explained also by the small partial-correlation coefficient between
X_1 and X_4 when X_2 and X_3 are held constant. This partial-
correlation coefficient is given as $r_{14.23} = 0.1340$.

Analysis of Variance in X_1. These conclusions are further
indicated by the nature of the β squares and the β cross-product
terms. From the first equation in Table 62 it is seen that the
various proportions of variance in X_1 are accounted for as
follows:

60.25 per cent by correlation with first-semester English grades.

  2.17 per cent by correlation with verbal scholastic-aptitude
      tests.

  0.43 per cent by correlation with College Board English exami-
      nations.

13.58 per cent by indirect correlation with first-semester English
      grades and verbal scholastic-aptitude tests.

  4.98 per cent by indirect correlation with first-semester English
      grades and College Board English examinations.

  0.61 per cent by indirect correlation with verbal scholastic-
      aptitude tests and College Board English examinations.

17.98 per cent by correlation with other factors independent of
      first-semester English grades, verbal scholastic-aptitude
      test grades, and College Board English examinations.

The small percentages attributable to College Board English
examination grades, either directly or indirectly, are apparent
from these statistics. Evidently, under conditions existing at
the woman's college, grades on the College Board English

[1] *Cf.* p. 451.

examination were of little value for predicting how well the students would do in their college freshman English courses.[1]

Another approach to the study of variance in X_1 could be made as follows: It was noted above for three variables that[2]

$$\sigma^2 = r_{12}^2\sigma_1^2 + r_{13.2}^2\sigma_{1.2}^2 + \sigma_{1.23}^2$$

For four variables,

$$\sigma_1^2 = r_{12}^2\sigma_1^2 + r_{13.2}^2\sigma_{1.2}^2 + r_{14.23}^2\sigma_{1.23}^2 + \sigma_{1.234}^2$$

which may be expressed in proportions as follows:

$$1 = r_{12}^2 + r_{13.2}^2\frac{\sigma_{1.2}^2}{\sigma_1^2} + r_{14.23}^2\frac{\sigma_{1.23}^2}{\sigma_1^2} + \frac{\sigma_{1.234}^2}{\sigma_1^2}$$

This expression means that the total variance in X_1 is composed of four parts as follows: the part that is due to total simple linear correlation with X_2, the part that is due to partial correlation with X_3 when X_2 is held constant, the part that is due to partial correlation with X_4 when X_2 and X_3 are held constant, and the part due to other causes independent of X_2, X_3, and X_4. The expression $r_{13.2}^2\frac{\sigma_{1.2}^2}{\sigma_1^2}$ describes the proportion of the variance in X_1 that is explained as a result of adding X_3 to the regression equation, while $r_{14.23}^2\frac{\sigma_{1.23}^2}{\sigma_1^2}$ describes the proportion of the variance in X_1 that is explained as a result of adding X_4 to the regression equation; the influences of X_3 and X_4 that result from their association with X_2 are already contained in $r_{12}^2\sigma_1^2$. By substituting the values of the four above terms in the illustrated problem, it becomes

$$1.00000 = 0.80238 + 0.07369\,\frac{381.46895}{1,930.3155} + 0.017957\,\frac{353.358}{1,930.3155} + \frac{346.9940}{1,930.3155}$$

or

$$1.00000 = 0.80238 + 0.01456 + 0.00329 + 0.17977$$

[1] It will be noted, however, that $r_{14} = 0.49$ so that approximately 25 per cent [$=(.49)^2$] of the variation in X_1 may be estimated from knowledge of X_4 alone.

[2] *Cf.* Chap. XVI, Eq. (33), p. 428.

From this expression it may be said that 80.2 per cent of the variance in X_1 is accounted for by total correlation with X_2, a further 1.4 per cent is accounted for by additional correlation with X_3, and a further 0.3 per cent is accounted for by additional correlation with X_4, the remaining 18 per cent being due to other influences independent of X_2, X_3, and X_4.   In other words, by making a four- instead of a three-variable correlation problem, that is, by including the College Board English examination grades, only an additional 0.3 per cent of the variance in second-semester English grades is explained.

CHAPTER XVIII

NORMAL FREQUENCY SURFACE

THE BIVARIATE HISTOGRAM

The study of frequency surfaces begins logically with a geometrical representation of a bivariate frequency distribution known as a "bivariate histogram." To visualize the histogram that would represent the distribution of Table 25 (page 326), consider an ordinary checkerboard. Let the side and top of the board be calibrated with the class-interval scale shown in Table 25, and let 81 checkers be taken to represent the 81 students. On the checkerboard square in the row headed 60– and the column headed 120-, let one checker be placed; on the square in the row headed 100– and the column headed 60–, let two checkers be placed; on the square in the row headed 100– and the column headed 100-, let one checker be placed; and so on, until all the squares on the checkerboard for which there are frequencies in Table 25 are covered with the proper number of checkers piled on top of each other.

If the checkers were square rather than round, they would stand up better and fill in all the area, helping to support each other. If they were square, the resulting figure would resemble a histogram for the given bivariate frequency distribution. A picture of what such a histogram would look like is given in Fig. 121.

In the foregoing example the heights of the various piles of checkers represented the frequency of each cell. It would be possible however, so to adjust the vertical scale that the heights of the piles of checkers represented the relative frequency of each cell. If the checkers were square, giving a histogram proper, then, further, it would be possible to adjust the vertical scale so that the volume of each pile of square checkers measured the relative frequencies. For example, since the class intervals are 20 units each and the area of any cell is thus 400 square units, the height of a pile of checkers taken to measure a relative frequency of, say 0.08, would be 0.0002 unit.   This would, of course, be very small; but then, in any model, the vertical unit could be taken sufficiently large to offset this.   That is, instead of letting $\frac{1}{4}$ inch represent 1 unit (the thickness of one checker, say), it would be possible to let 10,000 inches represent 1 unit.   Then 0.0002 units would be the equivalent of a pile of eight checkers.

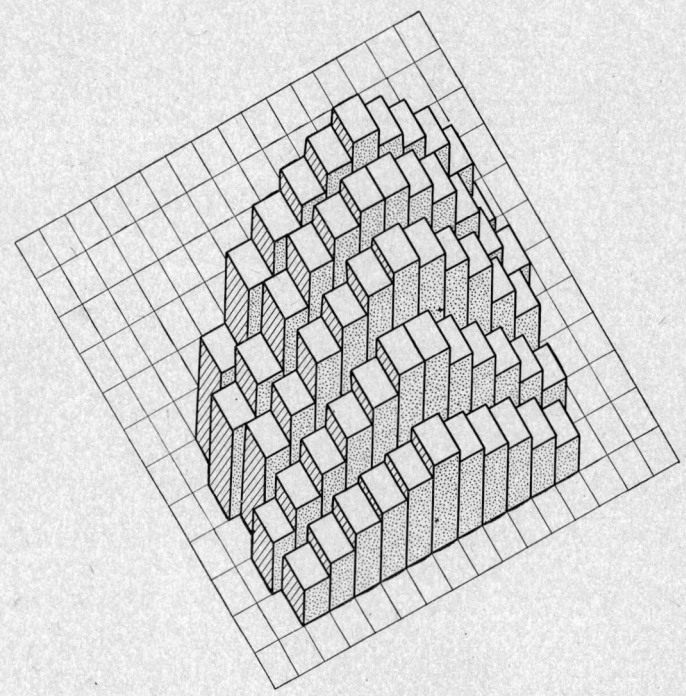

Fig. 121.—Histogram representation of a bivariate frequency distribution. Rectangular blocks on the other side of the mean point are presumably obscured from view.

Suppose, now, that a histogram is constructed so that volumes of the square checkers erected on each cell represent the relative frequency of that cell, and suppose that the number of cases is indefinitely increased and at the same time the size of the class intervals is made infinitesimally small.   The result would be a solid figure the top of which would tend to trace out a smooth surface.   This would be a frequency surface.   A frequency surface is thus the limit approached by a bivariate histogram as the number of cases is indefinitely increased and the sizes of the class intervals indefinitely reduced. If an area is traced out in the X_1X_2 plane, the relative frequency of cases falling in this area is given by the volume under the surface over that area.

FREQUENCY SURFACES

Frequency surfaces may assume all sorts of shapes. They may be symmetrical and bell-shaped, or they may be distorted by skewness or excessive peakedness or flatness, depending on the types of forces underlying the variation in the two variables. First will be considered the case of a bivariate surface for variables that are normally distributed and are independent of each other.

Bivariate-surface, Independent Variables. A monovariate frequency distribution, it will be recalled, showed the relative frequency of occurrence of various values of a given variable. A joint, or bivariate, frequency distribution shows the relative frequency of occurrence of various pairs of values of the two given variables. Suppose, for example, that a marksman is shooting at a target. The scatter of dots about the center of Fig. 122 may be taken to illustrate the results of a large number of such shots. The position of any particular shot relative to the center of the target may be indicated by the amount of its horizontal deflection (call it x_2) and by the amount of its vertical deflection (call it x_1). The relative frequencies of various types of shots may consequently be indicated by the relative frequencies of various combinations of horizontal and vertical deflections, that is to say, of various pairs of values of x_1 and x_2.

The relative frequency of shots in any given area of the target, the x_1x_2 plane shown in Fig. 122, may be indicated by the density of shots in that area or by the volume of some frequency surface constructed over the x_1x_2 plane. The use of the surface for this purpose is illustrated in Fig. 123.

It will be noted that the shots tend to be distributed symmetrically around the center of the target. No tendency for large vertical deviations to be associated with large horizontal deviations in either a positive or a negative direction is evident. Also, no tendency for vertical deviations to vary in any particular way with horizontal deviations is apparent.

Normal Bivariate-surface, Independent Variables.   Figure 123 illustrates the normal bivariate-surface independent variables; it

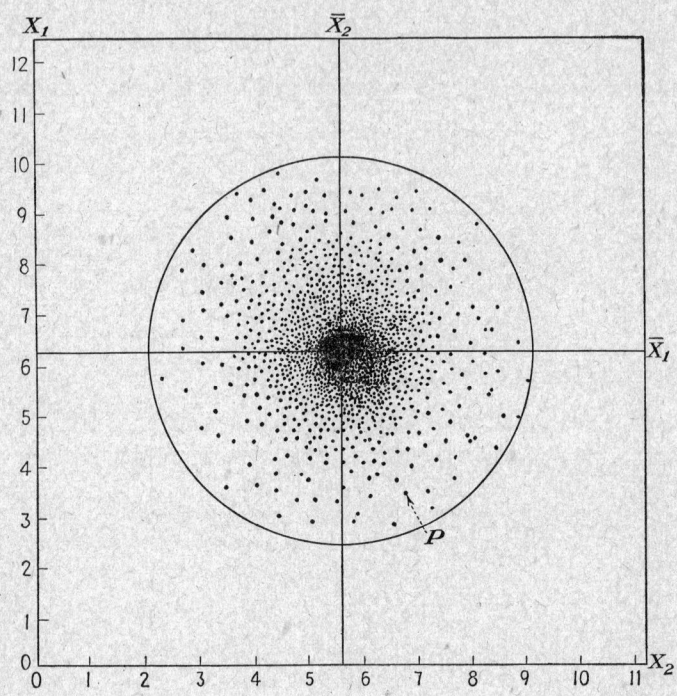

Fig. 122.—Distribution of shots at a target, representing a symmetrical bivariate distribution.

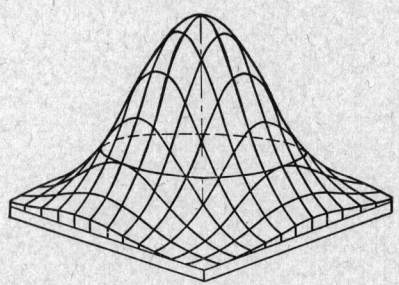

Fig. 123.—A normal bivariate frequency surface, independent variables.   [Here $\sigma_1 = \sigma_2$].

and the example described above illustrate the characteristics of a bivariate distribution where there is no correlation between the two variables. This may be summarized as follows: There is no correlation, that is to say, the variables are independent of each other, because (1) for any given value of X_1, the distribution of values of X_2 is the same, with the same mean and standard deviation, as for any other value of X_1; (2) for any given value of X_2, the distribution of values of X_1 is the same, with the same mean and standard deviation, as for any other value of X_2. When each variable is the result of a set of forces that will produce a normal frequency distribution in that variable alone and when the two sets of forces operate independently of each other, the result will be a normal bivariate frequency distribution with no correlation. The easiest way of generating a normal bivariate frequency surface is to suppose that a form of the normal frequency curve is held in a position perpendicular to the base plane, as in Fig. 124. A knob is fixed to the top of the frequency curve at B, and the center of the base line of the frequency curve is fixed at A, so that it can revolve but so that the line BA always remains perpendicular to the base plane CD.

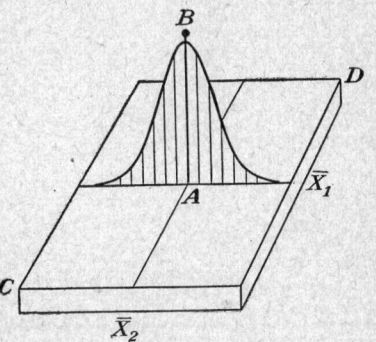

FIG. 124.—The normal curve, revolution of which will produce Fig. 123.

If the form of this normal frequency curve is revolved in a complete cycle until it reaches its original position again, the frequency curve will "describe" the surface of the bivariate normal frequency surface for independent variables, and it will be like a system of symmetrically concentric circles such as that shown in Fig. 123. For such a distribution of pairs of observations X_1 and X_2, $r = 0$, for the x_1x_2 products are distributed equally in the four quadrants, minus products canceling plus products.

Mathematical Representation of Normal Bivariate-surface, Independent Variables. *Use of the $\bar{X}_1$ and $\bar{X}_2$ as the Origin.* As noted in the discussion of Fig. 122, the various X_1X_2 points plotted in a bivariate plane may, with no difficulty, be described in terms of their distances from the respective means. This has the effect of shifting the axes so that the new axes are the lines drawn perpendicular to the means of the respective scales; the vertical line drawn through $\bar{X}_2$ in Fig. 122 is the x_1-axis, and the horizontal line drawn through $\bar{X}_1$ in Fig. 122 is the x_2-axis. Vertical and horizontal deviations from the center of the circle are x_1 and x_2 variates. For many purposes it is more convenient to use this method of describing points in a bivariate plane than to use the original scales as the point of reference. In the following pages, the more frequent appearance of x_1 and x_2, instead of the capital letters, will be understood to signify the shift from reference to the original axes to reference to the axes with the origin at the means of the two variables.

Probability of Each Variate Taken Separately. If x_1 is a normally distributed variate above and below the $\bar{X}_1$ and is completely independent of x_2, the probability or relative frequency of any value of x_1 between x_1 and $x_1 + dx_1$, whether associated with large or with small values or with positive or negative values of x_2, will be given by

$$dP(x_1) = \frac{1}{\sigma_1 \sqrt{2\pi}} e^{-\frac{x_1^2}{2\sigma_1^2}} dx_1 \tag{1}$$

Similarly, if x_2 is a normally distributed variate and is completely independent of x_1, the probability or relative frequency of any value of x_2 between x_2 and $x_2 + dx_2$, whether associated with large or with small values of x_1 or with positive or negative values of x_1, will be given by

$$dP(x_2) = \frac{1}{\sigma_2 \sqrt{2\pi}} e^{-\frac{x_2^2}{2\sigma_2^2}} dx_2 \tag{2}$$

Joint Probability of Two Variables. The joint probability or joint relative frequency of an x_1 between x_1 and $x_1 + dx_1$ occurring in association with an x_2 between x_2 and $x_2 + dx_2$ is the product of the above two probabilities. In other words, the joint probability of the two variables occurring in pairs of any combination is given by

$$dP(x_1 x_2) = \frac{1}{\sigma_1 \sqrt{2\pi} \, \sigma_2 \sqrt{2\pi}} e^{-\frac{x_1^2}{2\sigma_1^2} - \frac{x_2^2}{2\sigma_2^2}} dx_1 \, dx_2 \tag{3}$$

which reduces to the following form:

$$dP(x_1 x_2) = \frac{1}{\sigma_1 \sigma_2 2\pi} e^{-\frac{1}{2}\left(\frac{x_1^2}{\sigma_1^2} + \frac{x_2^2}{\sigma_2^2}\right)} dx_1\, dx_2 \qquad (4)$$

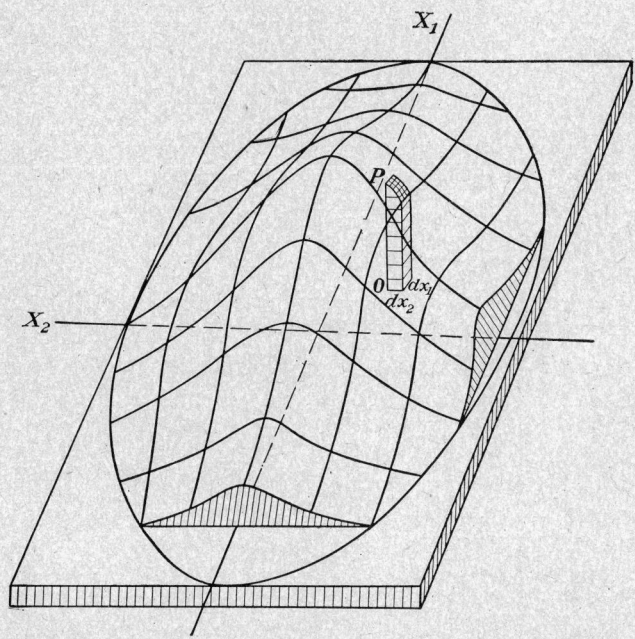

FIG. 125.—A normal bivariate frequency surface, independent variables. [Here $\sigma_1 > \sigma_2$].

Geometrically, the $dP(x_1 x_2)$ expressed in Eq. (4) describes the volume of a column with breadth and width of dx_1 and dx_2 and a height equal to $\frac{1}{\sigma_1 \sigma_2 2\pi} e^{-\frac{1}{2}\left(\frac{x_1^2}{\sigma_1^2} + \frac{x_2^2}{\sigma_2^2}\right)}$. Such a column is shown at P in Fig. 125.

The normal bivariate surface may be described, therefore, as follows:

$$f(x_1 x_2) = \frac{1}{\sigma_1 \sigma_2 2\pi} e^{-\frac{1}{2}\left(\frac{x_1^2}{\sigma_1^2} + \frac{x_2^2}{\sigma_2^2}\right)} \qquad (5)$$

If the two standard deviations are equal, the normal probability surface is circular like Fig. 123. Horizontal planes parallel to the base will intersect the figure in the form of circles becoming smaller as the plane is elevated.   Any vertical plane parallel with the x_1-axis (a line through the $\bar{X}_1$) will intersect the figure in the form of a normal curve with a standard deviation equal to σ_1; and any vertical plane parallel with the x_2-axis will intersect the figure in the form of a normal curve with a standard deviation equal to σ_2.   If the two standard deviations are equal, these normal curves will be identical.

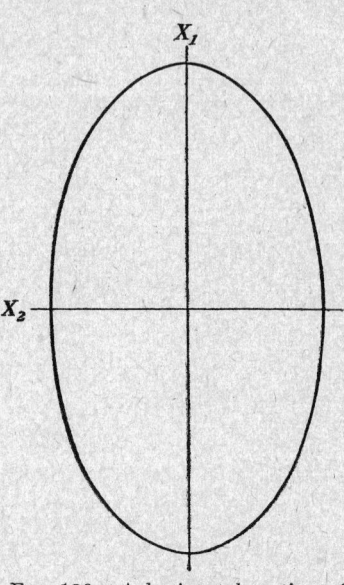

Fig. 126.—A horizontal section of the frequency surface of Fig. 125.

If, however, the two standard deviations are not equal, the normal bivariate surface will be elliptical in form, as shown in Fig. 125, rather than circular. Vertical planes drawn as before will nevertheless bisect contours of normal curves.   The vertical normal curves will have standard deviations equal to σ_1, and the horizontal normal curves will have standard deviations equal to σ_2.   Horizontal planes parallel to the base in Fig. 125 will intersect the figure in the form of ellipses, which will become smaller as the plane is elevated.   Figure 126 is the sort of ellipse that would be obtained by the intersection of a plane horizontal to the base plane of Fig. 125.   The equation for the ellipse shown in Fig. 126 is

$$0.3x_1^2 + 6.7x_2^2 - 32 = 0$$

or

$$x_1 = \pm \sqrt{\tfrac{320}{3} - \tfrac{6.7}{3}x_2^2}$$

Pairs of x_1 and x_2 that satisfy this equation are:

x_2	x_1
0	±10.3
±0.5	±10.0
±1.0	± 9.2
±1.5	± 7.5
±2.0	± 4.2
±2.18	0

Bivariate-surface, Correlated Variables.   Instead of two independent variables, suppose there is a set of paired variables in which is displayed a marked tendency for positive correlation, so that large values of X_1 are associated with large values of X_2, and vice versa.   This is the same as to say that positive values

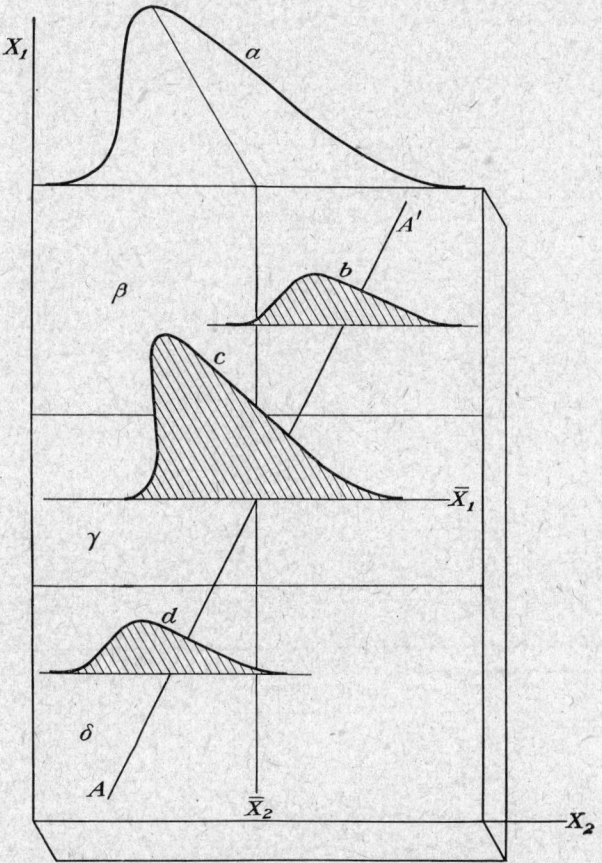

Fig. 127.—Horizontal view of correlated variables.

of x_1 occur predominantly with positive values of x_2 and negative values of x_1 occur predominantly with negative values of x_2, the small x's measuring in each case the deviations from respective means.   Assume that each distribution taken separately is a symmetrical one like a in Fig. 127 and a in Fig. 128.   In Fig.

127 let a represent the frequency curve of the total distribution of the X_2 variable. Then suppose this frequency distribution of all the variants of the variable X_2 is cross-classified into three groups, (1) those X_2's associated with large values of X_1, (2) those associated with the ordinary or average range of values of X_1, and (3) those associated with small values of X_1.

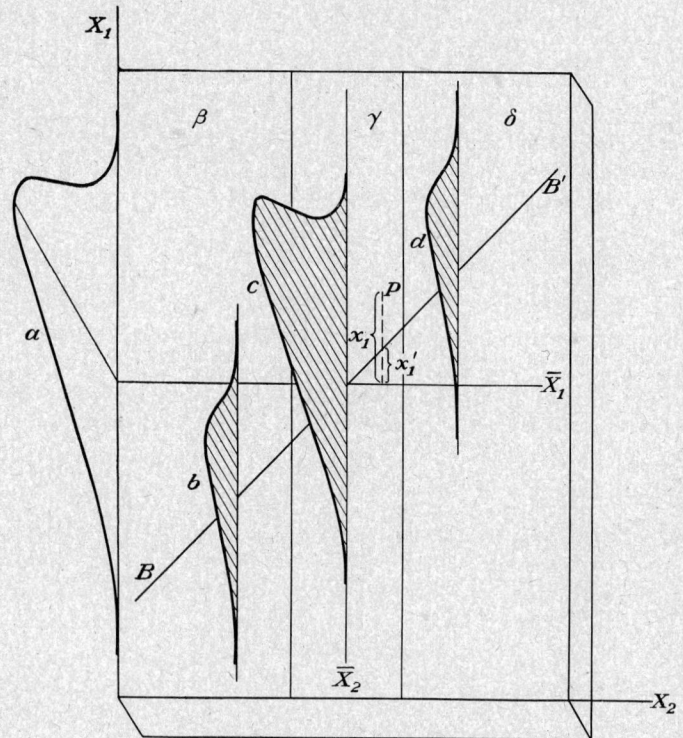

Fig. 128.—Vertical view of correlated variables.

The plane is accordingly divided vertically into three parts representing the range of (1) large values of X_1 (this part of the plane is labeled β in Fig. 127); (2) ordinary or average range of X_1 values, represented in the figure by γ; and (3) small values of X_1, represented by δ in the figure.

By summarizing in a group those variates of X_2 associated with large values of X_1 (those in the range of β in Fig. 127), and under the assumption that large values of X_2 are associated with large values of X_1, a frequency distribution like b, whose mean would be larger than the $\bar{X}_2$ of the total population of variables X_2, would be obtained. The line AA' intersects the base of the frequency curve b at its mean point.

By summarizing in a group the X_2 variables in the γ range of Fig. 127, a frequency distribution of X_2 variables like c would be obtained; then the one showing the X_2 variables associated with X_1 in the range of δ would give a frequency distribution like d. The line AA' in Fig. 127 also passes through the mean of the frequency curve d. In other words, the means of curves b, c, and d, all lie on the same straight line, AA'.

The X_1 variable is treated in a similar manner in Fig. 128, in which a represents the frequency curve of all of the values of the X_1 variable. This frequency distribution of all the X_1 variables is then cross-classified into three groups, (1) those associated with small values of X_2, (2) those associated with ordinary or average range of values of X_2, and (3) those associated with large values of X_2. The plane of Fig. 128 is accordingly divided horizontally into three parts, representing the range of (1) small values of X_2 (this part of the plane is labeled β in Fig. 128); (2) ordinary or average range of X_2 values, represented in the figure by γ; and (3) large values of X_1, represented by δ in the figure. By summarizing in one frequency distribution the variates of X_1 associated with small values of X_2 (those in the range of β in Fig. 128), under the assumption that small values of X_1 are associated with small values of X_2, a frequency distribution like b, whose mean is smaller than the mean of the total population of variable X_1, would be obtained.

By summarizing in one group the X_1 variables in the range γ of the X_2 variable, a frequency distribution of X_1 variables like c would be obtained; the group of X_1 variables associated with X_2 in the range of δ will give a frequency distribution like d. The line passing through the means of these three frequency distributions would be like BB' in Fig. 128.

Normal Correlation Surface, Correlated Variables. A bivariate frequency distribution showing the joint variation of two correlated variables would thus appear to be represented by a frequency surface that is turned so as to make an angle with the x_1- and x_2-axes. A picture of a normal bivariate frequency surface for correlated variables is shown in Fig. 129. Figures 127 and 128 constitute analyses of the frequencies of Fig. 129 that divided the surface into three parts, first up and down and second left and right. The three figures, therefore, are an attempt to view the same distribution in three different ways. If any cross section is taken of the surface represented by Fig. 129, parallel to the X_1-axis, the cross section will have the form of a normal frequency curve with its mean on the line bb'. Any cross section

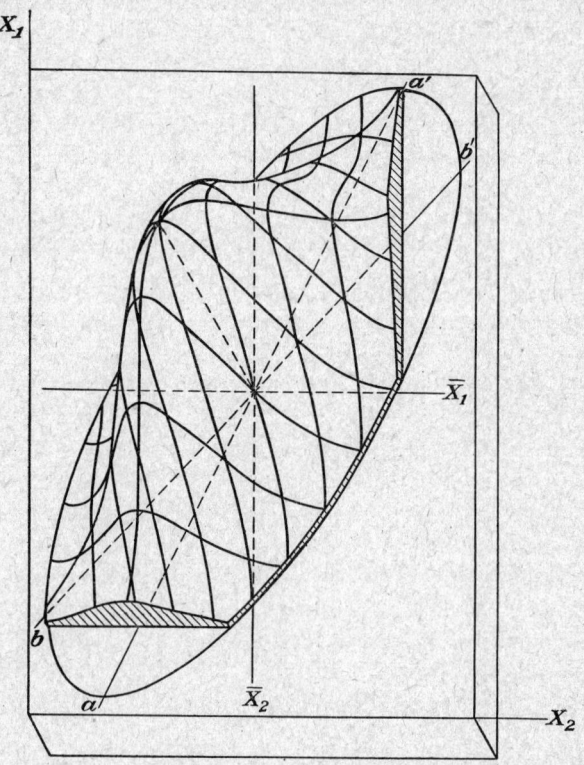

Fig. 129.—A normal bivariate frequency surface, correlated variables.

of this surface taken parallel to the X_2-axis will have the form of a normal frequency curve with its mean on the line aa'. Such cross sections are similar in character to the frequency curves b, c, and d, discussed in connection with Figs. 127 and 128, respectively. Typical cross sections are likewise shown in Fig. 129.

Careful study of Figs. 127 to 129 will aid greatly in the understanding of the theory of correlation. They serve also as the basis for comprehending the theoretical explanation in the ensuing section.

Derivation of Equation for Bivariate Normal Frequency Distribution, Correlated Variables. *Equation of a Rotated Ellipse.* A quadratic equation of the general form

$$aX_1^2 + 2hX_1X_2 + bX_2^2 + 2gX_1 + 2fX_2 + c = 0 \qquad (6)$$

is an ellipse under the following conditions:[1]

$$ab - h^2 > 0 \qquad \text{and} \qquad D \neq 0$$

where

$$D = \begin{vmatrix} a & h & g \\ h & b & f \\ g & f & c \end{vmatrix} = abc + hgf + gfh$$
$$- af^2 - ch^2 - bg^2$$

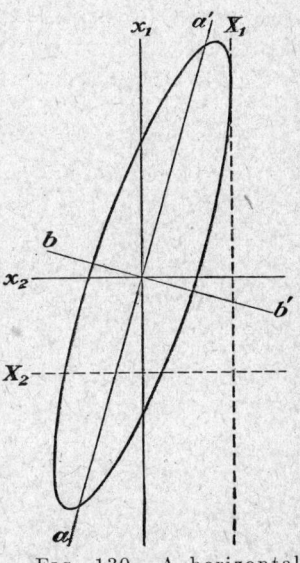

For example, the equation

$$X_1^2 - 4X_1X_2 + 6X_2^2 - 24X_1$$
$$+ 64X_2 + 144 = 0 \quad (6')$$

is an ellipse like that shown in Fig. 130, expressed with reference to the large X_1X_2-axes. The center of the ellipse is at $X_1 = 4$, $X_2 = -4$.[2]

The equation for an ellipse with reference to the axes passing through its center is[3]

Fig. 130.—A horizontal cross section of a normal bivariate surface, correlated variables.

$$a'x_1 + 2h'x_1x_2 + b'x_2^2 + c' = 0 \qquad (7)$$

where $a' = a$, $h' = h$, $b' = b$, and $c' = D/(ab - h^2)$.

For Eq. (6') the new form is

$$x_1^2 - 4x_1x_2 + 6x_2^2 - 32 = 0 \qquad (7')$$

---

[1] FINE, H. B., and H. D. THOMPSON, *Coordinate Geometry*, pp. 137–138.

[2] The center of the ellipse is found by solving the following two equations for X_1 and X_2:

$$aX_1 + hX_2 + g = 0$$
$$hX_1 + bX_2 + f = 0$$

In this problem, $a = 1$, $h = -2$, $g = -12$, $b = 6$, and $f = 32$.

[3] *Cf.* FINE and THOMPSON, *op. cit.*

Following are the solutions for Eqs. (6′) and (7′), from which Fig. 130 was drawn, the two equations describing the same ellipse:

EQUATION (6′)	EQUATION (7′)

Solution:			Solution:		
$X_1 = 2X_2 + 12 \pm \sqrt{-2(X_2^2 + 8X_2)}$			$x_1 = 2x_2 \pm \sqrt{32 - 2x_2^2}$		
X_2	X_1		x_2	x_1	
0	$12 \pm \sqrt{0} = 12$		0	$0 \pm \sqrt{32}$	$= \quad 5.7 - 5.7$
-1	$10 \pm \sqrt{14} = 13.74$	6.3	± 1	$\pm 2 \pm \sqrt{30}$	$= \pm 7.5 \mp 3.5$
-2	$8 \pm \sqrt{24} = 12.9$	3.1	± 2	$\pm 4 \pm \sqrt{24}$	$= \pm 8.9 \mp 0.9$
-3	$6 \pm \sqrt{30} = 11.5$	0.5	± 3	$\pm 6 \pm \sqrt{14}$	$= \pm 9.7 \pm 2.3$
-4	$4 \pm \sqrt{32} = 9.7$	-1.7	± 3.5	$\pm 7 \pm \sqrt{7.5}$	$= \pm 9.7 \pm 4.3$
-5	$2 \pm \sqrt{30} = 7.5$	-3.5	± 4	$\pm 8 \pm \sqrt{0}$	$= \pm 8$

The equations of the axes of the ellipse are obtained by finding the positive root of λ in the following equations:

$$h'\lambda^2 + (a' - b')\lambda - h' = 0$$

or, in this case,

$$-2\lambda^2 - 5\lambda + 2 = 0$$
$$\lambda = 2.85$$

The equation for the major axis of the ellipse is therefore $x_1 = 2.85x_2$, and the equation for the minor axis is $x_2 = -2.85x_1$.

Referred to its own major and minor axes, the equation of the ellipse is $Ax_1^2 + Bx_2^2 + C = 0$, where A and B are obtained from

$$A + B = a' + b' \qquad AB = a'b' - h'^2 \qquad C = c'$$

and the condition that $A - B$ has the same sign as h'. For this ellipse it is thus found that $A = 0.3$ and $B = 6.7$. The equation for this ellipse referred to its own axes (see Fig. 125) is

$$0.3x_1^2 + 6.7x_2^2 - 32 = 0$$

Mathematical Representation of a Bivariate Normal Correlation Surface. It was noted above that the bivariate normal surface in which x_1 and x_2 are independent of each other (that is, in which no correlation exists between them) is of the form

$$dP(x_1x_2) = \frac{1}{2\pi\sigma_1\sigma_2} e^{-\frac{1}{2}\left(\frac{x_1^2}{\sigma_1^2} + \frac{x_2^2}{\sigma_2^2}\right)} dx_1 dx_2 \qquad (8)$$

The constant term, $1/2\pi\sigma_1\sigma_2$, is a constant dependent on the values of the two standard deviations in any particular instance. The product of this constant times the term $e^{-\frac{1}{2}\left(\frac{x_1^2}{\sigma_1^2}+\frac{x_2^2}{\sigma_2^2}\right)}$ gives, for various values of x_1 and x_2, the height of the bivariate surface from the base (the distance OP in Fig. 125). If a horizontal plane parallel with the base plane is drawn through the normal bivariate surface at a distance OP from the base plane, the intersection of the plane and the bivariate surface will be an ellipse (as in Fig. 126) if the standard deviations are unequal; the intersection will be a circle (as in Fig. 123) if the two standard deviations are equal. Such a plane represents the locus of all points distant OP from the base plane, and the passing of such a horizontal plane through the bivariate surface is equivalent to setting the expression $e^{-\frac{1}{2}\left(\frac{x_1^2}{\sigma_1^2}+\frac{x_2^2}{\sigma_2^2}\right)}$ equal to a constant which is equivalent to putting

$$\frac{x_1^2}{\sigma_1^2} + \frac{x_2^2}{\sigma_2^2} = c$$

This equation represents a circle if $\sigma_1 = \sigma_2$ and an ellipse if $\sigma_1 \neq \sigma_2$.

The smaller the constant c, the smaller will be the circle or ellipse until, at the peak of the bivariate surface a very small circle or ellipse will be found—finally, just a point.

If the two variables are correlated, two changes occur. (1) The ellipse is rotated. (2) The ellipse is narrowed. If before correlation the surface is circular in form, owing to the fact that the standard deviations are equal, the existence of correlation will cause the circle to be converted into a rotated ellipse, narrowing the circle to an elliptical form. If before correlation the surface is elliptical in form, owing to the fact that the standard deviations are unequal (see Fig. 126), the existence of correlation will cause the ellipse to rotate and also to become narrower. This phenomenon is explained as follows:

If larger than average values of X_1 cause X_2 to be larger than average and smaller than average values of X_1 cause X_2 to be smaller than average, the pull exerted on X_2 values is indicated by the arrows in Fig. 131. The larger the X_1, the more pull will be exercised upon X_2 to make it larger than its average. This is indicated by making arrow (1) longer than arrows (2), (3), and (4), which, respectively, represent the degree to which successively smaller values of X_1 affect values of X_2, until, by the time X_1 becomes smaller than average (below the line $\bar{X}_1$), arrow (4′) points to the negative pull, that is, causing X_2 to be less than its average.

When correlation exists, this means that bivariate frequencies located in quadrant II, where X_1 is larger and X_2 is smaller than average, tend to move over to quadrant I, where X_2 and X_1 are both larger than average. Bivariate frequencies already located in quadrant I are less affected. Similarly, bivariate frequencies in quadrant IV tend to move to quadrant III, where

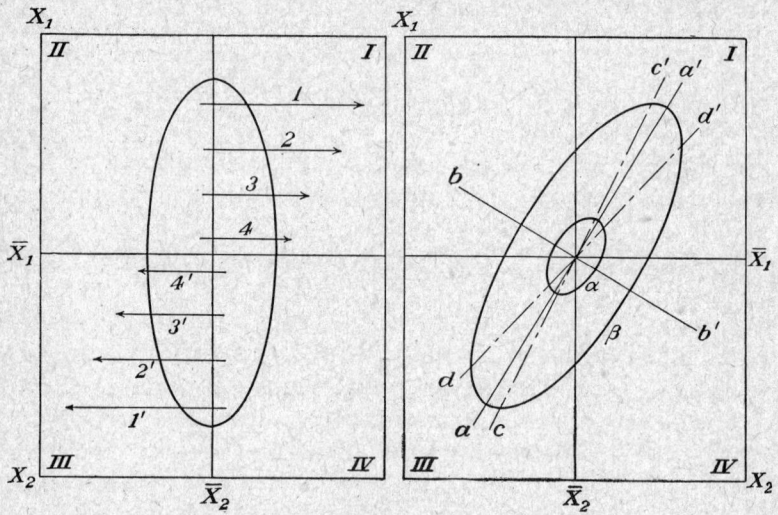

Fig. 131.—Illustrating the difference between the nonexistence and existence of correlation in a normal bivariate frequency surface.

both X_2 and X_1 are smaller than average, while bivariate frequencies in quadrant III are less affected. The result is that the rotated ellipse becomes narrowed as shown in the part of Fig. 131 at the right. Any horizontal plane parallel to the base of a correlated bivariate (Fig. 129) will intersect the bivariate frequency surface in the form of an ellipse such as that shown in the right half of Fig. 131—large ellipses near the base plane, and smaller and smaller ellipses as the horizontal plane is raised higher and higher from the base. These ellipses have the equation

$$ax_1^2 + 2hx_1x_2 + bx_2^2 + c = 0$$

As already noted, the middle term $2hx_1x_2$ is present in the equation because of the fact that the ellipse is rotated and now described in terms of axes other than its own, although the origin remains the center of the ellipse. The middle term is thus present because of correlation, which causes the rotation of the ellipse. This middle term is generally called the "product term" because it is the product of the two variables. When there is no correlation, this middle term disappears.[1] The narrowing of the ellipse, as will be seen, results in the increase in the value of the constant term $\dfrac{1}{2\pi\sigma_1\sigma_2}$.

Since the normal bivariate surface in which X_1 and X_2 are correlated is thus elliptical in form but rotated and narrower than the elliptical surface representing uncorrelated bivariates, the distribution of probabilities or relative frequencies will be given by an expression of the form

$$dP(x_1x_2) = ke^{-\frac{1}{2}(ax_1{}^2+2hx_1x_2+bx_2{}^2)}\, dx_1\, dx_2 \qquad (9)$$

This is the general formula for a normal bivariate frequency distribution of correlated variables. The remainder of the argument, which appears in the Appendix to this chapter, shows how the parameters k, a, h, and b may be evaluated in terms of the moments of X_1 and X_2. When the proper values of the parameters are inserted, the formula is as follows:[2]

$$dP(x_1x_2) = \frac{1}{2\pi\sigma_1\sigma_2\,\sqrt{1-r^2}}\, e^{-\frac{1}{2(1-r^2)}\left(\frac{x_1{}^2}{\sigma_1{}^2} - 2r\frac{x_1x_2}{\sigma_1\sigma_2} + \frac{x_2{}^2}{\sigma_2{}^2}\right)}\, dx_1\, dx_2 \quad (10)$$

This probability expression describes a normal bivariate frequency distribution such as that graphed in Fig. 129. The rotated position is reflected in the fact that the exponent of e has a middle "product term." The fact that the surface is narrower than it would be if there were no correlation is reflected in the character of the constant term, which is larger than the constant term of a normal bivariate frequency surface of uncor-

---

[1] See p. 475.
[2] See Appendix, pp. 492–496.

related variables.[1]   In other words, because r cannot be greater than 1,

$$\frac{1}{2\pi\sigma_1\sigma_2 \sqrt{1 - r^2}} \geqq \frac{1}{2\pi\sigma_1\sigma_2}$$

The degree to which the constant term in the correlated surface is larger depends upon the value of r.   If $r = 0$, the constant term becomes identical with the constant term of the uncorrelated surface.   If $r = 1$, the constant term of the correlated surface becomes infinitely large, reflecting the fact that when $r = 1$ the surface becomes so narrowed that it is a plane, all points being on the line of regression.

LINES OF REGRESSION

In the discussion of Fig. 127 it was pointed out that the line AA' passes through the means of frequency distributions a, b, and c.   Similarly, in the discussion of Fig. 128, it was said that the line BB' passes through the means of frequency distributions a, b, and c.   In the discussion of Fig. 129 the line aa' was said to pass through the means of any frequency distribution made by a vertical plane parallel with the x_1-axis, and the line bb' was said to pass through the means of any frequency distribution made by a vertical plane parallel with the x_2-axis.   These two lines are thus the progressions of the means for the normal bivariate surface.   As will be shown shortly, they are also the least-squares lines that might be fitted to the surface.   In both senses, therefore, they are the lines of regression for the surface.

If there is no correlation, as illustrated by Figs. 122, 123, and 126, the two lines of regression correspond with the major and minor axes of the ellipse, that is, with the axes represented by the $\bar{X}_1$ and $\bar{X}_2$ lines of Fig. 122 or Fig. 126.   By hypothesis, in the uncorrelated bivariate surface the mean of any frequency distribution made by a vertical plane parallel to the x_1-axis will be on the $\bar{X}_1$ line, and the mean of any frequency distribution made by a vertical plane parallel to the x_2-axis will be on the $\bar{X}_2$ line.   When the surface is rotated and narrowed, as a result of correlation, it is part of the hypothesis that the normal symmetry

---

[1] The narrowing is due to a stretching upward of a given volume.   As indicated, in the limiting situation ($r = 1$), the surface becomes a vertical plane stretching to an infinite height and having an infinitesimal thickness.

of the surface remains and accordingly the means remain in a straight line, but a straight line at an acute angle rather than perpendicular to the original axis.

Mathematical Representation of Lines of Regression. The bivariate normal correlation surface in terms of probabilities has been found to be described as follows:

$$dP(x_1 x_2) = \frac{1}{2\pi\sigma_1\sigma_2 \sqrt{1-r^2}} e^{\frac{1}{2(1-r^2)}\left(\frac{x_1^2}{\sigma_1^2} - 2r\frac{x_1 x_2}{\sigma_1 \sigma_2} + \frac{x_2^2}{\sigma_2^2}\right)} dx_1 \, dx_2 \quad (11)$$

A line of regression, for example, the line of regression of x_2 on x_1, is a general description of the law of relationship by which for a given value of x_1 the most probable value of x_2 may be determined. Equation (11) describes the joint probability of any bivariate $x_1 x_2$. The probability of any value of x_2 occurring with some specified value of x_1, say $\hat{x}_1$, will be as follows:

$$dP(\hat{x}_1 x_2) = \frac{1}{2\pi\sigma_1\sigma_2 \sqrt{1-r^2}} e^{-\frac{1}{2(1-r^2)}\left[\left(\frac{\hat{x}_1}{\sigma_1}\right)^2 - 2r\frac{\hat{x}_1 x_2}{\sigma_1 \sigma_2} + \frac{x_2^2}{\sigma_2^2}\right]} dx_1 \, dx_2$$

$$(12)$$

If $(\hat{x}_1/\sigma_1)^2$ is factored from the exponent of e, the equation becomes

$$dP(\hat{x}_1 x_2) = \frac{1}{2\pi\sigma_1\sigma_2 \sqrt{1-r^2}} e^{-\frac{(\hat{x}_1)^2}{2\sigma_1^2(1-r^2)}} e^{-\frac{1}{2(1-r^2)}\left(\frac{x_2^2}{\sigma_2^2} - 2r\frac{\hat{x}_1 x_2}{\sigma_1 \sigma_2}\right)} dx_1 \, dx_2$$

$$(13)$$

The square of $\dfrac{x_2^2}{\sigma_2^2} - 2r \dfrac{\hat{x}_1 x_2}{\sigma_1 \sigma_2}$ is completed by adding $\dfrac{r^2(\hat{x}_1)^2}{\sigma_1^2}$, which must also be subtracted to keep the value of the whole expression unchanged. This subtracted part may be conveniently put with the other $(\hat{x}_1)^2$ term so that the final result of these operations is as follows:

$$dP(\hat{x}_1 x_2) = \frac{1}{2\pi\sigma_1\sigma_2 \sqrt{1-r^2}} e^{\frac{-(\hat{x}_1)^2 - r^2(\hat{x}_1)^2}{2\sigma_1^2(1-r^2)}} e^{-\frac{1}{2(1-r^2)}\left(\frac{x_2}{\sigma_2} - r\frac{\hat{x}_1}{\sigma_1}\right)^2} dx_1 \, dx_2$$

$$(14)$$

Upon simplifying the exponents and splitting up the constant term and the $dx_1 dx_2$, this expression becomes

$$dP(\hat{x}_1 x_2) = \frac{1}{\sigma_1\sqrt{2\pi}}\,e^{-\frac{(\hat{x}_1)^2}{2\sigma_1{}^2}}\,dx_1\,\frac{1}{\sigma_2\sqrt{1-r^2}\sqrt{2\pi}}\,e^{-\frac{\left(x_2-r\frac{\sigma_2}{\sigma_1}\hat{x}_1\right)^2}{2\sigma_2{}^2(1-r^2)}}\,dx_2$$

$$(15)$$

Since the first factor is a constant ($\hat{x}_1$ being given), Eq. (15) shows that the probability of an x_2 for a given value of x_1 is proportional to the probability of a normally distributed variate whose mean is $r\dfrac{\sigma_2}{\sigma_1}\hat{x}_1$ and whose standard deviation is $\sigma_2\sqrt{1-r^2}$. (It will be recalled that the general equation for the normal curve is $\dfrac{1}{\sigma\sqrt{2\pi}}\,e^{-\frac{x^2}{2\sigma^2}}\,dx$). Accordingly, the most probable value of x_2 for specified values of x_1, that is, the line of regression of x_2 on x_1, is as follows:

$$x'_2 = r\frac{\sigma_2}{\sigma_1}x_1$$

The standard deviation or scatter about this line is $\sigma_2\sqrt{1-r^2}$.

From Eq. (15) it is seen that the locus of all points representing the means of x_2 for a given x_1 is $x_2 = r\dfrac{\sigma_2}{\sigma_1}\hat{x}_1$, which is the equation of the line of regression of x_2 on x_1. The line of regression of x_1 on x_2 is given by interchanging x_1 and x_2 in the above argument. As indicated above, these two lines are the same as those that might be fitted to the distribution by the method of least squares. From Eq. (15) it is also shown that the standard deviation of x_2 for a given x_1 (in other words, the scatter at any point of the line of regression) is independent of the selected value of x_1, for it is always equal to $\sigma_2\sqrt{1-r^2}$.

NORMAL MULTIVARIATE FREQUENCY "SURFACE"

When a bivariate distribution is described in geometrical terms, one of the dimensions can be used to measure the frequencies. This is not possible for distributions involving more than two variables. In the three-variable case, for example, all three dimensions must be used to indicate the variations in the variables themselves, and none is left to measure the frequencies.

Resort is had in multivariate problems to the use of densities to measure frequencies. Such a device could have been used in the monovariate or bivariate case; instead of having the frequency of any interval represented by the height of a rectangle erected on the interval, it could be assumed that the cases were represented by points on a line, and the more points crowded into any given interval on the line, *i.e.*, the greater the density of points in the interval, the greater would be the frequency of that interval. Likewise, in the bivariate case, instead of representing the frequency of cases in any given two-dimensional cell by the height of a rectangular pile of checkers set up on that cell, it would be possible to look upon the various cases as points in the two-dimensional plane; the frequency of points in any cell would then become the density of points in that cell.

This is the device used to measure frequencies in the multivariate case. For a trivariate distribution, for example, the various cases are looked upon as points in three-dimensional space, and the density of these points in any given three-dimensional cell becomes the measure of the relative frequency of cases in that cell. A trivariate frequency "surface," if it may be so called, is in reality a trivariate density function. The same idea may be carried over by analogy to distributions of four or more variables, although no graphical representation can actually be made of such distributions.

The properties of a normal multivariate "surface" or density function are merely generalizations of the properties of a normal bivariate surface. Whereas in the latter case, loci of equiprobability (*i.e.*, loci of constant level on the frequency surface) were ellipses in the $x_1 x_2$-plane, in the multivariate case loci of equiprobability (*i.e.*, loci of equal density in the N-dimensional space) are ellipsoids in the $X_1, X_2, \ldots, X_N$ space. A picture of a three-dimensional ellipsoid is given in Fig. 132. This represents a contour of equiprobability for a trivariate normal distribution in which there is no correlation. Similar ellipsoids, some larger, some smaller, would represent other contours of equiprobability, and the whole distribution could be represented by a nest of such ellipsoids. The elliptical contours representing a high degree of probability are, of course, the contours close to the center, the center itself being the point of maximum probability (maximum density). As one goes off from the center in a straight line in any direction whatsoever, the change in probability (density) is in accordance with the normal law. If the variables are measured in standard-deviation units, the ellipsoids become spheres and the distribution becomes symmetrical in all directions.

When there is correlation between the variables, the ellipsoids of equiprobability becomes tilted with respect to the various axes and flattened out. If the variables are measured in standard-deviation units, the degree of tilting in any direction is directly related to the amount of the correlation between the variables concerned. The greater the multiple correlation between the variables, the narrower or flatter the ellipsoids become. In

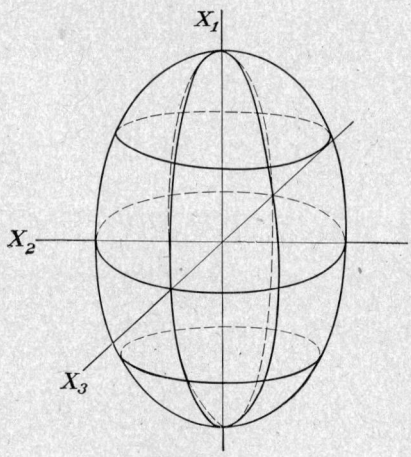

Fig. 132.—Ellipsoid of equiprobability for a trivariate normal frequency distribution.

the limit in which there is perfect correlation between all the variables, the whole distribution reduces to a line through the origin at an angle of approximately $54\frac{3}{4}$ degrees ($\cos^{-1} 1 \sqrt{3}$) with all the axes (assuming the variables are measured in σ units).

As in the simpler case, a plane or hyperplane of regression represents the locus of the mean values of one variable for various combinations of the other variables. For a normal multivariate distribution, the deviations from any plane of regression are all normally distributed with a constant standard deviation for any one plane.

All the properties of a normal bivariate distribution thus carry over to a normal multivariate distribution, the only difference being that ellipses of equiprobability and lines of regression now become ellipsoids and hyperplanes of higher dimensions. Basically, the character of the distribution is essentially the same.

NONNORMAL BIVARIATES AND MULTIVARIATES

If a bivariate or multivariate distribution does not approach the normal form, much of the conventional correlation analysis loses its significance. In some cases, by taking logarithms or reciprocals a nonnormal distribution may be transformed into a normal distribution.[1] In some instances, a multivariate distribution may be normal with respect to its variations about the means of the rows and columns but the means of the rows or means of columns may trace out a curve of regression. In other instances, the regressions of the means may be linear, or planar, but the deviations around these lines, or planes, of regression may be either nonnormally distributed or normally distributed with varying standard deviations.

If, in the case of two variables, the regressions are linear, the initial arguments presented for the use of the product-moment formula for r are still valid even for nonnormal distributions.[2] Large values of X_1 would still tend in general to be associated with large values of X_2 (or with small values if the correlation is negative), and a formula based upon the product deviations would give a good measure of the association between the two variables. If the distribution of cases around the lines of regression is skewed, however, or if the standard deviation varies from one part of the line to another, the scatter about the lines of regression loses its significance as a measure of typical variability. Great care must be taken in these cases in using an average scatter to determine the degree of error in an estimate based on the line of regression. When the distributions are not normal, the rule that two-thirds of the cases tend to lie between plus and minus $\sigma_{i.j}$ no longer holds.

Finally, if the bivariate distribution is not normal, even the product-moment formula may cease to be a statistic of special significance in characterizing the distribution. In the normal case, if the two means, the two standard deviations, and r are all known, the bivariate distribution is fully determined. In the nonnormal case, other measures similar to measures of skewness

---

[1] See Chap. XV, pp. 377–396.
[2] See Chap. XIII, pp. 338–353.

and kurtosis in the monovariate case may be of equal if not greater importance in describing the bivariate distribution. These considerations should always be borne in mind when r is used to measure correlation between nonnormally distributed bivariates.

Similar statements may also be made about nonnormal multivariate distributions. Here the higher dimensionality multiplies the possibilities of skewness, kurtosis, and other departures from normality.[1]

APPENDIX

DERIVATION OF THE EQUATION FOR THE NORMAL BIVARIATE FREQUENCY SURFACE, CORRELATED VARIABLES

The normal bivariate surface in which X_1 and X_2 are correlated is elliptical in form but rotated and narrower than the elliptical surface representing uncorrelated bivariates. The distribution of the probabilities or relative frequencies is given by an expression of the following form:

$$dP(x_1 x_2) = ke^{-\frac{1}{2}(a'x_1^2 + 2h'x_1x_2 + b'x_2^2)} \, dx_1 \, dx_2 \qquad (16)$$

in which the constants k, a', h', and b' may be evaluated in terms of the moments of X_1 and X_2.

First it is to be noted that

$$\iint P(x_1 x_2) \, dx_1 \, dx_2 \quad = 1 \qquad \text{(i)}$$
$$\iint P(x_1 x_2) x_1 \, dx_1 \, dx_2 \quad = 0 \qquad \text{(ii)}$$
$$\iint P(x_1 x_2) x_2 \, dx_1 \, dx_2 \quad = 0 \qquad \text{(iii)}$$
$$\iint P(x_1 x_2) x_1^2 \, dx_1 \, dx_2 \quad = \sigma_1^2 \qquad \text{(iv)}$$
$$\iint P(x_1 x_2) x_2^2 \, dx_1 \, dx_2 \quad = \sigma_2^2 \qquad \text{(v)}$$
$$\iint P(x_1 x_2) x_1 x_2 \, dx_1 \, dx_2 = r\sigma_1\sigma_2 \qquad \text{(vi)}$$

Equation (i) is true since the sum of all probabilities or relative frequencies is necessarily one. Equations (ii) and (iii) are true because x_1 and x_2 represent deviations from the means of X_1 and X_2. Thus $\iint P(x_1 x_2) x_1 \, dx_1 \, dx_2$ is equivalent to $\frac{\Sigma f}{N} x_1$, which equals zero. Likewise,

$$\iint P(x_1 x_2) x_2 \, dx_1 \, dx_2 = \frac{\Sigma f}{N} x_2 = 0$$

Equation (iv) is another form of $\frac{\Sigma f}{N} x_1^2$, which is equal to the variance of X_1; Eq. (v) is equivalent to $\frac{\Sigma f}{N} x_2^2$, which is equal to the variance of X_2; and Eq. (vi) is equivalent to $\frac{\Sigma f}{N} x_1 x_2$, which is equal to $r\sigma_1\sigma_2$, since $r = \Sigma f x_1 x_2 / N\sigma_1\sigma_2$.

[1] For a more complete consideration of the problem of nonnormality, see Smith and Duncan, *Sampling Statistics*, Chap. 18.

Second it is to be noted that, with reference to its rotated axes, aa' and bb', the equation of the ellipse representing the intersection of the frequency surface by a horizontal plane at a distance $e^{-\frac{C}{2}}$ from the base plane is as follows:

$$A x_1'^2 + B x_2'^2 = C$$

where x_1' and x_2' represent the coordinates of a point with reference to the axes aa' and bb', that is to say, x_1' measures the perpendicular distance of a point from aa' and x_2' measures the perpendicular distance of a point from bb'. If the areal element[1] $dx_1\, dx_2$ is also expressed in terms of the $x_1' x_2'$ coordinates, it becomes $dx_1\, dx_2 = dx_1'\, dx_2'$.* The whole probability function thus becomes

$$dP(x_1' x_2') = k e^{-\frac{1}{2}(A x_1'^2 + B x_2'^2)}\, dx_1'\, dx_2' \tag{17}$$

But this is the form of a normal frequency surface for uncorrelated variables, so that, as seen above, pages 474–475,

$$A = \left(\frac{1}{\sigma_1'}\right)^2 \qquad B = \left(\frac{1}{\sigma_2'}\right)^2 \qquad \text{and} \qquad k = \frac{1}{\sigma_1' \sigma_2' 2\pi}$$

since there is no cross-product term, $H = 0$.

[1] It will be recalled that $dP(x_1 x_2) = F(x_1 x_2)\, dx_1\, dx_2$ is represented geometrically by the volume under the surface $F(x_1 x_2)$ cut off by a hollow pipe, erected on a rectangle in the $x_1 x_2$ plane, the sides of which are dx_1 and dx_2 (see Fig. 125, p. 475). To express the whole probability distribution in terms of the new $x_1' x_2'$ coordinates, the area of the pipe's base, $dx_1\, dx_2$ must be transformed into these new coordinates as well as the height of the pipe, $F(x_1 x_2)$.

* The transformation of coordinates is of the form

$$x_1 = x_2' \sin \alpha + x_1' \cos \alpha$$
$$x_2 = x_2' \cos \alpha - x_1' \sin \alpha$$

where α is the angle that aa' makes with the x_2-axis. *Cf.* FINE and THOMPSON, *Coordinate Geometry*, p. 120. Since, in general, $dx_1\, dx_2$ equals, within differentials of higher order,

$$\begin{vmatrix} \dfrac{\delta x_2}{\delta x_2'} & \dfrac{\delta x_1}{\delta x_2'} \\[2ex] \dfrac{\delta x_2}{\delta x_1'} & \dfrac{\delta x_1}{\delta x_1'} \end{vmatrix} dx_1'\, dx_2'$$

it follows that

$$dx_1\, dx_2 = \begin{vmatrix} \cos \alpha \ \sin \alpha \\ -\sin \alpha \ \cos \alpha \end{vmatrix} dx_1'\, dx_2' = dx_1'\, dx_2'$$

since $\cos^2 \alpha + \sin^2 \alpha = 1$. *Cf.* WILSON, E. B., *Advanced Calculus*, pp. 133–134.

The distribution function, Eq. (17), may therefore be written as follows:

$$dP(x_1'x_2') = \frac{1}{\sigma_1'\sigma_2'2\pi}\, e^{-\frac{1}{2}\left[\left(\frac{x_1'}{\sigma_1'}\right)^2 + \left(\frac{x_2'}{\sigma_2'}\right)^2\right]}\, dx_1'\, dx_2' \qquad (18)$$

where σ_1' and σ_2' are the standard deviations of the new variables x_1' and x_2'. It will be noted that this transformation has not changed the probability of a given $x_1 x_2$ combination but has merely expressed it in terms of a new set of coordinates. Accordingly, $P(x_1 x_2) = P(x_1'x_2')$, where x_1' and x_2' are derived by a linear transformation from x_1 and x_2.*

Finally, it will be noted that in any equation of the second degree the product of the coefficients of the squared terms minus the square of one-half the coefficient of the cross-product term is invariant (that is, its value remains unchanged) under simple translations and rotations.[1] Accordingly, the following relationships hold:

$$AB - H^2 = a'b' - h'^2$$

or since $H = 0$,

$$AB = a'b' - h'^2$$

But inasmuch as $A = (1/\sigma_1')^2$, $B = (1/\sigma_2')^2$, it follows that

$$AB = \frac{1}{(\sigma_1'\sigma_2')^2} = a'b' - h'^2$$

From this it follows that

$$k = \frac{\sqrt{a'b' - h'^2}}{2\pi}$$

Use will now be made of these relationships to derive the values of a', b', and h'.

As noted above, since

$$\int_{-\infty}^{\infty} \int_{-\infty}^{\infty} k e^{-\frac{1}{2}(a'x_1{}^2 + 2h'x_1x_2 + b'x_2{}^2)}\, dx_1\, dx_2 = 1$$

then

$$\int_{-\infty}^{+\infty} \int_{-\infty}^{+\infty} e^{-\frac{1}{2}(a'x_1{}^2 + 2h'x_1x_2 + b'x_2{}^2)}\, dx_1\, dx_2 = \frac{1}{k} = \frac{2\pi\sigma_1'\sigma_2'}{1}$$

$$= \frac{2\pi}{\sqrt{a'b' - (h')^2}} \qquad (19)$$

If both sides of Eq. (19) are differentiated with respect to a', it is found that

---

* See footnote *, p. 493.

[1] Cf. FINE and THOMPSON, op. cit., p. 131.

$$-\frac{1}{2}\int\int x_1^2 e^{-\frac{1}{2}(a'x_1{}^2+2h'x_1x_2+b'x_2{}^2)}\,dx_1\,dx_2 = -\frac{1}{2}\frac{2\pi b'}{[a'b'-(h')^2]^{\frac{3}{2}}}$$

$$= -\frac{1}{2}\frac{b'}{k[a'b'-(h'^2)]}$$

By canceling out $-\frac{1}{2}$ and multiplying the equation by k, the left side is equal to σ_1^2 [see Eq. (iv), page 492], and it is found that

(a) $$\sigma_1^2 = \frac{b'}{[a'b'-(h'^2)]} \qquad \text{or} \qquad b' = \sigma_1^2[a'b'-(h'^2)]$$

If similar procedure is followed after differentiating Eq. (19) with respect to b', it is found that

(b) $$\sigma_2^2 = \frac{a'}{[a'b'-(h'^2)]} \qquad \text{or} \qquad a' = \sigma_2^2[a'b'-(h'^2)]$$

If both sides of Eq. (19) are differentiated with respect to h', it is found that

$$-\int\int x_1x_2 e^{-\frac{1}{2}(a'x_1{}^2+2h'x_1x_2+b'x_2{}^2)}\,dx_1\,dx_2$$

$$= -\frac{1}{2}\frac{2\pi(-2h')}{[a'b'-(h')^2]^{\frac{3}{2}}} = -\frac{(-h')}{k[a'b'-(h'^2)]}$$

in which, if multiplied through by k, the left side equals $-\sigma_1\sigma_2 r_{12}$ [see Eq. (vi)], and hence the whole expression reduces to

$$\sigma_1\sigma_2 r_{12} = \frac{-h'}{[a'b'-(h'^2)]}$$

or

(c) $$h' = -\sigma_1\sigma_2 r_{12}[a'b'-(h'^2)]$$

From Eqs. (a), (b), and (c), it follows that

(d) $$b' = \frac{\sigma_1^2}{\sigma_2^2}a' \qquad h' = -\frac{\sigma_1 r_{12}}{\sigma_2}a'$$

$$\sqrt{a'b'-(h')^2} = \frac{a'\sigma_1}{\sigma_2}\sqrt{1-r^2}$$

Equations (a), (b), and (c) are three equations from which the values of a', b', and h' may be expressed in terms of σ_1, σ_2, and r. The direct evaluation of a', b', and h' from these equations is not a simple matter, however, and it is easier to proceed as follows: From Eqs. (a), (b), and (c), it is possible to express b' and h' in terms of a', as noted above in Eq. (d). It will also be recalled that

(e) $$k = \frac{\sqrt{a'b'-(h')^2}}{2\pi} = \frac{a'\sigma_1\sqrt{1-r^2}}{2\pi\sigma_2}$$

By substituting equivalent values, Eq. (16) may accordingly be written as follows:

$$dP(x_1 x_2) = \frac{a'\sigma_1 \sqrt{1-r^2}}{2\pi\sigma_2} e^{-\frac{a'\sigma_1^2}{2}\left(\frac{x_1^2}{\sigma_1^2} - 2r\frac{x_1 x_2}{\sigma_1 \sigma_2} + \frac{x_2^2}{\sigma_2^2}\right)} dx_1\, dx_2 \qquad (20)$$

The double sum $\iint dP(x_1 x_2) = 1$, however, so that, from Eq. (20), it follows that

$$\int\int \frac{\sigma_1 \sqrt{1-r^2}}{2\pi\sigma_2} e^{-\frac{a'\sigma_1^2}{2}\left(\frac{x_1^2}{\sigma_1^2} - 2r\frac{x_1 x_2}{\sigma_1 \sigma_2} + \frac{x_2^2}{\sigma_2^2}\right)} dx_1\, dx_2 = \frac{1}{a'} \qquad (21)$$

If both sides of Eq. (21) are differentiated with respect to a', it is found that

$$-\int\int \frac{\sigma_1 \sqrt{1-r^2}}{2\pi\sigma_2} e^{-\frac{a'\sigma_1^2}{2}\left(\frac{x_1^2}{\sigma_1^2} - 2r\frac{x_1 x_2}{\sigma_1 \sigma_2} + \frac{x_2^2}{\sigma_2^2}\right)}$$
$$\left[\frac{\sigma_1^2}{2}\left(\frac{x_1^2}{\sigma_1^2} - 2r\frac{x_1 x_2}{\sigma_1 \sigma_2} + \frac{x_2^2}{\sigma_2^2}\right)\right] dx_1\, dx_2 = -\frac{1}{(a')^2}$$

Multiplication of both sides by $-a'$ and expansion of terms then give the following:

$$\int\int \left(\frac{x_1^2}{2}\right) \frac{a'\sigma_1 \sqrt{1-r^2}}{2\pi\sigma_2} e^{-\frac{a'\sigma_1^2}{2}\left(\frac{x_1^2}{\sigma_1^2} - 2r\frac{x_1 x_2}{\sigma_1 \sigma_2} + \frac{x_2^2}{\sigma_2^2}\right)} dx_1\, dx_2$$
$$-\int\int \left(r\frac{\sigma_1}{\sigma_2} x_1 x_2\right) \frac{a'\sigma_1 \sqrt{1-r^2}}{2\pi\sigma_2} e^{-\frac{a'\sigma_1^2}{2}\left(\frac{x_1^2}{\sigma_1^2} - 2r\frac{x_1 x_2}{\sigma_1 \sigma_2} + \frac{x_2^2}{\sigma_2^2}\right)} dx_1\, dx_2$$
$$+\int\int \left(\frac{\sigma_1^2}{2\sigma_2^2} x_2^2\right) \frac{a'\sigma_1 \sqrt{1-r^2}}{2\pi\sigma_2} e^{-\frac{a'\sigma_1^2}{2}\left(\frac{x_1^2}{\sigma_1^2} - 2r\frac{x_1 x_2}{\sigma_1 \sigma_2} + \frac{x_2^2}{\sigma_2^2}\right)} dx_1\, dx_2 = \frac{1}{a'}$$

But the left side is equal to

$$\frac{1}{2}\int\int x_1^2 dP(x_1 x_2) - r\frac{\sigma_1}{\sigma_2}\int\int x_1 x_2 dP(x_1 x_2) + \frac{\sigma_1^2}{2\sigma_2^2}\int\int x_2^2 dP(x_1 x_2)$$

which, according to Eqs. (iv) to (vi), is equal to

$$\frac{1}{2}(\sigma_1^2) - r\frac{\sigma_1}{\sigma_2}(r\sigma_1\sigma_2) + \frac{\sigma_1^2}{2\sigma_2^2}(\sigma_2^2) = \sigma_1^2(1 - r^2)$$

Hence,

$$\sigma_1^2(1 - r^2) = \frac{1}{a'} \qquad \text{or} \qquad a' = \frac{1}{\sigma_1^2(1 - r^2)}$$

If this value of a' is substituted in Eq. (20), it will give an equation in which all the parameters have been evaluted in terms of the moments as follows:

$$dP(x_1 x_2) = \frac{1}{2\pi\sigma_1\sigma_2 \sqrt{1-r^2}} e^{-\frac{1}{2(1-r^2)}\left(\frac{x_1^2}{\sigma_1^2} - 2r\frac{x_1 x_2}{\sigma_1 \sigma_2} + \frac{x_2^2}{\sigma_2^2}\right)} dx_1\, dx_2 \qquad (22)$$

PART V

Study of Dynamic Variability

CHAPTER XIX
INDEX NUMBERS

One of the most widely used statistical methods is the procedure that gives rise to the summarizing or expression of data in the form of index numbers. It is an application to a practical problem of simple principles of ready comparison, principles of averaging to obtain summary figures, and principles of stratified sampling. Today, the method of index numbers is applied in five large fields, as follows:

1. The measurement of the general price level, or the measurement of general exchange value.

2. The measurement of groups of prices, such as wholesale prices, retail prices, or wages.

3. The measurement of the general quantity of production or trade with indexes of physical production, trade, or employment.

4. The measurement of the general volume of business or trade with indexes of the value of production or trade, or with so-called "barometers."

5. Miscellaneous, including a wide variety of uses, some of which are given below on pages 511–513.

History of Index Numbers. General use of the device known as an "index number" to serve as a comprehensive method of summarization is of recent origin. Like most of the modern technique of statistics it has been developed since 1900. But the fundamental idea is an old one. According to Warren and Pearson, as early as 1738 Dutot made price comparisons showing that a group of representative commodities cost twelve times as much in 1735 as they did in 1508.[1] In 1764, an Italian, G. R.

---

[1] WARREN, GEORGE F., and FRANK A. PEARSON, *Prices* (1933), pp. 18–20, containing other interesting examples of attempts to measure changes in general price level prior to the middle of the nineteenth century.

Carli, attempted an investigation into the effect of the discovery of America upon the purchasing power of money; he constructed a very simple index number of prices, using only three commodities, grain, wine, and oil. He combined the prices of these three commodities in order to compare their average level in 1750 with the level of the same commodities in 1500.* The gold movement from the New World to European countries aroused speculation throughout the mercantile period with respect to the relationship between prices and the amount of money in circulation. Locke and Hume laid the groundwork for the statement of what is now known as the quantity theory of money. Speculations of the seventeenth and eighteenth centuries, however, with the exception of Carli's unusual attempt, were without the assistance of any measurement of the general price level.

Concern about the problem was brought to a new height during the Napoleonic Wars, when prices were fluctuating widely; and again during and following the Greenback era in the United States the question of the relationship between the general price level and the money supply became associated with inflationary issue of paper money. In the decade preceding the Civil War the discoveries of gold in California served to arouse interest in the question of the effect of increased supplies of gold upon the general price level.

Twentieth-century economists, already interested in the quantity theory of money by reason of the accumulation of these historical experiences, were provoked to continued and diligent study by the development of the South African gold mines since the 1890's, accompanying world-wide general rising prices until the First World War. During the First World War and the subsequent period of maladjustment, with countries all over the world alternately on and off the gold standard, speculation in monetary theory became of such general interest that the problem preoccupied some economists almost to the exclusion of other fields of study.

Meanwhile the statistical technique of measuring general price change by the index-number device was developed; by 1798,

* MITCHELL, WESLEY C., "Index Numbers of Wholesale Prices in the United States and Foreign Countries," Bureau of Labor Statistics, *Bulletin* 284, p. 7; *cf.* also reprint of Part I, "The Making and Using of Index Numbers," *Bulletin* 656 (1938), p. 7.

Sir George Schuckburg-Evelyn formulated a plan for making index numbers of prices.[1] The efforts of the early statisticians in this direction were accorded but scant approval by the economists, who were apparently suspicious of "political arithmetic." Ricardo said that it is impossible to determine "the value of a currency" by its "relation not to one, but to the mass of commodities."[2] Early in the nineteenth century mathematicians were more interested in the application of the theory of probabilities in the fields of astronomy, biology, anthropology, and geology. The great exponents of the developing technique in the application of statistical theory to the social sciences, such as Quételet, were busy with problems in the realm of ethics and morals; but about the middle of the nineteenth century came powerful support for the application of these principles to economic statistics.

William Stanley Jevons claimed that the works of Quételet abundantly proved that many subjects in the social sciences are so hopelessly intricate that they can be analyzed only by the use of averages and by trusting to probabilities as the form of generalization. He constructed indexes of wholesale prices in order to measure the value of gold and invoked the theory of probabilities as justification of his claim that the rise in prices was connected with the change in the value of gold, saying that "the odds are 10,000 to 1 against a series of disconnected and casual circumstances having caused the rise of prices—one in the case of one commodity, another in the case of another—instead of some general cause acting over them all." The general cause acting over them all was considered to be the change in the value of gold.[3]

In 1887 Prof. F. Y. Edgeworth began a series of contributions to the problem of index numbers as a method of summarizing trends in price statistics. He brought to bear upon the field of the social sciences the mathematical theory of probability. He saw clearly that it is a problem of applying a strictly a priori

[1] "An Account of Some Endeavors to Ascertain a Standard of Weight and Measure," *Philosophical Transactions of the Royal Society of London*, Part I, Art. viii, pp. 132–185; citation from Wesley C. Mitchell, *Business Cycles—The Problem and Its Setting* (1928), p. 191.

[2] *Ibid.*, p. 193.

[3] *Ibid.*, p. 195.

theory to an analogous situation, but he insisted that the theory of probability applied.[1]   Later, the theoretical application of probabilities to the problem of measuring social phenomena, and particularly the general price level, was taken up by C. M. Walsh, who published in 1901 a treatise on the measurement of the price level and later published a book entitled *The Problem of Estimation*, which further developed the application of probability theory to economics.[2]

Since about 1915 the important problem of the technique of index-number construction has been attacked by a number of scholars.   Prof. Wesley C. Mitchell was a pioneer in the exploration of the technical problems involved and a major part of their solution; others have done important work of this character during recent years, especially the economists and statisticians in government or semigovernment agencies, such as the Bureau of Labor Statistics and the Federal Reserve Board.

Interpretation of the problems involved in the making of index numbers may be facilitated by analysis of two of the main principles involved: (1) the concepts of absolutes vs. relatives, and (2) the application of the theory of stratified sampling to the particular problem of the making of an index number.

Conversion of Absolute Numbers to Relative Numbers. *Absolutes.*   An absolute is an expression of the number of things being considered, measured by an appropriate unit, as 1,000 bushels of wheat or 50 acres of land.   A simple absolute taken by itself is of little importance.   The number of people in a country is of no particular significance unless a comparison is desired, for example, a comparison with the natural resources of the country or with the population at some other point in time or in some other country.

Prices are ordinarily conceived of as absolutes; that is, saying that the price of wheat today is one dollar a bushel refers to the objective thing, namely, the concrete one dollar.   It is true that this particular absolute has a ratio aspect when it is thought of

[1] PERSONS, W. M., "Statistics and Economic Theory," *Review of Economic Statistics*, Vol. **7**, (1925), pp. 185–186.   Also cited in Wesley C. Mitchell, *Business Cycles—The Problem and Its Setting*, (1928), p. 197.

[2] *The Measurement of General Exchange-Value*, pp. 553–574, cited in Wesley C. Mitchell, "Index Numbers of Wholesale Prices in the United States and Foreign Countries," Bureau of Labor Statistics, p. 9.

as a measure of the value of wheat. But when thought of merely as one of the goods in an exchange, the dollar can rationally be considered to be an absolute. Prices accordingly are referred to as "absolutes."

Relatives. In tabular form a ready visualization is often accomplished by converting absolutes to relatives of some selected base. For example Table 63 shows data on three important types of productive activity in the United States.

TABLE 63.—ESTIMATED VALUE OF SELECTED TYPES OF PRIVATE CONSTRUCTION ACTIVITY IN THE UNITED STATES

Years	New factory construction		Farm construction		New nonfarm residential construction	
	Millions of dollars	Index*	Millions of dollars	Index*	Millions of dollars	Index*
Annual average 1926–1929	640	100	468	100	4,066	100
1932	78	12	125	27	641	16
1933	128	20	175	37	314	8
1937	391	61	360	77	1,530	38
1938	192	30	345	74	1,515	37
1939	200	31	340	73	1,860	46
1940	337	53	360	77	2,077	51

Source: *Survey of Current Business*, Vol. 21 (February, 1941), p. 21.
* Each index is on the base, average 1926–1929 = 100.

Considerable difficulty is encountered in obtaining a clear mental picture of the comparative changes in these three series by study of the absolutes themselves. Was the decline in new factory construction more severe in the 1932–1933 depression than the falling off in new residential construction? Did farm construction suffer more severely than new residential nonfarm construction? Such questions, involving comparative judgments, can be answered much more quickly if each series is converted into relatives or simple indexes upon a common base period. This is illustrated in Table 63, in the columns presenting the indexes with average 1926–1929 as the base.

Simple index numbers, or relatives, of this sort involve the notion of comparing with unity. The mind more readily grasps expressions in round numbers than in odd numbers; it further reduces mental effort if the round numbers are in multiples of 10. From this fact arises the practice of relating prices or other quantity figures or absolutes of any kind to each other in such a way as to get a comparison based upon 1, 10, 100, 1,000, etc. If based upon 1, they are called "proportions"; if based upon 100, they are called "percentages." They are all relatives, or indexes. Most commonly in the United States and in Great Britain and many other countries, 100 is used, although a few, notably Australia, use 1,000.

Even where there is but one price series, it is simpler to comprehend the significance of change if the absolute prices are converted to a relative form. For example, the changes in price of coffee per pound, as shown in Table 64, are easier to trace from period to period when expressed in relatives. Thus,

TABLE 64.—PRICE OF COFFEE
Annual averages in New York market of No. 7 Rio coffee
(In dollars per pound)

Item	Symbol	1926	1933	1934	1941
Price, lb............	p	0.182	0.078	0.098	0.080
Relative............	$(100/0.182)p$	100	43	54	44

Source: Bureau of Labor Statistics, *Wholesale Prices* (June and December issues of specified years).

let 1926 be considered 100 and the prices in other years related to it. The arithmetic involved is simple in principle and contains two steps: (1) dividing the series throughout by the base selected, which may more conveniently be done by multiplying throughout by the reciprocal of the base and (2) multiplying by 100. This method, illustrated in Table 64, makes the figure for the base period equal to 100, and the rest fluctuate as percentages of the base.

Another elementary idea is involved in the making of relatives, and that is the reduction of nonhomogeneous sets of figures to a homogeneous base for purposes of comparison and to simplify interpretation of relative change among nonhomogeneous things. For example, the prices of coffee per pound at different times, the prices of canned peaches per dozen cans, and the prices of wheat per bushel are all three presented in Table 65 for comparison with each other.

It is difficult to compare the price of coffee per pound with the price of wheat per bushel on the one hand and with the price of canned peaches per dozen cans on the other, as they fluctuate from time to time; but if all are changed to relative numbers, by the method already described, with 1926 as a base period, the comparison may easily be made. This is illustrated in Table 66.

TABLE 65.—PRICES OF COFFEE, CANNED PEACHES, AND WHEAT[1]

Item	1926	1933	1934	1941
Coffee........................	0.182	0.078	0.098	0.080
Canned peaches..............	1.993	1.146	1.403	1.528
Wheat.......................	1.496	0.724	0.932	0.993

Source: Bureau of Labor Statistics, *Wholesale Prices.*
[1] Prices of canned peaches are annual averages, quoted in dollars per dozen cans; prices of wheat are of No. 2 hard, Kansas City, quoted in dollars per bushel.

Relatives Using a Base Period in a Time Series. Price relatives, and the relatives shown in Tables 65 and 66, illustrate relatives using a base period in a time series. Three fundamental precautions must be observed in the use of such relatives.

TABLE 66.—PRICE RELATIVES OF COFFEE, CANNED PEACHES, AND WHEAT
Average 1926 = 100

Item	1926	1933	1934	1941
Coffee.................................	100	43	54	44
Canned peaches........................	100	58	70	77
Wheat.................................	100	48	62	66

1. It is almost always advisable and sometimes it is necessary to know the absolute figures as well as the relatives—else misinterpretation or even misrepresentation is likely to result. A classic example of a use of relatives that produced misinterpretation and may perhaps have even been intended to be misrepresentation was the evidence presented in 1932 by some notable protectionist "statesmen" in the United States Congress. Following are some of the statistics they issued for public consumption:

TABLE 67.—SOME OF THE LARGE INCREASES IN IMPORTS DURING THE FIRST
8 MONTHS OF 1932
(In percentages)

Commodity	Percentage Increase in Imports
Cod and other salt and pickled fish from Denmark...	3,729.8
Salmon, fresh or frozen, from Japan...............	2,511.8
Fish in airtight containers from Canada...........	4,669.9
Cheese from Denmark.............................	136.3
Wrapping paper (other than kraft) from Sweden....	615.9
Pig iron from Sweden.............................	181.0
Pig iron from the United Kingdom................	611.3
Wool and other yarns from the United Kingdom....	221.2
Long-staple cotton from Egypt and British India, but transshipped from the United Kingdom:	
Egypt..	1,283.1
British India...................................	1,128.1
From Canada, fresh pork........................	237.9
Dried peas from New Zealand....................	477.3

The purpose of these statistics was to prove that a veritable flood of foreign goods was threatening to inundate this country, put out of business all its domestic producers, and lower the wages of domestic workers. But the statistics are not what they seem to be. Some of the items were so very small in the aggregate in January, 1932 (the date they began to increase according to the table), that they were not even listed in the extensive classified list of imports that is published monthly by the Department of Commerce. If an exceedingly small item is increased by 1,000 per cent, it is still small. Each time it increases 1,000 per cent, it is only eleven times as large as before; 2,000 per cent means twenty-one times as large. In January, 1932, the amount of pig iron imported into the United States from Sweden and the United Kingdom combined was less than 460 tons, worth about $4,500, which, compared with United States domestic production, was a mere nothing. The imports in January, 1932, of wrapping paper other than kraft from Sweden amounted to $2,025. The imports in the same month of Egyptian cotton, transshipped from the United Kingdom, amounted to $982. The last item is particularly enlightening; it will be noted that the specification "transshipped from the United Kingdom" is carefully made. Most cotton of this type comes to the United States directly from Egypt and is not essentially competitive with American-grown cotton.

2. The meaning of a percentage figure is often ambiguous, and study of its background is necessary before it can be properly understood. An illustration of the misinterpretation of a percentage figure can again be found in the arguments of American protectionists. When it is alleged that our tariffs are already too high, the protectionists like to reply that they are not too high. To prove their statement they point to the fact that a large percentage of the imports are on the "free list," that is, that a large proportion of imports into the United States are charged no duty at all. This argument sounds plausible, but its *non sequitur* quality becomes evident when it is realized that the tariffs on dutiable goods are so high that they are virtually excluded from entering; it is thus the virtual exclusion of certain dutiable imports that causes a large proportion of imports to be goods on the free list. If the entire 100 per cent of imports were on the free list, it would mean, not that the tariff was not high, but that the tariff was so high that none of the dutiable goods could come in.

3. In a series of coordinate relatives, it is necessary to know the base and to specify it for the information of others. For example, death-rate figures are quite meaningless unless the comparison is known. The death rate may be expressed as so many deaths per 1,000 people or per 100 people, and the statistician should indicate which comparison is made. Death rates for a given disease may be expressed as the number of deaths per 1,000 people afflicted by the disease rather than as the number of deaths per 1,000 people whether exposed to it or not; again, the nature of the comparison should be specified.

In simple index numbers like those given as examples in Tables 64 and 66, it is essential to know that the base is 1926 or the average of 1926–1929, as the case may be. This should always be indicated somewhere in the title or subcaptions of the table or in a footnote.

Presumption of Normality in the Selected Base. When a series of coordinate relatives is constructed by relating a series of absolutes to some selected base, the base tends to be regarded as the normal level. Indexes in the series greater than 100 are looked upon as above normal, or above par, and indexes less than 100 are looked upon as below normal. Since this tendency exists, it is always desirable to give study to the matter of selecting the base.   Is it in fact the one that is at normal level, or is one of the other absolutes of the series at normal level?

For example, in the illustration given in Table 63, should the annual average of new factory construction, 1926–1929, be regarded as normal?   Was there, on the average, a normal amount of new nonfarm residential construction in those years? It might reasonably be argued that taking 3 years as a base is better than taking only 1 year, because an average of 3 years might tend to offset extreme fluctuations and produce comparisons that would tend to be better than if only 1 year were used as a base.   Thus the average of the 3 years might be about normal for each of the three types of construction compared, whereas if only 1 year were taken one or the other of the three types might have had an exceptionally high or low year.

On the other hand, it may be pointed out that the years 1926–1929 covered a range of years in which a great construction boom reached its peak.   Consequently, all types of construction were above normal in all three of those years; some writers claim this was the peak of the greatest and longest construction boom in history.   Construction was at a high level such as it might not be expected to reach again for many years, at least if the length of construction booms is some seventeen years from peak to peak, as some say it is.   It may therefore be argued that 1937 would be a better base to take, even if only 1 year is used. In that year the general level of economic activity seemed to be nearer to a normal or equilibrium than any other year in recent history, and certainly nearer normal than the boom year of 1929.   But the year 1937 would be a poor base year for strike statistics because of the great disturbances in the coal industry in that year.

Selection of the base has an important effect upon subsequent judgments as to the trends of the three series.   If the average 1926–1929 is taken as the base, all three of the construction activities were still below normal in the year 1940, as the indexes in Table 63 show; but if 1937 is taken as the base, the 1940 level of new factory construction would be 86, the 1940 level of farm construction would be 100, and the level of new nonfarm residential construction would be 136.   If 1937 is considered normal, in the years 1926–1929 new factory construction averaged 63 per cent above normal, farm construction averaged 30 per cent above normal, and new nonfarm residential construction was 166 per cent above normal.

The data shown in Table 64 and the indexes presented in Tables 65 and 68 may also be used to illustrate the effect of the base selected. In Table 66 and Fig. 133, the year 1926 is the base and the prices of coffee, canned peaches, and wheat are each set at 100 in that year; subsequent years are indexed accordingly. From 1926 to 1933 the greatest decline occurred in the price of coffee, the next greatest occurred in the price of canned peaches, and the decline in the price of wheat was com-

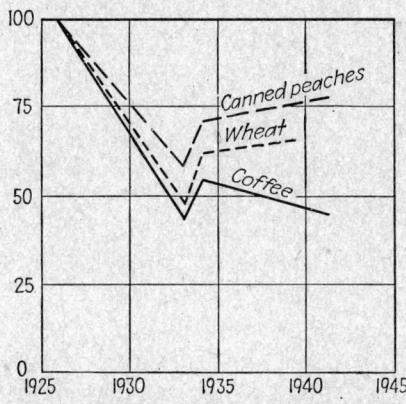

Fig. 133.—Indexes of prices of wheat, canned peaches, and coffee. 1926 = 100.

paratively the least. Their relative recovery was in the same order, and all three were below normal in 1941.

But if it is considered that they were at normal levels in 1941 so that all are called 100 for that year, a quite different picture is obtained, as shown in Table 68 and Fig. 134. If these prices

TABLE 68.—PRICE RELATIVES OF COFFEE, CANNED PEACHES, AND WHEAT
1941 = 100

Item	1926	1933	1934	1941
Coffee.....................................	228	98	122	100
Canned peaches.........................	130	75	92	100
Wheat..................................	151	73	94	100

were normally related to each other in 1941, then in 1926 the price of coffee was more than twice normal, the price of wheat was well above 50 per cent over normal, and the price of canned peaches was 30 per cent over normal. Moreover, Fig. 134 and Table 68 seem to indicate that it was the price of canned peaches that was farthest below normal in 1933; the price of coffee was only slightly below normal.

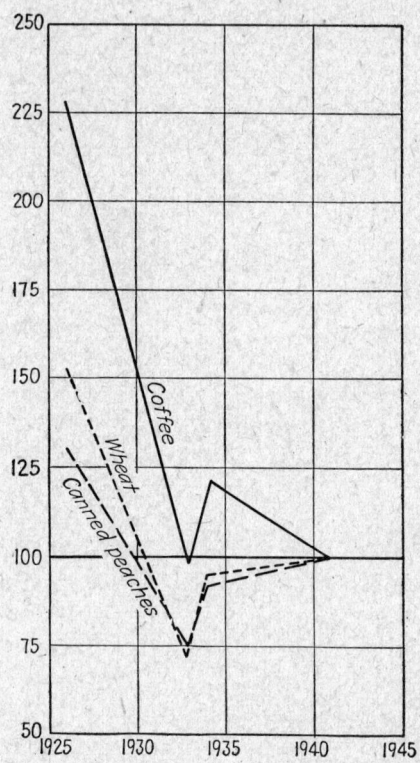

Fig. 134.—Indexes of prices of coffee, canned peaches, and wheat.   1940 = 100.

For most comparisons, a year too remote in the past is not a desirable base. For a long time, 1913, or an average of the years 1909–1914, was looked upon as the best base period to use, because it was the last normal period before the First World War. The farm bloc in Congress continued as late as 1941 to insist that farm prices should be permitted to rise to the par that existed before the First World War; but in 1941–1942, as farm prices began to rise at a more rapid rate than other prices so that they passed parity, the farm bloc began to insist upon a new definition of parity. The long survival of 1909–1914 as a base illustrates, not the general desirability of having a remote base period, but merely the power of the farm bloc. Ordinarily, general economic change over a 28-year period is sufficiently great to make such a base undesirable.

In the 1920's, accordingly, most comparisons came to be made, not with prewar 1913, but with the average of 1923–1925 or with the single year 1926; these years persisted as a base period much longer than might ordinarily be expected because the extreme decline of the depression of the early 1930's made it difficult to select a new base period. Finally, however, as the years of the Second World War passed, the period immediately preceding it came to be regarded as the best base for current comparisons. In the early 1940's the average for the years 1935–1939, or one of those years, began to be adopted as the base period.[1]

Relative Parts of a Whole. A single absolute quantity is often divided into several parts, and these several parts are expressed as percentages or proportions of the whole. These are properly called, not "index numbers," but simply "relatives," although they could be referred to as "constituent relatives." The term index numbers, used with strict propriety, refers to a series of relatives that is a composite of a more or less large number of series of relative numbers. The series of relatives may be combined to form a series of index numbers by any one of a number of methods of aggregating or averaging, as will be explained later in this chapter. Accordingly, in strict usage when an index is an average of relatives, the term relative should be reserved for the separate ingredients and the term index should

---

[1] In the *Survey of Current Business*, Vol. 22 (November, 1942), the index of prices received by farmers was still reported on the base of the average of 1909–1914 prices, the index of wholesale prices was still based on the 1926 average, and the index of retail prices was based on the average for 1923–1925; but the cost-of-living index was based on the average 1935–1939, and the indexes of the purchasing power of the dollar (wholesale, retail, and farm) were based upon the 1935–1939 average. The indexes of national income and industrial production were on the average 1935–1939 base. The index of some manufacturing data, such as orders, shipments, and inventories, were based upon the averages for the single year 1939. The *Survey of Current Business*, Vol. 22 (December, 1942) published the Bureau of Labor Statistics indexes of wage-earner employment and weekly wages in manufacturing industries, revised, with the average of the year 1939 as the base.

be used for the composite.   Yet this distinction is often honored in the breach as well as in the observance, and the student must expect to find the term index used in place of relative.

An important item to remember in the use of constituent relatives is that a relative increase or decrease does not necessarily mean an absolute increase or decrease in the subgroup. The absolute of the subgroup may, indeed, move in the opposite direction from that indicated by the relative figures.   Constituent relatives are useful when it is required to see clearly the relative changes.   If absolute changes are desired, the raw data must be examined.   Table 69 is an example of the use of constituent relatives.   It reveals the necessity of attention to the absolute as well as the relative figures.

TABLE 69.—DEATH RATES PER 100,000 POLICYHOLDERS FROM SELECTED CAUSES

Weekly premium-paying industrial business, Metropolitan Life Insurance Company

Specified causes of death	Annual rate per 100,000*			Percentage distribution of specified causes		
	1940	1941	1942	1940	1941	1942
All....................	531.6	553.9	501.6	100.00	100.00	100.00
Diabetes mellitus..............	31.1	33.8	30.2	5.85	6.10	6.02
Appendicitis....................	8.6	7.6	5.4	1.62	1.37	1.08
Influenza and pneumonia........	74.5	79.5	47.2	14.01	14.35	9.41
Tuberculosis (all forms)..........	44.9	44.0	41.9	8.45	7.94	8.35
Syphilis.......................	12.4	11.0	10.0	2.33	1.98	1.99
Cancer (all forms)..............	102.1	103.8	102.2	19.21	18.74	20.37
Diseases of the heart...........	233.3	245.9	236.7	43.89	44.39	47.19
Motor-vehicle accidents..........	17.2	20.2	21.3	3.24	3.65	4.25
Suicides.......................	7.5	8.1	6.7	1.41	1.46	1.34

Source: Metropolitan Life Insurance Company, *Statistical Bulletin*, March, 1942, p. 11.
* Policyholders, based upon first 3 months of each year.

In order to illustrate the necessity of presenting the absolute figures as well as relative figures when constituent relatives are used, Table 70 is drawn up with a few items taken from Table 69. Study of the percentage distribution shown in Table 70 would appear to indicate that the death rate from suicides increased between the years 1940 and 1942.   Actually, it decreased. Merely its relative position became more important.   The percentage distribution, in the absence of attention to the absolute figures, would also lead to a tendency to exaggerate the rise in the death rate from automobile accidents. These misleading results are due to the change in the size of the totals for the respective years considered—from 107.8 in 1940 to 115.4 in 1941 and to 80.8 in 1942.

TABLE 70.—DEATH RATE PER 100,000 POLICYHOLDERS FROM SELECTED CAUSES

Weekly premium-paying industrial business, Metropolitan Life Insurance Company

Specified causes of death	Annual rate[1]			Percentage distribution of specified causes		
	1940	1941	1942	1940	1941	1942
All................................	107.8	115.4	80.8	100.00	100.00	100.00
Influenza and pneumonia......... ...	74.5	79.5	47.2	69.11	68.89	58.56
Appendicitis....................	8.6	7.6	5.4	7.97	6.59	6.70
Suicides........................	7.5	8.1	6.7	6.96	7.02	8.31
Motor-vehicle accidents..........	17.2	20.2	21.3	15.96	17.50	26.43

[1] Per 100,000 policyholders, based upon first 3 months of each year.

Especially when a small number of rates are being considered, as in Table 70, it is necessary to study both the rates and the percentage distribution. Actually, the study of rates is required to answer the question: Is the rate from suicides greater in 1942 than in 1941? Study of the percentage distribution of specified causes is required to answer the questions: In 1942 were motor-vehicle accidents a more important cause of death than influenza and pneumonia combined? Did motor-vehicle accidents become relatively more important from 1940 to 1942 as compared with the other specified causes? Important questions are answered by each of the sets of figures; what is necessary to avoid is the use of the wrong set of figures to answer a given question.

Great Variety of Simple Index Numbers in Use. Hundreds of simple index numbers are in use, and the number has been increasing rapidly since the First World War. Indexes of the simple type illustrated in Tables 63, 65, and 68 exist for nearly every separate industrial activity, for thousands of prices, for retail sales, wholesale sales, inventories, consumption of certain types of goods, and for many other things related to economic

and social activity. Index numbers measuring production
from month to month in a large list of industries have been compiled and published by the Board of Governors of the Federal
Reserve System and other agencies. Indexes of marketing of
fish, dairy products, livestock, wool, and poultry and eggs have
been compiled by the Bureau of Foreign and Domestic Commerce;
and indexes of the marketing of cotton, fruits, grains and vegetables, lumber, and other natural products are compiled by the
same bureau. This bureau has also compiled and published a
large number of simple relative figures for new orders and unfilled
orders in a number of manufacturing industries, including iron
and steel, paper, lumber, textiles; and another series of index
numbers of commodity stocks of manufactured goods and of raw
materials, such as chemicals, foodstuffs, metals, textile materials,
and rubber products. These indexes are published currently in
the *Current Survey of Business* by the United States Department
of Commerce. In the League of Nations publications, indexes of
world stocks of foodstuffs and certain raw materials are available.

The United States Department of Commerce has recently
begun the compilation and publication of indexes of transportation for the United States. These monthly indexes include a
combined index of all types of transportation, commodity and
passenger, and also indexes by types of transportation, such as
an index of air transportation and a combined index of intercity
motorbus and truck transportation. The indexes are published
monthly with the base period 1935–1939 = 100 and appear in
the *Survey of Current Business*.[1] This publication contains
other illustrations of the many uses of index numbers.

The use of either subordinate or coordinate relatives to aid
in the interpretation of series of data does not involve the application of the theory of statistics or the principles of sampling,
although the gathering of the raw data may have involved the
use of the latter. The rules of comparability must be considered
when numbers are converted into relatives, however, as indicated in the discussion above. When a whole series of these
simple index numbers, or relatives, are combined into a composite index number, it is necessary to make application of the

[1] The transportation indexes are described in the *Survey of Current
Business*, Vol. 22 (September, 1942), pp. 20–28; Vol. 23 (May, 1943), pp.
26–27.

theory of statistics. The principles of stratified sampling apply to the construction of these composite index numbers.

Index Numbers. *Application of Sampling Technique.* Index numbers are combinations of a large number of single series of relatives by some method of aggregating or averaging. In the field of prices, indexes of farm prices, of cost of living, of retail prices, of wholesale prices, of wages, and of exchange rates are some of the index numbers obtainable. Also, indexes of industrial production, of trade activity, of retail trade, and of employment are found in various sources. All these indexes are combinations of numerous series of relatives.

From consideration of the various purposes for which index numbers may be used, it should immediately be apparent that a difficulty is involved. How, for example, is it possible to get together all the facts in the United States regarding all wholesale prices from time to time, or all wages, or all retail prices, or all production or consumption activities? The answer, of course, is that it is not possible, or certainly not feasible, but that a sample of some kind must be used. When a composite is made up of several series, how shall they be weighted? Should they be considered of equal importance, and if not how shall their relative importance be determined in making up the composite? It is upon the basis of the principles of sampling that such index numbers are justified. As Prof. Edgeworth once said, the task is to extricate from fallible observations a mean apt to represent the general trend of prices, wages, production, or whatever is being measured.[1]

The demonstration by eighteenth- and nineteenth-century statisticians, such as Süssmilch and Quételet, that a hitherto unsuspected regularity lay hidden in numerical data about social phenomena encouraged economists and social scientists in the belief that known variations that had been measured might be fair samples of the more numerous unknown variations. Furthermore, the construction of a great variety of composite index numbers by different investigators using different methods has produced results of such consistency as to inspire confidence in their use.[2]

[1] *Cf.* MITCHELL, WESLEY C., *Business Cycles—The Problem and Its Setting* (1928), p. 204.

[2] *Cf.* MITCHELL, WESLEY C., "Index Numbers of Wholesale Prices in the

To grasp the significance of an index number, it is not sufficient to have reference only to the summary picture it presents. Just as in the case of an average of one frequency distribution, so in the case of index numbers, the distribution of cases is of great importance. An index number is really a series of averages based upon a series of frequency distributions—one frequency distribution for each time period—of which the index number itself is an average of some sort. A study based upon this idea was made by Wesley C. Mitchell in his analysis of year-to-year fluctuations of the prices recorded in the wholesale price bulletins of the Bureau of Labor Statistics, covering prices from 1891 to 1918 and including 232 to 348 commodities. He found that the price changes from year to year formed a fairly symmetrical frequency distribution each year, and hence he concluded that "when it can be shown that phenomena are distributed approximately in this fashion, their average can safely be accepted as a significant measure of the whole set of variations, since even the deviations from the average are then grouped in a tolerably definite and symmetrical fashion about the average."[1]

Such an analysis seemed to establish as satisfactory the use of an average to summarize price change from year to year; but index numbers frequently extend over a considerable period of time so that the general level of wholesale prices of 1942, for example, is compared with 1926 as a base or with 1935–1939. Year-to-year fluctuations may occur in a manner such that the average may be used to summarize; but what of change compared with some year more remote in the past? In order to test the reliability of the method of index-number construction in this regard, Prof. Wesley C. Mitchell applied the technique of taking several samples; in one sample he took 242 commodities, in another 50 commodities, and in a third sample 25 commodities at wholesale prices and constructed three sample index numbers for the period 1890–1913. He found that the results from the smaller samples were strikingly close to those of the larger sample.[2]

United States and Foreign Countries," Bureau of Labor Statistics, *Bulletin* 284, p. 11.

[1] *Ibid.*, pp. 17–18.

[2] *Ibid.*, p. 38. The theory of sampling errors does not apply in a way that makes possible mathematical tests from a single sample.

Stratified Sampling Method Applied. Others have also found that whenever the principles of stratified sampling have been followed in the construction of index numbers of wholesale prices, the results obtained are similar to the results obtained by the use of all available data. This inspired confidence in index numbers extending back through the years, for which fewer price series are available in published records, and at the same time increased the belief that such an average expression of prices in the form of index numbers is a valid summary picture of general price change.

It is upon the basis of the principle of stratified sampling that it is possible to measure by index numbers, such things as the cost of living, or the volume of production, or the general wholesale price level. Also, it is upon the basis of the theory of sampling that credence can be given to index numbers; in addition, it is due to this very fact that it is necessary to examine the constituent parts of an index number to be sure that it measures what it purports to measure and that it is applicable to any particular problem for which it is desired to use an index number.

It is necessary to notice that stratified sampling is applied to the making of index numbers. For example, take the problem of measuring general price movement. This is not a case in which there is an infinite number of items, although the universe is a very large number, and the number for which data are given is probably less than the number for which data are unavailable, particularly in the case of retail prices or wages. In the case of wholesale prices the available data cover a larger portion of the universe.

Not only is there not an infinite number of items, but the number of available items is often not a very large one. For example, some index numbers are based upon less than 50 individual index-number series. However, the universe from which the items are taken is one concerning which a priori knowledge exists. According to such a priori knowledge, a representative sample can be obtained by a conscious or deliberate proportional selection of items from the various known strata of the universe. For example, it is known, in the case of wholesale prices, that the universe is made up of prices of foods, prices of metals, prices of forest products, prices of various raw materials, prices of semimanufactured products in a number of fields that can be classified, and prices of final goods at wholesale, to enumerate a few of the known strata of this universe. Knowing that such strata exist in the universe, the sample can be made proportional by a deliberate stratified random sampling procedure that would ensure proper representation in the sample of all the various strata known to exist in the universe.[1]

Variety of Purposes of Index Numbers. As a historical proposition, the original all-pervading purpose of an index number was to measure general exchange value, that is to say, to explain the relationship between prices, in their general or average movement, and the value of money and credit.

At the present time, however, a large number of general indexes of prices and other phenomena are currently published; but few even of the general price indexes purport to be a measure of the value of money. General indexes of retail prices, indexes of wages and pay-roll totals, indexes of prices of farm prices, metal products, manufactured goods, and raw materials, as well as general wholesale prices, are now available. Which of these price indexes really measures the value of money?

Some statisticians and economists have held that a real measure of the changes in the value of money and credit should include, not only wholesale prices, but also wages, rent, and other prices, including retail prices and perhaps the prices of securities. Samples of each kind of price should be included in the index of prices that aims to measure general exchange value. On this theory, Carl Snyder, at that time statistician for the

---

[1] *Cf.* KING, W. I., *Index Numbers Elucidated*, especially pp. 64–66. This, of course, often turns out to be a counsel of perfection in practice. The principle is based upon the assumption that in each of the strata designated the available data can be sampled successfully at random; and in practice this is often not true. For illustration, in gathering prices for an index of wholesale prices such subgroups of prices, or strata, as sulphuric acid and Portland cement are standardized, while house furnishings are not. From the point of view of obtaining the best possible results with the minimum amount of price gathering, and presumably with limited funds for the purpose, it would be sound practice to abandon the counsel of perfection and spend less money gathering prices of standardized articles and more gathering prices of nonstandardized articles. The resulting disproportionate amount of prices in the respective subgroups can then be countered by the required adjustments in the weights used to combine the series of relatives into index numbers.

Federal Reserve Bank of New York, compiled an "index of general price level," including wholesale and retail prices, wages, rents, etc., but for certain reasons he excluded security prices. After careful study, these various components were given certain weights in the general composite. It should be pointed out that this index of general price level was originated for the special purpose of deflating data on bank clearings. Since bank clearings included payments for all these things, Snyder believed that an index of prices based upon these components could be used to cancel out that part of change in total bank clearings due to price change and obtain thereby an index of physical volume of trade. Even if it is granted that this index of general price level is valid as a deflator of bank clearings, it still remains a question whether or not it measures the exchange value of money.

It could be argued with considerable force that such a general measure is impracticable because of the difficulty of getting adequate samples of rents, for example. And in any case, such a general measure of prices does not really give the measure of change in the purchasing power of money. The general purchasing power of money may be a far more flexible and possibly sensitive factor than this general price average would indicate. A general price average would include an overweight of prices largely controlled by custom, or of prices in which resistance to change is very great for some other reason, as, for example, because of public regulation, taxation, or their indirect effects. The true measure of change in general exchange value may be more nearly approximated by the wholesale price index and perhaps even by the group of more sensitive wholesale prices.

It is not the purpose here to carry this argument to a conclusion but merely to suggest its unsettled state. It may be significant that the Bureau of Labor Statistics has published reciprocals of its several indexes of prices—wholesale, retail, cost-of-living, and farm products—as indexes of the purchasing power of the dollar in those respective fields. The question of how to measure general exchange value, or the purchasing power of money, continues to be a controversial one. Meanwhile, index numbers continue to serve enormously useful special purposes whether or not collectively or individually they measure general exchange value. In his *Treatise on Money*, J. M. Keynes appears to suggest that the exchange should be looked upon as a number of relatively noncompeting groups of markets and that there may be no such thing as a general purchasing power of money.[1]

In the light of such theoretical difficulties hindering the proper measurement of the purchasing power of money by using reciprocals of price indexes, recent attempts have been made to construct indexes of the purchasing power of money by other means. One notable contribution is the index of purchasing power constructed by Murray Shields; this combines monetary data, *viz.*, demand deposits, foreign deposits in the United States, foreign bank deposits in Federal reserve banks, volume of money in circulation, and cash in the vaults of commercial banks.[2]

Construction of Index Numbers. *Principal Methods.* Prof. Irving Fisher of Yale University, in a comprehensive study of the mathematics of index-number making, found several hundred kinds of formulas for calculating index numbers; but it is quite unnecessary to be disturbed by this fact, since as he himself says, only a few of them are of any value. There are two principal methods of calculating index numbers now in use and generally recognized as adequate for most purposes, but other methods are occasionally used and will therefore be described. The most commonly used are (1) the weighted average-of-relatives method and (2) the weighted aggregative method. Other methods sometimes used are (3) the simple average-of-relatives method and (4) the simple aggregative method. Various alternative ways of applying these methods are possible. For example, in the case of the simple average of relatives, sometimes the median is used instead of the arithmetical mean in order to avoid extreme variations; it is advisable to use the median especially for very small samples. These methods will be taken up in the order (3), (1), (4), and (2), which is the logical method of treating them, rather than in the order of their prevalence in use, which is that given above.

Simple Average-of-relatives Method. Referring again to the simple case of the prices of coffee, wheat, and canned peaches, already used, perhaps the first method that would suggest itself

---

[1] *Cf.* also BECKHART, B. H., *The New York Money Market*, Vol. 2, and KING, *op. cit.*, pp. 189–216.

[2] "A Measure of Purchasing Power Inflation and Deflation," *Journal of the American Statistical Association*, Vol. 35 (1940), pp. 461–470.

to anyone desiring to obtain a summary figure representing average price change would be to add up the relatives and divide by their number, as follows:

TABLE 71.—COMPOSITE INDEX NUMBER OF THE PRICES OF COFFEE, WHEAT, AND CANNED PEACHES
1926 = 100

Commodity	1926	1933	1941
Coffee	$\dfrac{p_0}{p_0} = 100$	$\dfrac{p_1}{p_0} = 43$	$\dfrac{p_2}{p_0} = 44$
Canned peaches	$\dfrac{p_0'}{p_0'} = 100$	$\dfrac{p_1'}{p_0'} = 58$	$\dfrac{p_2'}{p_0'} = 77$
Wheat	$\dfrac{p_0''}{p_0''} = 100$	$\dfrac{p_1''}{p_0''} = 48$	$\dfrac{p_2''}{p_0''} = 66$
Average	$3)\overline{300}$	$3)\overline{149}$	$3)\overline{187}$
	100	50	62

The resulting composite index number shows that on the average these three prices fell to 50 in 1933 in comparison with 100 in 1926 and then rose on the average to 62 in 1941 in comparison with 100 in 1926. Reducing this method to symbols,
Let p_0, p_1, p_2 represent the prices of coffee.

p_0', p_1', p_2' represent the prices of canned peaches.

p_0'', p_1'', p_2'' represent the prices of wheat.

The relatives that appear in Table 71 are thus shown also in symbols. For example, the ratio p_2''/p_0'' corresponds to 66—in these symbolical presentations the multiple 100 is always "understood" and not actually written in the formula. The averages for the three would be expressed by symbols in Table 72:

TABLE 72

1926	1933	1941
$\dfrac{\dfrac{p_0}{p_0} + \dfrac{p_0'}{p_0'} + \dfrac{p_0''}{p_0''}}{3}$	$\dfrac{\dfrac{p_1}{p_0} + \dfrac{p_1'}{p_0'} + \dfrac{p_1''}{p_0''}}{3}$	$\dfrac{\dfrac{p_2}{p_0} + \dfrac{p_2'}{p_0'} + \dfrac{p_2''}{p_0''}}{3}$

These averages are represented by the letter P, and when N commodity prices are averaged, instead of only three, for n years,

instead of only 3, the series of averages of relatives is represented symbolically as follows:

$$P_{00} = \frac{\sum \frac{p_0}{p_0}}{N} \qquad P_{01} = \frac{\sum \frac{p_1}{p_0}}{N} \; \dots \; P_{0n} = \frac{\sum \frac{p_n}{p_0}}{N} \qquad (1)$$

The capital N refers to the number of prices, and the small subscript n refers to the number of years, or number of time periods,
which might be months or weeks as well as years. In general,
the subscripts to the series of p's represent the time periods, and
0 is assigned to the base time period, at which the relative equals
100. The average of the relatives likewise equals 100 in the
base time period. The primes refer to different commodities.

Weighted Average-of-relatives Method. The simple average of
relatives involves the assumption that changes in the several
prices to be combined are of equal importance; but this may not
be true. Consequently, the idea of weighting the component
price relatives in accordance with weights that are considered to
reflect their relative importance has been developed.

The weights are commonly based upon some rational consideration such as the quantities consumed in a given representative year, the quantities produced, family budget figures, or
some other criterion. Suppose, after considering all available
information on the subject, changes in the price of a pound of
coffee are considered thrice as important as changes in the price
of a dozen cans of peaches and changes in the price of wheat per
bushel are judged twice as important as changes in the price of a
pound of coffee. Convenience of calculation will be attained
if the numbers used as weights are so arranged that they will
sum up to 1, 10, or 100, because the averaging process will then
be a simple matter of changing decimal points in the sum of the
weighted relatives. Such a manipulation of the quantities
representing weights will have no effect on the final answer and
will reduce the amount of work considerably if the problem is a
long one involving, say, several years of monthly indexes. In
the illustration used above, the weights are as follows:

> Coffee, $3 = w$
> Canned peaches, $1 = w'$
> Wheat, $6 = w''$

A weighted average-of-relatives index number of these three commodities would be calculated as illustrated in Table 73.

TABLE 73.—INDEX NUMBER OF THE PRICES OF COFFEE, WHEAT, AND CANNED PEACHES
Weighted average of relatives, 1926 = 100

Commodity	1926	1933	1941
Coffee...................	100 × 3 = 300	43 × 3 = 129	44 × 3 = 132
Canned peaches.........	100 × 1 = 100	58 × 1 = 58	77 × 1 = 77
Wheat.................	100 × 6 = 600	48 × 6 × 288	66 × 6 × 396
Weighted average.....	10)1000	10)475	10)605
	100	47.5	60.5

In symbolic language, the weighted average of relatives illustrated in Table 73 is as follows:

$$P_{00} = \frac{\sum w \frac{p_0}{p_0}}{\Sigma w} \qquad P_{01} = \frac{\sum w \frac{p_1}{p_0}}{\Sigma w} \qquad P_{02} = \frac{\sum w \frac{p_2}{p_0}}{\Sigma w} \qquad (2)$$

Instead of weighting by arbitrary weights, the actual quantities of the articles consumed or produced in the base year are sometimes used as weights, if such data are available. The quantities of the base year or base period are retained throughout, instead of getting the new quantities each year or each time period, for two reasons: (1) because it is difficult if not impossible to get quantity figures for every year and (2) because the proportions between these quantities are not likely to change greatly over short periods of time. If, after a given base period has been used for some time, it is discovered that one or several of the quantity weights are at variance with current conditions that seem to be likely to persist, the system of weights may be revised. In the various index numbers it constructs, the Bureau of Labor Statistics keeps continually on the watch for such changing conditions and when desirable changes the weighting system.

The symbols for quantity weights are series of q's, as follows:

q_0 = quantity of coffee in 1926
q_1 = quantity of coffee in 1933
q_2 = quantity of coffee in 1941

$q_0' =$ quantity of canned peaches in 1926
$q_1' =$ quantity of canned peaches in 1933
$q_2' =$ quantity of canned peaches in 1941

Wheat would be the same arrangement of a series of q'''s. The resulting index number, using base-year quantities as weights for the relatives averaged, would be as follows:

$$P_{00} = \frac{\sum q_0 \dfrac{p_0}{p_0}}{\Sigma q_0} \qquad P_{01} = \frac{\sum q_0 \dfrac{p_1}{p_0}}{\Sigma q_0} \qquad P_{02} = \frac{\sum q_0 \dfrac{p_2}{p_0}}{\Sigma q_0} \quad (3)$$

Simple Aggregative Method. As suggested by its name, a simple aggregative index is the sum of the absolute prices, without first changing them to relatives. Thus the raw prices of coffee, canned peaches, and wheat for 1926, then for 1933, and then for 1941 would be added together to give the index. This seems to be combining nonhomogeneous things, and it is; nevertheless, there is one famous and at one time widely used index that was based upon this method. Such was Bradstreet's index of wholesale prices, which continued in use for many years. Following is an illustration of the method of Bradstreet's index of wholesale prices:[1]

Prices, Dollars per Pound

0.0007	Connellsville coke, southern coke
0.001	Bituminous coal, brick, iron ore
0.002	Anthracite coal
0.003	Salt
0.004	Bessemer pig iron
. . .	. . . .
0.34	Alcohol
0.50	Australian wool
0.52	Quicksilver
0.84	Rubber
9.8530	The sum, which is the index

According to this method, the index number of prices does not assume the form of a relative, but appears as follows:

[1] A good description of Bradstreet's index is contained in W. C. Mitchell, "Index Numbers of Wholesale Prices in the United States and Foreign Countries," Bureau of Labor Statistics, *Bulletin* 284, pp. 161–165. Other price indexes are also discussed in that source, such as Dun's, Gibson's, the *Annalist*, War Industries Board, Federal Reserve Board, and the Bureau of Labor Statistics.

TABLE 74.—BRADSTREET'S INDEX

1933	Index	1934	Index
October...............	$9.0512	January..............	$8.8329
November............	8.8480	February............	9.0110
December............	8.8126	March..............	9.2627

The index can readily be converted into a series of relatives upon any chosen base; the *Survey of Current Business* published Bradstreet's index converted into relatives, with the monthly average of 1926 = 100 until November, 1937, when compilation of the index was discontinued.[1]

Little rational justification can be mustered to the defense of such an index as Bradstreet's, except that it worked well. Using approximately 96 commodities, it gave an index number that reflected accurately the changes in wholesale prices, as tested by more elaborately conceived and compiled indexes of wholesale prices later introduced into the field. Bradstreet's index was the pioneer in the history of price indexes in the United States, having been started in 1897. The conversion of all prices into prices per pound gives the effect of a concealed weighting, but no logical basis can be found for such a system of weighting. The symbolic expression of this index is as follows:

$$\Sigma p_0, \ \Sigma p_1, \ \Sigma p_2, \ . \ . \ . \ , \ \Sigma p_n \tag{4}$$

When reduced to relatives and some base is taken as 100, it is as follows:

$$P_{00} = \frac{\Sigma p_0}{\Sigma p_0}, \qquad P_{01} = \frac{\Sigma p_1}{\Sigma p_0} \ \cdot \ \cdot \ \cdot \ P_{0n} = \frac{\Sigma p_n}{\Sigma p_0} \tag{5}$$

While the concealed weighting system of Bradstreet's index is accidental, or haphazard, depending upon the units in which goods are quoted, it has the effect of making the high-priced articles dominant. Its success as a good index of price change was due to the fact that there was a skillful or at least a pro-

[1] *Cf. Current Survey of Business*, Supplement, Vol. 18 (1938) p. 168. Monthly figures for the index are available from 1903 and annual figures from 1890. See 1932 Supplement, pp. 28–29 and 1936 Supplement, p. 15. Also see Bureau of Labor Statistics, *Bulletin* 173 (July, 1915).

pitious use of stratified sampling in the selection of the prices used.

Weighted Aggregative Method. In making index numbers by the aggregative method, it is usually considered that weights are required, for the same reason that they are regarded as necessary in constructing an index number by the average-of-relatives method. The most reasonable kind of weight would seem to be the quantities of the several commodities produced or consumed or marketed. Such figures have become increasingly available since the time when such indexes as Bradstreet's were originally conceived and developed.

The last four or five decennial censuses of the United States have included more and more complete data on physical quantities of production and, more recently, data on retail and wholesale trade; and, in the years since the First World War, yearly figures have been available on physical quantities of goods in stock and physical production of some goods, through the activities of the United States Departments of Commerce and Agriculture. If it is assumed that the method of weighting is one that uses actual quantity figures, there are two methods of weighting the price aggregates in order to construct the index number. The first method is called "weighting by base-year quantities." The second method is called "weighting by given-year quantities."

The desirability of weighting by base-year quantities has a twofold explanation: (1) In spite of the increased availability of quantity figures, there are still many commodities for which quantity figures are not easily available for every year; but a large number of such quantity figures, classified so as to be useful for weighting purposes, are available for the census years. (2) With few exceptions, the proportional changes in the quantities or value weights from year to year are not sufficiently great to cause large errors if these proportions are assumed to remain constant for several years in succession. Adjustments in the quantity or value weights can be made in the case of rapidly growing or rapidly declining industries, but the necessity for such changes within 10-year periods will not include a very large number of commodities. As a purely practical matter, the choice of base-year weighting instead of given-year weighting gives adequate results with much less statistical calculation, as well as much less statistical research in seeking data for use as weights.

United States Bureau of Labor Statistics. *Construction of Index Illustrated by Practice of an Official Bureau.* In the United States, the Bureau of Labor Statistics is one of the most important official compilers of index numbers of various kinds. From its publications can be illustrated how the various matters discussed above are brought into practice and how diligent must be the researcher, how alert the statistician, to new problems of weighting, sampling, and the like.

In 1943 the Bureau of Labor Statistics of the United States Department of Labor was compiling and publishing weekly, monthly, and annual index numbers of wholesale commodity prices. In a revision made in 1927, when the base period was changed from the 1913 average to the 1926 average, a new weighting system was adopted; it was then decided to revise the quantities used as weighting factors every 2 years, as the results of each new biennial census of manufactures became available. At the same time, the number of price series was increased from 404 to 550. Another revision was made in 1931, when the number of price series was changed from 550 to 784 and some rearrangement of the items in the groups and subgroups was made. No change was made in 1931 in the method of calculating the indexes. In December, 1942, according to the *Survey of Current Business*, the monthly index of wholesale prices compiled by the Bureau of Labor Statistics was made up of 889 quotations.[1]

The weights used for farm products are based on averages for 3-year periods, changed every 2 years in order to keep the weights up to date. Thus, for the years 1932 and 1933, the weights used for farm prices were based upon averages of quantities marketed in the years 1927, 1928, and 1929; and for the years 1934 and 1935 the weights used for farm-products prices were based upon averages of quantities marketed in the years 1929, 1930, and 1931. For all other groups of commodity prices, the weights used are averages of quantities produced for sale, to

[1] *Survey of Current Business*, Vol. 22 (December, 1942), p. S-3. On the history of its compilation, weighting, etc., see Bureau of Labor Statistics, *Bulletin* 181, 415, 453, 521; "Wholesale Prices," *Serial* No. R1434 (December, 1941); "Revised Method of Calculation of the Wholesale Price Index of the United States Bureau of Labor Statistics," *Serial* No. R.666.

which has been added the average of imports for consumption, in the last two completed census periods. For example, for the years 1932 and 1933, the weights were based on average census data (plus imports for consumption) for the years 1927 and 1929, whereas for the years 1934 and 1935 the weights were based on average census data (plus imports for consumption) for the years 1929 and 1931. In cases where census data are lacking, estimates are made of the quantities of the various commodities marketed, based on the best information available from governmental and reliable private sources; and these estimates are used as weighting factors. Commodities are added or dropped from time to time as they become important or cease to be important in the markets.[1]

During the period of depression following 1932, when the data on manufactured output became violently disrupted, the weights based upon averages of the years 1929–1931 were retained. Most of the prices continued in 1943 to be weighted by the averages of the 1929–1931 census data, but for certain commodity groups new weights had begun to be based upon special studies of those groups. Thus, in April, 1941, the Bureau published a study of the "Wholesale Price Trends of Carpets and Rugs" revising its price series for this group. This study included new weights for the prices in this group, according to their "importance in the country's markets in 1939."

The quantity weight used for each of the series, the unit in which each is priced, and the 1939 value of each item expressed as a percentage of the aggregate value of all carpet and rug items in the Bureau's indexes are shown in Table 75.

The use of data for 1939 departed from the "general practice of using the 1929 and 1931 data for weighting in the Bureau's

[1] If a "price" index, as contrasted with a "realized price" index, is desired, it is necessary to keep the weights constant. In constructing a realized price index the weights may be changed, but in revising the weights the index must be calculated by using both sets of weights for the overlapping year or period when the change is made. By "realized price" is meant the dollars covering the transaction, divided by the units involved in the transaction. When the lack of continuity of specifications makes it hard to define the commodity, as with automobiles, the dollars of sales for each general type (sedans, coupes, etc.) divided by the number of such units, in other words, the "realized price," has received the endorsement of competent price experts as an acceptable quotation to use in price statistics.

TABLE 75

Price series	Unit in which priced	Weight
Axminster ¾ carpets...............	Lineal yard	7,077
Axminster 9 × 12 rugs............	Each	2,015
Plain velvet ¾ carpets.............	Lineal yard	6,424
Plain velvet 1¼ carpets............	Square yard	7,861
Wilton 9 × 12 rugs...............	Each	612

Source: Bureau of Labor Statistics, mimeographed publication, "Wholesale Price Trends of Carpets and Rugs," April, 1941, pp. 16–17.

wholesale price indexes," in order to provide weights for the individual items that reflected their relative importance more nearly in accordance with present-day sales. The Axminster type has long been the most popular. The relative importance of Wilton carpets and rugs has increased considerably since the depression of the early 1930's, and they have regained much of their earlier popularity. Prior to the depression and before plain velvets became popular, the importance of Wiltons, on a dollar basis, was almost as great as that of Axminster carpets and rugs. During the depth of the depression, when consumer incomes were greatly reduced, there was a lessened demand for Wiltons, apparently because they were much more expensive, on the average, than Axminsters.

The study of the carpet and rug price series is presented to illustrate the alertness of the Bureau in relation to the problem of compiling and publishing its indexes of wholesale prices. Its activity extends to other groups of price series as well. For example, beginning with January, 1938, the results of a survey of farm-machinery wholesale prices were incorporated for the first time in the Bureau of Labor Statistics general indexes of wholesale prices. In 1941 the Bureau began publishing weekly index numbers of waste and scrap materials, carrying the index back to January, 1939. In "Wholesale Prices" (June, 1941), the Bureau published a monthly index of standard machine-tool prices, including 11 types of standard nonspecialty machine tools, carrying the index back to January, 1937. These new indexes are calculated on August, 1939, as a base; the monthly index of wholesale prices continued in 1943 to be based on the average of 1926 as 100.

Method of Computation Illustrated. The weighted aggregative method of computing an index number of prices is illustrated in Table 76, using only five price series. The five price series selected for illustration are those for carpets and rugs, for which the Bureau's weights are shown in Table 75. A procedure similar to that illustrated in Table 76 is used by the Bureau, but with 889 price quotations instead of 5.

TABLE 76.—WORK SHEET ILLUSTRATING CALCULATION OF WEIGHTED AGGREGATIVE INDEX
Base-period weights

Commodity	Average price		Weights q_0	Weighted price	
	1935–1939 p_0	1941 p_1		1935–1939 p_0q_0	1941 p_1q_0
(1)	(2)	(3)	(4)	(5)	(6)
Axminster $\frac{3}{4}$ carpets......	1.567	2.014	7,077	11,090	14,253
Axminster 9×12 rugs...	22.745	27.936	2,015	45,831	56,291
Plain velvet $\frac{3}{4}$ carpets....	1.772	2.356	6,424	11,383	15,135
Plain velvet $1\frac{2}{4}$ carpets...	2.581	3.266	7,861	20,289	25,674
Wilton 9×12 rugs......	40.007	50.521	612	24,484	30,919
$\Sigma =$	......	......	.....	113,078	142,272
$\times (100/\Sigma p_0q_0)$	......	......	.....	$= 100.00$	$= 125.82$
				$P_{01} = \Sigma p_1q_0/p_0q_0$	

Source: CUTTS, JESSE M., and SAMUEL J. DENNIS, "Revised Method of Calculation of Wholesale Price Indexes," *Journal of the American Statistical Association*, Vol. 32 (1937); also reprinted by the Bureau of Labor Statistics as *Serial* No. 666.

Accordingly, the index number of the wholesale prices of carpets and rugs is 100.00 for the years 1935–1939, the base period, and 125.82 for 1941. The latter figure is obtained by taking $P_{01} = \Sigma p_1q_0/\Sigma p_0q_0$. From the system of symbols already introduced, the symbolic presentation of this form of index number is as follows:

$$P_{00} = \frac{\Sigma p_0q_0}{\Sigma p_0q_0}, \quad P_{01} = \frac{\Sigma p_1q_0}{\Sigma p_0q_0}, \quad P_{02} = \frac{\Sigma p_2q_0}{\Sigma p_0q_0} \cdots P_{0n} = \frac{\Sigma p_nq_0}{\Sigma p_0q_0} \quad (6)$$

This is illustrated in the figures of Tables 75 and 76, the 1941 index being $\frac{142,272}{113,078} \times 100 = 125.82$.

Price Indexes and Quantity Indexes. *Aggregative Index Using Given-year Weights.* If given-year quantity weights are available and used for computing an index, it must be noted that the following system of ratios would merely give an index of changing aggregate values, without distinguishing which part of the change is due to price change and which part to quantity change:

$$R_{00} = \frac{\Sigma p_0 q_0}{\Sigma p_0 q_0}, \qquad R_{01} = \frac{\Sigma p_1 q_1}{\Sigma p_0 q_0}, \qquad R_{02} = \frac{\Sigma p_2 q_2}{\Sigma p_0 q_0} \cdots$$

$$R_{0n} = \frac{\Sigma p_n q_n}{\Sigma p_0 q_0}$$

Such an index is an index of aggregate value, made up partly of changes in quantity and partly of changes in price. In order, therefore, to extract from it that part of the change which is due solely to price change, the base-year prices must be multiplied throughout by the given-year weights. This fact makes the given-year weighting method a very long one to calculate; it loses the advantage, inherent in the aggregative index weighted by base-year quantities, of having a constant divider in securing the index. In addition, the method of weighting by given-year quantities necessitates the two sets of cross products for each year—each year's prices multiplied by that year's quantities and by the base-year quantities. Following is the symbolic expression of the aggregative index of prices weighted by given-year quantities:

$$P_{00} = \frac{\Sigma p_0 q_0}{\Sigma p_0 q_0}, \qquad P_{01} = \frac{\Sigma p_1 q_1}{\Sigma p_0 q_1}, \qquad P_{02} = \frac{\Sigma p_2 q_2}{\Sigma p_0 q_2} \cdots$$

$$P_{0n} = \frac{\Sigma p_n q_n}{\Sigma p_0 q_n} \quad (7)$$

Index of Quantities Weighted by Prices. An advantage of the given-year weighting method is that an index of quantities weighted by prices can be obtained as a by-product, with comparatively little additional calculation. The same numerators as those used in Eq. (7) can be used to calculate an index of quantity change weighted by given-year prices. For each year, given-year prices are multiplied by base-year quantities, and these aggregates are used as dividers. This will give an index of quantity weighted by given-year prices, as follows:

$$Q_{00} = \frac{\Sigma p_0 q_0}{\Sigma p_0 q_0}, \qquad Q_{01} = \frac{\Sigma p_1 q_1}{\Sigma p_1 q_0}, \qquad Q_{02} = \frac{\Sigma p_2 q_2}{\Sigma p_2 q_0} \cdots \quad (8)$$

Unfortunately, this advantage in the given-year weighting method is largely imaginary because the quantity data are not available soon enough for short periods of time to make it practicable to construct monthly or weekly indexes. In any case, it is also possible to obtain a quantity index weighted by given-year prices, using the following equation, which would provide a much simpler method:

$$Q_{00} = \frac{\Sigma p_0 q_0}{\Sigma p_0 q_0}, \qquad Q_{01} = \frac{\Sigma p_0 q_1}{\Sigma p_0 q_0}, \qquad Q_{02} = \frac{\Sigma p_0 q_2}{\Sigma p_0 q_0} \cdots \quad (9)$$

Quantity indexes are constructed, however, by other methods, usually with more general application of stratified sampling and with other weights than prices, largely because of the difficulty of obtaining quantity data. Not only are these other methods more convenient to calculate, but they make it possible to handle matters having to do with weighting and bias in the results. In using equations like Eqs. (8) and (9), it is often very difficult to appraise the inaccuracies due to bias inherent in the method.

Quantity Indexes and Business Barometers. *Indexes of Quantity of Trade or Production.* Several statisticians and economists made attempts, especially in the years immediately following the First World War, to construct an index that would trace variations in the physical volume of production or trade. Pioneer efforts to construct such indexes, based upon scant material and with little in the way of a statistical theory to guide them, were made before the First World War by Wesley C. Mitchell, Irving Fisher, and Edwin W. Kemmerer. During the war and postwar period important progress was made, especially by Edmund E. Day, Warren M. Persons, and others. In 1923, the latter published an index of trade for the United States, beginning with the year 1903.* The index of production is based very heavily on the index of employment; it might therefore fail to reflect properly the results of technological advance.

---

* "An Index of Trade for the United States," *Review of Economic Statistics*, Preliminary Vol. 5 (April, 1923), pp. 71–78. *Cf.* also GARFIELD, FRANK R., "General Indexes of Business Activity," *Federal Reserve Bulletin*, Vol. 26 (1940), pp. 495–501.

After these experiments by pioneering individuals, several government agencies and privately financed research organizations took up the task of developing indexes of trade and production. The most widely known and now most currently used index of industrial production for the United States is that compiled and regularly published in the *Federal Reserve Bulletin* by the Research Division of the Board of Governors of the Federal Reserve System. This index is compiled from 95 individual series of monthly data, representing about 85 per cent of the total industrial production of the United States. The series include 22 durable-goods manufacturing industry series, 63 nondurable-goods manufacturing industry series, and series representing production of fuels and metals. This index is also regularly reproduced in the *Survey of Current Business*, published by the United States Department of Commerce.[1] A reproduction of the entire index, with its component parts, 1923–1940 by months, with the average 1935–1939 = 100 as the base, can be found in the *Federal Reserve Bulletin*.[2]

It is characteristic of the indexes of physical volume of production or trade that they consist of combinations of various series upon the basis of stratified sampling, the weights for the representative series being devised upon a priori knowledge concerning the importance of certain groups of activity in relation to the whole of business activity. These indexes treat the separate series statistically before putting them together. For example, they remove seasonal variation and trend from the separate series and thus average together the cycles of the various separate series into the composite. The method of averaging employed is generally the aggregative method, although since 1940 the Federal Reserve Board uses an average of relatives weighted by quantities so that the final result is equivalent to what would be obtained by using the weighted aggregative method.[3]

---

[1] *Federal Reserve Bulletin*, Vol. 13 (February, March, 1927), Vol. 17 (February, September, 1931), Vol. 18 (March, 1932); for adjustments made necessary by the 1942 world war, see Vol. 27 (1941), pp. 878–881; *cf. Survey of Current Business*, Vol. 20 (1940), pp. 11–17.

[2] Vol. 26 (1940), pp. 825–882; see also "Answer to Critics of the Index," pp. 1047–1049. See also WOODLIEF, THOMAS, and MAXWELL R. CONKLIN, "Measurement of Production," *Federal Reserve Bulletin*, Vol. 26 (1940), pp. 912–924.

[3] See WOODLIEF and CONKLIN, *op. cit.*

Computation of Weights Illustrated. The index of manufactures published by the Federal Reserve Board is weighted by the total value added by manufacture in the case of all manufacturing industries, and the index of mineral production is weighted by value of mineral products. The sum of these two is the index of production. The individual production series of which the manufacturing index is composed are weighted, as nearly as possible, according to the same principle.[1] Accordingly, the total value added by manufacturing industries in 1937, as reported by the United States census, was distributed among the 16 groups represented in proportion to the value added for each

TABLE 77.—RELATIVE IMPORTANCE OF INDUSTRY GROUPS AND SELECTED INDUSTRIES INCLUDED IN THE FEDERAL RESERVE BOARD INDEX OF INDUSTRIAL PRODUCTION

(Per cent of total with 1937 weights)

Series		1937 Weights
Industrial production		100.00
Manufactures		84.80
Durable manufactures	37.93	
Iron and steel	11.00	
Machinery production	10.81	
Transportation equipment	5.92	
Nonferrous metals and their products	2.81	
Lumber and its products	4.39	
Stone, clay, and glass products	3.00	
Nondurable manufactures	46.87	
Textiles and their products	11.22	
Leather and its products	2.28	
Manufactured food products	10.92	
Alcoholic beverages	1.84	
Tobacco products	1.24	
Paper and its products	3.13	
Printing and publishing	6.44	
Petroleum and coal products	2.14	
Products of chemicals	6.27	
Rubber products	1.39	
Minerals		15.20
Fuels	13.01	
Metals	2.19	

Source: Condensed from *Federal Reserve Bulletin*, Vol. 26 (1940), p. 919.

[1] For industry series in which census data on value added by manufacture are not available other criteria had to be used, such as total value of manufactured product, raw materials consumed, or man-hours worked. See *ibid.*, pp. 917–918.

group, and then derived group totals were subdivided among industries and finally among individual products in a similar manner. Each individual series is thus assigned a hypothetical value-added figure, which is then divided by the relative of the 1935–1939 compared with 1937 in order to convert 1937 value-added figures to 1935–1939 base. The derived 1935–1939 figures for each series are then expressed as percentages of their own total to obtain the weights. These percentages represent the estimated relative importance of each series in the 1935–1939 base period and are the weights applied to the relatives in combining them into the index of production. Table 77 reproduces a summary of these weights.

Using the weights shown in Table 77, the equation for the Federal Reserve Board's index of industrial production is as follows:

$$P_{0n} = \sum \left(w \frac{q_n}{q_0} \right) \tag{10}$$

in which

$$w = \frac{p_{37} q_0}{\Sigma p_{37} q_0}$$

p_{37} represents the value (or value added) per unit of output in the weight-base period.

Barometers, or Indexes, of General Business Conditions. Some composite indexes purport to be barometers or indexes of business and trade in general. These indexes are of two types: (1) A single series is sometimes believed to be a barometer of general business conditions and (2) a number of indexes of trade activity are combined in order to measure general business conditions.

Of the first type, the most prominent one at present is probably the index of electrical-power production, which is compiled from quantity figures published by the Geological Survey. The index of activity in the steel industry at one time was looked upon as a good barometer of general business conditions because so many industries are dependent upon steel or steel products. The trends in the average of security market prices are sometimes taken as a barometer of coming business conditions, or at least as a measure of existing conditions. In wartime, the security markets often reflect conditions and war information that are not generally publicized.

A good example of the second type of index of general business conditions is that published currently by the *New York Times* and formerly by the *Annalist*. This index has been widely used and until October, 1937, was reproduced in the *Survey of Current Business*, published by the United States Department of Commerce.

A more comprehensive example of this second type of index of business conditions is one that has evolved from the pioneer work of Carl Snyder, whose procedure was based upon the theory that the fluctuations in total bank clearings are made up of two variables: (1) price change and (2) change in physical volume of trade. By constructing a price deflator, which has already been discussed, and then by using this deflator to cancel out from aggregate bank clearings that part due to price changes, he sought to obtain an index of physical volume of trade for the years 1875–1924.[1]   Modifications and refinements were made in the construction of this index by Leroy M. Piser, so that it was known as the Snyder-Piser index of volume of trade for the United States. It included 89 series, classified as follows: productive activity, 46 series; primary distribution, 13 series; distribution to consumer, 8 series; financial activity, 6 series; general (such as life insurance, postal receipts, electrical-power corporations, farmers, and communication), 5 series; and finally debits outside New York City. Thus it came to be based upon the principle of stratified sampling. This index of volume of trade and production is published monthly by the Federal Reserve Bank of New York in its *Monthly Review of Credit and Business Conditions*.[2]

Various forecasting services compile their respective indexes of business conditions according to their particular interpretation as to what should best be included in such an index and how best to weight various factors. Carefully worked out indexes of the marketing of farm products and forestry products are now available as a result of the efforts of the Bureau of Agricultural Economics in the United States Department of Agriculture. These are reproduced in the *Survey of Current Business*. The

---

[1] SNYDER, CARL, "A New Clearings Index of Business for Fifty Years," *Journal of the American Statistical Association*, Vol. 19 (1924), pp. 329–335.

[2] JOHNSON, NORRIS Q., "New Indexes of Production and Trade," *Journal of the American Statistical Association*, Vol. 33 (1938), pp. 341–348.

Bureau of Foreign and Domestic Commerce also publishes indexes of domestic commodity stocks, and of world stocks of certain outstanding industries, which constitute good barometers of the related business conditions.[1]

ADJUSTMENT OF INDEXES TO BENCH MARKS

Ideal Conditions for Stratified Sampling Nonexistent. In order to produce results approximating those of true random sampling, conditions favorable to random sampling in the subgroups or strata must exist. For one thing, this means that there must be large numbers of items from which to draw within each subgroup. It also means that the number of sample items must be sufficient to avoid the disadvantages of small samples. The law of large numbers must be given opportunity to produce the results of true random selection within each stratum; such is the *sine qua non* of truly successful stratified sampling. Under such conditions the method of selection causes no accumulation of bias. Such ideal conditions do not exist with reference to any known index number, not even the Bureau of Labor Statistics index of wholesale prices, which contains a total of more items than any other index.

Nevertheless, the pattern of stratified sampling can with considerable advantage be adopted as the guide to procedure in the construction of indexes of all types. Following this pattern the investigator first works out a system of classification of the data for which an index is to be compiled. Using the subgroups of this classification, he can then proceed according to the principles of stratified random sampling so far as it is possible to do so. When he finds that conditions ideal for random sampling in a subgroup fail to exist, the investigator must resort to subjective means to secure results that he believes will be representative.

Inasmuch as all indexes contain, in some part, data that have been collected and processed by the use of such subjective methods, employed in the absence of ideal sampling conditions, it is desirable wherever possible for the statistician to find bench marks with which he can compare the results of his sampling

[1] *Survey of Current Business*, Vol. 20, Annual Supplement (1940), pp. 88–164. For a more complete discussion of barometers of general business conditions see Wesley C. Mitchell, *Business Cycles—The Problems and Its Setting*, (1928), pp. 291–330; Joseph L. Snider, *Business Statistics;* and Garfield, *op. cit.*

procedure. A common-sense appraisal of the over-all result is the most generally used bench mark to judge whether or not the results are satisfactory; but this method presupposes an unusual amount of a priori knowledge and of scientific critical judgment on the part of the statistician.   Sometimes more objective bench marks may be found to aid the statistical worker along his thorny path.   These will be illustrated in the ensuing sections.

Reasons Why Indexes Require Adjustment.   The reasons why indexes require adjustment to bench marks do not necessarily arise from faulty application of the method of stratified sampling. They arise from the nature of the universe from which the sample is taken.   In connection with most types of data collected for the construction of indexes, the universe is a discrete rather than a continuous one; in other words, the universe consists of comparatively small numbers of units, each of which constitutes a comparatively large proportion of the whole universe.   Often they cannot be considered as representative of each other.

When such a comparatively small universe is subdivided, in order to apply the stratified sampling technique, the strata constitute universes with still smaller numbers.   Added to this is the usual fact that only a portion of this remaining small number is accessible to the data collector; in some cases, unavoidable bias itself constitutes a part of the reason for the accessible portion.   Under such circumstances it is almost impossible to realize the essential condition of randomness of selection in the respective strata, and consequently stratified sampling technique gives less satisfactory results.

Such is the situation with respect to sample data collected from business firms, especially manufacturing enterprises.   In some of the subdivisions, corporate enterprise is on so large a scale that only a few firms represent a large portion of that stratum.   In all subdivisions, the size of the sample return measures, not only changes in the trends it is desired to measure, but also success or failure of the collecting agency in persuading firms to report.   The statistical technique of comparing identical firms from month to month reduces but does not altogether obviate the cumulative error resulting from this weakness.

In addition, growth of an industry, and hence growth in pay rolls, in output, in stocks of materials, or in whatever is the subject of investigation, occurs not only in existing firms; but part of the growth is in the rise of new firms in the industry. In some strata, perhaps the steel and machinery industries, expansion or contraction of existing firms (and hence those reporting in a stratified sample) may accurately reflect proportionately a rise or fall in business in that strata. But in other strata, like some branches of the textile industry or the food industry, the expansion or contraction of existing firms (and hence those reporting in a stratified sample) may not at all reflect proportionately the rise or fall in business.

In heavy industry, where plant and equipment constitute a large proportion of the business investment, cyclical changes of the sample might well be much greater than cyclical changes in the universe. This would follow if the large firm, with heavy investment in plant and equipment, tended to curtail production instead of lowering prices when faced with declining business prospects.

In some branches of the clothing and food industries, in which small investment in plant and equipment and large numbers of small firms predominate, cyclical changes may be smaller in the sample than in the universe. The birth of new firms or resumption of activity by old firms is the principal manner of expansion in such strata. The death of old firms is the principal means of decline. The reporting firms are quite likely to be the ones that would not die at a rate so rapid as the average rate in the industry.

Circumstances like those just described constitute only an illustration of the type of problem facing the statistician, who must continually endeavor to improve the sample of reporting firms. Great as his efforts and ingenious as his imagination, may be the resulting sample is likely to show bias.

For bench marks in connection with adjustment of indexes of employment and pay rolls, statisticians have made use of the successive issues of the census of manufactures, often called the Biennial Census of Manufactures, which appeared in 1914, 1919, and each odd year thereafter, including 1939. For years after 1939 it should be possible to get similar bench-mark data from the records of the Social Security Administration.

By using the census-of-manufactures data as bench marks, it has been possible to check up on the monthly or weekly sample results obtained by the sampling process and to adjust them for any bias that is disclosed by such a check. As each new set of manufacturing census data became available, which was about two years from the time it was taken, such indexes could be adjusted to the census data for errors that had accumulated since the last census. In the meantime, the results of the sample were relied upon as the best available information; and at the same time subjective sampling procedures were continually studied with a view to improvement wherever possible. To this end, the adjustment procedure often discloses areas in which the sampling results are especially in need of improvement.

The method of making such adjustment will be illustrated, not so much as a valuable statistical device in itself, but as an example to the student of the care and attention to form, procedure, cross checking, and the like, required of a good statistician. Thus the following instructions, together with the form used, are presented as an exhibit to help the student visualize how a statistician plans his work and works his plan.

Method of Adjustment Illustrated. A good example of an index adjusted to United States census bench marks is the monthly index of pay rolls and employment published by the Bureau of Labor Statistics. The method of adjustment is reproduced by permission of the Bureau of Labor Statistics and is applied to a monthly index of pay rolls in the metal stamping, enameling, and japanning and lacquering industry of New Jersey.[1] The adjustment is carried out on Form BLS 1238, June, 1940, presented here in Table 78.

The raw data, which have been adjusted for the 1937 and earlier census figures or bench marks, but remain to be adjusted for 1939 census data, are entered by months in columns (3), (9), and (13); the sums and averages (S and I) for each of these columns are then entered. In column (17), using the lower part entitled "Formula if L is not available,"[2] enter the United States census figure for 1937 and 1939 (Z_1 and Z_3). Calculate the ratio Z_3/Z_1, and enter in the space provided, therefore, 0.933280

---

[1] The work on New Jersey data was done by a Work Progress Administration project sponsored by the New Jersey State Labor Department for the construction of monthly indexes of pay rolls and employment in manufacturing industries, January, 1923–December, 1940. One of the authors was called upon to serve as consultant and director of the project.

[2] The part labeled "Formula if L is available" is used with a blanket adjustment method involving several census periods.

in Table 78. Copy S_1 from column (3), in the space provided in column (17), that is, in Table 78, 883.82; this number multiplied by the ratio Z_3/Z_1 equals S_3', entered in the space provided, in Table 78, that is, 824.85.

In column (13) calculate R_3 by finding ΣnI for the year 1939 [the n for each month is found in column (12)]. $\Sigma nI =$ January $nI +$ February $nI +$ March $nI \cdots +$ December nI, including an nI for each of the 12 months.

In column (18) enter S_3', copying it from the last row of column (17). Enter S_3, copying it from column (13). Subtract S_3 from S_3' and enter the difference in the next row of column (18). Copy R_3 [from column (13)] in the next row of column (18). This value, R_3, divided into the figure in the preceding row, $S_3' - S_3$, gives the value of d. Enter d in the last row of column (18). This is the adjustment parameter. It is now used to adjust the series by months as follows:

In columns (4), (10), and (14) enter $1 + nd$ for each month. These values should be obtained on a calculating machine as follows: Put 1.000000 in the machine, and add it. Put d on the keyboard, being careful to place it correctly for the decimal point. Subtract once, and record the answer for $1 + nd$ in January, 1937. Subtract twice more (making -3 altogether), and record the answer for $1 + nd$ in February, 1937. Subtract twice more (making -5 altogether), and record the answer for $1 + nd$ in March, 1937. Subtract once more (making -6 altogether), and record the answer for $1 + nd$ in April, 1937. The values for $1 + nd$ in May, June, July, and August are the same as $1 + nd$ for April, March, February, and January, respectively. They can be found by reversing the above process on the calculator until 1.000000 remains in the machine and d on the keyboard. For September add d once and record $1 + nd$ for that month. Add d four more times (making 5 altogether), and record $1 + nd$ for October. By following a similar procedure, guided by n in columns (2), (8), and (12), values of $1 + nd$ are calculated and entered for each month through December, 1939.

Enter in columns (5), (11), and (15) the indexes in columns (3), (9), and (13), multiplied, respectively, by the $1 + nd$ for the corresponding month in columns (4), (10), and (14). Add for each year, and enter sums, which equal K, S_2', and S_3'. Divide

TABLE 78.—ADJUSTMENT OF MONTHLY INDEXES TO BIENNIAL CENSUS FIGURES

Continuation method

U.S. Bureau of Labor Statistics Form B.L.S. 1238 June, 1940

								Pay rolls				Metal stamping, enameling, japanning and lacquering			New Jersey
								Emp., P.R., etc.				Industry number and name			Area and State
(1)	(2)	(3)	(4)	(5)	(6)		(7)	(8)	(9)	(10)	(11)	(12)	(13)	(14)	(15)
				Year 1, 1937					Year 2, 1938				Year 3, 1939		
Month	n	Index I	Factor $1+nd$ F	First approx. $F \cdot I$ J	Second adjustment m	mh	Adjusted index $J+\cdot mh$ I'	n	Index I	Factor $1+nd$ F	Adjusted index $F \cdot I'$ I''	n	Index I	Factor $1+nd$ F	Adjusted index $F \cdot I$ I'
Jan.	−1	65.47	0.999564	65.44	1	−0.002	65.44	23	53.93	1.010025	54.47	140	52.66	1.061023	55.87
Feb.	−3	69.66	0.988092	69.57	2	−0.004	69.57	31	49.20	1.013512	49.86	150	55.83	1.065381	59.48
Mar.	−5	71.01	0.997821	70.86	3	−0.006	70.85	40	53.98	1.017435	54.92	159	60.61	1.069304	64.81
Apr.	−6	72.93	0.997385	72.74	4	−0.008	72.73	50	53.90	1.021794	55.07	167	62.30	1.072791	66.83
May	−6	72.33	0.997385	72.14	5	−0.010	72.13	60	54.17	1.026153	55.59	174	60.78	1.075842	65.39
June	−5	71.97	0.997821	71.81	5	−0.010	71.80	70	53.40	1.030511	55.03	180	60.35	1.078458	65.08
July	−4	67.11	0.998257	66.99	5	−0.010	66.98	80	50.50	1.034870	52.26	185	54.76	1.080637	59.18
Aug.	−2	73.09	0.999128	73.03	5	−0.010	73.02	90	51.67	1.039229	53.70	189	62.53	1.082380	67.68
Sept.	1	81.53	1.000436	81.57	4	−0.008	81.56	100	52.28	1.043588	54.56	192	65.98	1.083688	71.50
Oct.	5	91.87	1.002179	92.07	3	−0.006	92.06	110	54.82	1.047946	57.45	194	74.04	1.084560	80.30
Nov.	10	82.57	1.004359	82.93	2	−0.004	82.93	120	52.85	1.052305	55.61	195	76.48	1.084996	82.98
Dec.	16	64.28	1.006974	64.73	1	−0.002	64.73	130	52.68	1.056664	55.67	195	79.02	1.084996	85.74
Sum S_1		883.82		883.88 K			883.80 S_1'	S_2	633.38		654.19 S_2'	S_3	765.34		824.84 S_3'
Ave. I_1		73.65		73.66			73.65 I_1'	I_2	52.78		54.52 I_2'	I_3	63.78		68.74 I_3'
												R_3136	529.90	$R_3 = \Sigma nI$ for year 3	

(16) To find h, year 1 only

$$h = (S_1 - K)/40$$

$S_1 = \Sigma I$ = sum of given indexes	S_1	883.82
$K = \Sigma J$ = sum of approx. indexes	K	883.88
Numerator = difference	$S_1 - K$	-0.06
Parameter for second adj.	h	-0.002

If $S_1 - K$ is less than 0.05 regardless of sign, do not find h. Strike out J in the heading of column (5), and substitute the symbol I'.

(17) To find S_3'

Formula if L is available:

$$S_3' = LZ_3$$

Census figure, year 3	Z_3	
Converting factor	L	
$S_3' = LZ_3$	S_3'	

Formula if L is not available:

$$S_3' = S_1 \left(\frac{Z_3}{Z_1}\right)$$

Census figure, year 1	Z_1	2.034	870.00
Census figure, year 3	Z_3	1.899	104.00
Ratio	$\frac{Z_3}{Z_1}$	0.933 280	
S_1 from column (3)	S_1	883.82	
$S_3' = S_1 \left(\frac{Z_3}{Z_1}\right)$	S_3'	824.85	

(18) To find d

$$d = \frac{S_3' - S_3}{R_3}$$

S_3' from column (17)	S_3'	824.85
S_3 from column (13)	S_3	765.34
Numerator = difference	$S_3' - S_3$	59.51
Denominator = R_3 from col. (13)	R_3	136 529.90
Adjustment parameter	d	0.000 435875

Checks:

S_1', col. (7) = S_1, col. (3)

I_1', col. (7) = I_1, col. (3)

S_3', col. (15) = S_3', col. (17)

Signature and date

Source: The method here illustrated was supplied by Sidney W. Wilcox, Chief Statistician of the Bureau of Labor Statistics. *Cf.* Bureau of Labor Statistics, *Bulletins* 610, (October, 1934), 3987 (November, 1936), 4189 (January, 1937), and 4382 (April, 1937), on revised indexes of factory employment. The revised indexes appear currently in the monthly bulletin on "Employment and Pay Rolls," *Serial* No. R589, and the back figures are published in full from 1919 to date in *Federal Reserve Bulletin*, Vol. 24 (1938), pp. 838–866. *Cf.* also recommendations of the Committee on Government Statistics in "Recent Progress in Employment Statistics" by Aryness Joy, *Journal of the American Statistical Association*, Vol. 29 (1934), pp. 355–371.

each of these by 12, and enter the quotients in the next row. Thus, in Table 78, $K = 883.88$, $S_2' = 654.19$, and $S_3' = 824.84$; and divided by 12 these become 73.66, 54.52, and 68.74.

In column (16) enter the S_1 and K_1, as indicated in the table; subtract K from S_1, and enter the difference. Divide this difference by 40, and enter the quotient in the next row. This figure is h, the parameter for the second adjustment. If $S_1 - K$ is smaller than 0.05, regardless of sign, do not calculate h. In the problem illustrated, $S_1 - K = -0.06$; hence h is calculated and found to be -0.002.

If h is calculated, enter in column (6), for each month, mh; that is, in January enter h, in February enter $2h$, in March enter $3h$, in April enter $4h$, in May to August, inclusive, $5h$; thereafter declining each month, with $2h$ in November and h in December. Enter in column (7) the sum of the figures for the respective months in columns (5) and (6). The sum of column (7) is equal to S_1'. If h is not used, the sum of column (5) is taken as S_1'; that is, if h is ignored, $K = S_1'$.

CHAPTER XX

RATIONAL BASIS OF THE ANALYSIS OF TIME SERIES

Elements of Variation in Time Series. The elements of variation contained in an ordinary time series may be illustrated by building up a hypothetical time series. The first element in the time series is *long-time growth*, or *trend*. People living in the twentieth century are accustomed to the idea that things grow, or progress. Table 79, column (1), shows years and months for 3 years, and column (2) shows a set of figures that grow at the constant difference of 0.2 per month. This column of figures is plotted in Fig. 135 (AA') and is a picture of the growth, or trend, in the hypothetical time series.

Time series are also likely to have *seasonal variations*. Many economic and social phenomena vary from season to season in a similar manner each year. This is most evident in the case of activities affected by weather, such as agricultural production; but such patterns of seasonal variation occur in other events as well. Suppose the seasonal variation in the hypothetical time series is such that November is usually 58 per cent above the average month, July is usually only 43 per cent as large as the average month, etc., as indicated in Table 80 showing the index of seasonal variation for the hypothetical time series.

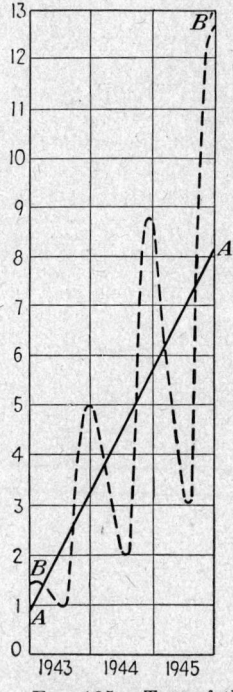

Fig. 135.—Two of the component parts of a hypothetical time series. AA' = annual trend, BB' = assumed trend, modified by annual seasonal variation.

Figure 136 is a graph of this seasonal variation as it occurs year after year, 1943, 1944, and 1945.

543

TABLE 79.—HYPOTHETICAL TIME SERIES BUILT UP

(1)	(2)	(3)	(4)	(5)
Year and month	Growth or trend	Seasonal variation put in	The cycle	The cycle put in
1943:				
January........................	1.0	1.45	100	1.45
February......................	1.2	1.49	101	1.50
March.........................	1.4	1.41	102	1.44
April..........................	1.6	1.33	103	1.37
May...........................	1.8	1.19	106	1.26
June..........................	2.0	1.04	109	1.13
July..........................	2.2	0.95	112	1.06
August........................	2.4	1.01	115	1.16
September.....................	2.6	2.42	120	2.90
October.......................	2.8	4.00	122	4.88
November......................	3.0	4.74	124	5.88
December......................	3.2	5.02	125	6.28
1944:				
January.......................	3.4	4.93	126	6.21
February......................	3.6	4.46	130	5.80
March.........................	3.8	3.84	140	5.38
April..........................	4.0	3.32	150	4.98
May...........................	4.2	2.77	160	4.43
June..........................	4.4	2.29	180	4.12
July..........................	4.6	1.98	200	3.96
August........................	4.8	2.02	210	4.24
September.....................	5.0	4.65	160	7.44
October.......................	5.2	7.44	140	10.42
November......................	5.4	8.53	112	9.55
December......................	5.6	8.79	111	9.76
1945:				
January.......................	5.8	8.41	109	9.17
February......................	6.0	7.44	107	7.96
March.........................	6.2	6.26	105	6.57
April..........................	6.4	5.31	103	5.47
May...........................	6.6	4.36	101	4.40
June..........................	6.8	3.54	99	3.50
July..........................	7.0	3.01	90	2.71
August........................	7.2	3.02	85	2.57
September.....................	7.4	6.88	75	5.16
October.......................	7.6	10.87	65	7.07
November......................	7.8	12.32	60	7.39
December......................	8.0	12.56	55	6.91

TABLE 80.—SEASONAL VARIATION
(In percentages of the average month)

January	145	May	66	September	93
February	124	June	52	October	143
March	101	July	43	November	158
April	83	August	42	December	157

When the seasonal variation and trend are combined, a line like BB' in Fig. 135 is produced; the data are shown in column (3) of Table 79. To obtain each monthly value for the line BB' each monthly coordinate of the line AA', that is, the growth element in the time series, has been multiplied by the index of seasonal variation for the corresponding month. This has the effect of redistributing the total of the 12 monthly figures of the growth line in such a manner as to make them properly reflect the seasonal element. Thus the trend figure for January is multiplied by 1.45 (or 145 per cent) while the April trend figure is multiplied by 0.83 (or 83 per cent).

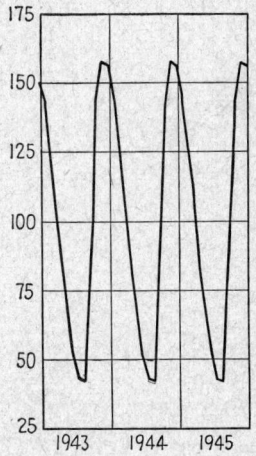

FIG. 136.—Seasonal variation in the hypothetical time series. See Table 80.

A third element of variation in time series is *cyclical fluctuation*, which may extend over several years. For example, Fig. 137 shows the rising and the falling movement of a cyclical fluctuation by months that occurs over a period of 3 years; this is shown also in column (4) of Table 79. In column (5) of Table 79 and in Fig. 138 are shown the effect of combining also the cyclical movement. The figures for the respective months are now altered according to whether the cycle is carrying them upward or downward, and the percentage figures for the cycle, shown in column (4), depict this upward and downward swing of the cycle. The cycle is put into the data by multiplying each monthly figure in column (3) by the corresponding monthly index of the cycle found in the same row of column (4). The results are shown in Fig. 138, which is the final hypothetical time series; the data for it are in column (5) of Table 79.

Two important effects of combining the growth element and the seasonal-variation element are noticeable from Fig. 135. In the first place, the combination has a tendency to obscure the trend. It is still clear in line BB' that there is a rising tendency, but the wide sweeps of the seasonal fluctuations tend to conceal the exact nature of the rise; for without the line AA' in Fig. 135 it would be difficult to visualize precisely what the slope of this trend actually is. In the second place, the combination definitely

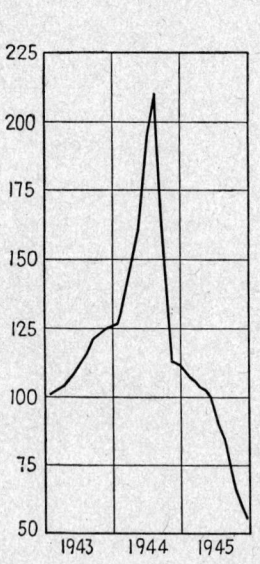

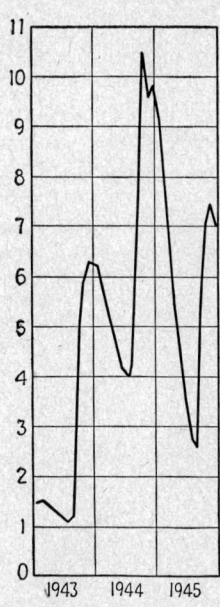

Fig. 137.—The cycle in the hypothetical time series. See Table 79, column (4).

Fig. 138.—All three component elements of the hypothetical time series combined. See Table 79, column (5).

distorts the shape of the seasonal variation, in two ways: (1) It causes the valleys and peaks to be thrown out of line arithmetically. (2) It minimizes the size of the seasonal variation where trend is low and exaggerates the size of the seasonal variation where trend is high.

From Fig. 138 it is clear that the effect of including the cyclical movement is further to obscure the trend or growth element and to distort still more the character of the seasonal variation. It is in approximately this condition that most time series exist in their raw state. Raw data of time series contain in varying degrees elements of all three of these types of fluctuation. Some have little seasonal variation, some have a great deal, and some have none. Many have rising trends following population and general growth, while a few have declining trends because they represent decaying or disappearing types of economic or social activities. In practically all time series, cycles of varying length and varying amplitude occur.

In addition to the three elements illustrated by the hypothetical case, most time series contain *fluctuations due to unusual or residual occurrences*, such as the effects of floods, storms, or strikes. This gives four elements or types of fluctuation and these four types of fluctuation serve as a good classification for an empirical start in the analysis of time series.[1]

GENESIS AND PURPOSES OF THE TIME-SERIES ANALYSIS

The hypothetical problem just illustrated consisted in a synthesis. The study of time series is analysis—a reversal of the procedure that has just been demonstrated. This breaking up of time series into its constituent elements, and the various complications involved, constitutes the subject of time-series analysis.

Why do economists, social scientists, and statisticians analyze time series? What started them along this line of procedure, and what are its advantages? The answers to these or other questions as to the significance of time-series analysis have in general a threefold basis: (1) interest in the population problem and the discovery of the law of organic growth, (2) concern for the general problem of the so-called "business cycle," and (3) preoccupation with the variety of problems associated with seasonal influences upon business and social life.

Rational Trends. *Historical Background.* In 1798, Thomas Robert Malthus, a minister of the gospel and a political economist, wrote an *Essay on the Principle of Population*, in which he advanced the fundamental principle that the law of growth of population is geometric—population, he said, tends to grow in a geometric progression. The curve representing population

---

[1] This is the conventional classification of types of fluctuation that occur in time series; it was presented in detail by W. M. Persons of the Harvard Committee of Economic Research and published in the *Review of Economic Statistics*, Preliminary Vol. 1. See also articles by the same author in the *American Economic Review*, Vol. 6 (1916), pp. 739–769, and *Publications of the American Statistical Association*, Vol. 12 (1917), pp. 602–642.

growth would accordingly be a positive exponential curve,
similar in character to the curve representing the growth of a
principal sum of money at compound interest.

While some of the doctrines of Malthus regarding the controls
to population growth are no longer accepted as tenable, the
fundamental principle of the tendency of population to grow
geometrically has not only been accepted with regard to population theory but has been widely applied in other fields.   To
people of the twentieth century this principle seems almost
axiomatic, for they are familiar with the history of the nineteenth
century, when the statistics show such a growth of population
and such a development of many kinds of activities according to
this principle of geometric progression.

The principle of growth was not so obvious to those living at
the time of Malthus, nor to those living in the middle of the
nineteenth century.   Consequently, it was startling and new to
see the same principle applied to growth in certain economic and
social phenomena, as was done by William Stanley Jevons, an
English economist, in his celebrated book on *The Coal Question*
(1865).   Chapter IX of that book is entitled Of the Natural Law
of Social Growth.   In this he propounds the idea that many of
the phenomena of economic and social life follow the same law
of organic growth as population.   In some, the progressive rate
of geometric growth is greater than that of population; in some,
less; but in all the growth is geometric.   In another chapter of
the same book, Jevons applied this principle and tested it with
reference to England's progress in industry.   His contribution
was of the nature of the proposal of a hypothesis that served as a
challenge to mathematically minded economists like himself
and others and soon stimulated the development of ideas as to
how best to write the equation for the curve that would represent growth of population.   By such an equation, it was thought,
population could be forecast far into the future as well as for
intercensus years.

Population Curves.   In 1891, A. S. Pritchett suggested that
an equation of the form $P = a + bt + ct^2 + dt^3$ would fit the
curve of population growth.   The subject of equations for the
population curve became one of wide concern to population
students, economists, and scientists in general, as well as of practical interest in obtaining accurate estimates of population

between the dates of taking the census. In 1907, Raymond
Pearl proposed that the form of this equation should be

$$P = a + bt + ct^2 + d \log t.*$$

The problem was again approached by G. Udny Yule, an English
statistician, in 1925;[1] and in later years the discussion was
continued.[2]

Perhaps the most striking contribution on the subject is that
of Raymond Pearl and Lowell J. Reed, who in 1920 advanced the
idea that the population curve should not continue to rise
indefinitely but should level off after some period of time and
that thus the population curve showing the law of growth would
not follow the compound-interest curve indefinitely. Rather, it
would resemble the curve shown in Fig. 145 in Chap. XXI.

The mathematical characteristics of this curve and its equations are presented by these joint authors in the *Journal of the
Royal Statistical Society* for 1927.† As will be clear from a glance
at Fig. 145, the shape of this curve indicates about the growth of
population or the law of organic growth that the first period
of relatively slow arithmetical growth is followed by a period
of very rapid arithmetical growth but that finally a period of
slowing down of this rapid arithmetical growth occurs so that the
curve at the top assumes an asymptotic character.

Early Population Theories. Quételet remarked that Malthus's
doctrine resolved itself essentially to the proposition that, under
the most favorable industrial circumstances, population could
grow no more rapidly than in an arithmetical progression,
although, of course, he stated the geometric law of growth as a

---

* Knibbs, George H., "The Laws of Growth of Population," *Journal of
the American Statistical Association*, Vol. 21 (1926), p. 381.

[1] *Journal of the Royal Statistical Society*, Vol. 88 (1925), pp. 1–62, which
contains an excellent historical summary of the problem of curve fitting to
population growth.

[2] Reed, L. J., and Raymond Pearl, "On the Summation of the Logistic
Curve," *Journal of the Royal Statistical Society*, Vol. 90 (1927), pp. 729–746.
The mathematics of the curve was discovered, say the authors, by Verhulst,
according to Quételet writing in 1838, and was again applied to population
by Pearl and Reed in 1920. *Cf.* Pearl, Raymond, *Studies in Human
Biology* (1924), Chap. XXIV, The Curve of Population Growth.

† *Op. cit.*

tendency. It could grow only in arithmetical progression because it would be kept down to that rate by the fact that subsistence grows only in arithmetical progression. He also pointed out that the theory of population growth up to the time he was writing (1836) had not been developed to the point where it could be considered "dans le domaine des sciences mathématiques, auquel elle semble spécialement devoir appartenir."[1] Even so, Quételet himself never went to the point of developing a mathematical equation expressing the law of population growth, although in other ways his contributions as a population theorist are outstanding. However, he did reach the point of suggesting that the law of population growth is like that of a body traveling through a resisting medium that tends to attain a limiting velocity.

Yule suggested that this analogy probably inspired Verhulst, professor of mathematics at the École Militaire, to a controversy with Quételet on the subject. The problem of devising a mathematical law of population growth was actively studied by Verhulst for a number of years. He fitted logistic curves to the population histories of several countries for as many years as data were available, but the limited amount of data did not inspire confidence in the results.[2] This work of Verhulst seems to have been forgotten until the time of the Pearl-Reed studies of 1920. Pearl and Reed's discovery of the law of population growth in the mathematical form developed by them was independent. As Yule says, they seemed to have been unaware of the formulation by Verhulst.

Basis for Rationalizing Trends. The attempt is made by students of the law of population growth to rationalize the fitting of such a logistic curve to experienced growth of population in many parts of the world, and at different times, by basing their reasoning upon the following points:

[1] *Sur l'homme* (Bruxelles, Louis Hauman et Comp. 1836), pp. 283, 287.

[2] *Notice sur la loi que la population suit dans son accroissement* (correspondance mathématique et physique publiée par A. Quételet, 1838), tome 10 (also numbered tome 2 of the third series), pp. 113–121; and by the same author, "Recherches mathématiques sur la loi d'accroissement de la population," *Nouveaux mémoires de l'Académie Royale des Sciences et Belles-Lettres de Bruxelles*, tome 17 (1845), pp. 1–38; "Deuxième mémoire sur la loi d'accroissement de la population," *ibid.*, tome 20 (1847), pp. 1–32. Citations from G. Udny Yule, *op. cit.*, p. 57.

1. The construction of such a curve through the plotted points showing actual population growth in a large number of places produces a good fit.

2. Biological experiment under controlled conditions, with other species than man, produces increases in numbers in a manner following such a curve. Thus Pearl made such an experiment with fruit flies under controlled conditions.[1]

3. Studies of trends in birth rates and death rates, in their relation to population growth, appear to fit into the theory that the law of population growth follows this curve.

4. Studies of death rates by age distribution of the population and the relationship between age composition and total death rate and birth rate of a population appear to fit into the law of population thus formulated.[2]

5. While it is true that the parabolas of earlier writers fit empirically the population growth wherever tried, such a curve fit cannot be rationalized, because the extension of the parabola goes on to infinity. On the other hand, the logistic curves of the Verhulst, Pearl-Reed, or Gompertz variety approach a limit in an asymptotic manner, which seems to be a more rational manner in which to view the law of population growth.

6. The asymptotic limit that it is assumed population is approaching can be closely approximated by study of the circumstances surrounding the determination of the factors influencing population growth.

Thus, it is recognized in this theory of the law of population growth that should technological changes comparable with the industrial revolution occur, the asymptotic limit might have to

---

[1] *Cf.* Pearl, R., *The Biology of Death*, pp. 253–254. Cited in Yule *op. cit.*, p. 22.

[2] These ideas have reached the general public as well as the scientific group, through such articles as Robert A. Kuczynski, "The World's Future Population," *The New Republic*, May 7, 1930; Aaron Hardy Ulm, "Our Falling Birth Rate Is Studied by Experts," *The New York Times*, Mar. 2, 1930; Louis I. Dublin (Statistician of the Metropolitan Life Insurance Company), "America Approaching Stabilized Population," *The New York Times*, Mar. 4, 1930; and by the same author, "Our Aging Population: Its Vital Effects," *The New York Times*, Jan. 4, 1931. *Cf.* also Dublin, Louis, I., and Alfred J. Lotka, "On the True Rate of Natural Increase," *Journal of the American Statistical Association*, Vol. 20 (1925), pp. 305–339; and Dublin, Louis I., "The Statistician and the Population Problem," *ibid.*, Vol. 20 (1925), pp. 1–12.

be raised and that the law of population growth over a period of centuries may be conceivably a series of ogive-like cycles.

Criticism of Rationalized Trends. However, this rationalistic view of curve fitting to population and the attainment in this manner of a mathematical law of population growth have not gone unchallenged. Prof. A. L. Bowley, an outstanding English statistician, says, "I regret that so much prominence has been given to the logistic equation. It certainly has the merit, and the danger, of mathematical neatness, and it expresses what may be regarded as a fundamental law of population—that is, that population cannot increase indefinitely in constant geometric progression. There is, however, no reason *a priori* to suppose that the damping down of the increase is of so regular or uniform a nature that a mathematical function of the same form represents it in all times and in all places, and none *a priori* to justify the use of a linear term (out of all possible functions) for this purpose. We should rather anticipate that the form of the function would be neither general nor linear. The justification for the logistic form is purely empirical, and, in fact, we are asked to accept it because it does give results which agree with the records of certain populations. Any other curve which gives as good an agreement has similar claims for representing the series of records. The closeness of the agreement is, I think, unduly accented by the very small vertical scales used by Dr. Pearl and Mr. Yule. . . ."[1]

T. H. C. Stevenson, another English statistician, rather prosaically declares that he finds sufficient explanation, without resort to logistic curves, for the rapid decline in birth rates since the end of the nineteenth century, in the dissemination of knowledge of contraception.[2]

. More recently, the whole question of the rationality of curve fitting was taken up in an admirably thorough manner by George H. Knibbs, whose findings are apparently that the mechanical process of the curve fitting is empirical and must be accepted as empirical but that the law of population growth may be conveniently expressed by such equations when it is

---

[1] From remarks on Yule's paper, *op. cit.*, p. 76.

[2] "The Laws Governing Population," *Journal of the Royal Statistical Society*, Vol. 88 (1925), pp. 63–76.

thoroughly understood how those equations apply, and also their limitations.[1]

It is natural to scientists to be skeptical, particularly of other scientists' startling discoveries, and the student of social science must get used to such controversies and pick and choose for himself what he believes to represent progressive development of human knowledge and what merely overzealous creative imagination. It is in these attempts to explain phenomena that the progressive development of human knowledge occurs.

Application of Rational Trends to Social Philosophy. It was pointed out above that Jevons had advanced the hypothesis that the law of organic growth applies also to social and economic phenomena. Following the example of the population curve-fitting group, scientific curiosity turned to the discovery of a rational conception of curve fitting to social, biological, and economic phenomena in order to replace purely empirical methods. As Wesley C. Mitchell has pointed out,[2] "A step toward such a conception is represented by the frequent interpretation of certain trend lines as showing the 'growth factor.' Statisticians dwell with satisfaction upon their demonstrations that certain industries have expanded decade after decade at a substantially uniform rate, or at a rate which has changed in some uniform way. They take almost as much pleasure in contemplating the somewhat similar rates at which different industries have grown in given periods and countries. Nor are they at a loss for explanation of these uniformities. In view of the increase in population characteristic of the great commercial nations and of the advance in industrial technique, it seems scarcely fanciful to think of modern society as 'tending' to produce an ever larger supply of goods for the satisfaction of its wants. On this basis, cyclical fluctuations appear as alternating accelerations and retardations in the pace of a more fundamental

[1] "Laws of Growth of Population," *Journal of the American Statistical Association*, Vol. 21 (1926), pp. 381–398; and Vol. 22 (1927), pp. 49–59.

[2] *Business Cycles—The Problem Stated and Its Setting*, (1928), pp. 221–224; *cf.* PRESCOTT, RAYMOND B., "Law of Growth in Forecasting Demand," (1928), *Journal of the American Statistical Association*, Vol. 17 (1922), pp. 471–479. Later, Leroy E. Peabody fitted such a curve to railway traffic in the United States, "Growth Curves and Railway Traffic," *Journal of the American Statistical Association*, Vol. 19 (1924), pp. 476–483.

process.   Secular trends, in short, are taken to measure economic progress generation by generation.   ·

"A bold speculation of this sort has been ventured by Raymond B. Prescott. He suggests that perhaps 'all industries, whose growth depends directly or indirectly upon the ability of the people to consume their products,' pass through similar phases in the course of their development. Four stages seem to be common.

1. Period of experimentation.
2. Period of growth into the social fabric.
3. Through the point where the growth increases, but at a diminishing rate.
4. Period of stability.

"On this basis, Prescott suggests that the secular trends of all such industries may be represented by a single type of curve— that yielded by the Gompertz equation. Every country may have a different rate of growth, and so may every industry, because no two industries have the same combination of influences. They will trace the same type of curve, however, even though the rate of growth is different."

More recently, an ambitious and carefully studied attempt to rationalize the whole subject of trends in economic phenomena was made by Simon S. Kuznets, of the National Bureau of Economic Research.[1] Kuznets analyzes the various factors making for growth, and also making for slowing up of growth, under the following items:

1. On the side of growth:
   Population increase.
   Changes in demand.
   Technological changes.
2. On the slowing up of growth:
   Slackening of technological progress.
   Retarding influence of other slower industries.
   Funds available for expansion decrease in relative size as industry grows.
   Competition of later developing industries in other countries.

[1] *Secular Movements in Production and Prices* (1930); in 1943, Kuznets's work is still the best statistical study of this type. For more recent trend studies of a different type, see Edwin Frickey, *Economic Fluctuations in the United States, 1866–1914* (1942), and Norman J. Silberling, *The Dynamics of Business* (1942). These studies use subjective methods for analyzing trends and cycles.

Kuznets fits logistic curves to a large number of production series and also fits appropriate curves to the corresponding price series. It should be noted that this type of rationalization does not apply to price series, and as a rule the curves that Kuznets fits to his price series were merely parabolas and represented empirical trends. One of the most interesting results of his work is his discovery and analysis of "secondary trends."

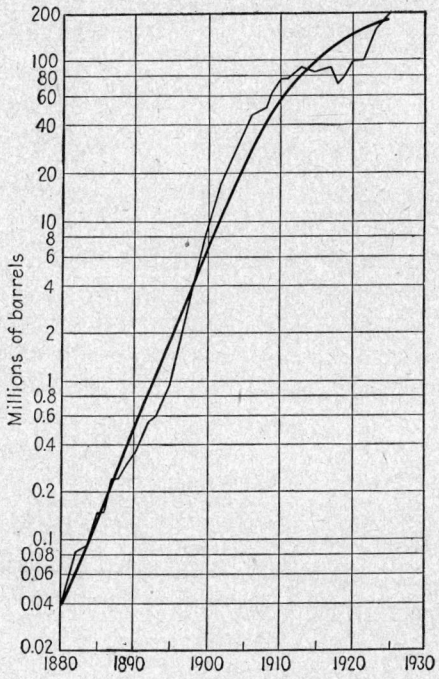

Fig. 139.—Production of Portland cement in the United States with logistic trend line, 1880–1924.

Thus, from a large variety of data, he took out the long-time growth, upon the assumption of the existence of a logistic growth element, and he found, not only cycles, but also longer wavelike movements of 11 to 20 years. This is illustrated by Figs. 139 to 141, reproduced from his book and showing the type of analysis as applied to cement production and prices, 1880–1924.[1] As seen in Fig. 139, the heavy line represents the logistic curve, and there are long sweeps of the actual data in waves above and below

[1] *Op. cit.*, pp. 100–101, reproduced by permission of the author.

this growth curve, as well as cyclical movements of shorter duration. Figure 140 shows a parabola fitted to the course of

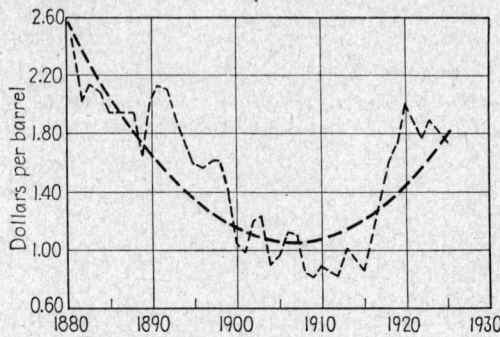

FIG. 140.—Factory prices of Portland cement in the United States, original data and primary trend, 1880–1924.

prices of cement during the same period. Figure 141 shows the long wavelike movements in production and in prices, with the relative fluctuations of the actual data above and below these

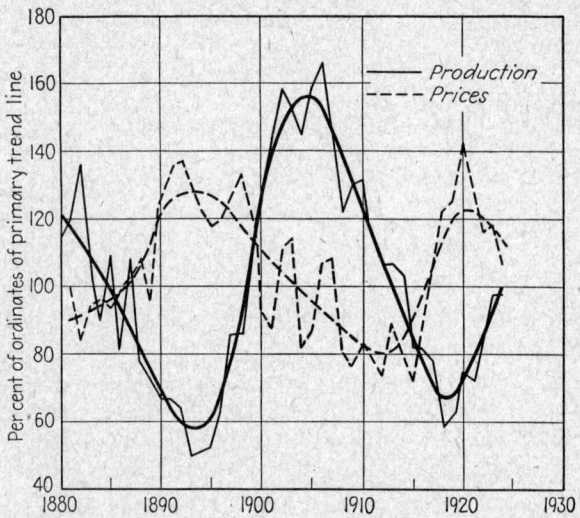

FIG. 141.—Production of and prices of Portland cement in the United States, 1880–1924. Secondary trends and minor cycles.

secondary trends. Kuznets calls the logistic growth curve the "primary trend line," and the heavy, black, wavelike line in Fig. 141 represents the secondary trends of the production of cement. The actual data fluctuate above and below these secondary trends in major and minor cycles.

Before the publication of Kuznets's work these longer movements had been studied by C. A. R. Wardell.[1] Wardell called the movements "major cycles" rather than secondary trends, and his method of analysis was quite different from that followed by Kuznets. He also attempted to give an explanation of the major business cycle that Kuznets rejects.[2] In 1927, also, there appeared in Russian a discussion of the whole problem of major cycles, which contains a report by Kondratieff and a counter-reply by D. T. Oparin. To explain these major cycles Kondratieff developed the theory that they are essentially cycles of expansion and contraction in the growth of the basic capital equipment of a country.

Thus, starting with the desire to define the law of population growth more precisely and to bring the population problem into the realm of mathematical treatment, scholars have carried on by analogy into other fields; so far as economics is concerned, the principal result so far is the discovery of these long wavelike movements. Not only do the theoretical economists need to explain the old-fashioned business cycle (which was always a rather vague concept), but they now are challenged to explain (1) secondary secular movements or major business cycles, (2) ordinary business cycles, and (3) minor business cycles. The analysis of time series, then, must include some additional types of fluctuations from those described in a preliminary manner at the beginning of the chapter.

The following classification of movements is now suggested.[3]

1. *Trend,* or *long-time growth,* which appears to be logistic in character and for which a mathematical formula may be rational.

2. *Cyclical movements* of three types, for which a rational mathematical formula is not appropriate.

    a. Secondary secular movements or major cycles.

    b. Cycles (the old theoretical business cycle).

    c. Minor cycles.

[1] *An Investigation of Economic Data for Major Cycles,* Thesis (University of Pennsylvania, 1927).

[2] *Op. cit.,* pp. 265–266.

[3] *Cf.* classification suggested by Prof. Willford I. King, which is similar, in "Principles Underlying the Isolation of Cycles and Trends," *Journal of the American Statistical Association,* Vol. 19 (1924), p. 468.

3. *Seasonal variations*, for which a mathematical formula is not rational.

4. *Irregular fluctuations*, such as those due to wars, epidemics, floods, or strikes. These are called "residual fluctuations" and may follow the normal curve.[1]

Empirical Trends. Trend analysis, that is to say, the application of mathematical processes in order to obtain equations describing direction of movement of a time series, may be applied, not only for rational ends indicated in the discussion of the law of organic growth, but also empirically where no a priori knowledge about the character of growth or law of movement or trend exists. Indeed, the search for such a law may have no bearing on the analysis; the trend may be sought for the purpose of isolating and studying cyclical movements. When trends are found without seeking to verify some hypothesis concerning a law of growth but merely with respect to given data, they are empirical trends.

Application of Empirical Trends to Cycle Analysis. The third factor mentioned at the beginning of this chapter as a force stimulating statistical analysis of time series has been the abstract study of the business cycle. Such abstract analysis has challenged the mathematical economist and the statistician to discover and to apply methods of statistical analysis that would measure the cycle.

Economic history of the modern era has been one of alternating periods of relative prosperity and relative depression and has also been characterized by periods of more or less violent speculative activity. The Mississippi Scheme and the South Sea Bubble burst in France and England in 1720, and there occurred commercial crises of major importance in 1763, 1772, 1783, and 1793. During the eighteenth century these recurring periods of crisis excited much discussion, but eighteenth-century writings dealt mainly with the dramatic surface events and did not develop a theory explaining them. And indeed the fundamental principles of economics were not formulated until the latter half of the eighteenth century. The publication of Adam Smith's *Wealth of Nations* in 1776 is usually taken as the debut of economics as a science.

---

[1] See pp. 285–297, and 570, 648.

While a group of economists following Adam Smith developed a theoretical explanation of the operation of economic forces under normal conditions, or in the long run, another group that assumed the role of critics of the "economists" developed theories of the business cycle. These were such men as Sismondi, Rodbertus, and Karl Marx. J. C. L. Simonde de Sismondi, an Italian Swiss, had originally been a thorough convert of Adam Smith and *laissez faire* and had become the Continental expositor of his theories; but as he said, writing in 1818 and referring to the depression of 1815–1817, he was deeply affected by the commercial crisis that Europe had experienced and by the cruel sufferings of the industrial workers that he had witnessed in Italy, Switzerland, and France and that all reports showed to have been at least as severe in England, in Germany, and in Belgium.[1] He set about developing a theory to explain the recurrence of such periods, and in his work are found many of the ideas current even today concerning the origin and explanation of the business cycle. He suggested that the business cycle is due to the faulty organization of the capitalist system and that the system is planless and therefore needs planning. He also suggested the explanation that what is needed is a better distribution of income. He suggested the oversaving hypothesis. His principal explanation is the inequality in the distribution of incomes resulting in glutting of the markets and the production of crises and depressions.

The idea that commercial crises are cyclical in character evolved early in the nineteenth century; some even went so far as to advance the theory that they occur every 7 or every 11 years. In 1875, this led the economist and statistician, W. S. Jevons, to propound a theory that the business cycle is due to cycles that occur in sun spots, which it had been discovered have a rhythm of about 11 years.[2] During the latter half the nineteenth century a number of statistical attempts to discover the business cycle were made. The attempts used the idea of smoothing out the irregular fluctuations in the curves of raw data and

---

[1] MITCHELL, *op. cit.*, pp. 4–5. The historical material here given on the business cycle is taken principally from this source.

[2] For a more complete discussion of the history of business-cycle theory than it is possible to give here, see *ibid.* and also Ernst Wagemann, *Economic Rhythm*, (1930), either of which contains further bibliographical references.

thereby clarifying the cyclical movements. The earliest examples of such statistical work appear to be in 1884.[1]

Both Jevons and the later experimenters of the nineteenth century were content with attempts to discover cyclical movements in separate individual series. In 1909, Beveridge in England; in 1911, Julin in France; and in 1913, Mortara in Italy conceived the idea of combining a number of series into a composite statistical measure of the business cycle. The work of carrying out this task was then largely taken over by the American statisticians, in the construction of the so-called "barometers" of business conditions that have been described in Chap. XIX Index Numbers. The period up to about 1914 may be characterized as one during which interest in the subject of the business cycle was intense. Economists were in sharp controversy with the business-cycle theorists—denying emphatically the implications that they drew from their analysis of the statistics available and from their theoretical explanations of the business cycle. At the same time, the disturbing theories of the business-cycle students had greater claim to general interest because they touched upon a more vital and present thing than was customarily dealt with by the conventional economist. The conventional economist was explaining how things tend to happen under normal conditions, and the business-cycle theorists loudly proclaimed that we never live under "normal conditions" and that the theories of the economist were therefore useless. At the same time, the interest of the practical businessman was aroused by the desire for knowledge of the relationship between his own particular business and the general business cycle.

Development of Technique for Time-series Analysis. The pressure to develop a statistical technique to analyze the problem was thus very great, and the accumulation of available statistical material to analyze had been rapid for a number of years. The technique that developed assumed two general characteristics, one of which has since been extensively used, the other less frequently.

The first method of technique that developed was the discovery statistically of the cycle in time series by the removal of the

[1] POYNTING, J. H., and R. H. HOOKER, "A Comparison of the Fluctuations in the Price of Wheat and in the Cotton and Silk Imports into Great Britain," *Journal of the Royal Statistical Society*, Vol. 47 (1884), pp. 34–64.

trend from a series of annual data. Trends were fitted empirically to the data by the method of least squares or some other method—most commonly by the method of least squares—using relatively short periods of time, say 9 to 19 years. The cyclical movements then were the measures of the movements of the data above and below the empirical trend. Prof. Willford I. King said, "Any particular type of fluctuation in which we happen to be interested can be successfully studied only when most of the other kinds of fluctuations have been eliminated."[1]

This is, of course, the *raison d'être* for the empirical trend analysis, which is primarily for the purpose of isolating the ordinary and the minor cycles. The major cycles or secondary secular movements are best studied by the Kuznets methods that have been described and illustrated. The methods of analysis used are essentially similar to those employed in empirical trend analysis, but the Kuznets logistic trend lines may be rationalized in terms of a law of organic growth.

The second method of technique that developed was the attempt to apply harmonic analysis or the periodogram to series of economic data, a different application of the method of least squares. This was the work of Henry L. Moore of Columbia University in his application of Fourier's theorem, the mathematics of which Fourier had developed a century ago in his *Théorie des mouvements de la chaleur dans les corps solides* and for which he was feted by the Académie des Sciences in 1812.

Prof. Moore applied the mathematics of the periodogram to the records of rainfall in the corn belt of the United States, working out the periodogram equations for the cycles of rainfall; he discovered similar cycles in crops and introduced the harmonic analysis into modern statistical method. He says:[2] "The principal contribution of this essay is the discovery of the law and cause of economic cycles. The rhythm in the activity of economic life, the alternation of buoyant, purposeful expansion with aimless depression, is caused by the rhythm in the yield per acre of the crops; while the rhythm in the production of the

---

[1] *Journal of the American Statistical Association,* Vol. 19 (1924), p. 468.

[2] *Economic Cycles: Their Law and Cause* (1914). *Cf.* CRUM, W. L., "Periodogram Analysis," Chap. XI in H. L. Reitz, *Handbook of Mathematical Statistics* (1924). Also BRUNT, DAVID, *The Combination of Observations* (1931), Chaps. XI and XII.

crops is, in turn, caused by the rhythm of changing weather, which is represented by the cyclical changes in the amount of rainfall.   The law of the cycles of rainfall is the law of the cycles of the crops and the law of economic cycles."

The mathematics of the harmonic analysis are somewhat complex, and this method has not attained the popularity that has been attached to the removal of empirical trend by using straight lines or second- or third-degree polynomials, where the mathematical analysis involved is quite simple.

Use of Functions of Arc Tangent and Orthogonal Polynomials in Trend Analysis.   In recent years two modified forms of the conventional trend analysis by the method of least squares have been developed.   In 1928, it was suggested that the inverse trigonometric function, or arc tangent, could be adapted to measuring trends in series behaving in the following manner:[1]

1. A downward tendency approximating a straight line but of such nature that projection of a straight line into the future would lead to absurd results, that is, negative or ridiculously small positive values when comparatively large positive values only are possible.

2. Approximately a linear growth or decline, followed by an abrupt change in level (rise or drop) and subsequent resumption of the early tendency.

3. Approximately a straight-line trend interrupted by a sharp rise or drop, followed by another abrupt change in level and subsequent resumption of the early movement at the same or a different level.

The method was used successfully in fitting a trend to the annual prices of International Paper common stock for the period 1900–1926 and to the annual index of wholesale prices in the United States, 1900–1928.

The orthogonal analysis is a method invented for reducing the amount of arithmetical calculation involved in fitting polynomials to time series by the method of least squares, especially second- and third-degree polynomials or polynomials of higher degree.   The fitting of a polynomial of higher than second degree to a time series involves laborious calculations, particularly if a considerable period of time is covered.   This laborsaving method

<hr />

[1] CARMICHAEL, F. L., "The Arc Tangent in Trend Determination," *Journal of the American Statistical Association*, Vol. 23 (1928), pp. 253–262.

is described in detail, together with tables of values to facilitate its use, in Chap. XXII.[1]

[1] See pp. 600–615. Also *cf.* JORDAN, CHARLES, "Approximation and Graduation According to the Principle of Least Squares by Orthogonal Polynomials," *The Annals of Mathematical Statistics*, Vol. 3 (1932), pp. 257–357. *Cf.* ROMANOVSKY, V., "Note on Orthogonalizing Series of Functions and Interpolation," *Biometrika*, Vol. 19 (1927), pp. 93–99; JORDAN, CHARLES, "Sur une série de polynomes dont chaque somme partielle représente la meilleure approximation d'un degré donné suivant la méthode les moindres carrés," *Proceedings of the London Mathematical Society*, Vol. 20 (1921), pp. 297–325; and DIEULEFAIT, CARLOS E., "La determinación de la tendencia secular en las series económicas," Gabinete de Estadística, Rosario, Argentine Republic (Santa Fe), Universidad Nacional del Litoral (1932), pp. 1–52. *Cf.* FISCHER, R. A., *Statistical Methods for Research Workers* (4th ed., 1932), pp. 133–142.

CHAPTER XXI

TREND ANALYSIS

Empirical Trend vs. Rational Trend. Both empirical and rational trends are obtained by analysis from raw data; the difference between the two is that a rational trend can be explained in terms of long-time growth or decline, whereas an empirical trend has no meaning per se. The empirical trend is a useful tool of analysis, as will be seen in the ensuing discussion.

In the preceding chapter the attempt was made to convey the idea that a rational trend is one that is found for its own sake; it has a rational explanation and is useful as a method of interpretation in itself. While it may be true that the rationalization that is made with respect to such trends is preliminary or even tentative, nevertheless the original intent is to make a rational use of them. Empirical trends are those for which there is admittedly no rational basis at the start, being used merely as a convenient method of removing from the data longer time movements that obscure the shorter time cyclical fluctuations.

Empirical trends in themselves may have no rational significance as a description of any type of long-time growth, or movement. An empirical trend calculated for a period of 9 years at a point in time coincident with the peak of a secondary secular movement would presumably be in the form of a parabola. At another point in time, a 9-year trend analysis may give a straight line, or a logarithmic line. If a trend line happened to be calculated for a period of time from the low point of a secondary secular movement to the high point of another, the empirical trend might assume the form of a Verhulst growth curve; but it may have no such significance as a law of growth in that case, being simply the result of happening to take an empirical trend for that period of time. An examination of the heavy black curve representing the secondary trends in cement production (Fig. 141, page 556) will help to make clear what is meant by these statements.

Detecting Cycle by Removing Empirical Trend. While empirical trends may have no rational significance per se, the fitting of an empirical trend to the annual data of a time series will make it possible to isolate the residuals from the trend. These residuals constitute the cycles and minor cycles of the period analyzed. The first clear statement of the analysis of time series by this method was made by W. M. Persons in 1915.[1] The method is illustrated by examples at the end of this chapter.

Thus the function of empirical trend analysis is to obtain an approximation to some longer term movement for the purpose of eliminating this in order to study shorter term movements of a cyclical or accidental character. The empirical trend may approximate a segment of a long-term cyclical movement, or it may approximate a portion of long-term growth in the series that might itself have rational explanation. What the empirical trend measures depends upon the circumstances in each problem, and the discovery of the rational nature of an empirical trend depends upon a priori knowledge.

Methods of Fitting Trend. Three methods of fitting trend to time series can be distinguished: (1) the method of least squares, (2) the method of selected points, and (3) the method of averages.

Fitting a Trend Line by the Method of Least Squares. Figure 142 represents a plane in which there are seven points, $P_1, \ldots, P_7$. To simplify the arithmetic an uneven number of points is taken, and the middle point is selected for the location of the y-axis.[2] Accordingly, t varies from -3 to $+3$. The coordinates of the points, as may be observed from the figure, are as follows:

$$P_1(t = -3, y_1) \qquad P_2(t = -2, y_2) \qquad P_3(t = -1, y_3)$$
$$P_4(t = 0, y_4) \qquad P_5(t = 1, y_5) \qquad P_6(t = 2, y_6) \qquad P_7(t = 3, y_7)$$

---

[1] *American Economic Review,* December, 1916, pp. 739–769; *Publications of the American Statistical Association,* June, 1917, pp. 602–642; *Harvard Review of Economic Statistics,* Preliminary Vol. 1 (1919). *Cf.* MITCHELL, W. C., *Business Cycles—The Problem Stated and Its Setting,* pp. 200, 212–213, 328–330.

[2] For statistical purposes it is more convenient to take a more recent year as the time origin than that of the birth of Christ. Thus, if a given set of data run from 1927, say, to 1937, it might be convenient to choose 1932 as the zero year. If this were done, then 1933 would be $t = 1$, 1935 would be $t = 3$, 1929 would be $t = -3$, etc.

The corresponding points on the straight line to be found, for example, point A in the figure, may be represented by the following coordinates:

$$(t = -3, y'_1) \quad (t = -2, y'_2) \quad (t = -1, y'_3)$$
$$(t = 0, y'_4) \quad (t = 1, y'_5) \quad (t = 2, y'_6) \quad (t = 3, y'_7)$$

The general form of the equation for a straight line in a field of coordinates y and t is $y = a + bt$, and for this line the equation is as follows:

$$y' = a + bt \tag{1}$$

The line is determined for the particular case by finding values of a and b.

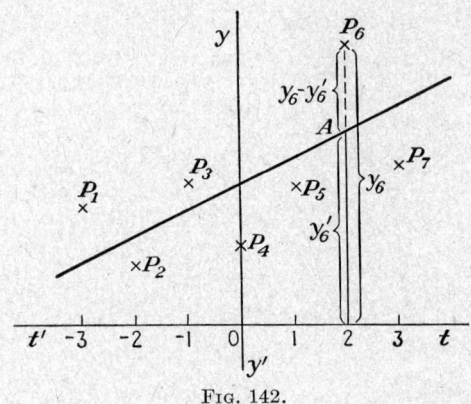

FIG. 142.

The line that is sought is the one from which the sum of the squared deviations of the points from the line is less than such a sum with respect to any other line. This is the least-squares criterion.

The vertical residuals of particular points from the line are as follows, as illustrated in Fig. 142 for P_6:

$$r_1 = y_1 - y'_1$$
$$r_2 = y_2 - y'_2$$
$$\cdots \cdots$$
$$r_6 = y_6 - y'_6 \quad \text{(illustrated by } P_6 \text{ in Fig. 142)}$$
$$r_7 = y_7 - y'_7$$

Some of these variations (designated as r) are negative, for example, at P_7, while others are positive, as at P_6. When squared, however, they are all positive and the conditions that must be satisfied according to the least-squares criterion for a line that will best fit these points is that Σr^2 = minimum, in other words, that

$$\Sigma(y - y')^2 = \text{minimum} \tag{2}$$

The value of y', from Eq. (1), may be substituted; Eq. (2) then becomes

$$\Sigma(y - a - bt)^2 = \text{minimum} \tag{3}$$

The condition under which Eq. (3) is true is that the total differential is equal to zero, in other words, that

$$d(\Sigma r^2) = \frac{\partial(\Sigma r^2)}{\partial a}\,da + \frac{\partial(\Sigma r^2)}{\partial b}\,db = 0$$

Inasmuch as da and db cannot be equal to zero, this gives the two conditions that[1]

$$\left.\begin{aligned}
\frac{\partial(\Sigma r^2)}{\partial a} &= \frac{\partial}{\partial a}\,\Sigma(y - a - bt)^2 = \Sigma 2(y - a - bt) = 0 \\
\frac{\partial(\Sigma r^2)}{\partial b} &= \frac{\partial}{\partial b}\,\Sigma(y - a - bt)^2 = \Sigma 2t(y - a - bt) = 0
\end{aligned}\right\} \tag{4}$$

and hence the following two equations, by canceling out the 2's and carrying out the summations:

$$\Sigma y = Na + b\Sigma t \tag{i}$$
$$\Sigma ty = a\Sigma t + b\Sigma t^2 \tag{ii}$$

In these two equations, all the terms are known, except a and b; because $\Sigma t = 0$ and Σy is the sum of the known y's of the seven points $P_1, \ldots, P_7$. The Σt^2 is

$$9 + 4 + 1 + 0 + 1 + 4 + 9$$

Because $\Sigma t = 0$, values for a and b can be found as follows:

$$a = \frac{\Sigma y}{N} \qquad \text{from Eq. (i)}$$

$$b = \frac{\Sigma ty}{\Sigma t^2} \qquad \text{from Eq. (ii)}$$

[1] In the case under consideration, it is not necessary to be concerned with the possibility that these same conditions might also hold true for a maximum or a minimum, since the conditions of the problem indicate that it is a minimum.

Accordingly, the equation for the line of best fit, by the criterion of least squares, is as follows:

$$y' = \frac{\Sigma y}{N} + \frac{\Sigma ty}{\Sigma t^2} t \qquad (5)$$

Numerical Illustration. As a more concrete illustration, values will be assigned to the y's of the seven points, as follows (t coordinates remaining as before):

$$P_1(y = 5) \qquad P_2(y = 2) \qquad P_3(y = 7) \qquad P_4(y = 4)$$
$$P_5(y = 6) \qquad P_6(y = 10) \qquad P_7(y = 8)$$

An orderly work sheet will be set up in order to find Σy, Σty, and Σt^2. N, of course, is equal to 7.

WORK SHEET FOR FINDING BEST-FITTING STRAIGHT LINE FOR SEVEN GIVEN POINTS

t	y	ty	t^2
−3	5	−15	9
−2	2	−4	4
−1	7	−7	1
0	4	0	0
1	6	6	1
2	10	20	4
3	8	24	9
		50	
$\Sigma t = 0$	$\Sigma y = 42$	−26	$\Sigma t^2 = 28$
		$\Sigma ty = 24$	

The equation for the best-fitting line according to the least squares criterion is therefore as follows [see Eq. (5)]:

$$y' = \tfrac{42}{7} + \tfrac{24}{28}t$$

or

$$y' = 6 + 0.86t$$

It will be well to note what the equation says. First, with each unit increase of t, the line (that is, the value of y') rises by 0.86. This value, 0.86, is called the "slope" of the line; and it is the tangent of the angle that the line makes with the t-axis or with any line parallel to the t-axis. Second it says that, when $t = 0$, $y' = 6$. This means that the line passes through the y-axis at a point $+6$ from the t-axis (when the y-axis is located at the middle point in time).

If the y-axis were shifted from its present location to the position $t = -3$, everything else remaining in its original position, the value of the t coordinates of all the points P will change to accord with the new location of the y-axis. Also, it is to be noted that the above equation would then become

$$y' = [6 - 3(0.86)] + 0.86t$$

or

$$y' = 3.42 + 0.86t$$

since 3.42 will be the intercept on the new y-axis.

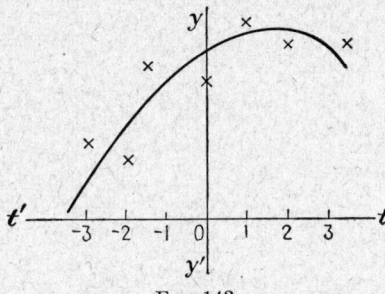

Fig. 143.

Fitting Second- or Third-degree Curves. Second-, third-, or even high-degree curves may similarly be fitted by the method of least squares. It may happen that the points are distributed in such a manner that a straight line does not fit. For example, Fig. 143 shows seven points that would be better fitted by a parabola. The general form of the equation for such a curve is

$$y' = a + bt + ct^2$$

The equations for finding values of a, b, and c, for such a best-fitting parabola, are worked out on precisely the same principles as those for finding a and b for the best-fitting straight line.[1] That is to say, the equation $y' = a + bt + ct^2$ is fitted to the points so that

$$\Sigma(y - y')^2 = \text{minimum} \tag{6}$$

and when the value of y' is substituted in this equation, it becomes

[1] For a better method of fitting polynomials by the method of least squares, see Chap. XXII, Orthogonal Polynomial Trends.

$$\Sigma(y - a - bt - ct^2)^2 = \text{minimum} \qquad (7)$$

When this expression is differentiated with respect to a, b, and c, following the same method as in Eqs. (4), (i), and (ii), the equations for finding a, b, and c are obtained, as follows:

$$\Sigma y = Na + b\Sigma t + c\Sigma t^2 \qquad \text{(i)}$$
$$\Sigma ty = a\Sigma t + b\Sigma t^2 + c\Sigma t^3 \qquad \text{(ii)}$$
$$\Sigma t^2 y = a\Sigma t^2 + b\Sigma t^3 + c\Sigma t^4 \qquad \text{(iii)}$$

A work sheet such as the following form (leaving out columns for the uneven powers of t; they will presumably all be zero since the zero value of t is selected in the middle of an odd number of years) is used for finding values of a, b, and c.

WORK SHEET FOR FINDING BEST-FITTING PARABOLA FOR SEVEN GIVEN POINTS

t	y	ty	t^2y	t^2	t^4
. . . .	. . . .	. . . .	. . . .	. . . .	. . . .
. . . .	. . . .	. . . .	. . . .	. . . .	. . . .
$\Sigma t = \cdots$	$\Sigma y = \cdots$	$\Sigma ty = \cdots$	$\Sigma t^2y = \cdots$	$\Sigma t^2 = \cdots$	$\Sigma t^4 = \cdots$

Since $\Sigma t = 0$, when the sums of the columns in the work sheet are substituted in Eqs. (i), (ii), and (iii) above, the three unknowns a, b, and c may be found by solutions of these.

Probability Theory Is Not Applied.   It must be remembered that the application of the least-squares criterion for obtaining the line that best fits a time series does not involve the application of the theory of least squares in the sense that the trend line obtained is a most probable line, expressive of a law of movement or growth in the probability sense.[1]   As originally applied, the theory of least squares had a definite connection with the theory of probabilities because it was devised as a method of obtaining a measure of the most probable orbit of a comet, etc. In the fitting of a trend line to a single time series there is no multiplicity of cases fluctuating in a normal distribution about the

[1] *Cf.* KUZNETS, SIMON S., *Secular Movements in Production and Prices* (1930), p. 62, who cites W. H. R. Lexis, *Zur Theorie der Massenerscheinungen in der menschlichen Gesellschaft* (Freiburg, *i.B.*, F. Wagner, Ed: 1877), pp. 31–33. See also TINTNER, GERHARD, "The Analysis of Economic Time Series," *Journal of the American Statistical Association*, Vol. 35 (1940), pp. 93–100.

trend line.   The use of the least-squares criterion in trend fitting for time series is merely the application by analogy of a method that produces desired results; it gives an objective criterion for finding the line of best fit.   If the analyst can be satisfied with a less objective method, he may use, for example, the method of selected points, which will now be described.

Methods of Selected Points.   One of the simplest methods of determining the trend of a time series is to make the trend "line" pass through certain points selected as representative of normal values.   This line[1] may be drawn in a purely freehand fashion, or a mathematical equation may be determined such that it is satisfied by the coordinates of the selected points.

To determine a unique mathematical equation in a given case the number of selected points must be taken equal to the number of parameters in the equation.   Thus, if a straight-line trend seems appropriate, two normal years are selected (preferably near the ends of the series) and the values of a and b in the equation $y' = a + bt$ are so determined that the equation is satisfied by the values of t and y for the selected points.   If a parabolic trend of the type $y' = a + bt + ct^2$ is deemed appropriate, then three normal points must be selected to determine the values of a, b, and c.   In general, if a polynomial of the nth degree is taken to portray the course of the trend, viz., $y' = a + bt + ct^2 + \cdots + kt^n$, then there must be n selected points.   The polynomial is the simplest type of mathematical equation to employ for this purpose.   Other, more "rational" types may also be fitted by this method, however, and its use in fitting a simple logistic curve is described below.

The actual process of finding the mathematical equation of the chosen type that is satisfied by the selected points consists in solving n simultaneous equations, n being the number of selected points (or the number of parameters to be determined).   Thus if (t_1,y_1) and (t_2,y_2) are the coordinates of the selected points, the straight line $y' = a + bt$ passing through these points is given by the solution of the following equations for a and b:

$$y_1 = a + bt_1$$
$$y_2 = a + bt_2$$

[1] "Line" is here used in the generic sense; it may be either straight or curved.

For example, if the time scale is such that $t_1 = 3$ and $t_2 = 9$ and if the y values for these years (or months) are[1] $y_1 = 68$ and $y_2 = 110$, then a and b are found by solving the equations

$$68 = a + 3b$$
$$110 = a + 9b$$

These yield $a = 47$ and $b = 7$; hence the equation for the given trend is $y' = 47 + 7t$.

If the equation to be fitted is a second-degree parabola $y' = a + bt + ct^2$ and if (t_1,y_1), (t_2,y_2), and (t_3,y_3) are the coordinates of the selected points, then a, b, and c are determined by solving the equations

$$y_1 = a + bt_1 + ct_1^2$$
$$y_2 = a + bt_2 + ct_2^2$$
$$y_3 = a + bt_3 + ct_3^2$$

Three equations are more difficult to solve than two; but if the time scale is chosen so that $t_1 = 0$, then these reduce to

$$y_1 = a$$
$$y_2 = a + bt_2 + ct_2^2$$
$$y_3 = a + bt_3 + ct_3^2$$

or

$$y_2 - y_1 = bt_2 + ct_2^2$$
$$y_3 - y_1 = bt_3 + ct_3^2$$

and two equations are obtained for determining b and c, the value of a being y_1. For example, if the selected points are

$(t_1 = 0, \; y_1 = 68)$ $(t_2 = 6, \; y_2 = 110)$ $(t_3 = 12, \; y_3 = 200)$

then $a = 68$ and b and c may be found from the solution of the equations

$$110 - 68 = 6b + 36c$$
$$200 - 68 = 12b + 144c$$

The results are $b = 3$ and $c = \frac{2}{3} = 0.67$; hence, the parabola which passes through the given points is

$$y' = 68 + 3t + 0.67t^2, \quad \text{origin at } t_1 = 0$$

When higher degree polynomials are fitted in this way, the simultaneous equations may be solved by repeated substitution,

---

[1] These values may be actual values or values estimated as normal.

or special methods making use of finite differences may be employed.[1]

Method of Averages. Even less refined methods of fitting lines to data than those already described could be applied; in fact, the analyst could, if he so desired, merely draw the line that seems to fit the plotted data. The objection to this method is that it is too subjective—no two people would draw the same line. A certain degree of objectivity is secured by applying the method of selected points, which has already been described, or by using a modification of that method, namely, the method of averages. The method of averages merely suggests a refinement in the selection of the points. It can be illustrated by the fitting of a straight line, but it could be applied to curves as well.

WORK SHEET FOR FITTING A STRAIGHT-LINE TREND BY THE METHOD OF AVERAGES

t	y	
1	5	
2	2	$t_3 = 3, \quad y'_3 = 5$
3	7	For $t = 3$, y is taken as the average of the first five
4	4	y's; that is, $\frac{25}{5} = 5$.
5	7	
6	8	
7	15	For $t = 8$, y is taken as the average of the last five
8	19	y's; that is, $\frac{75}{5} = 15$.
9	18	$t_8 = 8, \quad y'_8 = 15$
10	15	

The trend line is the straight line passing through the two points $t = 3$, $y' = 5$ and $t = 8$, $y' = 15$. Following the same procedure as that used in the method of selected points, the parameters a and b are found by solving the following two equations:

$$5 = a + 3b$$
$$15 = a + 8b$$

from which it is found that $b = 2$ and $a = -1$, so that the trend line is $y' = -1 + 2t$.

Method of Moving Averages. Ordinarily the method of moving averages is used with monthly data, but it could be used with annual data if an appropriate number of years over which to

---

[1] For the latter, the reader is referred to E. T. Whittaker and G. Robinson, *The Calculus of Observations* (1924), Chap. I.

average or smooth the data could be determined.   The difficulty of determining the proper number of years for the averaging period is one of the objections to this method; another objection is that it does not give an equation of trend.   The method of moving averages is explained in Chap. XXIII, Seasonal Variation.

Advantages of the Method of Least Squares.   The advantage of using the least-squares line is that it gives a line from which the residuals add up to zero and when squared are a minimum; this supplies an objective criterion to the fit of the line.   In addition, the least-squares method of trend fitting is a very flexible device that can be widely applied and varied according to the type of line desired.   If a complex trend line is desired, a mathematical procedure based upon the least-square criterion is handily available.   The method of orthogonal polynomials explained in the next chapter, for example, is an application of the method of least squares.

ILLUSTRATIONS OF RATIONAL TRENDS

As indicated in the preceding chapter, rational trends are likely to be logistic in character.   The simplest type of logistic curve is of the form $y = ab^t$, which may readily be reduced to a straight line if the equation is expressed in logarithms, as follows: $\log y = \log a + t \log b$.

Trend of a Dying Institution.   If the early development, growth, and arrival at maturity of a new economic institution follow the pattern suggested by Raymond B. Prescott, as explained in the preceding chapter, presumably the disappearance of a dying institution would follow a reversal of that pattern. Thus, it would die slowly at first, then rapidly, and then slowly again until it finally disappeared.   If such is the case, the appropriate equation to use is one of the Verhulst, Pearl-Reed, or Gompertz types of curves.   However, an economic institution that is disappearing from the economic system might depart in another manner; it might be struck a sudden devastating blow by a new development that caused it to die or decline according to the simple logistic curve $y = ab^t$.   Such appears to be the case with respect to a certain type of commercial bank credit known as "open-market commercial paper."   Many authorities on money and credit believe this to be a dying institution in this country; and accordingly the downward trend illustrated in Table 81 and Fig. 144 may be considered a rational trend.[1] The data used are annual average monthly volumes of open-market commercial paper outstanding; and Table 81 is a work sheet for calculating the straight-line logarithmic trend line for these data, following the method indicated on pages 566 to 568. Here, however, the straight line is fitted to the logarithms of the data instead of to the data themselves.

The equation for this trend line is $y' = ab^t$, so that, by the rule of logarithms,

$$\log y' = \log a + t \log b$$

The two least-squares equations that would be obtained by the method explained above are as follows:[2]

$$\Sigma \log y = N \log a + \log b \Sigma t$$
$$\Sigma t \log y = \log a \Sigma t + \log b \Sigma t^2$$

Upon substituting the sums taken from the appropriate columns of Table 81, this gives

$$36.18035 = 23 \log a$$
$$-38.41844 = 1,012 \log b$$

from which

$$\log a = 1.57306 \quad \text{and} \quad \log b = -0.037963$$

Therefore, the equation of the best-fitting (according to the least-squares criterion) logarithmic trend in this case is

$$\log y' = 1.57306 - 0.037963t$$

When a logarithmic straight line is fitted to a time series by the method of least squares, it is the sum of the squares of the ratio residuals that is made a minimum—and not the sum of the squares of the actual residuals as is the case where an arith-

---

[1] For explanations of the demise of open-market commercial paper see B. H. Beckhart, *The New York Money Market*, Vol. 3, pp. 242–246; O. A. Greef, *The Commercial Paper House in the United States* (1938), pp. 123–127; P. Hunt, *Portfolio Policies of Banks in the United States* 1920–1929 (1940), pp. 11–38.

[2] See pp. 566–567.

TABLE 81.—WORK SHEET FOR CALCULATING ANNUAL INDEX OF NORMAL
AND TREND
Straight-line logarithmic trend
DATA: Open-market commercial paper outstanding. Annual averages of
monthly data
(In millions of dollars)
Equation of trend: $\log y' = 1.57306 - 0.037963t$

Year	Raw data y	$\log y$	t	$t \log y$	t^2	log of trend $\log y'$	Trend y'	Index of computed trend $\frac{y}{y'}$
....	....	....	−13					
....	....	....	−12					
1919	1,084	2.03503	−11	−22.38533	121	1.99065	979	110.7
1920	1,113	2.04650	−10	−20.46500	100	1.95269	897	124.1
1921	749	1.87448	−9	−16.87032	81	1.91473	822	91.1
1922	768	1.88536	−8	−15.08288	64	1.87676	753	102.0
1923	834	1.92117	−7	−13.44819	49	1.83880	690	120.9
1924	873	1.94101	−6	−11.64606	36	1.80084	632	138.1
1925	743	1.87099	−5	−9.35495	25	1.76288	579	128.3
1926	629	1.79865	−4	−7.19460	16	1.72491	531	118.4
1927	585	1.76716	−3	−5.30148	9	1.68695	486	120.4
1928	494	1.69373	−2	−3.38746	4	1.64899	446	110.8
1929	322	1.50786	−1	−1.50786	1	1.61102	408	78.9
1930	489	1.68931	0	0	0	1.57306	374	130.7
1931	264	1.42160	1	1.42160	1	1.53510	343	77.0
1932	106	1.02531	2	2.05062	4	1.49713	314	33.8
1933	95	0.97772	3	2.93316	9	1.45917	288	33.0
1934	156	1.19312	4	4.77248	16	1.42121	264	59.1
1935	174	1.24055	5	6.20275	25	1.38324	242	71.9
1936	188	1.27416	6	7.64496	36	1.34528	222	84.7
1937	296	1.47129	7	10.29903	49	1.30732	203	145.8
1938	239	1.37840	8	11.02720	64	1.26936	186	128.5
1939	198	1.29667	9	11.67003	81	1.23139	170	116.5
1940	234	1.36922	10	13.69220	100	1.19343	156	150.0
1941	317	1.50106	11	16.51166	121	1.15547	143	221.7
....	....	....	12					
....	....	....	13					
		36.18035	....	−38.41844	1,012	....	...	2,496.4
$N = 23$	.....	$\Sigma \log y$	....	$\Sigma t \log y$	Σt^2			$\Sigma y = y'$

Source: Compiled from the Annual Report of the Federal Reserve Board, 1929, p. 121;
1935, p. 174; and from the *Survey of Current Business*, Annual Supplement, (Vol. 20, 1940),
p. 47,

metical straight line is fitted.[1] It is the following expression
that is minimized:

$$\Sigma(\log y - \log y')^2$$

which is the same as

$$\sum \left(\log \frac{y}{y'} \right)^2$$

If the logarithm is expanded in a power series, this sum is seen
to be roughly equivalent to

$$\sum \left(\frac{y - y'}{y'} \right)^2$$

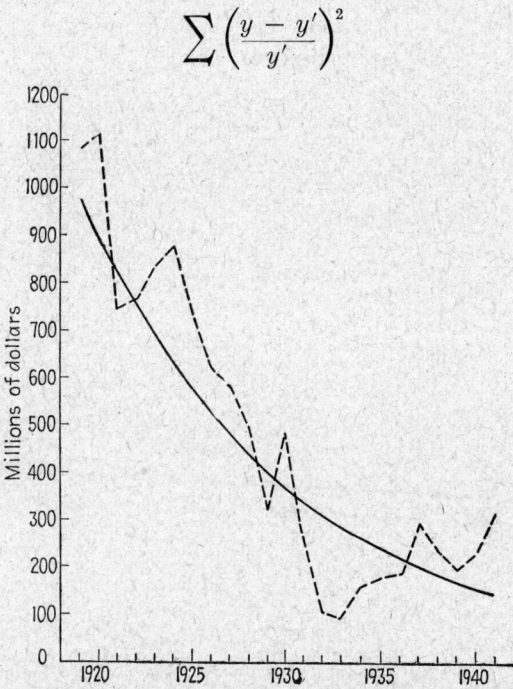

Fig. 144.—Open-market commercial paper outstanding in the United States,
1919–1941.   Logistic trend fitted by method of least squares.

For a dying institution, open-market commercial paper outstanding showed remarkable vigor in the years 1933–1941, and
perhaps the monetary economists were premature in their
predictions.   Whether or not they were is a matter for the
future to reveal.

[1] *Cf.* pp. 566–567.

Trend of a Growing Institution.   *Method of Selected Points Illustrated.*   If the hypothesis made by Raymond B. Prescott can be demonstrated or illustrated in real life, it should surely be done by the development of the automobile during the past three or four decades.   Table 82 and Fig. 145 give an illustration of the fitting of a rational trend that purports to represent this type of growth, constituting thereby a test of this hypothesis.[1] They also illustrate the method of fitting a logistic curve of the Pearl-Reed type by using selected points.

The equation of the curve may be written in the form

$$y' = \frac{k}{1 + m} \tag{8}$$

in which $m = e^{a+bt}$.

It is thus required to find three parameters k, a, and b, which is more conveniently done by first converting the equation into logarithms, as indicated in the work sheet.

By using annual data, consisting of monthly average output of passenger cars and trucks each year from 1903 to 1941, a graph was made and from its examination the following selected points were adopted:

1909	1922	1935
$t_0 = 0$	$t_1 = 13$	$t_2 = 26$
$y_0 = 10$	$y_1 = 250$	$y_2 = 320$

The values of the parameters k, a, and b may be found by using the following equations:[2]

$$\left. \begin{aligned} k &= \frac{2y_0 y_1 y_2 - y_1^2 (y_0 + y_2)}{y_0 y_2 - y_1^2} \\ a &= \log_e \frac{k - y_0}{y_0} \\ b &= \frac{1}{n} \log_e \frac{y_0 (k - y_1)}{y_1 (k - y_0)} \end{aligned} \right\} \tag{9}$$

in which n is defined as $t_2 - t_1$.

[1] Explained on pp. 553–555.

[2] *Cf.* PEARL, RAYMOND, *Studies in Human Biology*, (1924), Chap. XXIV; *The Biology of Population Growth* (1925), p. 22.   Citations used from F. E. Croxton and D. J. Cowden, *Applied General Statistics* (1939), pp. 444–445, 852–853.

Thus, for the problem illustrated,

$$k = \frac{2 \times 10 \times 250 \times 320 - 250 \times 250 \times 330}{10 \times 320 - 250 \times 250}$$

$$= \frac{5(128 - 1{,}650)}{\frac{22}{25} - 25} = \frac{-7{,}610}{-23.72}$$

$$= 320.82630$$

$$a = \log_e \frac{320.82630 - 10}{10}$$

$$= \log_e 31.082630$$

$$= 2.302585 \log_{10} 31.082630$$

$$= 2.302585(1.4925178)$$

$$= 3.4366491$$

$$b = \frac{1}{13} \log_e \frac{10(320.82630 - 250)}{250(320.82630 - 10)} = \frac{2.302585}{13} \log_{10} \frac{70.82630}{7{,}770.6575}$$

$$= 0.1771219 \; (\log_{10} 0.00911458)$$

$$[\log_{10} 0.00911458 = 7.9597368 - 10]$$

$$= 0.1771219 \; (-2.0402632)$$

$$= -0.3613753$$

As indicated in Table 82, the values for m for various values of t are conveniently found by the use of logarithms; thus, since

$$m = e^{a+bt}$$
$$\log m = \log_{10} e(a + bt) \quad [\text{since } \log_{10} e = 0.43429]$$
$$= 0.43429(a + bt)$$

or, for the example illustrated,

$$\log m = 0.43429(3.4366491 - 0.3613753t)$$
$$= 1.4925023 - 0.1569417t$$

For the year 1909, when $t = 0$, the value of $\log m$ is 1.4925023, as may be seen from the work sheet (Table 82), and the values of $\log m$ for other values of t are obtained by the successive algebraic subtraction of the constant -0.1569417 through the years preceding 1909 and by successive algebraic addition of the constant -0.1569417 through the years subsequent to 1909. These are the logarithms of m for the various values of t, that is, for the various years. In the next column of the work sheet, the antilogarithms are entered, which, when added to 1, are divided into the constant k in order to find the trend values for each year. These steps are shown in the next three columns of Table 82. An index of normal, that is, y/y', is also calculated.

TABLE 82.—WORK SHEET FOR CALCULATING INDEX OF NORMAL AND TREND
Logistic trend of the Pearl-Reed type
DATA: Automobile production in the United States.   Annual averages of
monthly data
(In thousands of cars)

Year	t	$\log m$	m	$1 + m$	$y' = \dfrac{k*}{1 + m}$	y	$\dfrac{y}{y'}$
1903	−6	2.4341525	271.7393	272.7393	1.176	0.9	76.5
1904	−5	2.2772108	189.3261	190.3261	1.686	1.9	112.7
1905	−4	2.1202691	131.9073	132.9073	2.414	2.1	87.0
1906	−3	1.9633274	91.90234	92.90234	3.453	2.8	81.1
1907	−2	1.8063857	64.03030	65.0303	4.933	3.7	75.0
1908	−1	1.6494440	44.61122	45.61122	7.034	5.4	75.8
1909	0	1.4925023	31.08152	32.08152	10.000	10.9	109.0
1910	1	1.3355606	21.65515	22.65515	14.161	15.6	110.2
1911	2	1.1786189	15.08757	16.0876	19.942	17.5	87.8
1912	3	1.0216772	10.51177	11.5118	27.869	31.5	113.0
1913	4	0.8647355	7.32380	8.3238	38.543	40.4	104.8
1914	5	0.7077938	5.10263	6.1026	52.572	47.4	90.2
1915	6	0.5508521	3.55510	4.5551	70.432	80.8	114.7
1916	7	0.3939104	2.47691	3.4769	92.273	134.8	146.1
1917	8	0.2369687	1.72571	2.7257	117.704	156.2	132.7
1918	9	0.0800270	1.20234	2.2023	145.675	97.6	67.0
1919	10	−0.0769147	0.83769	1.8377	174.581	161.1	92.3
1920	11	−0.2338564	0.58364	1.5836	202.588	185.6	91.6
1921	12	−0.3907981	0.40663	1.4066	228.082	134.7	59.0
1922	13	−0.5477398	0.28331	1.2833	249.999	212.0	84.8
1923	14	−0.7046815	0.19739	1.1974	267.938	336.2	125.5
1924	15	−0.8616232	0.13752	1.1375	282.040	300.2	106.4
1925	16	−1.0185649	0.095815	1.0958	292.773	355.5	121.4
1926	17	−1.1755066	0.066756	1.0668	300.748	358.4	119.2
1927	18	−1.3324483	0.046511	1.0465	306.568	283.4	92.4
1928	19	−1.4893900	0.032405	1.0324	310.758	363.2	116.9
1929	20	−1.6463317	0.022577	1.0226	313.742	446.5	142.3
1930	21	−1.8032734	0.015730	1.0157	315.858	279.7	88.6
1931	22	−1.9602151	0.010959	1.0110	317.348	199.1	62.7
1932	23	−2.1171568	0.007636	1.0076	318.394	114.2	35.9
1933	24	−2.2740985	0.0053199	1.0053	319.128	160.0	50.1
1934	25	−2.4310402	0.0037065	1.0037	319.640	229.4	71.8
1935	26	−2.5879819	0.0025824	1.00258	320.001	328.9	102.8
1936	27	−2.7449236	0.0017992	1.00180	320.250	371.2	115.9
1937	28	−2.9018653	0.0012535	1.00125	320.426	400.7	125.0
1938	29	−3.0588070	0.0008734	1.00087	320.547	207.4	64.7
1939	30	−3.2157487	0.0006085	1.00061	320.631	298.1	93.0
1940	31	−3.3726904	0.0004239	1.00042	320.692	372.4	116.1
1941	32	−3.5296321	0.0002954	1.00030	320.730	403.2	125.7
....	..	....	....	....	....	.....	$\sum \dfrac{y}{y'} = 3{,}788.7$†

Source: Data from *Statistical Abstract of the United States*, 1933, p. 334; and *Survey of Current Business*, Annual Supplement, Vol. 12 (1932), and current issues, *passim*.
  * $k = 320.82630$.   See p. 579.
  † If the curve had been fitted according to the least-squares criterion, this sum would approximate a hundred times the number of years, that is, 3,900.

The results lend support to the hypothesis that automobile production in the United States had a growth during those years following the law of the Pearl-Reed logistic curve. The goodness

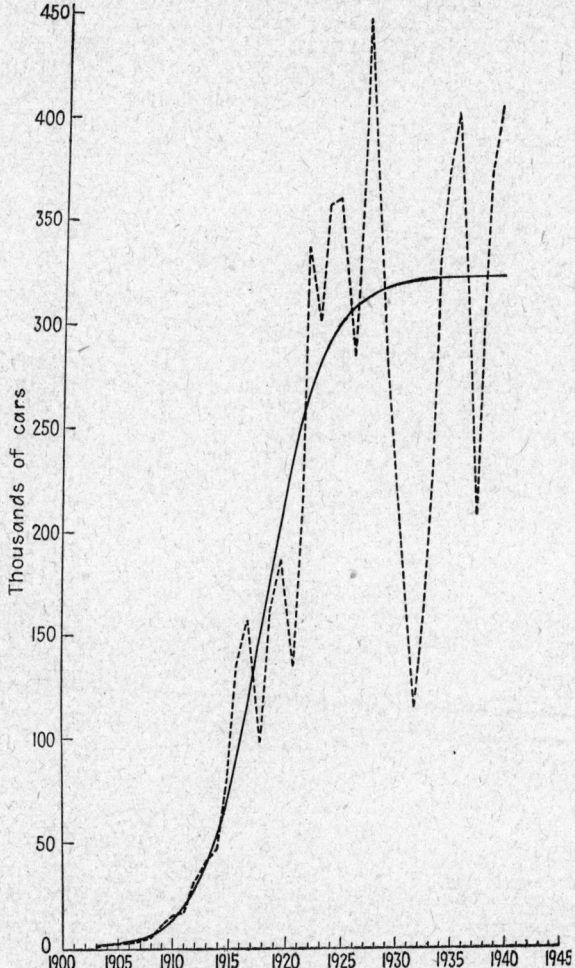

Fig. 145.—Automobile production in the United States, 1903–1941. Pearl-Reed curve fitted by method of selected points.

of fit of the trend is attested to, not only by the plotting of the curve with the data in Fig. 145, but also by the fact that the sum of the ratios of the raw data to the trend equals approximately a hundred times the number of years.

ILLUSTRATIONS OF EMPIRICAL TRENDS

The distinction between rational trends and empirical trends lies, not in the method of calculation, but in the interpretation and analytical use of the trend after it is calculated. Yet, in the case of empirical trends, it frequently suffices to fit a trend line of very simple character. Thus a straight line may be quite adequate in some cases.

Straight-line Trend. Table 83 contains a work sheet for calculating a straight-line trend in open-market commercial paper outstanding for the period 1931–1941. Rationalization of this trend is uncertain—it may be the commencement of a new period of growth in what was supposed to be a dying institution,

TABLE 83.—WORK SHEET FOR CALCULATING INDEX OF NORMAL AND TREND
Straight line

DATA: Open-market commercial paper outstanding. Annual averages of monthly data

(In millions of dollars)

Equation of trend: $y' = 206 + 12.49t$ (origin at 1936)

SOURCE: Annual Report of the Federal Reserve Board, 1929, p. 121; 1935, p. 174. *Survey of Current Business*, Annual Supplement, Vol. 20 (1940), p. 47 and current issues, *passim*.

(1) Year	(2) Raw data y	(3) t	(4) t^2	(5) ty	(6) Trend y'	(7) Index of computed trend $\dfrac{y}{y'}$
1931	264	−5	25	−1,320	144	183.3
1932	106	−4	16	−424	156	67.9
1933	95	−3	9	−285	168	56.5
1934	156	−2	4	−312	181	86.2
1935	174	−1	1	−174	194	89.7
1936	188	0	0	0	206	91.3
1937	296	1	1	296	218	135.8
1938	239	2	4	478	231	103.5
1939	198	3	9	594	243	81.5
1940	234	4	16	936	256	91.4
1941	317	5	25	1,585	268	118.3
	2,267	0	110	1,374	. . .	1,105.4*
$N = 11$	Σy	Σt	Σt^2	Σty		$\sum \dfrac{y}{y'}$

* This total is a cross check on the work sheet; it should equal a hundred times the number of years. Failure to check precisely is due to rounding.

or it may be merely a cyclical movement. At any rate, for the period of 11 years selected the trend analysis makes possible a better study of the shorter term cyclical or residual movements in the data.

The work sheet contains all the information necessary to calculate the equation of trend, which in this case is of the simple form, $y' = a + bt$. As seen in Eq. (5), the equation is found by the following:

$$y' = \frac{\Sigma y}{N} + \frac{\Sigma ty}{\Sigma t^2} t$$

From the work sheet, for this particular problem,

$$\Sigma y = 2{,}267 \qquad \Sigma t = 0 \qquad \Sigma t^2 = 110 \qquad \Sigma ty = 1{,}374 \qquad N = 11$$

Accordingly,

$$a = \frac{2{,}267}{11} = 206$$

$$b = \frac{1{,}374}{110} = 12.49$$

and the equation of trend is $y' = 206 + 12.49t$ (origin at 1936). It is necessary to specify the origin in order to know for which year $t = 0$. If the origin were 1931, the equation would be $y' = 144 + 12.49t$ (origin at 1931); this equation describes the same straight line as $y' = 206 + 12.49t$ (origin at 1936).

Column (6) of the work sheet contains the solutions of the trend equation for the respective values of t. Thus, for 1933, $t = -3$, and the solution of the trend equation for that year is $y' = 206 + (-3)(12.49) = 168$.

Column (7) is the index of computed trend, each y of the raw data divided by the corresponding y' of the trend, and the result expressed as a percentage. Thus, 264 is 183.3 per cent of 144.

Polynomial Empirical Trends. *Laborsaving Devices.* It is possible to find a second-degree, third-degree, or higher degree polynomial trend by the methods already illustrated. To fit a second-degree polynomial, according to the least-squares criterion, the work sheet would be like that illustrated in skeleton form on page 570. But it is better, for practical use, to introduce two important sets of laborsaving devices before proceeding to fit the higher order polynomial trends. The first set of laborsaving devices has to do with economy of calculation in the work sheet; the second set has to do with solving the equations for different values of t, therefore, with computing trend values for various years.

Economy of Calculation in the Work Sheet. As already noted, an economy was obtained by taking an odd number of years and making the median year the origin, so that $\Sigma t = 0$, $\Sigma t^3 = 0$, and similarly the total of all odd powers of t will be equal to zero; hence, columns in the work sheet for odd powers of t are not required. In addition, the entry of columns in the work sheet for the even powers of t may be avoided because Σt^2, Σt^4, Σt^6, etc., can be computed from formulas. It can be shown by algebraic derivation[1] that, if t runs integrally from $t = \pm 1$ to $t = \pm (n - 1)$, in which $n = \dfrac{N + 1}{2}$, *i.e.*, $n = t$ (terminal value) $+ 1$,

$$\left. \begin{aligned} \sum t^2 &= \frac{n(n - 1)(2n - 1)}{3} \\ \sum t^4 &= \sum t^2 \left(\frac{3n^2 - 3n - 1}{5} \right) \\ \sum t^6 &= \sum t^2 \left[\frac{3n^2(n^2 - 2n) + 3n + 1}{7} \right] \end{aligned} \right\} \quad (10)$$

By similar algebraic computation Σt^8 can be evaluated in terms of n, but it is preferable to use orthogonal polynomials if a trend equation of fourth or higher degree is sought.

A second economy for the work sheet is secured by using a subtotal summation procedure by which aggregates S_1, S_2, S_3, S_4, etc., are obtained. From these aggregates algebraic formulas are used to compute as follows:

$$\left. \begin{aligned} \Sigma y &= S_1 \\ \Sigma ty &= nS_1 - S_2 \\ \Sigma t^2 y &= n^2 S_1 - (2n + 1)S_2 + 2S_3 \\ \Sigma t^3 y &= n^3 S_1 - (3n^2 + 3n + 1)S_2 + 6(n + 1)S_3 - 6S_4 \end{aligned} \right\} \quad (11)$$

in which $n = \dfrac{N + 1}{2}$.

---

[1] *Cf.* Ross, FRANK A., "Formulae for Facilitating Computation in Time Series Analysis," *Journal of the American Statistical Association*, Vol. 20 (1925), pp. 75–79. For method of proof see footnote 1 p. 586.

TREND ANALYSIS

TABLE 84.—ECONOMICAL WORK SHEET FOR CALCULATING POLYNOMIAL TREND, ALGEBRAIC ILLUSTRATION
Method of least squares

Year			Data	Sets of subtotals		
	T	t	y	First	Second	Third
(1)	(2)	(3)	(4)	(5)	(6)	(7)
1937	1	-2	y_1	y_1	y_1	y_1
1938	2	-1	y_2	$y_1 + y_2$	$2y_1 + y_2$	$3y_1 + y_2$
1939	3	0	y_3	$y_1 + y_2 + y_3$	$3y_1 + 2y_2 + y_3$	$6y_1 + 3y_2 + y_3$
1940	4	1	y_4	$y_1 + y_2 + y_3 + y_4$	$4y_1 + 3y_2 + 2y_3 + y_4$	$10y_1 + 6y_2 + 3y_3 + y_4$
1941	5	2	y_5	$y_1 + y_2 + y_3 + y_4 + y_5$	$5y_1 + 4y_2 + 3y_3 + 2y_4 + y_5$	$15y_1 + 10y_2 + 6y_3 + 3y_4 + y_5$
			S_1	S_2	S_3	S_4

The subtotal summation process is illustrated algebraically in Table 84 and arithmetically in Table 85. The sum of column (4), S_1, is merely Σy. Column (5) contains the first set of subtotals, which is obtained on the adding machine by taking a subtotal after entry of each item in column (4); the first subtotal in column (5) will thus be the first item of column (4), therefore, y_1, the second subtotal in column (5) will be $y_1 + y_2$, the third subtotal will be $y_1 + y_2 + y_3$, etc. S_2 is the sum of these subtotals.

The second set of subtotals, column (6), consists of subtotals of the figures in the preceding column, column (5); thus the first subtotal in column (6) is y_1, the second subtotal is $2y_1 + y_2$, the third subtotal is $3y_1 + 2y_2 + y_3$, etc. S_3 is the sum of the second set of subtotals.

The third set of subtotals, column (7), consists of the subtotals of figures in column (6); and S_4 is the sum of this third set of subtotals.

This process of taking subtotals and aggregating the subtotals by columns to obtain S_2, S_3, S_4 can be repeated to as many as desired, depending on how high degree a polynomial is to be fitted. If carried as far as S_4, a third-degree polynomial can be fitted.

A cross check on the work sheet is noted in Table 85: S_1 is equal to the final subtotal in column (5), S_2 is equal to the final subtotal in column (6), S_3 is equal to the final subtotal in column (7), etc.

TABLE 85.—ECONOMICAL WORK SHEET FOR CALCULATING POLYNOMIAL
TREND, ARITHMETICAL ILLUSTRATION

(Method of least squares)

Year			Data	Sets of subtotals		
	T	t	y	First	Second	Third
(1)	(2)	(3)	(4)	(5)	(6)	(7)
1937	1	-2	2	2	2	2
1938	2	-1	5	7	9	11
1939	3	0	8	15	24	35
1940	4	1	7	22	46	81
1941	5	2	9	31	77	158
			31	77	158	287
			S_1	S_2	S_3	S_4

From Table 84 it can be readily seen that algebraically

$$S_1 = y_1 + y_2 + y_3 + \cdots + y_N$$
$$S_2 = Ny_1 + (N-1)y_2 + (N-2)y_3 + \cdots + y_N \qquad (12)$$
$$S_3 = \frac{N(N+1)}{2} y_1 + \frac{(N-1)N}{2} y_2 + \frac{(N-2)(N-1)}{2} y_3$$
$$+ \cdots + y_N$$

For the coefficient of y_1 in this sum is equal to the sum of the natural numbers from 1 to N, therefore, $\sum_1^N T$, which equals $\frac{N(N+1)}{2}$; the coefficient of y_2 is the sum of the natural numbers from 1 to $N-1$, which equals $\frac{(N-1)N}{2}$; etc.[1]

$$S_4 = \frac{N(N+1)(N+2)}{6} y_1 + \frac{(N-1)(N)(N+1)}{6} y_2 + \cdots + y_N$$

[1] This may be demonstrated as follows:
$$\Sigma T = 1 + 2 + 3 + 4 + \cdots + N$$
Also,
$$\Sigma T = N + (N-1) + (N-2) + (N-3) + \cdots + 1$$
By adding,
$$2\Sigma T = (N+1) + (N+1) + (N+1) + (N+1) + \cdots + (N+1)$$
$$= N(N+1)$$
and hence

$$\sum T = \frac{N(N+1)}{2}$$

For the coefficient of y_1 is the sum of $\dfrac{N(N+1)}{2}$ as N goes from 1 to N; this sum equals $\dfrac{N(N+1)(N+2)}{6}$; etc.

It will be convenient to express these sums in the following manner:

$$S_1 = \Sigma y$$
$$S_2 = \Sigma(N+1-T)y$$

In the case of y_1, $N+1-T = N$. In the case of y_2
$$N+1-T = N-1.$$
In the case of y_3, $N+1-T = N-2$. Etc.

$$S_3 = \sum \frac{(N+1-T)(N+2-T)}{2}\,y$$

In the case of y_1, $\dfrac{(N+1-T)(N+2-T)}{2} = \dfrac{N(N+1)}{2}$. In the case of y_2, $\dfrac{(N+1-T)(N+2-T)}{2} = \dfrac{(N-1)N}{2}$. Etc.

$$S_4 = \sum \frac{(N+1-T)(N+2-T)(N+3-T)}{6}\,y$$

In the case of y_1,
$$\frac{(N+1-T)(N+2-T)(N+3-T)}{6} = \frac{N(N+1)(N+2)}{6}.$$
In the case of y_2,
$$\frac{(N+1-T)(N+2-T)(N+3-T)}{6} = \frac{(N-1)N(N+1)}{6}.\quad \text{Etc.}$$

$$\tag{13}$$

In the above equations, if T is replaced by $t + \bar{T} = t + \dfrac{N+1}{2}$

and if, by definition, $n = \dfrac{N+1}{2}$, these equations become

$$S_1 = \Sigma y$$
$$S_2 = n\Sigma y - \Sigma ty$$
$$2S_3 = \Sigma(n-t)^2 y + n\Sigma y - \Sigma ty$$
$$6S_4 = \Sigma(n-t)^3 y + 3\Sigma(n-t)^2 y + 2n\Sigma y - 2\Sigma ty$$

$$\tag{14}$$

in which the unmarked Σ refers to summations with respect to t from $+\dfrac{N-1}{2}$ to $-\dfrac{N-1}{2}$. If these equations are expanded and similar terms assembled, Eqs. (11) are obtained.

TABLE 86.—WORK SHEET FOR CALCULATING TREND—SECOND-DEGREE
POLYNOMIAL
Method of least squares
DATA: Consumer expenditures for personal appearance and comfort.
Annual data in millions of dollars
SOURCE OF DATA: *Survey of Current Business*, October, 1942, p. 24.

Year	t	y	Sets of subtotals	
			First	Second
1929	−6	655	655	655
1930	−5	630	1,285	1,940
1931	−4	540	1,825	3,765
1932	−3	427	2,252	6,017
1933	−2	347	2,599	8,616
1934	−1	393	2,992	11,608
1935	0	441	3,433	15,041
1936	1	503	3,936	18,977
1937	2	545	4,481	23,458
1938	3	543	5,024	28,482
1939	4	540	5,564	34,046
1940	5	568	6,132	40,178
1941	6	653	6,785	46,963
		6,785	46,963	239,746
		S_1	S_2	S_3

By using Eqs. (11), page 584, the following values are obtained:

$$\Sigma y = 6,785$$
$$\Sigma ty = 7(6,785) - 46,963 = 532$$
$$\Sigma t^2 y = 49(6,785) - 15(46,963) + 2(239,746) = 107,512$$

By using Eqs. (10) the following values are obtained:

$$\Sigma t^2 = \frac{7(6)(13)}{3} = 182$$

$$\Sigma t^4 = 182 \frac{(147 - 21 - 1)}{5} = 182(25) = 4,550$$

To find the second-degree polynomial trend equation these values
may be substituted in Eqs. (7), (i) to (iii), page 570, as follows:

(i) $6,785 = 13a + 182c$

(ii) $532 = 182b$ $b = 2.923$

(iii) $107,512 = 182a + 4,550c$

(i′) $\underline{94,990 = 182a + 2,548c}$ (i) × 14

         $12,522 = \qquad 2,002c$ $c = 6.2547$

(iii) $107,512 = 182a + 4,550c$
(i'') $\underline{169,625 = 325a + 4,550c}$ (i) $\times$ 25
$62,113 = 143a$ $a = 434$

Accordingly, the second-degree polynomial equation of trend for the problem illustrated is $y' = 434 + 2.923t + 6.2547t^2$ (origin at 1935).

Finding Trend Values by Method of Finite Differences. The equation for a trend line having been found, the problem is to compute from this equation the values of y' pertaining to a given set of years. Direct substitution is laborious. Finite differences provide an easier method. The keystone of the latter method is the fact that the nth difference of a polynomial of the nth degree is constant. Hence, that constant nth difference having been determined, the other differences, and ultimately the desired trend values themselves, can all be computed by merely reversing the differencing process, *i.e.*, by simple addition.

In the equation $y' = a + bt + ct^2$ the first difference, by definition, would be

$$\Delta^1 y' = a + b(t + 1) + c(t + 1)^2 - a - bt - ct^2 = b + 2ct + c$$

and, by definition, the second difference would be

$$\Delta^2 y' = b + 2c(t + 1) + c - b - 2ct - c = 2c$$

TABLE 87.—BUILDING UP A POLYNOMIAL BY FINITE DIFFERENCES

(1)	(2)	(3)	(4)	(5)	(6)
t	Fourth difference $\Delta^4 y'$	Third difference $\Delta^3 y'$	Second difference $\Delta^2 y'$	First difference $\Delta^1 y'$	Polynomial (trend) values y'
-4	-1	6	-48	220	305
-3	-1	5	-42	172	525
-2	-1	4	-37	130	697
-1	-1	3	-33	93	827
0	-1	2	-30	60	920
1	...	1	-28	30	980
2	...	..	-27	2	1,010
3	...	..	....	-25	1,012
4	...	..	....	....	987

Table 87 illustrates the building up of a polynomial by finite differences. The polynomial here is of the fourth degree, and hence its fourth differences are all identical.

A figure in a given line of column (6) algebraically added to the figure in the same line of column (5) gives the next figure for column (6); thus, $305 + 220 = 525$, $525 + 172 = 697$, etc. Similarly, a figure in a given line of column (5) added algebraically to the figure in the same line of column (4) gives the next figure for column (5); thus, $220 - 48 = 172$, $172 - 42 = 130$, etc. The same general rule applies to the figures in columns (2) and (3); thus, $-48 + 6 = -42$, $-42 + 5 = -37$, etc., and $6 - 1 = 5, 5 - 1 = 4$, etc.

In the polynomial illustrated in Table 87, the polynomial is known to have a constant fourth difference. Hence, if the polynomial value and the differences of any one line are all known, then the differences and polynomial values for all other lines above or below the given line can be readily computed. Thus, if for $t = 0$, it is known that the polynomial value $y' = 920$, $\Delta^1 y_0' = 60$, $\Delta^2 y_0' = -30$, $\Delta^3 y_0' = 2$, and the constant fourth difference is equal to -1, then, by working from right to left and up and down, the other values in the tables can be built up. The first set of variable differences, in this case the third, can be built up cumulatively from the known $\Delta^3 y_0' = 2$ and the constant difference -1. It is to be noted that in a downward direction, in this table, this constant difference is -1; so in building up from the bottom to the top the constant difference is algebraically $-(-1)$, or $+1$. This rule follows also for the building up of the other differences.

TABLE 88.—AID FOR COMPUTING FINITE DIFFERENCES AT $t = 0$ IN POLYNOMIAL $y' = a + bt + ct^2 + dt^3 + \cdots$

Parameter	(1) $\Delta^1 y_0'$	(2) $\Delta^2 y_0'$	(3) $\Delta^3 y_0'$	(4) $\Delta^4 y_0'$	(5) $\Delta^5 y_0'$
b	1				
c	1	2			
d	1	6	6		
e	1	14	36	24	
f	1	30	150	240	120

This method is of general validity and can be used to find values of a polynomial of any degree from knowledge of its value for one year and its differences for that same year. Fortunately, it is relatively easy to calculate the y' or polynomial value and the various differences for the year $t = 0$. If the form of the polynomial is $y' = a + bt + ct^2 + dt^3 + et^4 + \cdots$, then the polynomial value for $t = 0$ is $y' = a$. The first, second, and higher order differences for $t = 0$ can be computed with the help of Table 88.

The figures in Table 88 give the weights by which the parameters b, c, d, e, f, etc., must be multiplied to give the difference specified at the top of each column, as follows:

$$\Delta^1 y_0' = b + c + d + e + \cdots$$
$$\Delta^2 y_0' = 2c + 6d + 14e + 30f + \cdots$$
$$\Delta^3 y_0' = 6d + 36e + 150f + \cdots$$
$$\Delta^4 y_0' = 24e + 240f + \cdots$$
$$\Delta^5 y_0' = 120f + \cdots$$

For a particular polynomial, each of these equations, of course, terminates with the coefficient of t^n. Thus, for a second-degree polynomial $y' = a + bt + ct^2$, the formulas for the differences at $t = 0$ would be $\Delta^1 y_0' = b + c$ and $\Delta^2 y_0' = 2c$, the higher differences being zero since the second difference is the same for all values of t. For a third-degree polynomial,

$$y' = a + bt + ct^2 + dt^3$$

the formulas would be $\Delta^1 y_0' = b + c + d$, $\Delta^2 y_0' = 2c + 6d$, and $\Delta^3 y_0' = 6d$. For a fourth-degree polynomial

$$y' = a + bt + ct^2 + dt^3 + et^4$$

the differences would be $\Delta^1 y_0' = b + c + d + e$,

$$\Delta^2 y_0' = 2c + 6d + 14e, \qquad \Delta^3 y_0' = 6d + 36e$$

and $\Delta^4 y_0' = 24e$.

For higher degree polynomials, the table can be readily extended by the rule that a figure in a given line of a given column is equal to the number of the column multiplied by the sum of the two figures in the line above situated in the given column and in the column to the left, respectively. For example, $36 = 3(6 + 6)$; $24 = 4(0 + 6)$; etc.[1]

The use of finite differences to compute the trend values of a second-degree polynomial is illustrated in Table 89. The trend is $y' = 434 + 2.923t + 6.2547t^2$ (origin at 1935), calculated above in Table 86 for data on consumer expenditures for personal appearance and comfort in the United States, 1929–1941.

In Table 89, the constant second difference is known to be 12.509; the first difference for $t = 0$ is 9.2,* and the trend value for $t = 0$ is $y' = 434.0$. These are first entered in the work

TABLE 89.—WORK SHEET FOR COMPUTING TREND VALUES BY METHOD OF FINITE DIFFERENCES

Equation of trend: $y' = 434 + 2.923t + 6.2547t^2$
Value of $y'_0 = 434$
Value of $\Delta^1 y'_0 = 2.923 + 6.2547 = 9.1777$
Constant $\Delta^2 y' = 12.509$

Year	t	$\Delta^2 y'$	$\Delta^1 y'$	y'
1929	−6	......	−65.9	641.5
1930	−5	......	−53.4	575.6
1931	−4	......	−40.8	522.2
1932	−3	......	−28.3	481.4
1933	−2	......	−15.8	453.1
1934	−1	......	−3.3	437.3
1935	0	12.509	9.2	434.0
1936	1	......	21.7	443.2
1937	2	......	34.2	464.9
1938	3	......	46.7	499.1
1939	4	......	59.2	545.8
1940	5	......	71.7	605.0
1941	6	......	......	676.7

sheet; then, since the constant second difference is positive, the remainder of the column of first differences is obtained by successively subtracting 12.509 to obtain first differences for earlier years and by successively adding 12.509 to obtain first differences for later years. Obtaining the trend values is illustrated as follows: $434.0 + 9.2 = 443.2$, $443.2 + 21.7 = 464.9$, etc.; for values before 1935, $434.0 - (-3.3) = 437.3$, $437.3 - (-15.8)$

[1] *Cf.* WHITTAKER and ROBINSON, *op. cit.*, pp. 1–7.

* The first differences may be rounded without causing cumulative error.

= 453.1, etc. Beginning at the top of the table, it will then be found that $641.5 - 65.9 = 575.6$, $575.6 - 53.4 = 522.2$, etc.

While the explanation of the method of finite differences may be extended, its use in solving second-degree polynomials for various values of t is much more expeditious than the method of obtaining solutions to the equation for the various values of t by substitution in the equation. The labor involved in the longer method is great if the number of years is large or if the polynomial is of higher than a second degree. In contrast, the method of finite differences may be used without difficulty, and the arithmetic involved is always simple addition or subtraction.

A danger inheres in the use of finite differences, namely, that any error in the higher order differences is cumulated as the lower order differences are computed. For this reason, when the trend line is determined the coefficients of the higher powers of t should be carried out to a larger number of places than would be regarded as significant. If, for example, the coefficient of t^4 is rounded off to the fifth place, the maximum error in the fourth difference is $24 \times 0.000005 = 0.00012$, over a 7-year period. If the other coefficients have also been rounded off to the last place indicated, then the maximum error in

$$\Delta^3 y_0' = 6(0.00005) + 36(0.000005) = 0.00048$$

in

$$\Delta^2 y_0' = 2(0.0005) + 6(0.00005) + 14(0.000005) = 0.00137$$

in

$$\Delta^1 y_0' = 0.005 + 0.0005 + 0.00005 + 0.000005 = 0.0055555$$

TABLE 90.—MAXIMUM CUMULATED ERRORS IN DIFFERENCES AND POLYNOMIAL VALUES

Error in $\Delta^4 y' = 0.000120$

t	$\Delta^3 y'$	$\Delta^2 y'$	$\Delta^1 y'$	y'
0	0.000480	0.001370	0.005555	0.050000
1	0.000600	0.001850	0.006925	0.055555
2	0.000720	0.002450	0.008775	0.062480
3	0.000840	0.003170	0.011225	0.071255
4	....	0.004100	0.014395	0.082480
5	....	....	0.018495	0.096875
6	....	....	....	0.115370

and in $y_0' = 0.05$. Thus, by the time y_6', the seventh year, for example, has been computed, the maximum error in that figure becomes $0.11+$. This is shown in Table 90.

The final error grows larger the further the work proceeds and thus makes it necessary to compute the coefficients of higher powers of t to several figures beyond the number of significant figures required in the computed trend values. A cross check on the method of finite differences would be to solve the polynomial equation for the terminal values of t.

The danger of cumulative error is reduced to a minimum by starting at $t = 0$ and accumulating upward through the $-t$'s and accumulating downward through the $+t$'s.

Analysis of Cycles by Empirical Trends. Data on plate-glass production in the United States, 1933–1941, have been selected, in order to illustrate how cycles may be studied by empirical trend analysis. Table 91 is a work sheet providing the figures needed to compute either a straight-line trend or any polynomial trend up to the third degree.

TABLE 91.—WORK SHEET FOR COMPUTING TREND AND INDEX OF NORMAL
Method of least squares

DATA: Production of plate glass, polished, in the United States
(In millions of square feet, monthly)
SOURCE: *Survey of Current Business*, Supplement, Vol. 20 (1940), p. 151;
Vol. 21 (February, 1941), p. 99, Annual (March, 1942), p. S-35.

Year	t	y	Sets of subtotals		
			First	Second	Third
1933	-4	7.2	7.2	7.2	7.2
1934	-3	7.9	15.1	22.3	29.5
1935	-2	15.0	30.1	52.4	81.9
1936	-1	16.5	46.6	99.0	180.9
1937	0	16.0	62.6	161.6	342.5
1938	1	7.1	69.7	231.3	573.8
1939	2	11.8	81.5	312.8	886.6
1940	3	13.7	95.2	408.0	1,294.6
1941	4	15.9	111.1	519.1	1,813.7
		111.1	519.1	1,813.7	5,210.7
		S_1	S_2	S_3	S_4

By using Eqs. (10), the values of Σt^2, Σt^4, and Σt^6 are found as follows:

$$\sum t^2 = \frac{n(n-1)(2n-1)}{3} = \frac{5(4)(9)}{3} = 60$$

$$\sum t^4 = \sum t^2 \left(\frac{3n^2 - 3n - 1}{5}\right) = 60\left(\frac{75 - 15 - 1}{5}\right) = 708$$

$$\sum t^6 = \sum t^2 \left[\frac{3n^2(n^2 - 2n) + 3n + 1}{7}\right]$$

$$= 60\left[\frac{75(25 - 10) + 15 + 1}{7}\right] = 60\left(\frac{1,141}{7}\right) = 60(163)$$

$$= 9,780$$

By using Eqs. (11), the values of Σty, $\Sigma t^2 y$, and $\Sigma t^3 y$ are found as follows:

$$\Sigma y = S_1 = 111.1$$
$$\Sigma ty = nS_1 - S_2 = 5(111.1) - 519.1 = 36.4$$
$$\Sigma t^2 y = n^2 S_1 - (2n + 1)S_2 + 2S_3$$
$$= 25(111.1) - 11(519.1) + 2(1,813.7)$$
$$= 694.8$$
$$\Sigma t^3 y = n^3 S_1 - (3n^2 + 3n + 1)S_2 + 6(n + 1)S_3 - 6S_4$$
$$= 125(111.1) - 91(519.1) + 36(1,813.7) - 6(5,210.7)$$
$$= 678.4$$

From these, two trend lines may be computed, first a straight line, and second a third-degree polynomial, as follows:

Straight-line trend:

$$y_1' = \frac{111.1}{9} + \frac{36.4}{60} t$$
$$y_1' = 12.3 + 0.607t \qquad \text{(origin at 1937)}$$

Third-degree polynomial trend:
The normal equations are

$$\Sigma y = Na + b\Sigma t + c\Sigma t^2 + d\Sigma t^3$$
$$\Sigma ty = a\Sigma t + b\Sigma t^2 + c\Sigma t^3 + d\Sigma t^4$$
$$\Sigma t^2 y = a\Sigma t^2 + b\Sigma t^3 + c\Sigma t^4 + d\Sigma t^5$$
$$\Sigma t^3 y = a\Sigma t^3 + b\Sigma t^4 + c\Sigma t^5 + d\Sigma t^6$$

in which all the sums of the odd powers of t are equal to zero, so that the equations for finding a, b, c, d are as follows:

(i)	$111.1 = \quad 9a + 60c$	
(ii)	$36.4 = \quad 60b + 708d$	
(iii)	$694.8 = \quad 60a + 708c$	
(iv)	$678.4 = 708b + 9,780d$	
(ii′)	$\underline{429.52 = 708b + 8,354.4d}$	(ii) $\times$ 11.8
(iv) − (ii′)	$248.88 = \qquad\qquad 1,425.6d$	$d = 0.17457$
(iii)	$694.8 = \quad 60a + 708c$	
(i′)	$\underline{1,310.98 = 106.2a + 708c}$	(i) $\times$ 11.8
(i′) − (iii)	$616.18 = \quad 46.2a$	$a = 13.34$

Substituting d in Eq. (ii), $b = -1.45325$
Substituting a in Eq. (i), $c = -0.14891$

The third-degree polynomial trend equation is thus

$$y'_2 = 13.34 - 1.45325t - 0.14891t^2 + 0.17457t^3 \quad \text{(origin at 1937)}$$

By using the method of finite differences to solve for various trend values, from Table 88 above, at $t = 0$,

$$y'_2 = 13.34$$

and

$$\Delta^1 y'_2 = -1.45325 - 0.14891 + 0.17457$$
$$= -1.42759$$
$$\Delta^2 y'_2 = 2(-0.14891) + 6(0.17457)$$
$$= 0.7496$$
$$\Delta^3 y'_2 = 6(0.17457)$$
$$= 1.04742,$$

which is a constant difference in this case.

In Table 92, trend values are built up for the problem by using the method of finite differences. First, opposite $t = 0$, the value of y', the first, second, and third differences are entered. The constant third difference, 1.04742, is then subtracted successively in the $-t$ direction (upward in the table); it is then added successively in the $+t$ direction (downward in the table). For example, starting at $t = 0$, the second difference is 0.74960; the second difference at $t = -1$ is

$$0.74960 - 1.04742 = -0.29782$$

the second difference at $t = -2$ is

$$-0.29782 - 1.04742 = -1.34524; \text{ etc.}$$

Starting again at $t = 0$, the second difference is again 0.74960; the second difference at $t = +1$ is

$$0.74960 + 1.04742 = 1.79702; \text{ etc.}$$

The column of first differences is built up from the column of second differences. For example, starting at $t = 0$, the first

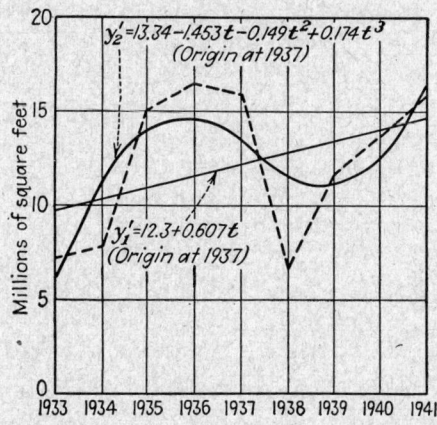

Fig. 146.—Production of plate glass, polished, in the United States, 1933–1941. Straight-line and third-degree polynomial trends shown with raw data.

difference is -1.42579; the first difference for $t = -1$ is then $-1.42579 - (-0.29782) = -1.12797$, the first difference for $t = -2$ is $-1.12797 - (-1.34524) = +0.21727$; etc. Again,

TABLE 92.—WORK SHEET FOR FINDING TREND VALUES BY METHOD OF FINITE DIFFERENCES

Equation of trend: $y_2' = 13.34 - 1.45325t - 0.14891t^2 + 0.17457t^3$

(origin at 1937)

Year	t	$\Delta^3 y_2'$	$\Delta^2 y_2'$	$\Delta^1 y_2'$	y_2'
1933	-4	....	-3.44008	6.05001	5.59
1934	-3	....	-2.39266	2.60993	11.64
1935	-2	....	-1.34524	0.21727	14.25
1936	-1	....	-0.29782	-1.12797	14.47
1937	0	1.04742	0.74960	-1.42579	13.34
1938	1	....	1.79702	-0.67619	11.91
1939	2	....	2.84444	1.12083	11.24
1940	3	....	....	3.96527	12.36
1941	4	....	....	....	16.32

starting at $t = 0$ with the first difference -1.42579, the first difference at $t = +1$ is $-1.42579 + 0.74960 = -0.67619$; the first difference at $t = +2$ is $-0.67619 + 1.79702 = 1.12083$; etc. The values of y_2' are found from the first differences in exactly the same manner as the first differences from the second differences.

The results of the trend analysis are shown graphically in Fig. 146. If it can be assumed that the period of 9 years covered by the whole period is a segment in a longer cyclical movement, the straight-line trend may be considered to measure a part of that longer cycle—part or all of its upward movement. The shorter cycle is then shown by the polynomial trend. Plate-glass production appears to have gone through one complete short cycle from about 1934 to about mid-1940.

CHAPTER XXII

ORTHOGONAL-POLYNOMIAL TRENDS

Great economy in trend analysis is secured by the use of orthogonal polynomials, especially if the trend desired is of higher degree than second-degree polynomial. It requires considerable space to explain and describe the method of orthogonal polynomials, which may seem to belie the fact of its economy in use, but the actual arithmetic of application is simple. When lines of regression involving more than three coefficients are fitted to time series by the least-squares criterion, the work of computation by the ordinary method increases very rapidly. Laborsaving devices introduced in the preceding chapter, including the use of the summation work sheet and the determination of Σt^2, Σt^4, Σt^6, etc., by formula, help to keep the amount of calculation at a minimum; but further reduction in the amount of calculation and particularly in the magnitude of the figures that have to be handled is obtained by using orthogonal polynomials.

A "polynomial" is an algebraic expression of the form

$$a + bt + ct^2$$

which, for example, is a polynomial in t of the second degree. A polynomial in t of the fourth degree would be

$$a + bt + ct^2 + dt^3 + et^4$$

and so forth. "Orthogonal" polynomials are polynomials that bear a certain relationship to each other, to be described below. The use of orthogonal polynomials involves merely a special method of computing the coefficients of a trend line; the method of fitting is still the method of least squares.

One of the greatest advantages of using orthogonal-polynomial trends is that, if the investigator decides to fit either a higher or lower degree trend line than what he has already derived, the amount of work involved in these further calculations is reduced to a minimum. In fact, no extra work at all would be required to determine the equation for a trend line of lower degree, while the determination of an equation for a trend line of higher degree would require only the calculation of quantities pertaining directly to the added term and would not necessitate any recalculations of other quantities. The work already done will therefore not be wasted.

Orthogonal Polynomials. Suppose a variable t has a set of values, say from 0 to 3. If each of these values is substituted in a polynomial in t, the polynomial will take on a corresponding set of values. Thus, if $p_1 = t - 1.5$ is a given polynomial in t, then, as t has the values 0, 1, 2, and 3, p_1 has values -1.5, -0.5, $+0.5$, and $+1.5$. Another polynomial in t, say

$$p_2 = t^2 - 3t + 1$$

will have a different set of values; in this instance, it will have the values 1, -1, -1, and 1 when t has the values 0, 1, 2, and 3, respectively.

Orthogonal polynomials are those that bear special relationships to each other. The necessary condition for two polynomials to be orthogonal to each other is that the sum of their product for all values of t shall be equal to zero. That this necessary condition is met by $p_1 = t - 1.5$ and $p_2 = t^2 - 3t + 1$ is readily seen. Thus, when $t = 0$,

$$p_1 p_2 = (t - 1.5)(t^2 - 3t + 1) = -1.5$$

when $t = 1$, $p_1 p_2 = +0.05$; when $t = 2$, $p_1 p_2 = -0.05$; and when $t = 3$, $p_1 p_2 = +1.5$. Hence,

$$\Sigma p_1 p_2 = -1.5 + 0.5 - 0.5 + 1.5 = 0$$

The polynomials $p_1 = t - 1.5$ and $p_2 = t^2 - 3t + 1$, accordingly, possess the orthogonal property.

In general, if a set of polynomials in t, say $p_1, p_2, p_3, \ldots, p_r$, form an orthogonal set, then it is necessary that

$$\left. \begin{array}{lll} \Sigma p_1 p_2 = 0 & \Sigma p_1 p_3 = 0 & \cdots \quad \Sigma p_1 p_r = 0 \\ \Sigma p_2 p_3 = 0 & \Sigma p_2 p_4 = 0 & \cdots \quad \Sigma p_2 p_r = 0 \\ \Sigma p_3 p_4 = 0 & \Sigma p_3 p_5 = 0 & \cdots \quad \Sigma p_3 p_r = 0 \end{array} \right\} \quad (1)$$

These are the general conditions that must be satisfied by orthogonal polynomials. Notice that they are equivalent to the conditions that the correlation between each pair of polynomials is zero.

Trend Line in Orthogonal Polynomials by the Method of Least Squares. The form of a trend-line equation that has so far been used is $y' = a + bt + ct^2 + dt^3 \ldots$. This is an arbitrary form, however, and it is to be noted that other forms of the identical equation are possible. This can be illustrated numerically as follows:

The equation $y' = 105.3 + 8.1t - 0.7t^2$ is identically the same as $y' = 115 + 6(t - 1.5) - 0.7(t^2 - 3t + 1)$, which may be proved by multiplying out the expressions in the latter equation and collecting like terms. If the use of the second form has any advantage over the use of the first, there is no reason why it may not be adopted.

Suppose, now, that instead of fitting a trend line in the form $y' = a + bt + ct^2 + dt^3$, the fitting process is carried out with respect to the form

$$y' = A + Bp_1 + Cp_2 + Dp_3 + Ep_4$$

in which p_1, p_2, p_3, and p_4 are polynomials in t of the first, second, third, and fourth degree, respectively, that are orthogonal to each other and to unity, that is to say, where p_1 is a polynomial in t of the form $p_1 = k_{10} + t$, p_2 is a polynomial in t of the form $p_2 = k_{20} + k_{21}t + t^2$, p_3 is a polynomial in t of the form

$$p_3 = k_{30} + k_{31}t + k_{32}t^2 + t_3, \text{ etc.}$$

and where $\Sigma p_1 = 0$, $\Sigma p_2 = 0$, $\Sigma p_3 = 0$, $\Sigma p_4 = 0$, and $\Sigma p_1 p_2 = 0$, $\Sigma p_1 p_3 = 0$, $\Sigma p_1 p_4 = 0$, $\Sigma p_2 p_3 = 0$, etc. With reference to the arithmetical illustration given above, which was a third-degree polynomial, this is equivalent to deriving a trend line of the form

$$y' = 115 + 6(t - 1.5) - 0.7(t^2 - 3t + 1)$$

instead of the usual form $y' = 105.3 + 8.1t - 0.7t^2$.

Either method will, of course, give the same result; for, whichever form is derived, it can be converted into the other by simple algebra. It is the purpose of this section to show the simplification gained by using the orthogonal-polynomial form rather than the usual form. The problem of finding the forms of the polynomials themselves, *i.e.*, the values of the k coefficients, will be left for a subsequent section.

If a trend line is put in the orthogonal-polynomial form

$$y' = A + Bp_1 + Cp_2 + Dp_3$$

and is then fitted by the method of least squares, *i.e.*, if A, B, C, and D are determined so that

$$\Sigma(y - y')^2 = \Sigma(y - A - Bp_1 - Cp_2 - Dp_3)^2$$

is made a minimum, the following conditions are obtained:

$$\Sigma(y - A - Bp_1 - Cp_2 - Dp_3) = 0$$
$$\Sigma p_1(y - A - Bp_1 - Cp_2 - Dp_3) = 0$$
$$\Sigma p_2(y - A - Bp_1 - Cp_2 - Dp_3) = 0$$
$$\Sigma p_3(y - A - Bp_1 - Cp_2 - Dp_3) = 0$$

or

$$\Sigma y = NA + B\Sigma p_1 + C\Sigma p_2 + D\Sigma p_3$$
$$\Sigma p_1 y = A\Sigma p_1 + B\Sigma p_1^2 + C\Sigma p_1 p_2 + D\Sigma p_1 p_3$$
$$\Sigma p_2 y = A\Sigma p_2 + B\Sigma p_1 p_2 + C\Sigma p_2^2 + D\Sigma p_2 p_3$$
$$\Sigma p_3 y = A\Sigma p_3 + B\Sigma p_1 p_3 + C\Sigma p_2 p_3 + D\Sigma p_3^2$$

But since 1, p_1, p_2, and p_3 form an orthogonal set (by assumption), it follows that $\Sigma p_1 = 0$, $\Sigma p_2 = 0$, $\Sigma p_3 = 0$, $\Sigma p_1 p_2 = 0$, $\Sigma p_1 p_3 = 0$, and $\Sigma p_2 p_3 = 0$. Hence the above equations reduce to

$$\Sigma y = NA$$
$$\Sigma p_1 y = B\Sigma p_1^2$$
$$\Sigma p_2 y = C\Sigma p_2^2$$

and

$$\Sigma p_3 y = D\Sigma p_3^2$$

and therefore

$$A = \frac{\Sigma y}{N}$$

$$B = \frac{\Sigma p_1 y}{\Sigma p_1^2}$$

$$C = \frac{\Sigma p_2 y}{\Sigma p_2^2} \qquad\qquad (2)$$

$$D = \frac{\Sigma p_3 y}{\Sigma p_3^2}$$

The simple form of these solutions will be noted. It will also be noted that the solution for A is independent of p_1, p_2, and p_3 and that the solution for B depends only upon p_1, the solution for C only upon p_2, and the solution for D only upon p_3. This means that the value of A would have been the same whether a first-, second-, or third-degree trend line had been fitted. Similarly, the value of B would have been the same whether a first-, second-, or third-degree trend had been fitted, and the value of C would have been the same whether a second- or third-degree trend line had been fitted. For if $y' = A + Bp_1$ had been fitted, the solutions would still have been

$$A = \frac{\Sigma y}{N} \quad \text{and} \quad B = \frac{\Sigma p_1 y}{\Sigma p_1^2}$$

If $y' = A + Bp_1 + Cp_2$ had been fitted, the solutions would still have been

$$A = \frac{\Sigma y}{N}, \quad B = \frac{\Sigma p_1 y}{\Sigma p_1^2}, \quad \text{and} \quad C = \frac{\Sigma p_2 y}{\Sigma p_2^2}$$

The addition of the term Cp_2 does not therefore change the values obtained for A or B, and the addition of the term Dp_3 does not change the values obtained for A, B, or C. It also can be seen that if a fifth term were added to the trend line, namely, Ep_4, making it a fourth-degree trend, the value of E would be given by $E = \Sigma p_4 y / \Sigma p_4^2$ and the values of A, B, C, and D would be the same as before. It is this simplicity and independence of the solutions of the least-squares equations when orthogonal polynomials are used that give the orthogonal-polynomial method its main advantage over the ordinary method.

Forms of Orthogonal Polynomials Used. The forms of the orthogonal polynomials to be used for fitting trends can be generalized; what is required is to find the k's in terms of the given values of t and the number of years involved. The condition has been laid down that $p_1 = k_{10} + t$, $p_2 = k_{20} + k_{21}t + t^2$, and $p_3 = k_{30} + k_{31}t + k_{32}t^2 + t^3$, etc., are to be polynomials of the first, second, and third degree in t, respectively, that are orthogonal to each other and to unity. The problem is to make use of this condition to determine values for the k's in terms of the given values of t. When this is done, it will be possible to find the actual values of A, B, C, and D, from the formulas of the preceding section.

By way of illustration, the forms of only p_1 and p_2 will be derived; the method can be readily extended to the determination of the forms of p_3 and of higher polynomials.

First, it is assumed that the time intervals T are measured from the mean $\bar{T}$, so that p_1 and p_2 become $p_1 = k_{10} + t$ and $p_2 = k_{20} + k_{21}t + t^2$, where $t = T - \bar{T}$. In addition, it is supposed that the time intervals to which the variable refers are equally spaced and without interruptions. According to these assumptions, t will have a mean of zero; its highest value will be $+ \dfrac{N-1}{2}$ and its lowest value $- \dfrac{N-1}{2}.$ * For example, if there are 5 years of data, the middle year will be 0, the first year -2, and the last year $+2$. If there are 4 years of data, the first year will be $- \dfrac{3}{2}$; the second year $- \dfrac{1}{2}$; the third year $+ \dfrac{1}{2}$; and the last $+ \dfrac{3}{2}.$

Accordingly, all the odd moments of t, such as $\Sigma t/N$, $\Sigma t^3/N$, and $\Sigma t^5/N$, will be zero; the even moments, such as $\Sigma t^2/N$, $\Sigma t^4/N$, and $\Sigma t^6/N$, are computable from simple formulas depending entirely on N, the number of years, as already noted in Chap. XXI.[1]

With these assumptions, the derivation of the form of the orthogonal polynomials, that is to say, the derivation of the values of k_{10}, k_{20}, and k_{21}, may now be undertaken. The condition that p_1, p_2, and 1 shall be orthogonal to each other requires that $\Sigma p_1 = 0$, $\Sigma p_2 = 0$, and $\Sigma p_1 p_2 = 0$. These equations may be written as follows:

$$\Sigma p_1 = \Sigma(k_{10} + t) = Nk_{10} + \Sigma t = 0 \qquad \text{(i)}$$
$$\Sigma p_2 = \Sigma(k_{20} + k_{21}t + t^2) = Nk_{20} + k_{21}\Sigma t + \Sigma t^2 = 0 \qquad \text{(ii)}$$
$$\Sigma p_1 p_2 = \Sigma p_2(k_{10} + t) = k_{10}\Sigma p_2 + \Sigma p_2 t = 0 \qquad \text{(iii)}$$

From these equations, the values of the k's can readily be obtained. Since $\Sigma t = 0$, (i) gives $Nk_{10} = 0$, or $k_{10} = 0$; and Eq. (ii) gives $Nk_{20} + \Sigma t^2 = 0$, or $k_{20} = - \dfrac{\Sigma t^2}{N}.$ From Eq. (ii), it is known that $\Sigma p_2 = 0$; hence, Eq. (iii) becomes $\Sigma p_2 t = 0$. Substituting the equivalent of p_2, this gives the condition,

$$\Sigma p_2 t = \Sigma(k_{20} + k_{21}t + t^2)t = k_{20}\Sigma t + k_{21}\Sigma t^2 + \Sigma t^3 = 0 \qquad \text{(iv)}$$

* These assumptions were made in the preceding chapter. *Cf.* Tables 84 to 86, Chap. XXI.

[1] *Cf.* pp. 584, 586.

Since both Σt and Σt^3 are equal to zero, this becomes

$$k_{21}\Sigma t^2 = 0$$

and hence k_{21} must be zero, since Σt^2 is not. The values of the k's, therefore, are as follows:

$$\left.\begin{aligned}
k_{10} &= 0 \\
k_{21} &= 0 \\
k_{20} &= -\frac{\Sigma t^2}{N}
\end{aligned}\right\} \quad (3)$$

and the forms of the polynomials p_1, p_2 are therefore

$$\left.\begin{aligned}
p_1 &= t \\
p_2 &= t^2 - \frac{\Sigma t^2}{N}
\end{aligned}\right\} \quad (4)$$

for

$$\Sigma t^2 = \frac{n(n-1)(2n-1)}{3}$$

in which

$$n = \frac{N+1}{2}*$$

Hence,

$$\frac{\Sigma t^2}{N} = \frac{N^2 - 1}{12}$$

Accordingly,

$$p_2 = t^2 - \frac{N^2 - 1}{12}$$

Similar methods of analysis may be used to derive the forms of p_3 and higher polynomials. The results obtained for polynomials up to the fifth degree may be listed as follows:[1]

$$\left.\begin{aligned}
p_1 &= t \\
p_2 &= t^2 - \frac{N^2 - 1}{12} \\
p_3 &= t^3 - \frac{3N^2 - 7}{20}\,t \\
p_4 &= t^4 - \frac{3N^2 - 13}{14}\,t^2 + \frac{3(N^2 - 1)(N^2 - 9)}{560} \\
v_5 &= t^5 - \frac{5(N^2 - 7)}{18}\,t^3 + \frac{15N^4 - 230N^2 + 407}{1,008}\,t
\end{aligned}\right\} \quad (5)$$

* *Cf.* Eqs. (10), Chap. XXI.

[1] *Cf.* FISHER, R. A., *Statistical Methods for Research Workers*, Section **27**.

Thus, it is to be noted that a trend line can be fitted in two different forms, by the method of least squares; it can be fitted in the form $y' = a + bt + ct^2 + dt^3 + \ldots$ (where $t = T - \bar{T}$) by the methods described in the preceding chapter, or it can be fitted in the form $y' = A + Bp_1 + Cp_2 + Dp_3 + \ldots$ by the method of orthogonal polynomials. If the orthogonal-polynomial form is used in the fitting process, the ordinary form of the trend equation can readily be derived from the results; it should be repeated that the criterion of fit in each case is the least-squares criterion.

Calculation of the Coefficients A, B, C, ... If the values of p_1, p_2, p_3, . . . given in Eq. (5) are substituted in formulas for A, B, C, etc. [Eqs. (2)], the following values are obtained:

$$A = \frac{\Sigma y}{N}$$

$$B = \frac{12}{N(N^2 - 1)} \sum ty$$

$$C = \frac{180}{N(N^2 - 1)(N^2 - 4)} \left(\sum t^2 y - \frac{N^2 - 1}{12} \sum y \right)$$

$$D = \frac{2{,}800}{N(N^2 - 1)(N^2 - 4)(N^2 - 9)} \left(\sum t^3 y - \frac{3N^2 - 7}{20} \sum ty \right)$$

$$E = \frac{44{,}100}{N(N^2 - 1)(N^2 - 4)(N^2 - 9)(N^2 - 16)}$$
$$\left(\sum t^4 y - \frac{3N^2 - 13}{14} \sum t^2 y + \frac{3(N^2 - 1)(N^2 - 9)}{560} \sum y \right)$$

$$F = \frac{698{,}544}{N(N^2 - 1)(N^2 - 4)(N^2 - 9)(N^2 - 16)(N^2 - 25)}$$
$$\left(\sum t^5 y - \frac{5(N^2 - 7)}{18} \sum t^3 y + \frac{15N^4 - 230N^2 + 407}{1{,}008} \sum ty \right)$$

$$(6)$$

In order to illustrate the algebraic procedure by which the above formulas are obtained, the formula for C will be derived, as follows:

$$C = \frac{\Sigma p_2 y}{\Sigma p_2^2}$$

But

$$p_2 = t^2 - \frac{N^2 - 1}{12}$$

Hence,

$$C = \frac{\sum \left(t^2 - \frac{N^2 - 1}{12}\right) y}{\sum \left(t^2 - \frac{N^2 - 1}{12}\right)^2}$$

$$= \frac{\sum t^2 y - \frac{N^2 - 1}{12} \sum y}{\sum t^4 - 2 \frac{N^2 - 1}{12} \sum t^2 + \frac{(N^2 - 1)^2}{144} N}.$$

The formula for $\frac{\Sigma t^2}{N}$, however, is $\frac{N^2 - 1}{12}$, and hence

$$\sum t^2 = \frac{N(N^2 - 1)}{12}$$

Likewise, the formula for $\frac{\Sigma t^4}{N}$ is $\frac{N^2 - 1}{12} \cdot \frac{(3N^2 - 7)}{20}$, and hence

$$\sum t^4 = \frac{N(N^2 - 1)}{12} \cdot \frac{(3N^2 - 7)}{20}$$

Therefore the denominator of C becomes

$$\frac{N(N^2 - 1)}{12} \cdot \frac{(3N^2 - 7)}{20} - \frac{2(N^2 - 1)}{12} \frac{N(N^2 - 1)}{12} + \frac{(N^2 - 1)^2}{144} N$$

Taking $N(N^2 - 1)/12$ out of each term,

$$\frac{N(N^2 - 1)}{12} \left[\frac{3N^2 - 7}{20} - \frac{2(N^2 - 1)}{12} + \frac{(N^2 - 1)}{12} \right]$$

which readily reduces to

$$\frac{N(N^2 - 1)}{12} \cdot \frac{(N^2 - 4)}{15} = \frac{N(N^2 - 1)(N^2 - 4)}{180}$$

Thus C has the formula given above. The formulas for the other coefficients can be obtained in the same way.

Equations (6) could be applied by using a work sheet with columns for the product terms indicated in order to obtain Σty, $\Sigma t^2 y$, $\Sigma t^3 y$, etc. Greater economy is obtained, however, by using the subtotal summation type of work sheet illustrated in the preceding chapter. By using such a work sheet, an expeditious method that involves only addition and is self-checking has been evolved for finding A, B, C, ... A brief description of this method, together with the mathematical analysis that justifies its use, will now be given.

α is defined as $\dfrac{\Sigma y}{N}$ so that

$$N\alpha = S_1 \tag{7}$$

and α' is defined as equal to α. Accordingly,

$$A = \alpha = \alpha' = \frac{\Sigma y}{N} = \frac{S_1}{N} \tag{i}$$

From Eqs. (14), Chap. XXI,

$$S_2 = \frac{N+1}{2} \sum y - \sum ty$$

and, by the definition of α,

$$S_2 = \frac{N(N+1)}{2}\, \alpha - \sum ty$$

If β is now defined as

$$\beta = \frac{2S_2}{N(N+1)} \tag{ii}$$

then

$$\beta = \alpha - \frac{2}{N(N+1)} \sum ty$$

But $\Sigma ty = \Sigma p_1 y$, since $p_1 = t$; and if β' is defined as $\beta' = 2\Sigma p_1 y / N(N+1)$,

$$\beta = \alpha - \beta'$$

and

$$\beta' = \alpha - \beta \tag{iii}$$

Since $B = \dfrac{12\Sigma p_1 y}{N(N^2 - 1)}$, it follows that

$$B = \frac{6}{N - 1}\beta' \tag{iv}$$

Again, from Eqs. (14), Chap. XXI, it is found that

$$2S_3 = \sum \left(\frac{N + 1}{2} - t\right)^2 y + \sum \left(\frac{N + 1}{2} - t\right) y$$

$$= \frac{(N + 1)^2}{4} \sum y - (N + 1) \sum ty + \sum t^2 y + S_2$$

in which α and β may be substituted for equivalents, so that

$$2S_3 = \frac{(N + 1)^2}{4} N\alpha - \frac{N(N + 1)^2}{2}(\alpha - \beta) + \sum t^2 y$$
$$+ \frac{N(N + 1)}{2}\beta$$

$$= -\frac{N(N + 1)^2}{4}\alpha + \frac{N(N + 1)^2 + N(N + 1)}{2}\beta + \sum t^2 y$$

$$= -\frac{N(N + 1)^2}{4}\alpha + \frac{N(N + 1)(N + 2)}{2}\beta + \sum t^2 y$$

But

$$\sum p_2 y = \sum \left(t^2 - \frac{N^2 - 1}{12}\right) y = \sum t^2 y - \frac{(N^2 - 1)}{12} \sum y$$

Hence

$$\sum t^2 y = \sum p_2 y + \frac{N^2 - 1}{12} \sum y = \sum p_2 y + \frac{(N^2 - 1)N}{12}\alpha$$

Therefore, making substitutions in the above value of $2S_3$,

$$2S_3 = -\frac{N(N + 1)^2}{4}\alpha + \frac{(N^2 - 1)N}{12}\alpha + \frac{N(N + 1)(N + 2)}{2}\beta$$
$$+ \sum p_2 y$$

$$2S_3 = \frac{-3N(N+1)^2 + N(N+1)(N-1)}{12}\,\alpha$$

$$+ \frac{N(N+1)(N+2)}{2}\,\beta + \sum p_2 y$$

$$= \frac{-N(N+1)(N+2)}{6}\,\alpha + \frac{N(N+1)(N+2)}{2}\,\beta + \sum p_2 y$$

Now, if γ is defined as

$$\gamma = \frac{6}{N(N+1)(N+2)}\,S_3 \tag{v}$$

then

$$\frac{2N(N+1)(N+2)}{6}\,\gamma = \frac{-N(N+1)(N+2)}{6}\,\alpha$$

$$+ \frac{3N(N+1)(N+2)}{6}\,\beta + \sum p_2 y$$

And if γ' is defined as $\gamma' = \dfrac{6}{N(N+1)(N+2)} \sum p_2 y,$

then

$$2\gamma = -\alpha + 3\beta + \gamma'$$

and

$$\gamma' = \alpha - 3\beta + 2\gamma \tag{vi}$$

and since $C = \dfrac{180}{N(N^2-1)(N^2-4)} \sum p_2 y$, it follows that

$$C = \frac{30}{(N-1)(N-2)}\,\gamma' \tag{vii}$$

In the same manner, it can be shown that if

$$\delta = \frac{24}{N(N+1)(N+2)(N+2)}\,S_4 \tag{viii}$$

and

$$\delta' = \frac{20}{N(N+1)(N+2)(N+3)} \sum p_3 y$$

then

$$\delta' = \alpha - 6\beta + 10\gamma - 5\delta \tag{ix}$$

$$D = \frac{140}{(N-1)(N-2)(N-3)}\,\delta' \tag{x}$$

As a result of the above analysis, from Eqs. (i), (ii), (v), and (viii), the following formulas are obtained:

$$\alpha = \frac{S_1}{N}$$

$$\beta = \frac{2}{N(N+1)} S_2$$

$$\gamma = \frac{6}{N(N+1)(N+2)} S_3$$

$$\delta = \frac{24}{N(N+1)(N+2)(N+3)} S_4$$

$$\epsilon = \frac{120}{N(N+1)(N+2)(N+3)(N+4)} S_5$$

$$\lambda = \frac{720}{N(N+1)(N+2)(N+3)(N+4)(N+5)} S_6$$

$$\quad(8)$$

The values of ϵ and of λ are indicated by extension, since the symmetrical pattern of these formulas is readily apparent. The numerators run 2!, 3!, 4!, 5!, 6!, 7!, etc., and the denominators run N, $N(N+1)$, $N(N+1)(N+2)$,

$$N(N+1)(N+2)(N+3), \text{ etc.}$$

Similarly, from Eqs. (i), (iii), (vi), and (ix), the following formulas are obtained:[1]

$$\alpha' = \alpha$$
$$\beta' = \alpha - \beta$$
$$\gamma' = \alpha - 3\beta + 2\gamma$$
$$\delta' = \alpha - 6\beta + 10\gamma - 5\delta$$
$$\epsilon' = \alpha - 10\beta + 30\gamma - 35\delta + 14\epsilon$$
$$\lambda' = \alpha - 15\beta + 70\gamma - 140\delta + 126\epsilon - 42\lambda$$

$$\quad(9)$$

and from Eqs. (i), (iv), (vii), and (x), the following formulas are obtained;

---

[1] For additional equations, see Fisher, *op. cit.*, or George W. Snedecor, *Statistical Methods* (1940), pp. 324–334, where the procedure is applied to problems of curvilinear correlation in which probability interpretation is valid.

$$A = \alpha'$$

$$B = \frac{6}{N-1}\,\beta'$$

$$C = \frac{30}{(N-1)(N-2)}\,\gamma'$$

$$D = \frac{140}{(N-1)(N-2)(N-3)}\,\delta'$$

$$E = \frac{630}{(N-1)(N-2)(N-3)(N-4)}\,\epsilon'$$

$$F = \frac{2,772}{(N-1)(N-2)(N-3)(N-4)(N-5)}\,\lambda'$$

$$(10)$$

Tables to Be Used in Orthogonal-polynomial Analysis to Save Calculations. All the explanation necessary for the application of the method of orthogonal polynomials to a problem has been given. Thus, from a work sheet providing the series of sums $S_1, S_2, S_3, \ldots$, Eqs. (8) could be used to find the series $\alpha, \beta, \gamma, \delta, \ldots$; from these, Eqs. (9) could be used to find the series $\alpha', \beta', \gamma', \delta', \ldots$; from these, Eqs. (10) could be used to find the series $A, B, C, \ldots$. The set of orthogonal polynomials fitting the data according to the least-squares criterion could then be written $y' = A + Bp_1 + Bp_2 + Cp_3 + \ldots$. From Eqs. (5), values of p_1, p_2, p_3 in terms of t could then be substituted, and the final equation of trend in terms of t would be found. But it is desirable to effect another economy, by use of three tables of values that are the same for all problems having the same number of years of data.

Thus, the use of Eqs. (8) will be greatly facilitated by the use of Table 93, a set of constants, $\dfrac{N(N+1)}{2}$, $\dfrac{N(N+1)(N+2)}{6}$, etc., worked out for various odd values of N, that is to say, for various numbers of years, from 11 to 41. The use of Eqs. (10) will be greatly facilitated by referring to Table 94 for the various values of the series of constants $\dfrac{N-1}{6}$, $\dfrac{(N-1)(N-2)}{30}$, $\dfrac{(N-1)(N-2)(N-3)}{140}$, etc. And the use of Eqs. (5) will be made easier by referring to Table 95 for the values of $\dfrac{N^2-1}{12}$, $\dfrac{3N^2-7}{20}$, $\dfrac{3N^2-13}{14}$, etc.

TABLE 93.—VALUES OF SPECIFIED VARIABLES DEPENDENT UPON THE NUMBER OF YEARS INCLUDED IN TREND CALCULATION

Odd numbers of years, from 11 to 41

N	$\dfrac{N(N+1)}{2}$	$\dfrac{N(N+1)(N+2)}{6}$	$\dfrac{N(N+1)(N+2)(N+3)}{24}$	$\dfrac{N(N+1)(N+2)(N+3)(N+4)}{120}$	$\dfrac{N(N+1)(N+2)(N+3)(N+4)(N+5)}{720}$
11	66	286	1,001	3,003	8,008
13	91	455	1,820	6,188	18,564
15	120	680	3,060	11,628	38,760
17	146	969	4,845	20,349	74,613
19	190	1,330	7,315	33,649	134,596
21	231	1,771	10,626	53,130	230,230
23	276	2,300	14,950	80,730	376,740
25	325	2,925	20,475	118,755	593,775
27	378	3,654	27,405	169,911	906,192
29	435	4,495	35,960	237,336	1,344,904
31	496	5,456	46,376	324,632	1,947,792
33	561	6,545	58,905	435,897	2,760,681
35	630	7,770	73,815	575,757	3,838,380
37	703	9,139	91,390	749,398	5,245,786
39	780	10,660	111,930	962,598	7,059,052
41	861	12,341	135,751	1,221,759	9,366,819

TABLE 94.—VALUES OF SPECIFIED VARIABLES DEPENDENT UPON THE NUMBER OF YEARS INCLUDED IN TREND CALCULATION

Odd numbers of years, from 11 to 41

N	$\dfrac{N-1}{6}$	$\dfrac{(N-1)(N-2)}{30}$	$\dfrac{(N-1)(N-2)(N-3)}{140}$	$\dfrac{(N-1)(N-2)(N-3)(N-4)}{630}$	$\dfrac{(N-1)(N-2)(N-3)(N-4)(N-5)}{2,772}$
11	1.666667	3.000000	5.142857	8.000000	10.909091
13	2.000000	4.400000	9.428571	18.857143	34.285714
15	2.333333	6.066667	15.600000	38.133333	86.666667
17	2.666667	8.000000	24.000000	69.333333	189.090909
19	3.000000	10.200000	34.971428	116.571428	370.909091
21	3.333333	12.666667	48.857143	184.571428	671.168831
23	3.666667	15.400000	66.000000	278.666667	1,140.000000
25	4.000000	18.400000	86.742857	404.800000	1,840.000000
27	4.333333	21.666667	111.428571	569.523895	2,847.619048
29	4.666667	25.200000	140.400000	780.000000	4,254.545454
31	5.000000	29.000000	174.000000	1,044.000000	6,169.090909
33	5.333333	33.066667	212.571428	1,369.904762	8,717.575757
35	5.666667	37.400000	256.457142	1,766.704762	12,045.714285
37	6.000000	42.000000	306.000000	2,244.000000	16,320.000000
39	6.333333	46.866667	361.542857	2,812.000000	21,729.090909
41	6.666667	52.000000	423.428571	3,481.523895	28,485.194805

TABLE 95.—VALUES OF SPECIFIED VARIABLES DEPENDENT UPON THE NUMBER OF YEARS INCLUDED IN TREND CALCULATION

Odd numbers of years, from 11 to 41

N	$\dfrac{N^2-1}{12}$	$\dfrac{3N^2-7}{20}$	$\dfrac{3N^2-13}{14}$	$\dfrac{3(N^2-1)(N^2-9)}{560}$	$\dfrac{5(N^2-7)}{18}$	$\dfrac{15N^4-230N^2+407}{1{,}008}$
11	10.000000	17.8	25.000000	96.000000	38.000000	190.666667
13	14.000000	25.0	35.285714	144.000000	45.000000	613.142862
15	18.666667	33.4	47.285714	259.200000	60.555555	702.412698
17	24.000000	43.0	61.000000	432.000000	78.333333	1,177.333333
19	30.000000	53.8	76.428571	678.857142	98.333333	1,857.333333
21	36.666667	65.8	93.571428	1,018.285714	120.555555	2,793.841270
23	44.000000	79.0	112.428571	1,470.857142	145.000000	4,044.000000
25	52.000000	93.4	133.000000	2,059.200000	171.666667	5,670.666667
27	60.666667	109.0	155.285714	2,808.000000	200.555556	7,742.412698
29	70.000000	125.8	179.285714	3,744.000000	231.666667	10,333.523809
31	80.000000	143.8	205.000000	4,896.000000	265.000000	13,524.000000
33	90.666667	163.0	232.428571	6,294.857142	300.555556	17,399.555556
35	102.000000	183.4	261.571428	7,973.485714	338.333333	22,051.619048
37	114.000000	205.0	292.428571	9,966.854142	378.333333	27,577.333333
39	126.666667	227.8	325.000000	12,312.000000	420.555556	34,079.555556
41	140.000000	251.8	359.285714	15,048.000000	465.000000	41,666.857143

Advantages of Method of Orthogonal Polynomials.   The method of orthogonal polynomials is a great timesaver whenever a trend of higher order than a second-degree polynomial is fitted.   While it has required several pages to describe the method, it will be noted that the actual solution of a problem requires little more than a page of figures besides the work sheet.   This is illustrated in Chap. XXIV.

But the saving of time is not the sole advantage of the method of orthogonal polynomials.   In addition, the set of orthogonal polynomials that is obtained when values for A, B, C, D, . . . , are obtained, that is to say,

$$y' = A + Bp_1 + Cp_2 + Dp_3 + \cdots$$

constitutes the solution for any one of several trend lines. Thus $y' = A + Bp_1$ is the straight-line trend; the addition of Cp_2 gives the second-degree polynomial trend; the addition of Dp_3 gives the third-degree polynomial trend, etc.   It is not necessary to recalculate values for A, B, C, . . . , for the various trends required.   If a problem has been worked out to include solutions for A, B, C, and D and subsequently it is decided that E is required, it can be found by adding one more column to the work sheet and finding the value of E without recalculating the values of A, B, C, and D.

This convenience of obtaining several types of trends from one orthogonal set comes from the fact that the terms of the orthogonal equation are linearly uncorrelated with each other.[1]

[1] See p. 600.

CHAPTER XXIII

TIME-SERIES ANALYSIS—SEASONAL VARIATION

Historical Background. The second major stimulus to the development of methods for analyzing time series, listed at the beginning of Chap. XX, was the troublesome effects of seasonal variations in economic activity. Writers on labor problems stress the evil effects for labor of wide seasonal fluctuations in some employments. The effects of seasonal variations upon the banking and credit system were emphasized during the nineteenth century and the early part of the twentieth century. Even as early as 1793, Alexander Hamilton advised that redemption of the public debt be carried on during the winter, for, said he, "it is a familiar fact that during the winter in this country, there is always a scarcity of money in the towns—a circumstance calculated to damp the price of stock."[1]

Jevons made an analysis of the effects of the "autumnal pressure" on the London money market and calculated the average monthly fluctuations in currency movement between the Bank of England and its branches (1855–1862) and the average monthly excess of payments or receipts of British coin at the Bank of England for the same period.[2] In 1890, George Clare analyzed the seasonal variations for the period from 1881 to 1890 in the circulation of the Bank of England, in public deposits, in "other deposits," in "other securities," in the "reserve," and in the "internal gold movements."[3] In 1902, J. P. Norton published a study of the New York money market in which he com-

---

[1] 28th Congress, 1st Session, *Executive Document*, 15, p. 199. *Cf.* MYERS, MARGARET G., *The New York Money Market*, Vol. 1, Origins and Development, p. 208. Other early references to seasonal fluctuations are *Hunt's Merchants' Magazine*, Vol. 20, p. 302, Vol. 39, p. 582; *Journal of Commerce*, Aug. 3, 1846.

[2] *Investigations in Currency and Finance* (Foxwell ed., 1909), pp. 158–159. *Cf.* MITCHELL, W. C., *Business Cycles—The Problem Stated and Its Setting*, (1928), pp. 199, 236.

[3] *A Money-Market Primer* (2d ed.), pp. 19, 24, 31, 42, 53, 55. *Cf.* SMITH, JAMES G., BENJAMIN H. BECKHART, and WILLIAM A. BROWN, *The New York Money Market*, Vol. 4, External and Internal Relations, p. 424.

puted the seasonal variation in loans, the peaks occurring on Mar. 4 and in July and December and the low points occurring at the beginning of the year, in May, and at the end of November.[1]   The outstanding statistical analysis of seasonal variations in the New York money market before the First World War is that prepared for the National Monetary Commission in 1910 by Prof. E. W. Kemmerer.[2]   In this study he analyzed seasonal variations in money rates, exchange rates, bond yields, currency movements, and deposits.   His analysis brought out the seasonal relationships in a striking manner, in spite of very strict limitations in available data at the time.   Much of his work is based upon data gathered by the questionnaire method.

Causes of Seasonal Variation.   Two types of underlying forces cause seasonal variations in economic activity: (1) climatic conditions giving rise to seasons in agricultural production, in out-of-door construction work, in the manufacture of clothing, in the use of fuel, and in traveling, etc., and (2) forces arising from convention, such as the Christmas and Easter trade and seasonal style convention.[3]   The effects of these various basic seasonal influences upon the New York money market and upon the banking and credit structure of the United States have recently been exhaustively studied and published in Vol. 4 of the previously mentioned studies of *The New York Money Market*, edited by Prof. Benjamin H. Beckhart of Columbia University.[4]

In large part the movement for banking reform in this country, which culminated in the studies of the National Monetary Commission and the Federal Reserve Act of 1913, was the result of the evil effects of seasonal fluctuations in the demands of trade giving rise to periodical stringencies in the money market and frequently initiating monetary panics.   Consequently, it was one of the most important aims of the Federal Reserve System to devise an elastic currency and credit system that would accommodate these seasonal demands.[5]   Thus banking reform in the United

[1] *Statistical Studies in the New York Money Market*, pp. 62–64.

[2] *Seasonal Variations in the Relative Demand for Money and Capital in the United States* (National Monetary Commission Publications), Vol. 22.

[3] *Cf.* MITCHELL, *op. cit.*, pp. 236–240.

[4] *The New York Money Market*, Vol. 4, External and Internal Relations, pp. 417–542.

[5] *The New York Money Market*, Vol. 2, Sources and Movements of Funds, pp. 155–374.

States is a case in which a long-recognized evil was finally statistically measured and evaluated and a reform in the system definitely resulted in improvement.

Not only in the field of banking' has the study of seasonal variation by statistical methods been stimulated. In addition, unemployment with all its economic, social, and psychological implications has aroused great concern about the measurement of such variation. Extended reference to the problem of seasonal unemployment was made at former President Hoover's Conference on Unemployment, in the Report and Recommendations of the Committee to Investigate Business Cycles and Unemployment.[1]

In the hearings before the Committee on Education and Labor, of the United States Senate, in 1928–1929, much material and discussion are devoted to the subject of the seasonal variations in employment in industries and trade.[2] Franklin D. Roosevelt, when governor of New York State, appointed a Committee on the Stabilization of Industry for the Prevention of Unemployment, which made its report to him in November, 1930, entitled Less Unemployment through Stabilization of Operations, in which the subject of seasonal variations in employment constituted an important part.

During the years leading up to the depression of the 1930's, much was written on seasonal variation in employment and its contemplated stabilization. Thereafter, the problem of cyclical unemployment and its solution by means of unemployment insurance and the entire social security program dominated the scene.[3]

[1] New York, 1923, pp. 6, 116–120, 161, 215.

[2] 70th Congress, 2d Session, "Unemployment in the United States," S.R.219.

[3] SMITH, EDWIN S., *Reducing Seasonal Unemployment*, The Experience of American Manufacturing Concerns (1931). DOUGLAS, PAUL H. and AARON, DIRECTOR, *The Problem of Unemployment*. This book devotes pp. 73–118 to the subject of seasonal variations and regularization of industry to stabilize such fluctuations. HANSEN, ALVIN H., and TILLMAN M. SOGGE, *Seasonal Irregularity of Employment in Minneapolis, St. Paul and Duluth* (Employment Stabilization Research Institute, November, 1931). BERRIDGE, W. A., "Employment and Income of Labor in the United States," in *International Unemployment* (a study of fluctuations in employment and unemployment in several countries, 1910–1930, Industrial Relations Institute, The Hague, Netherlands, 1932).

A familiar example of seasonal activity in the economic sphere is construction activity, which gives not more than two-thirds as much employment in the winter months, on the average, as in the summer. Some important manufacturing industries, too, such as the automobile, agricultural implements, and ready-made clothing industries, show a considerable seasonal fluctuation. To be sure, the busy season in some industries comes in the dull season for others, a fact that tends to level out the differences between the number employed in industry in its entirety in one month as compared with another. But this does not mean that the workers released by one industry are absorbed by another to a sufficient degree or with sufficient promptitude to obliterate the variations from month to month in the amount of their employment. Barriers of specialized skill, geography, and attachment to particular occupations and localities prevent anything like the dovetailing suggested by the figures of the total number employed.[1] Consequently, the statistics of total employment may show little seasonal variation, while at the same time large degrees of seasonal unemployment exist in many parts of the total. The fact that there is no seasonal variation or little seasonal variation in total employment does not solve the unemployment problem for the seasonally unemployed worker.

One reason why concern, statistically speaking, about the subject of seasonal variations in employment has been stimulated is because the opinion prevails that this particular type of unemployment is in large part avoidable. The movement to inaugurate unemployment insurance in the United States was partly based upon the belief that such a measure for the relief of unemployment would tend to regularize industries affected by seasonal unemployment. It is recognized that the greater problem of cyclical unemployment is less easily solved. The literature on the subject of unemployment insurance in the United States makes it clear that the movement is directed particularly toward the regularization of industry to eliminate as much as possible of the seasonal fluctuation in employment.[2]

With these problems in mind, students of the labor problem asked: What types of business are responsible for the largest

---

[1] McCabe, David A., chapter on Unemployment, in *Facing the Facts* (a symposium, 1932), pp. 324–325, 338–351.

[2] *Cf.* McCabe, *op. cit.*, pp. 344–346, 350.

part of this seasonal irregularity in employment? What are the peak and slack seasons of employment in different businesses, and what are the amplitudes of fluctuations? What can be done to make business less seasonal and less irregular? What is the cost of regularization plans in an industry, and how do such costs compare with the savings resulting from more regular use of capital investment? These are the types of exceedingly practical problems presenting themselves in this field of economics, and they have stimulated statistical research to take measurements of seasonal variations. They are of practical significance to employers and to investors and to workers. They are of great social and psychological significance to the social scientist, the economist, and the political theorist.

Methods of Measuring Seasonal Variations

It has been seen that the method of discovering trends either for their own sake (rational trends) or in order to remove them from the data, *i.e.*, to get rid of them (empirical trends), has been based upon curve-fitting technique. The technical problem involved is a simple one even though the mathematics may be complex in some cases. The simplicity of the idea is somewhat offset, however, by the irrational character of the procedure. This is a troublesome factor because it is the function of the statistician not only to apply mathematical analysis to statistics but also to explain what he does and why he does it. Enough has been included in Chaps. XX and XXI, to indicate the general character of this problem.

In the case of seasonal variation, the difficulties of the statistician are just the reverse; for while it has been possible to build up a perfectly rational procedure, upon the basis of the theory of averages, the technical problem involved has been found to be a complex one. The rational concept underlying the procedure of measuring seasonal variation is that, where a time series has a characteristic seasonal variation occurring year after year, it should be quite reasonable to depict a "typical," or average, seasonal variation for that time series.

In its abstract aspect, therefore, the concept is perfectly rational. Homogeneous variates are to be averaged to obtain a type. For example, it is proposed to average the amount by which January data are higher or lower than those of other months of the year, to average the amount by which February data are higher or lower than those of other months of the year, and so on, until a picture of the "type" of periodical movement that occurs every year is obtained, although each year may be slightly different from the type.   Moderate variations from the type are quite consonant with the theory of averages and their application to the problem of measuring seasonal variation.[1]

When the rational procedure is to be put into effect, however, difficulties of a technical character arise.   A time series of raw data that by a priori knowledge should have a distinctively regular seasonal variation may be selected.   A graph of the time series is made, and a seasonal variation occurring every year is revealed, but the seasonal periodicity in the raw data is distorted by other movements, namely, trend and cycle.   This was noted at the beginning of Chap. XX where a hypothetical time series was constructed.   It is clear that the data in their raw state cannot be averaged to find the typical seasonal periodicity. That is to say, January, 1937, is not homogeneous with respect to seasonal variation with January, 1940, because the relative position of the respective Januaries (1) as to trend and (2) as to cycles is not comparable.   In other words, averaging the raw data of all the Januaries in a series of data, all the Februaries, etc., for the 12 months of the year would be an irrational procedure.   This would not accord with the rational idea of seasonal variation outlined above because the averages of raw data would include averages of something in addition to seasonal variation.

Problem of Isolating Seasonal Variation.   To average the actual seasonal variation, it must be isolated from the other types of variation in the raw data.   The technical problem involved in the measurement of seasonal variation is thus how to isolate from the raw data that part of its fluctuation that is essentially seasonal in character.   When these other types of

---

[1] If the seasonal variation were measured weekly, rather than monthly, the principle would be the same.   The same principle may be used to measure periodicity by days within the month or within the week; and it may likewise be used to measure periodicity by hours within the day. Thus periodicity by days within the month of wage payments might have great economic value for some problems; and periodicity by hours within the day of consumption of electrical power might have significance in connection with some problems.   Seasonal variation is only one type of periodicity that can be measured by this method.

fluctuation have been removed from the raw data, by subtraction or division, all the residual Januaries can be rationally averaged, all the residual Februaries can be averaged, etc., in order to obtain a picture of the average position, respectively, of each month.

How can this be done? There are several answers to this question, and there is controversy as to just what is the best technical procedure. In his notable studies of seasonal variation made about 1910, Prof. Kemmerer devised a method for measuring seasonal variation separate from other fluctuations. At the time, it was the best that had been suggested.[1]

Another famous suggestion as to a method of isolating the seasonal periodicities from other types of fluctuations was made by W. M. Persons, when from 1915 to 1919 he developed his approach to the problems of time-series analysis, culminating in the establishment of the Harvard Economic Society's business barometer and the *Review of Economic Statistics*. Persons' method, called the "link relative method," expresses each monthly figure as a relative of the immediately preceding month; the seasonal pattern is found by averaging all the link relatives for the same month and taking any residual trend out of the chain relatives computed from these average link relatives.[2]

A third method of isolating the seasonal fluctuations and measuring them by an index of seasonal variation is that advocating simply the removal of trend from the data and then the averaging of the monthly ratio differences from the trend.[3] While this method removes the nonhomogeneous effects of trend, it does not remove those due to cyclical fluctuations. If taken over a sufficient period of time, the bias of the cyclical fluctuations will cancel so that a true index of seasonal variations would be

---

[1] *Op. cit.* *Cf.* criticism of Kemmerer's method by W. L. Hart, *Journal of the American Statistical Association*, Vol. 17 (1922). Kemmerer's work constitutes an important pioneer effort to solve the technical difficulties involved and helped direct attention to better solutions.

[2] *Review of Economic Statistics*, January, 1919, pp. 18–31; *Indices of Business Conditions* (1919). *Cf.* RIETZ, H. L., *Handbook of Mathematical Statistics*, pp. 151–155.

[3] FALKNER, HELEN D., "The Measurement of Seasonal Variation," *Journal of the American Statistical Association*, Vol. 19 (1924), pp. 167–179; ROBB, RICHARD A., "Variate Difference Method of Seasonal Variation," *ibid.*, Vol. 24 (1929), pp. 250–257.

obtained by averaging. One of the discoveries of recent years, however, is that seasonal variations change in the same time series from one era to another owing to new conditions; for such time series an index of seasonal variation based on a period of time covering two or more eras would be comparatively useless. Thus the criticism of the ratio-difference-from-the-trend method is that, if taken over a sufficient period of time to make it a valid measurement of seasonal variation, it would be taken for too long a time, *i.e.*, that two or more eras of typical seasonal fluctuation might be confused.

A number of other methods have been suggested, based upon the principles that have been outlined.[1] The most widely used and probably the best method is the 12 months' moving average method, of which a number of refinements have been suggested. Since this method is the one most extensively used, it is now described in detail and an illustration will be given.

Twelve Months' Moving Average Method. This method consists of the following steps:

1. Calculate a 12 months' moving average of the raw data, centering the moving average at the seventh month; thus, opposite July of the first year would be the average of the 12 months of that year; opposite August would be the average of the last 11 months of that year and the first month of the next year; and so on.

2. Divide the raw data serially by the 12 months' moving average. Inasmuch as the moving average would contain in it the elements both of trend and of major and minor cycles, the residuals of the raw data from the moving average (either by subtraction or division) would contain purely seasonal fluctuations.

---

[1] KING, W. I., "An Improved Method for Measuring the Seasonal Factor," *Journal of the American Statistical Association*, Vol. 19 (1924), pp. 301–313; CARMICHAEL, F. L., "Methods of Computing Seasonal Indexes: Constant and Progressive," *ibid.*, Vol. 22 (1927), pp. 339–354; JAY, ARYNESS, and THOMAS WOODLIEF, "Use of Moving Averages in the Measurement of Seasonal Variation,' *ibid.*, Vol. 23 (1928), pp. 241–252; BAUMANN, A. O., "Thirteen Months-Ratio-First Difference Method of Measuring Seasonal Variation," *ibid.*, Vol. 23 (1928), pp. 282–290; KUZNETS, SIMON, "Seasonal Patterns and Seasonal Amplitudes: Measurement of Their Short-time Variations," *ibid.*, Vol. 27 (1932), pp. 9–20; RIGGLEMAN, JOHN R., and IRA N. FRISBEE. *Business Statistics* (1932), pp. 226–242.

3. Make frequency distributions of the several months (see the example at the end of the chapter).

4. Find the median relatives for each month, using the median to avoid the influence of extreme fluctuations.

5. Express these median relatives as a percentage of their own average, thus giving an *index of seasonal variation.*

As a short cut, inasmuch as the result will be precisely the same, the 12 months' moving total may be used instead of the 12 months' moving average, thus saving the division throughout by 12.

Problem Illustrating Measurement of Seasonal Variation. *Calculating the Index of Seasonal Variation by the* 12 *Months' Moving Average Method.* The time series of monthly data on consumer installment-sale debt for household appliances in the United States has been selected to illustrate the calculation of an index of seasonal variation by the 12 months' moving average method. Table 96 is a work sheet for the calculations necessary to the problem. The data were recorded on this work sheet for the years 1929–1942 by months, the raw data appearing in column (1). Next, a 12 months' moving total was calculated; this appears in column (2), the moving total being "centered at the seventh month." For example, the figure 2,930 after July, 1929, in column (2) of the work sheet is the total of the 12 monthly figures for 1929; the figure 2,972 (opposite August, 1929) is the total of the next 12 monthly figures, beginning with February, 1929, and ending with January, 1930. Opposite each July is the total for that year; this constitutes a good cross check in the construction of the moving total.

To calculate the moving total, first put the 12 monthly figures for 1929 in the adding machine, and take a subtotal; then subtract the datum for January, 1929, and add the datum for January, 1930, and take a subtotal; then subtract the datum for February, 1929, and add the datum for February, 1930, and take a subtotal; and so on, until the end of the time series. Clear the machine, and then add independently the last 12 months of the time series; this should check with your last subtotal. If it does not check, a mistake has been made, which can be most readily found by checking up on the July subtotals for each year, beginning with the last one and going back until you find the mistake. These subtotals are the 12 months'

TABLE 96.—WORK SHEET FOR CALCULATING INDEX OF SEASONAL VARIATION
DATA: Consumer installment-sale debt, monthly, for household appliances,
end of month
(In millions of dollars)

Year and month	(1) Monthly raw data	(2) 12 months' moving total centered at 7th month	(3) Raw data divided by 12 months' moving total, per cent
1929:			
January...................	207		
February.................	199		
March....................	199		
April....................	217		
May.....................	237		
June....................	260		
July....................	273	2,930	9.32
August...................	274	2,972	9.22
September................	272	3,006	9.05
October..................	266	3,031	8.78
November.................	261	3,043	8.58
December.................	265	3,043	8.71
1930:			
January...................	249	3,031	8.22
February.................	233	3,010	7.74
March....................	224	2,984	7.51
April....................	229	2,953	7.75
May.....................	237	2,919	8.12
June....................	248	2,881	8.61
July....................	252	2,838	8.88
August...................	248	2,800	8.86
September................	241	2,766	8.71
October..................	232	2,734	8.48
November.................	223	2,701	8.26
December.................	222	2,666	8.33
1931:			
January...................	211	2,628	8.03
February.................	199	2,588	7.69
March....................	192	2,548	7.54
April....................	196	2,509	7.81
May.....................	202	2,471	8.17
June....................	210	2,434	8.63
July....................	212	2,397	8.84
August...................	208	2,357	8.82
September................	202	2,318	8.71
October..................	194	2,275	8.53
November.................	186	2,225	8.36
December.................	185	2,167	8.54

TABLE 96.—WORK SHEET FOR CALCULATING INDEX OF SEASONAL VARIA-
TION.—(*Continued*)

Year and month	(1) Monthly raw data	(2) 12 months' moving total centered at 7th month	(3) Raw data divided by 12 months' moving total, per cent
1932:			
January	171	2,101	8.14
February	160	2,028	7.89
March	149	1,954	7.63
April	146	1,881	7.76
May	144	1,813	7.94
June	144	1,749	8.23
July	139	1,685	8.25
August	134	1,628	8.23
September	129	1,575	8.19
October	126	1,528	8.25
November	122	1,484	8.22
December	121	1,447	8.36
1933:			
January	114	1,418	8.04
February	107	1,398	7.65
March	102	1,386	7.36
April	102	1,378	7.40
May	107	1,372	7.80
June	115	1,367	8.41
July	119	1,365	8.72
August	122	1,364	8.94
September	121	1,365	8.86
October	120	1,370	8.76
November	117	1,384	8.45
December	119	1,403	8.48
1934:			
January	113	1,422	7.95
February	108	1,441	7.49
March	107	1,456	7.35
April	116	1,468	7.90
May	126	1,479	8.52
June	134	1,490	8.99
July	138	1,502	9.19
August	137	1,515	9.04
September	133	1,528	8.70
October	131	1,544	8.48
November	128	1,561	8.20
December	131	1,578	8.30

TABLE 96.—WORK SHEET FOR CALCULATING INDEX OF SEASONAL VARIA-
TION.—(*Continued*)

Year and month	(1) Monthly raw data	(2) 12 months' moving total centered at 7th month	(3) Raw data divided by 12 months' moving total, per cent
1935:			
January	126	1,600	7.88
February	121	1,626	7.44
March	123	1,657	7.42
April	133	1,692	7.86
May	143	1,728	8.28
June	156	1,768	8.82
July	164	1,808	9.07
August	168	1,845	9.10
September	168	1,882	8.93
October	167	1,921	8.69
November	168	1,964	8.55
December	171	2,017	8.48
1936:			
January	163	2,075	7.86
February	158	2,143	7.37
March	162	2,211	7.33
April	176	2,281	7.72
May	196	2,353	8.33
June	214	2,428	8.81
July	232	2,512	9.24
August	236	2,596	9.09
September	238	2,683	8.87
October	239	2,772	8.62
November	243	2,863	8.49
December	255	2,952	8.64
1937:			
January	247	3,045	8.11
February	245	3,130	7.83
March	251	3,217	7.80
April	267	3,302	8.09
May	285	3,382	8.43
June	307	3,451	8.90
July	317	3,503	9.05
August	323	3,552	9.09
September	323	3,594	8.99
October	319	3,624	8.80
November	312	3,639	8.57
December	307	3,636	8.44

TABLE 96.—WORK SHEET FOR CALCULATING INDEX OF SEASONAL VARIA-
TION.—(*Continued*)

Year and month	(1) Monthly raw data	(2) 12 months' moving total centered at 7th month	(3) Raw data divided by 12 months' moving total, per cent
1938:			
January	296	3,610	8.20
February	287	3,571	8.04
March	281	3,525	7.97
April	282	3,475	8.12
May	282	3,420	8.24
June	281	3,371	8.34
July	278	3,330	8.35
August	277	3,290	8.42
September	273	3,253	8.39
October	264	3,218	8.20
November	263	3,183	8.26
December	266	3,154	8.43
1939:			
January	256	3,153	8.12
February	250	3,120	8.01
March	246	3,110	7.91
April	247	3,103	7.96
May	253	3,104	8.15
June	260	3,106	8.37
July	265	3,113	8.51
August	267	3,119	8.56
September	266	3,124	8.51
October	265	3,131	8.46
November	265	3,143	8.43
December	273	3,161	8.64
1940:			
January	262	3,182	8.23
February	255	3,205	7.96
March	253	3,232	7.83
April	259	3,259	7.95
May	271	3,284	8.25
June	281	3,309	8.49
July	288	3,338	8.63
August	294	3,366	8.73
September	293	3,397	8.62
October	290	3,430	8.45
November	290	3,474	8.35
December	302	3,523	8.57

Table 96.—Work Sheet for Calculating Index of Seasonal Variation.—(*Continued*)

Year and month	(1) Monthly raw data	(2) 12 months' moving total centered at 7th month	(3) Raw data divided by 12 months' moving total, per cent
1941:			
January	290	3,572	8.12
February	286	3,620	7.90
March	286	3,672	7.79
April	303	3,721	8.14
May	320	3,764	8.50
June	330	3,794	8.70
July	336	3,805	8.83
August	346	3,809	9.08
September	342	3,808	8.98
October	333	3,794	8.78
November	320	3,749	8.54
December	313	3,670	8.53
1942:			
January	294	3,559	8.26
February	285	3,425	8.32
March	272	3,262	8.34
April	258	3,089	8.35
May	241		
June	219		
July	202		
August	183		
September	169		
October			
November			
December			

Source: Holthausen, Duncan McG., "Monthly Estimates of Short-term Consumer
Debt, 1929–1942," *Survey of Current Business*, Vol. 22 (November, 1942), pp. 9–25.

moving total and can be tabulated in column (2) of the work
sheet, as in Table 96. The next step is to divide each monthly
raw datum by the corresponding moving total figure, expressing
the answer as a percentage figure in column (3). The figures in
column (3) are then tabulated in a system of frequency arrays
as in Fig. 147.

From Fig. 147 the median monthly relatives are read and
arranged as in Table 97.

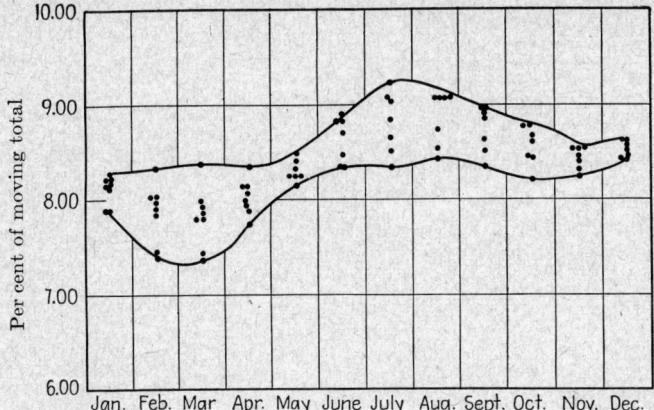

Fig. 147.—Frequency arrays, one for each month, of distributions of monthly ratios of raw data to 12 months' moving total. Column (3) of Table 96. Consumer installment-sale debt for household appliances in the United States, 1935–1942.

Column (1) of Table 97 consists of the median relatives read from Fig. 147; and these median relatives have only to be

TABLE 97.—INDEX OF SEASONAL VARIATION IN CONSUMER INSTALLMENT-SALE DEBT FOR HOUSEHOLD APPLIANCES IN THE UNITED STATES

Month	Medians	Index of seasonal variation[1]
January	8.13	96.2
February	7.95	94.0
March	7.82	92.5
April	8.05	95.2
May	8.25	97.6
June	8.72	103.2
July	8.85	104.7
August	9.10	107.6
September	8.88	105.0
October	8.64	102.2
November	8.50	100.6
December	8.55	101.1
Total	101.44	1,200.0
Average	8.4533+	

[1] This column consists of the medians expressed as percentages of their average. Thus 8.13 is 96.2 per cent of 8.4533+.

expressed as percentages of their own average to give the index of seasonal variation. This is done, giving the figures in column

(2) of Table 96. No adjustment is necessary because trend and cyclical influences were removed by the use of the 12 months' moving total as a divisor into the raw data, thereby isolating residuals each month that presumably contained seasonal varia-

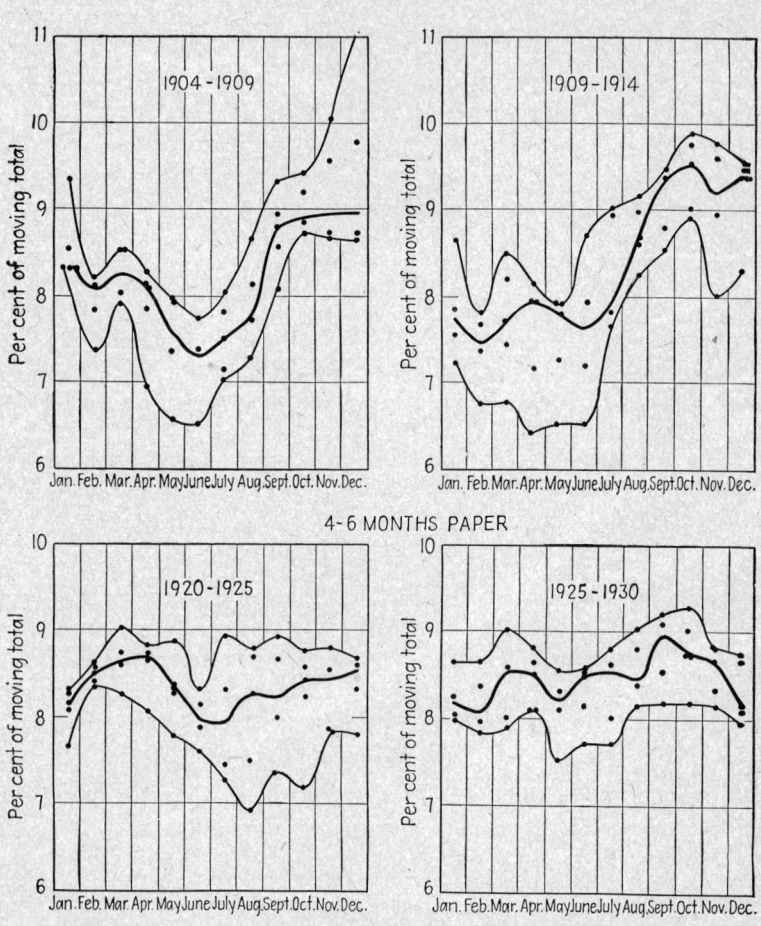

FIG. 148.—Studies in seasonal variations in commercial paper rates, before and since the establishment of the Federal Reserve System.

tions and chance fluctuations. By averaging, the chance fluctuations are canceled out, leaving in the index a description of relative seasonal movement. The theory of this method is based, of course, upon the use of a 12 months' moving average; but precisely the same arithmetical results are obtained by using the moving total instead, and it is a saving of a considerable number of division processes. In dividing by the 12 months' moving total instead of by the 12 months' moving average, the average residual percentage is 8.333+, whereas, in dividing by the 12 months' moving average, the average residual percentage would be 12 times 8.333+, or 100.00.

From the multiple frequency array, as in Figs. 147 and 148, it can be determined whether or not the seasonal variation is well defined. If the course of all the recorded ratios of raw data to the 12 months' moving total by months tends to run close to the course of the medians, then the seasonal variation is a well-defined one. If, however, the points are scattered in a wide range from the medians and the general swing of the data does not correspond to the movements of the median line, then the seasonal variation is not well defined. Such a result might be obtained if the type of the seasonal variation were changing, and in that case the data may be studied in groups of a smaller number of years. Figure 148 is included to present examples of poorly defined seasonal variation, as compared with well-defined cases of seasonal variation. The data studied are commercial paper rates in the New York money market before and after the inception of the Federal Reserve System. From the figure it is seen how well defined the seasonal variation in commercial paper rates was before the beginning of the Federal Reserve System—namely, for the periods 1904–1909 and 1909–1914. Also, it is seen how poorly defined is the seasonal variation for the periods 1920–1925 and 1925–1930—so poorly that there could hardly be said to have been any consistent seasonal periodicity whatever.[1]

METHOD OF DETECTING CHANGING SEASONAL VARIATION

Figure 149 is drawn to discover whether or not, during the years from 1929 to 1941, the seasonal variation in consumer installment debt for household appliances has changed.[2] The

[1] For a more complete discussion see *The New York Money Market*, Vol. 4, pp. 510–530.

[2] For other suggested methods of measuring changing seasonal variation see Julius Shiskin, "A New Multiplicative Seasonal Index," *Journal of the American Statistical Association*, Vol. 37 (1942), pp. 507–516; Henry A. Latané, "Seasonal Factors Determined by Difference from Average of Adjacent Months," *Journal of the American Statistical Association*, Vol. 37 (1942), pp. 517–522; Dudley J. Cowden, "Moving Seasonal Indexes," *Journal of the American Statistical Association*, Vol. 37 (1942), pp. 523–524.

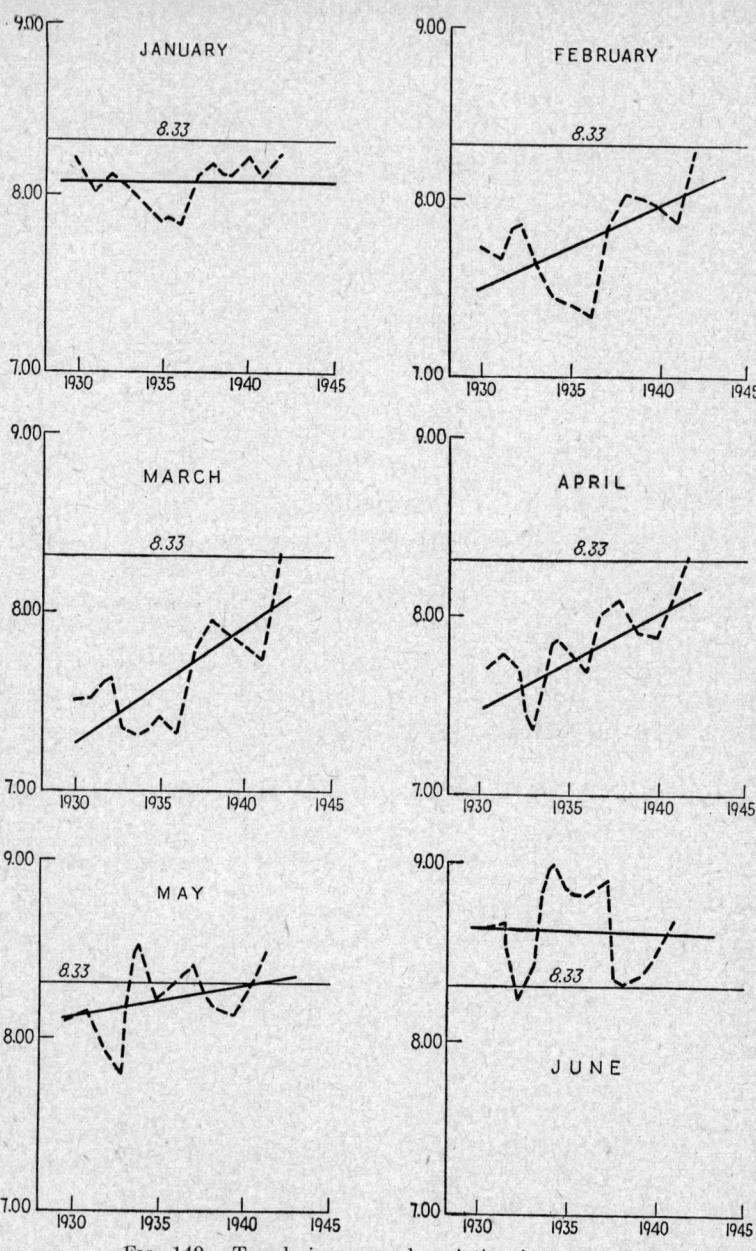

Fig. 149.—Trends in seasonal variation in consumer instalment-

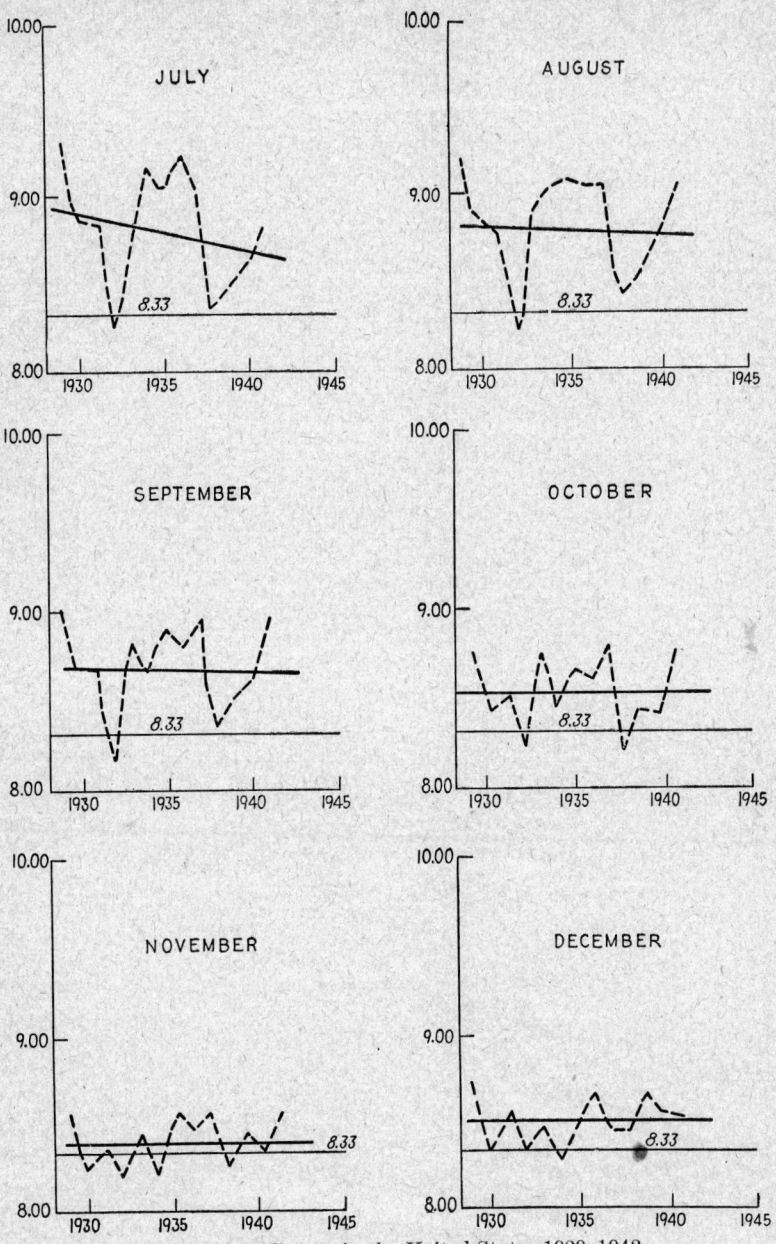

sale debt for household appliances in the United States 1929–1942.

figure is a plot of the ratios to 12 months' moving total shown in the last column of Table 96; a separate graph for each month has been drawn in Fig. 149.

The straight-line trends for each month were drawn in "at sight"; they were not fitted by a mathematical method. Figure 149 shows that the relative seasonal position of January, June, October, November, and December remained about the same during this period of years. But the relative seasonal amount of consumer installment debt was rising in the months of February, March, April, and May, while the relative seasonal quantity of consumer installment debt was declining in the months of July, August, and September.

Consequently, a more refined index of seasonal variation than the average of a period of years such as that shown in Table 97 and Fig. 148 can be obtained from Fig. 149. In fact, since these trends exist, a different index of seasonal variation for each year is required. For 1942 this index of seasonal variation can be obtained as indicated in Table 98.

TABLE 98.—COMPUTATION OF INDEX OF SEASONAL VARIATION IN CONSUMER INSTALLMENT-SALE DEBT FOR HOUSEHOLD APPLIANCES, 1942

Month	Ratios, read from trend lines in Fig. 149	Index of seasonal variation[1]
January	8.10	96.4
February	8.09	96.2
March	8.08	96.1
April	8.15	97.0
May	8.35	99.3
June	8.60	102.3
July	8.65	102.9
August	8.75	104.1
September	8.65	102.9
October	8.54	101.6
November	8.40	99.9
December	8.50	101.1
Total	100.86	1,200.0
Average	8.405	

[1] Obtained by expressing ratios in the first column as percentages of their own average.

CHAPTER XXIV

DETERMINATION OF CYCLE

Usually it is desirable to have current figures on a monthly basis, and to know how actual experience compares with what should be expected for the season and with normal growth. Can we estimate our position in the business cycle from month to month? Annual data adjusted for trend and a picture of undistorted seasonal variation, illustrated in the preceding chapters, do not go quite far enough. It is often necessary to remove trend and seasonal variation from monthly data in order to determine position in the cycle.

Cycle Determined by Adjusting Monthly Data. When monthly, instead of annual, data are analyzed, the empirical trend may be found by setting up a work sheet similar to Table 83 or 86 (pages 582, 588), depending upon the type of trend selected. The trend is then fitted by the method of least squares in a manner precisely similar to that demonstrated for annual data. Of course, if quite a number of years of monthly data are thus treated, the calculations become very extended, but the principle remains the same.[1] It is possible, however, to derive an approximation of the monthly trend equation from an annual trend equation. This is explained in the present chapter and may serve as an economizer of time in the analysis of monthly data.

Determination of Cycle in Annual Data. While the purpose of this chapter is to present a method for measuring the cycle in monthly data, it may be noted at the start that even if the object of analysis is to determine cycle in monthly data it is desirable first to study the annual data. Not only is this true because the monthly trend may be easily estimated from the annual trend, but it is also desirable because the general character

---

[1] Where trends are calculated for monthly data, involving long series, convenient short-cut methods of calculation have been devised. *Cf.* Ross, F. A., "Formulae for Facilitating Computations in Time Series Analysis," *Journal of the American Statistical Association*, Vol. 20 (1925), pp. 75–79; *cf.* also timesaving devices discussed in Chap. XXII.

of the results on a monthly basis can be visualized from the analysis of the annual figures and the annual data can be analyzed with a much smaller amount of computation. The analysis on an annual basis will help judge the kind of analysis required for the monthly data, whether to use a straight-line trend or a second- or third-degree polynomial trend. In addition, the analysis on an annual basis will help to decide the significance of the respective trends. This will now be illustrated by making use of monthly and annual averages of monthly data on consumer installment-sale debt for household appliances in the United States, 1929–1942.*

The work sheet is not reproduced here, but one similar to Table 91 (page 594) was constructed and the following set of subtotals was obtained: $S_1 = 2,842$; $S_2 = 18,159$; $S_3 = 89,614$; and $S_4 = 362,901$ (in millions of dollars). Using the method of orthogonal polynomials, which is the quickest method of finding at once the first-, second-, and third-degree polynomial trend lines by one set of calculations, the following results were obtained by the application of Eqs. (5) and (8) to (10), Chap. XXII (pages 605–612):

$$\alpha = \frac{2,842}{13} = 218.61538$$

$$\beta = \frac{18,159}{91} = 199.54945$$

$$\gamma = \frac{89,614}{455} = 196.95384$$

$$\delta = \frac{362,901}{1,820} = 199.39615$$

The values of the denominators in the above fractions were obtained from Table 93 (page 613). These calculations are carried to more places than are significant for the problem because they must be combined in multiple proportions to obtain the following results by using Eqs. (9) and (10), Chap. XXII (pages 611–612):

---

* HOLTHAUSEN, DUNCAN McG., "Monthly Estimates of Short-term Consumer Debt, 1929–1942," *Survey of Current Business*, Vol. 22 (November, 1942), pp. 9–25, 17.

$$\alpha' = 218.61538 \qquad A = 218.61538$$
$$\beta' = 19.06593 \qquad B = 9.53296$$
$$\gamma' = 13.87471 \qquad C = 3.15334$$
$$\delta' = -6.12367 \qquad D = -0.64948$$

Accordingly, the following set of orthogonal-polynomial trends is obtained; the first line is the straight-line trend; the first line combined with the second line is the second-degree polynomial trend; the first, second, and third lines combined give the third-degree polynomial trend:

$$y' = 218.61538 + 9.53296p_1$$
$$+ 3.15334p_2$$
$$- 0.64948p_3$$

that is to say, since $p_1 = t$, $p_2 = t^2 - 14$, and $p_3 = t^3 - 25t$ when $N = 13$ (see pages 605 and 615),

$$y' = 218.61538 + 9.53296t$$
$$+ 3.15334(t^2 - 14)$$
$$- 0.64948(t^3 - 25t)$$

The three possible trends are therefore the following (in millions of dollars):

Straight-line trend:

$$y' = 218.6 + 9.533t \quad \text{(origin at 1935)}$$

Second-degree polynomial trend:

$$y'' = 174.5 + 9.533t + 3.153t^2 \quad \text{(origin at 1935)}$$

Third-degree polynomial trend:

$$y''' = 174.5 + 25.77t + 3.153t^2 - 0.6495t^3 \quad \text{(origin at 1935)}$$

Table 99 is presented to show the raw annual data and the annual values of each of these three trends, which are also presented graphically in Fig. 150.

An annual increment averaging something less than 10 on a base of over 200 is not too great to deter the assumption that the straight-line trend roughly depicts rational long-term growth. If it is appropriate to suppose that installment-sale debt would tend to grow at the rate of population growth, which is presumably geometric, the trend line fitted should be a logarithmic

TABLE 99.—ANNUAL TREND ANALYSIS OF CONSUMER INSTALLMENT-SALE
DEBT FOR HOUSEHOLD APPLIANCES IN THE UNITED STATES, 1929–1942
(In millions of dollars)

Year	Raw data	Straight-line trend	Second-degree polynomial trend	Third-degree polynomial trend
1929	244	161	231	274
1930	236	171	206	206
1931	200	180	187	163
1932	140	190	174	143
1933	114	200	168	141
1934	125	209	168	152
1935	151	219	174	174
1936	209	228	187	203
1937	292	238	206	233
1938	277	247	232	263
1939	259	257	263	286
1940	278	266	301	301
1941	317	276	345	302
1942	*	286†	396†	287†

* Data available for only the first 9 months of the year; this year was not used in fitting
the trends.

† Extrapolated.

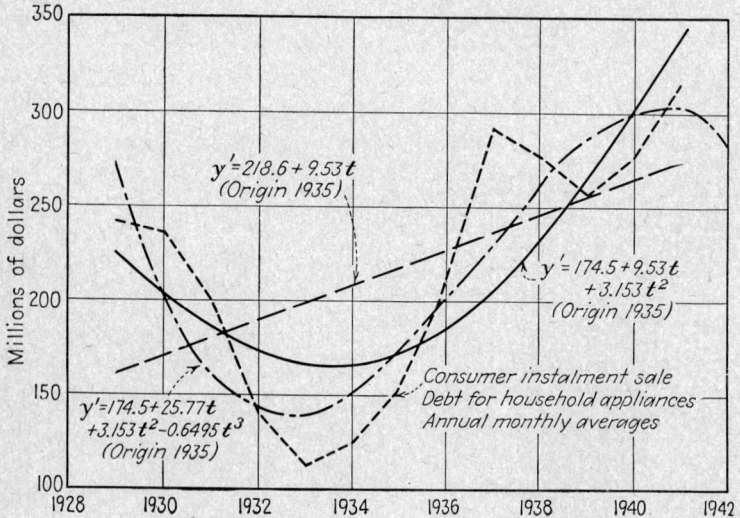

FIG. 150.—Annual trend analysis of consumer installment-sale debt for household appliances in the United States, 1929–1942.

trend; but for a short period of years the straight-line trend is an adequate approximation of the more appropriate logarithmic trend. The straight-line trend in the data presently studied may consequently be used as the base from which the major cycle in the data can be measured.

The second-degree polynomial trend shows a sharp rise for the later years, and if extrapolated beyond 1942 it would quickly approach infinity; it is not, therefore, a reasonable picture of rational growth. The straight line comes nearer to what would be the result if a logarithmic trend were fitted, if data covering a long enough period were available to afford sufficient perspective to obtain a growth curve.

TABLE 100.—CYCLICAL MOVEMENTS IN CONSUMER INSTALLMENT-SALE DEBT FOR HOUSEHOLD APPLIANCES IN THE UNITED STATES, 1929–1942

Year	Raw data, millions of dollars y	Straight-line trend, millions of dollars y'	Second-degree polynomial trend, millions of dollars y'''	Cycle, per cent $\dfrac{y'''}{y'}$ $(y' = 100)$	Cycle mixed with residuals, per cent $\dfrac{y}{y'}$ $(y' = 100)$
1929	244	161	274	170	152
1930	236	171	206	120	138
1931	200	180	163	90	111
1932	140	190	143	75	74
1933	114	200	141	70	57
1934	125	209	152	73	60
1935	151	219	174	79	69
1936	209	228	203	89	92
1937	292	238	233	98	123
1938	277	247	263	106	112
1939	259	257	286	111	101
1940	278	266	301	113	104
1941	317	276	302	109	114

The third-degree polynomial trend seems adequately to represent the rounded contour of a major cycle. Examination of Fig. 150, accordingly, leads to the conclusion that the straight-line trend can be used to depict growth in the data, and the third-degree polynomial trend can be used to measure the major cycle. As a consequence, the raw data divided by the straight-line trend should give a picture of the major cyclical movement in this period (plus the residual fluctuations);[1] and the third-degree polynomial trend divided by the straight-line trend gives a measure of the major cycle. Table 100 and Fig. 151 give the results of such computations. The column headed Cycle in Table 100 consists of the second-degree polynomial empirical trend divided by the straight-line empirical trend, giving as a result a smoothed measure of the major cycle. This is shown by the heavy line in Fig. 151. The column headed Cycle mixed

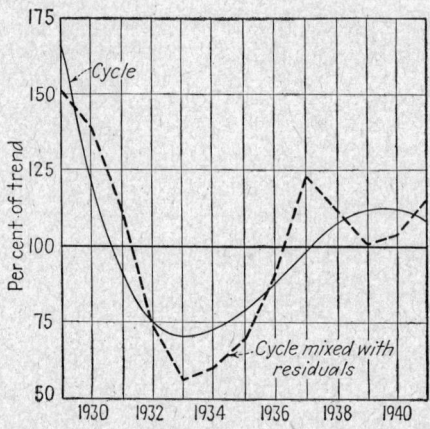

FIG. 151.—Cyclical study of consumer installment-sale debt for household appliances in the United States, 1929–1942.

with residuals in Table 100 consists of the raw data divided by the straight-line empirical trend, giving as a result the measure of the cycle mixed with residual fluctuations in annual data.[2] Both these columns are expressed as percentages, with the y' for each year equal to 100.

Determination of Cycle in Monthly Data. *Cycle Determined by Adjusting Monthly Data.* Monthly data, when examined to discover the cycle, must be adjusted not only for trend but also for seasonal variations. Adjusting monthly data for trend and seasonal variation in order to measure cyclical movements

---

[1] In addition, there might be minor cyclical movement, a fact that could be determined by further analysis of data extending over a longer period of time.

[2] See p. 570 for meaning of "residual fluctuations" in time series. In this instance, the residuals might include short-cycle fluctuations. See also Chap. XXV, pp. 659–661.

TABLE 101.—WORK SHEET FOR CALCULATING MONTHLY INDEX OF CYCLE
DESCRIPTION OF DATA: Consumer installment-sale debt for purchase of
household appliances, United States

SOURCE OF DATA: *Survey of Current Business*, Vol. 22 (1942), pp. 9–25, 17.

(1)	(2)	(3)	(4)	(5)	(6)
Year and month	Raw data, millions of dollars y	Monthly trend, millions of dollars $y'*$	Index of seasonal variation,† per cent Av. = 100	Monthly trend times index of S.V., millions of dollars $y' \times$ S.V.	Cycle, per cent $\dfrac{y}{y' \times \text{S.V.}}$
1940:					
January	262	262.0	96.2	252.0	104.0
February	255	262.8	94.0	247.0	103.2
March	253	263.6	92.5	243.8	103.8
April	259	264.4	95.2	251.7	102.9
May	271	265.2	97.6	258.8	104.7
June	281	266.0	103.2	274.5	102.4
July	288	266.8	104.7	279.3	103.1
August	294	267.6	107.6	287.9	102.1
September	293	268.4	105.0	281.8	104.0
October	290	269.1	102.2	275.0	105.4
November	290	269.9	100.6	271.5	106.8
December	302	270.7	101.1	273.7	110.3
1941:					
January	290	271.5	.....	261.2	111.0
February	286	272.3	.....	256.0	111.7
March	286	273.1	.....	252.6	113.2
April	303	273.9	.....	260.8	116.2
May	320	274.7	.....	268.1	119.4
June	330	275.5	.....	284.3	116.1
July	336	276.3	.....	289.3	116.1
August	346	277.1	.....	298.2	116.0
September	342	277.9	.....	291.8	117.2
October	333	278.7	.....	284.8	116.9
November	320	279.5	.....	281.2	113.8
December	313	280.3	.....	283.4	110.4
1942:					
January	294	281.1	.....	270.4	108.7
February	285	281.9	.....	265.0	107.5
March	272	282.7	.....	261.5	104.0
April	258	283.5	.....	269.9	95.6
May	241	284.3	.....	277.5	86.8
June	219	285.1	.....	294.2	74.4
July	202	285.9	.....	299.3	67.5
August	183	286.7	.....	308.5	59.3
September	169	287.4	.....	301.8	56.0
October					
November					
December					

* Equation of monthly trend: $y' = 219.0 + 0.796t$ (origin July, 1935).

† Necessary to copy this for only one year; this seasonal variation was calculated for illustrative purposes in Chap. XXIII, pp. 625–631.

involves the removal of trend and seasonal variation from the raw monthly data. The method is devised to produce an index or relative expression of raw data compared with what would be expected if only trend and seasonal variation were present in the data. Such analysis gives an answer to the question: How far are the raw data from month to month above or below what they would be if they were following the usual course of seasonal variation and the expected trend? In effect, the process is the reverse of that illustrated by a hypothetical series at the beginning of Chap. XX. The theory underlying the method of adjusting monthly data for seasonal variation and trend contains no tricks new to the student after mastering the material in the preceding chapters. It is quite simple in concept, though perhaps the arithmetical calculations involved are somewhat long.

Illustration of Method of Determining Cycle in Monthly Data. It should be pointed out at the start that measuring the cycle in monthly data is measuring the same cycle as was measured in the annual data, if the same trend is used. In this illustration the raw monthly data will be adjusted for the straight-line trend and for seasonal variation, so that the resulting series of monthly data will correspond to the figures given in the last column of Table 100, except that they will be monthly instead of annual figures. The annual averages of the monthly adjusted data obtained in this illustration should be equal to the annual percentages shown in the last column of Table 100.

Table 101 is a work sheet drawn up for the purpose of making the necessary calculations, on the assumption that (1) the index of seasonal variation and (2) the equation of trend on an annual basis have been calculated. The data used are monthly figures for consumer installment-sale debt for household appliances in the United States, 1929–1942. In the illustration only the period 1940–1942 is presented. It would be a good laboratory exercise for the student to work out the rest for himself and plot the resulting adjusted figures.

Column (2) of Table 101 contains the raw monthly data tabulated from the source.[1]

If a trend equation is in terms of annual figures, and the annual figures used are annual totals, the monthly trend equation will be

[1] HOLTHAUSEN, *op. cit.*

$$y' = \frac{a}{12} + \frac{b}{144}\,t$$

But if the annual figures are annual averages of monthly data, then the monthly equation of trend will be

$$y' = a + \frac{b}{12}\,t$$

Thus, b must be divided by 12 because in the monthly trend equation the annual increment is distributed among 12 parts (t now stands for months instead of years). In other words, if b is the annual increment, $b/12$ is the monthly increment. But if b is the annual increment of total annual data (sum of the 12 months each year), then to put it on a monthly basis it is necessary first to convert it to a monthly figure by dividing by 12; it is then still an annual increment and has to be divided by 12 again to obtain the monthly increment.

In the trend equation, a can be assumed to be at June–July of the origin year, and of course the origin may be shifted by changing accordingly the value of a. The origin is at the middle of the year, *i.e.*, between June and July. For example, the equation of trend found for the annual data on consumer installment-sale debt for household appliances is (in millions of dollars)

$$y' = 218.6 + 9.53t \quad \text{(origin at 1935)}$$

The data used in this illustration are annual averages of monthly data; so the monthly trend equation is (in millions of dollars)

$$y' = 218.6 + 0.796t \quad \text{(origin at June–July, 1935)}$$

in which unit of t is 1 month.

By adding algebraically half a monthly increment to 218.6, the origin is shifted to July, 1935, and the approximate equation of monthly trend is as follows (in millions of dollars):

$$y' = 219.0 + 0.796t \quad \text{(origin at July, 1935)}$$

Solving this equation for different values of t (from $t = 54$ at January, 1940, to $t = 86$ at September, 1942) gives the various monthly values of y' shown in column (3) of Table 101 under the caption Monthly Trend. Column (4) shows the index of seasonal variation, which in Chap. XXIII was calculated by the 12 months' moving total method. Column (5) shows seasonal variation and trend combined by multiplication, and column (6) is obtained by dividing the monthly items in column (2), the raw data, by the monthly items in column (5). By this last operation, both trend and seasonal variation are removed from the raw data; the resulting index gives an idea of how high or low the raw data are in comparison to what they might be expected to be according to usual seasonal variation and trend.

Data thus treated over a series of years disclose information about the time series that it is not possible to visualize from the raw figures. It makes possible the comparison between cyclical and minor cyclical fluctuations in time series otherwise concealed by disturbing elements of seasonal variation and trends. If this monthly analysis of the data on consumer installment-sale debt for household appliances in the United States were done for the entire period 1929–1942, the picture of monthly data would, of course, resemble the broken line of Fig. 151. The annual averages of the monthly data, which contain cyclical movements mixed with residual movements, would be equal to the figures shown in the final column of Table 100. In this connection it is to be noted that the annual averages of column (6) in Table 101 are equal to the corresponding annual figures in the last column of Table 100; for 1940 the annual average of the figures in column (6) of Table 101 is equal to 104, and for 1941 the annual average of the figures in column (6) of Table 101 is equal to 114.

From the results of calculations in Table 101 it may be concluded that consumer installment-sale debt for household appliances reached the peak of a cycle in May, 1941, remaining 10 to 17 per cent above normal throughout 1941. In 1942 a sharp decline materialized; in fact, this decline, on a monthly basis, was rapid after October, 1941. The raw data appear to indicate that the peak of the cycle occurred in August, but this is due to the effect of seasonal variation and trend. When seasonal variation and trend are taken into consideration, the cyclical peak is found to be in May, 1942. From July, 1940, to August, 1940, the raw data show an increase, but a cyclical decline occurred in that period. Removal of seasonal variation and trend makes it apparent that the appearance of a rise from

July, 1940, to August, 1940, was due to seasonal influences and trend.

Adjustment of data by removing seasonal variation and trend makes it possible to judge quickly whether or not consumer installment-sale debt for household appliances is rising (or falling) more rapidly than seasonal variation and trend would lead us to expect. The resulting figures are frequently described when published by saying that the data are "adjusted for seasonal variation and trend." Sometimes, if trend is unimportant or of dubious character, only seasonal variation is removed and the data are described as "adjusted for seasonal variation." Charts of such data appear frequently in financial publications and in the financial sections of metropolitan newspapers.

Measuring the Cycle Where Trend Is a Second- or Third-degree Polynomial. The rational growth of some data is better described by a second-degree polynomial, as discovered in Chap. XXI. When such is the case, it would be necessary to use a second-degree polynomial instead of a straight-line trend as illustrated in the preceding sections of this chapter.

A third-degree polynomial is not likely ever to resemble a rational growth element in a time series, but it may resemble the conformation of the major cycle during a specified period covered by data that are being analyzed. If it is desired not only to remove growth trend but also to remove from the data the effects of the major cycle in order to observe residuals that might be significantly described as a short cycle, the method described in the preceding sections could be used with monthly data, applying the same principles to the removal of a third-degree polynomial trend combined with seasonal variation that were applied to the removal of a straight-line trend combined with seasonal variation.

The general form of the second-degree polynomial annual trend is $y' = a + bt + ct^2$ where t is 1 year. The equation of the monthly second-degree polynomial trend, where the annual data are annual averages of monthly data, would be

$$y' = a + \frac{b}{12} t + \frac{c}{144} t^2$$

where t is 1 month.

The general form of the third-degree polynomial annual trend is $y' = a + bt + ct^2 + dt^3$ where t is 1 year. The equation of the monthly third-degree polynomial trend, where the annual data are annual averages of monthly data, would be

$$y' = a + \frac{b}{12} t + \frac{c}{144} t^2 + \frac{d}{1,728} t^3$$

in which t is 1 month.

If the data are annual totals, instead of annual averages, every item on the right side of the respective equations will be divided by 12.*

Danger in Extrapolating Trends. In the illustration on page 641 it was noted that the second-degree polynomial trend, if extended beyond the year 1941, would quickly go up to infinity. Thus the extrapolation, or extension, of this trend beyond 1942 very soon becomes an absurdity. This shows the need for caution in the projection, or extrapolation, of empirical trends.[1] Their projection for short periods of time (how long depends upon the conditions of each particular case) is a valuable aid in constructing barometric indexes.

A troublesome unsolved problem in time-series analysis is to know when trend is changing and also, for that matter, when seasonal variation may be changing. Neither the statisticians nor the economists have solved this problem, but they realize that it is ever present in time-series analysis. It is desirable, therefore, to be cautious about extending empirical trends into the future and to reexamine monthly data for seasonal variation at frequent intervals. A method for detecting changing trends in seasonal variation was explained and illustrated in the preceding chapter.

Method of Ratios vs. Method of Differences. In general, the method here presented for removing one or more types of variation from time series has been the method of division, or ratios. In other words, the raw data are expressed as percentages of computed trend and seasonal variation. This is not the only method of removing trend and seasonal variation from the monthly or annual raw data. Another type of approach is called

* See pp. 644–645.
[1] For further discussion in connection with economic forecasting, see Chap. XXV, pp. 661–671.

the "method of differences," which, in one of a number of forms, may be summarized as follows:

1. Assuming that the index of seasonal variation and the monthly trend have been calculated by one of the conventional procedures, the monthly trend values are multiplied by the index of seasonal variation.

2. The trend multiplied by seasonal variation (y_j') are now subtracted from the raw data (y_i).

3. This gives a series of $y_1 - y_1'$, $y_2 - y_2'$, . . . , being the arithmetical amount, in original units (pounds, dollars, etc.), by which the raw data are greater each month, or less, than the computed value for trend multiplied by the index of seasonal variation. These residuals of the raw data from trend and seasonal variation form a series $r_1, r_2, r_3, \ldots , r_n$ that would be a time series fluctuating arithmetically above and below zero, according to whether the raw data were above or below trend multiplied by seasonal variation, that is to say, according to whether the raw data were greater or less than values expected in view of the anticipated growth and seasonal fluctuation.

4. These residuals are in terms of the quantity units of the raw data. Consequently, it would be very difficult to compare the residual fluctuations of a series measured in bushels (say wheat production) with the residuals in dollars (say the price of wheat). It is necessary to find a common denominator in order to compare the residuals in various time series, obtained by the arithmetical difference method.

5. The common denominator used is the standard deviation in the residuals. σ_r will be simply $\sqrt{\Sigma r^2 / N}$, since their arithmetical average is zero. Each r divided successively by σ_r would give a series in terms of standard-deviation units that could thereafter be compared with other time series similarly treated. Various series, whether the original units were dollars, pounds, inches, etc., will now be reduced to terms of standard-deviation units and can all be plotted on the same scale, namely, a scale that is calibrated in standard deviations.

One important disadvantage in the method of differences persists even after the residuals are expressed in terms of their own standard deviations. The residuals will tend to be arithmetically greater when trend is at high values and arithmetically small when trend is at low values. This means that the impression will almost universally arise from such an analysis that as things grow they become subject to more violent fluctuations. In fact, when considered relative to the magnitudes from which variation occurs, these greater arithmetical variations may be really less important. The ratio method places at all times the proper proportional emphasis upon arithmetical fluctuations by expressing them as a ratio to the trend and seasonal variation.

On the other hand, by the same token the ratio method may tend to minimize the importance of fluctuations; for it may be possible that the proportional amount of change is not so significant as the actual amount of change. For example, the fact that the amount of unemployment is no greater proportionally may not necessarily dispose of the fact that the actual amount of unemployment at some particular time is very great and the corresponding personal problems distressing in the extreme.

Whatever method of statistics is used, it is necessary for the analyst to keep his eyes open to the effect the method itself may have upon his results.

PART VI
Forecasting

CHAPTER XXV

THE ART OF FORECASTING WITH STATISTICS

INTRODUCTION

Prevalence of Forecasts. *Ancient Origin of Pseudoscientific Forecasts.* The human desire to look into the future led, even in ancient times, to the rise of various forms of pseudoscientific forecasts. Oracles were frequently consulted as to the outcome of a contemplated military campaign, business venture, or love affair. Among the most famous of these was the Delphian oracle. Astrologists were, and still are, consulted for what the stars have to say; one of their most prominent devotees in modern times is said to be Adolf Hitler.

It was partly to disprove some of these astrological notions that statistical method was first undertaken on a scientific basis. In the seventeenth century an idea prevailed that the phases of the moon influenced health; also, health was supposed to be critical every seventh year and life particularly hazardous at the ages of forty-nine and sixty-three. Near the end of the seventeenth century studies of vital statistics by Capt. John Graunt of London and Casper Neumann of Germany disproved the connection between health and the phases of the moon as well as the fateful significance of every seventh year in life. Other similar superstitions were "debunked" by statistical studies. From the beginning of the history of the modern money market, attempts have been made to devise some way to forecast the course of financial affairs. For the Antwerp Bourse in 1543, Christopher Kurz is said to have contrived an astronomical method of making prophecies about the money market.[1]

[1] EHRENBERG, R., *Capital and Finance in the Age of the Renaissance,* p. 240.

Modern Scientific Forecasts. Although forecasting was thus once the special prerogative of soothsayers, today it has been placed upon a broader basis by the development of science. For one of the objectives of science is, precisely, to forecast. Science seeks to classify and determine relationships that may be used for purposes of prediction. Every scientific law is, in a certain sense, a forecast. It foretells what will happen under certain circumstances. The law of gravitation says, for example, that if a ball is dropped from a tall building it will fall with an acceleration of 32 feet per second per second. Boyle's law says that the pressure in a given container varies, and will vary, directly with the temperature and indirectly with the volume. Scientific astronomy makes it possible to forecast the tides, to construct the calendar for our mundane affairs, and, in addition, to forecast celestial events such as the date of the next visit of Halley's comet. There are no "ifs" or "buts" about the modern scientific forecasts in the realm of the natural or physical sciences.

Popular Dramatization of Forecasts. The depression of the 1930's did more than hundreds of books could have done to make people cycle-conscious. So general was the interest in cyclical behavior that by 1940 the Foundation for the Study of Cycles was set up as a nonprofit organization with an international committee composed of scientists and businessmen. This foundation proposed to help in the task of integrating the work of the thousands of scientists and statisticians who are contributing in various fields to the study of cycles. Not only have cycles been found to exist in the realm of business activity, but scientists in many other fields believe they have discovered cyclical behavior in their respective studies. For example, psychologists have discovered that human beings have regular ups and downs in their emotional life, following a cyclical pattern. Biologists have discovered what appear to be regular fluctuations in animal, insect, bird, and even fish populations. In 1937, Prof. William Hamilton of Cornell University, upon the basis of cycle studies, warned farmers and housewives of New York State to prepare for a scourge of mice in the winter of 1939–1940 and for another outbreak in 1943–1944. While it may still be too early to put the stamp of final scientific approval upon all these cyclical discoveries, they are nevertheless making important contributions to knowledge.

Some of the twentieth-century discoveries sound almost like the pseudoscientific superstitions of the Middle Ages. Thus in 1943 the public was advised "to look for skunks under your front porch about 1945." It was claimed that an answer could be given to such questions as: Will you feel happy or gloomy a month from today? Such statements were made as: If you are born in January, February, March, or April, the chances are you will live longer than people born in July, August, or September.[1] These notions about forecasting suggest a precision in statistical forecasts that they probably will never possess.[2]

Conditional Scientific Forecasts. A forecast, to be scientific, does not have to be unconditional; in fact, most forecasts in the realm of the social sciences and some in the realm of the physical sciences are hypothetical in character. Indeed, in its largest sense, forecasting must be taken to mean prediction of not only what will happen but what would happen under given hypothetical conditions. Not only must the predictions of the meteorologist and stockbroker be considered forecasts, but also predictions of the engineer as to the outcome of certain plans and the warnings of the economist as to the effect of certain proposed actions of Congress are forecasts. The latter are conditional forecasts.

Many predictions of coming events are hedged in by all sorts of weasel-like conditions. It may be said that private enterprise will disappear if Republicans are not elected. Or an economist may predict that a Congressional increase in tariff rates will cause exports to decline, provided that foreign countries do not offset our higher tariff by giving bounties to their exporters, or that foreign demand for American products does not increase for some unforseen reason, or that American exports do not become less costly to produce. Such forecasts are conditional, or hypothetical, in character.

The practical worth of a forecast depends, not on whether it is conditional or unconditional, but on how much knowledge the forecaster actually has of the relevant conditions. An unconditional forecast may be merely a wild guess and have little

---

[1] DEWEY, EDWARD RUSSELL, "Science Predicts the Future," *American Magazine*, Vol. 136 (1943), pp. 90–92.

[2] See More Exact Forecasting and Less Exact Forecasting, pp. 659–661. See also SMITH and DUNCAN, *Sampling Statistics and Applications*.

value, in spite of its uncompromising and categorical appearance, while a carefully drawn conditional forecast may be of great value, in spite of its "pussyfooting" aspect. In the case of the latter, it may be that the likelihood of the conditional factors is very slight and that they are mentioned only to guard the forecaster from unwarranted criticism. On the other hand, if the disturbing factor has a fair likelihood of occurrence, the nature of its effect might be forecast so that the recipient of the forecast could be on his guard against this factor; by watching it, he might know when to abandon his faith in the original forecast. For example, if a prediction of rain tomorrow is based merely on the fact that it looks somewhat cloudy today, the forecast would probably be of little value (in the sense that such forecasts would probably be wrong more often than they were right). In contrast, if a trained observer predicted rain after a thorough observation of the weather situation, this would have considerable value even if he hedged his prediction by saying that the rain might not occur if the wind in a neighboring area shifted before a certain time.

Qualitative vs. Quantitative Forecasts. Most forecasts are qualitative in character. The meteorologist says it will rain but does not always say how heavily. The economist may predict that the effect of an increase in the tariff will be to raise prices, but he does not often say to what degree. The meteorologist, on the contrary, may give the approximate time when rain is expected and how many inches are expected to fall; and the economist may try to estimate the average foreseen rise in prices. The latter would be quantitative forecasts.

It will be noted that forecasts may be quantitative in two ways, with reference to the degree of the predicted change and with reference to the time of occurrence. The success of forecasting must be judged, not only on the basis of whether the forecast was correct, but also on how far the forecast went in actually describing the future event—its quantity and its timing.

Illustrations of Modern Forecasts. In the modern world, forecasts are applied in many fields. Predictions of astronomical events, as already indicated, have been among the earliest and most successful forecasts. The movements of the moon, the planets, and other heavenly bodies have been computed with considerably accuracy so that their future course may be predicted with great precision. Forecasts of certain eclipses, for example, have been only a few seconds in error in timing. In this connection, it is interesting to note that the theory of least squares was largely developed in the attempt to forecast the paths of the heavenly bodies.

Closely akin to astronomical forecasts have been forecasts of weather conditions. Short-range forecasts are based mainly on wind conditions and barometric pressures, but long-range forecasts are sometimes attempted from the study of rainfall data, sunspots, and the like. In some instances, studies of growth rings in old trees have yielded weather data going back many years. These studies usually look for cyclical fluctuations that will indicate periods of high and low activity and permit long-range forecasting. Studies of average weather conditions and the dispersion around these averages also afford forecasts of the variability of conditions in different areas and hence suggest the more desirable airports and air routes.

Engineers make many forecasts. A water-power engineer will forecast the amount of power to be obtained from a dam of given size built in a given river. Another engineer may predict the breaking strength of given kinds of wire at different temperatures. Still another may predict the maximum load to be sustained by a given bridge.

From the laws of Mendel, biologists make predictions of results to be expected from crossbreeding. Agronomists will predict the average results to be obtained from the use of certain fertilizers, or certain methods of cultivation, or certain varieties of crops. Agricultural economists attempt to predict the effect of certain sized crops on the future prices of important commodities or the effect of certain prices on the future volume of production.

Business economists attempt many kinds of forecasts. From studies of factors closely related to the sale of a certain product in a given area where the trade has been well established, forecasts may be made of the sales to be obtained from new untapped areas of similar character. Other economic forecasts aim to predict the ups and downs of the business cycle in various lines of activity. Probably the greatest percentage of economic forecasts are devoted to predictions of the stock market—money rates, bond prices, and security prices.

These are but a few of the examples of forecasting. It is probably true that forecasting in all its ramifications is pandemic in modern life.

Use of Statistics in Forecasting. This chapter attempts to outline the use that may be made of statistical analysis in making forecasts. Details of the methods of forecasting are beyond the scope of this volume, which is not a book on forecasting but merely includes a chapter on the pattern of methods used in forecasting. A few examples will be given to illustrate these methods. The aim here is primarily to indicate the application of different statistical techniques to the problems of forecasting.

Statistics affords a basis for forecasting in two principal ways. (1) By studying monovariate and multivariate frequency distributions, statistics are used to forecast average results and the type and degree of dispersion around these results. (2) By means of time-series analysis, statistics are used to predict the course of events in time. Each of these applications to forecasting will be discussed in the ensuing pages.

FORECASTS FROM DISTRIBUTION STUDIES

Forecasts from Monovariate Distributions. If considerable data have been obtained, forecasts from monovariate distributions may yield good estimates of the mean, standard deviation, coefficient of skewness, and kurtosis of the population from which the data were derived. If such is the case, these population estimates may be used to forecast the character of future samples drawn from the given population.

Familiar matters relating to family care and health conventionally rely upon forecasting by use of monovariates. Suppose the frequency distribution, or monovariate, represents the weights of boys of specified age. The mean of that distribution is presumably normal weight for that age; the standard deviation and kurtosis describe expected variability. From such a monovariate and its statistics, it is commonly inferred whether or not a child is under normal weight and, if so, whether or not this deficiency is sufficient to cause alarm. Taken with other evidence it may be the basis for the application of timely therapeutic action.

In social control, monovariate distributions are used to standardize products involving the presumption of forecasting.

The fat content and standard deviation in fat content of milk that has been produced and sold in the past constitute a set of standards according to which it is ruled that milk sold in the future will conform; thus milk is graded according to standards found by frequency-distribution analysis. Methods of weight or content are used by the Bureau of Standards to set standards for many products, both in the raw state, such as grains of wheat, and in the final product, such as bread; and abnormal variations from these standards in the market are not permitted.

In business the use of monovariate distributions for forecasting is widespread. For example, the distribution in sizes of shoes sold by a retailer is used as the basis for forecasting his future sales and for determining his reorders of additional shoes. In such forecasting, the businessman is interested in forecasting each class in the distribution rather than in the distribution's average and standard deviation. A similar forecasting procedure is used by any retailer when he purchases articles that are sold by size, which include most articles of clothing. The wholesaler and the manufacturer also are interested in the same type of forecasting, so that they may profit by having the appropriate number of articles of various sizes continually ready for the consumer—if the articles are there, ready for him to buy when he comes, a minimum of consumers' sales will be lost.[1]

Forecasts from Bivariate Distributions. Bivariate data may likewise yield estimates of a bivariate population that may make it possible to forecast results of future samples. Suppose, for example, that it is found from a study of army records that there is a high correlation between the Army General Classification Test scores and the results obtained in a given electrical course. To be specific, suppose that the bivariate distribution of these two variables appears to be normal in form and it is estimated

---

[1] For another illustration of the use of monovariates in forecasting, see Robert J. Myers, "Comparison of Demographic Rates Assumed by the National Resources Committee with Actual Experience," *Journal of the American Statistical Association*, Vol. 38 (1943), pp. 201–209; also, for an example of such forecasting for the purpose of control of quality of manufactured product, see William B. Rice, "Quality Control Applies to Business Administration," *Journal of the American Statistical Association*, Vol. 38 (1943), pp. 228–232; *cf.* W. A. Shewhart, *Economic Control of Quality of Manufactured Product* (1931).

that the line of regression of electrical grades on Army General Classification Test scores is

$$E = 5 + 0.8T$$

with a first-order standard deviation of seven points. From this it is possible to make certain predictions regarding the future results of men taking the electrical course. Thus, it might be predicted that men who got 90 on the Army General Classification Test will get an average grade of 77 on the electrical course, half of them getting less than this and half getting more. If 70 is taken as the passing grade, it may be predicted that something like 84 per cent of the men whose score is 90 will pass the course, 70 being one standard deviation less than the average and the distribution being normal.[1]

Forecasts from Multivariate Distributions. Study of multivariate distributions may permit the same sort of forecasting as the study of bivariates. Suppose that a study of army salvage data shows that the length of service of wool socks is closely related to the amount of marching required of the troops and the average temperature of the area. Suppose, for example, that the plane of regression derived from the data is as follows:[2]

Length of life = 40 days − 3 (average miles marched per day) + 2 (average temperature)

Then, if the average miles marched is increased by 2 miles per day, the Army may predict that the average length of life of wool socks will probably decrease by 6 days. Or again, if the troops are shipped to an area in which the average temperature is 10 degrees warmer, the average length of life of the wool socks will be increased by 30 days. Or, in a third instance, if it is planned to send a force to a given area for which the average temperature is approximately 60 degrees and it is expected that the troops will march about 20 miles per day on the average,

---

[1] For illustrations of the use of bivariates for prediction in business, see Patricia Daly and Paul H. Douglas, "The Production Function for Canadian Manufactures," *Journal of the American Statistical Association*, Vol. 38 (1943), pp. 178–186; also see pp. 674–675.

[2] The correlation between length of life and temperature is assumed to be positive on the ground that, the warmer the climate, the less the use that would be made of wool and the more the use that would be made of cotton socks. See the discussion on planes of regression, pp. 448–455.

then it should have sufficient supplies of wool socks on hand to provide for new issues every 100 days on the average.[1]   If the study indicated that the first-order standard deviation about the plane of regression was about 5 days, the Army might keep on hand a large enough supply to replace socks every 85 days (that is to say, 100 minus three times the standard deviation, or $100 - 15 = 85$).

Errors of Forecasts.   In concluding this section on the use of monovariates, bivariates, and multivariates as forecasters, it must be noted that forecasts of the kind indicated are necessarily inexact.   They are based on the assumption that the population is exactly known.   When the population characteristics themselves have to be estimated, as they usually do, then the forecasts based upon these estimates will suffer from all the errors involved in the latter.   The more refined analysis that is required to take care of these errors of estimate of the population is beyond the scope of this book.   It is sufficient here to point out that the error of forecast based upon estimated population characteristics is greater than that based upon a known population. For example, if a plane of regression based upon sample estimates has a related standard deviation of five points, the probability of a forecast based on the plane being off by as much as two times five points in either direction (therefore, 2σ) will be, not the normal 5 per cent, but perhaps 10 per cent or more.   Everything depends on the size of the sample from which the original estimates of the population characteristics were made.

FORECASTING TRENDS WITH TIME SERIES

More Exact Forecasting.   If much is known about a particular time series, so that the nature of its growth and cyclical movements can be fairly well determined from rational considerations and if the remaining fluctuations are apparently random, forecasting from such a series can be put on much the same level as forecasting from distributions of the monovariate, bivariate, and multivariate type discussed above.   Careful estimates may be made of the growth, and these may be extrapolated for a short period of time into the future.   Distribution analysis of the random fluctuations will determine the range of

---

[1] For the summer season this would be less than for the winter season, but a stock level based on a 100-day turnover might be taken as normal.

fluctuations around the growth curve and will afford an estimate for the error of a forecast based solely on the growth element in the series.

Suppose, for example, that a logistic form of growth appears to be very logical for a certain type of data. If the data have reached a certain stage of development, the values of the next few periods may be forecast from an extrapolation of the logistic curve fitted to the past data. The amount of error in the forecast resulting from the random fluctuations around the normal growth may be estimated from the standard deviation of the residual fluctuations of the data from the fitted logistic curve.

Illustrations of the type of time series that would permit fairly exact forecasting are afforded by Fig. 54 in Chap. V and Figs. 144 and 145 in Chap. XXI.

Less Exact Forecasting. The real difficulty in most time-series analyses is to determine what is random and what is not random. Furthermore, it is often hard to work out any rational basis for specific forms of the trends and cycles.[1] In cases where there is no particular trend indicated by the rationale of the situation, forecasts must be of a rough-and-ready sort, and little can be done to determine the error of forecast.

Economic time series are generally of the sort that do not permit more exact statistical forecasts.[2] For this reason statistical analysis is usually only one of the elements entering into the making of economic forecasts. In some cases it plays a more important role than others, but nearly always the forecaster incorporates his statistical findings into a general appraisal of the situation. As indicated above, statistical analysis in these cases is itself largely intelligent guessing. The statistical part of an economic forecast is consequently merely the quantitative ingredient of the final forecast.

Public utilities, especially the telephone companies, are keenly interested in the subject of forecasting growth or trend elements in time series. In the telephone business the laying

---

[1] See discussion on rational vs. empirical trends, pp. 550–565.

[2] TINTNER, GERHARD, "The Analysis of Economic Time Series," *Journal of the American Statistical Association*, Vol. 35 (1940), pp. 93–101. WALLIS, W. ALLEN, and GEOFFREY H. MOORE, "A Significance Test for Time Series Analysis," *Journal of the American Statistical Association*, Vol. 36 (1941), pp. 401–409; Vol. 38 (1943), pp. 153–164.

out of plans and the construction of new exchanges necessitate some sort of forecast as to the future growth of the community. For years these companies have maintained elaborate and efficient research organizations whose business it is to forecast trends in growth of population as well as the geographical distribution of various types of business and residential areas in the communities served.

Most business enterprises, however, are more concerned about cyclical fluctuations than about trend or growth in time series. For this reason the greatest number of published forecasts have to do with the prediction of cyclical movements in business conditions.

FORECASTING CYCLES WITH TIME SERIES

All that has been said about the inexactness of forecasting trends by the use of time series applies equally to the forecasting of cycles with time series. Nevertheless, the practice of relying upon statistics as an aid to business is now so prevalent that statistics, along with accounting, has become one of the standard tools and one of the essential means of internal control of nearly all economic enterprises, as well as a guide to public policies of governmental agencies. Among its many commercial uses, business forecasting is one of the most important, and it is along this line that statistical analysis has been intensively developed in recent years. Today there are several important agencies that supply forecasting services. Among these are Standard & Poor's Corporation, Brookmire Economic Service, Moody's Investor's Service, Babson, and the Harvard Economic Society. In addition, many commercial banks such as National City, Cleveland Trust, and Chase National include forecasts of probable future business trends in their monthly letters. Supplementing these professional services are the statisticians and statistical departments of many large corporations, such as the American Telephone and Telegraph Company, which make forecasts for their own use.

American activity in this field has been internationally contagious. As early as 1921 the publication of the *Economic Bulletin of the Conjuncture Institute* was begun in Moscow; this publication was devoted to the study of business cycles and to the analysis of Russian statistics. Subsequently in nearly every important European country during the 1920's and 1930's forecasting services were organized, sometimes by the large universities. The League of Nations showed its intention of inaugurating forecasting on a world scale by appointing a Committee of Experts on Economic Barometers.[1]

The many possible occasions when forecasting is required in modern business can be shown by a few examples. A commercial banker granting a loan must forecast the probability of its being repaid; his judgment in this respect will depend on his forecast of the borrower's future earning power; this, in turn, depends on his estimation of probable future price stability in the borrower's business. Similarly, a collateral loan will involve a prediction, more or less precise, of the future value of the security offered as collateral. A manufacturer needs to forecast probable sales and probable prices of his own goods and of materials he has to purchase, so that he can profitably plan production and plant expansion. A public-utility operator needs to forecast population and industrial trends, construction and operating costs, and probable prices for the service, in order to determine when and where to build a railroad line, a gas main, a power plant, or a telephone exchange.

All these things are commonplace in economic life, but the growing complexity and interdependence of economic society have made it increasingly difficult for the average businessman to comprehend an existing situation in trying to formulate his programs for the future. He is not a statistical expert. His knowledge of methods of summarization and comparison goes usually little beyond a vague comprehension of averages. To aid him, it is the purpose of the various business forecasting agencies "to provide the basis for business, financial, and security market policy. Regardless of the inevitable margin of error in every forecast, business, financial, or security market policy which is geared to only a fairly intelligent estimate of future probabilities is more likely to be sound than is policy geared only to guess, or to no forecast whatsoever."[2]

---

[1] Cox, G. V., *An Appraisal of American Business Forecasts*, pp. 1–2.

[2] "A Forecaster's View of Forecasting," *Standard Statistics*, (June 15, 1931), p. 14. Also see BRATT, ELMER C., *Business Cycles and Forecasting* (1941), pp. 736–800; HARDY, CHARLES O., and GARFIELD V. COX, *Forecasting Business Conditions* (1927).

Forecasting General Business Conditions. One of the most important objects of economic forecasting is to predict general business conditions, that is to say, the cyclical position of general business. Good times and bad times are such important elements in determining the prosperity of individual lines of activity and of individual firms that the prospect for general business is probably the first thing any corporation executive wishes to know. Statistically, general business is properly measured by some index of all business activity. It is the summation of the whole and not merely one of the parts, although an index of a part, say an index of industrial production, may be taken as a barometer of the upswings and downswings of the whole. Such series are commonly called "business barometers."[1]

Forecasts of general business conditions are based upon one of two forecasting methods or a combination of the two. The first method is known as "historical analogy," the second as "crosscut analysis."[2]

The method of historical analogy is based on the assumption that in cyclical fluctuations history tends to repeat itself. In its cruder forms, this consists merely in forecasting the course of general business, subsequent to some disturbance, from the course of general business that followed a similar disturbance in the past. For example, the forecaster might undertake to predict the course of general business following the crisis of 1929 from the course of business following the crisis of 1873. In more carefully thought-out form, historical analogy becomes a business-cycle theory that attempts to explain how the interplay of economic forces causes general business now to rise and now to fall.

Crosscut analysis proceeds on the basis that the business situation is never the same and that each new upswing or downswing is the product of a set of factors different from those previously operative. To understand the given situation all the factors must be weighed as to their importance and a net appraisal of the situation derived.

[1] See pp. 530–535.
[2] For more elaborate classifications see Bratt, *op. cit.*, pp. 736–760; HANEY, L. H., *Business Forecasting* (1931), p. 195; DAY, E. E., "The Rôle of Statistics in Business Forecasting," *Journal of the American Statistical Association*, Vol. 33 (1938), p. 2.

In good forecasting, both methods are employed. If a certain cyclical theory appears to constitute a good explanation of past events, it is good forecasting practice to consider it in predicting future cycle changes. Nevertheless, careful study must be made to see whether the role played in the past by a particular industry or economic development is subsequently being played by some other industry or development. The user of historical analogy must always, therefore, be on guard for changes required in the statistical embodiment of the cyclical theory on which his analysis is based in order to keep it up to date in its assumptions. During the railroad era, statistics about railroads dominated the scene as good indicators of general business conditions; later, it was statistics about automobile production; perhaps the time will come when it will be aircraft production. Again, the present era is often regarded as the "iron age." Statistics of iron and steel production are often used as barometers of general business conditions because so many of the products of the modern age depend upon iron. Perhaps the time will come when the emphasis will shift, from the point of view of statistics, away from iron and steel production to the production of the lighter metals such as aluminum. Who can say when the world of business is changing from the one to the other?

Reflection along the lines indicated in the preceding paragraph leads to the conclusion that continuous crosscut analysis is needed as a means of verifying and justifying the use of the historical-analogy method.

Forecasting by Historical Analogy. One type of forecasting by historical analogy makes extensive use of the fluctuations in particular time series that appear to lead general business conditions. Examples of series that have been used as business barometers are indexes of stock-market prices, changes in unfilled orders of the United States Steel Corporation, machine-tool orders, and the loan-deposit ratio. These series, it is argued, will tend to lead changes in general business conditions, and important changes in general business conditions will first be made apparent by them. For example, a clear and consistent downswing in unfilled steel orders is presumed to presage a similar downswing in general business. Hence the latter is presumably forecasted from the former. In the case of the loan-deposit ratio, it is the attainment of certain critical levels that is significant; when high

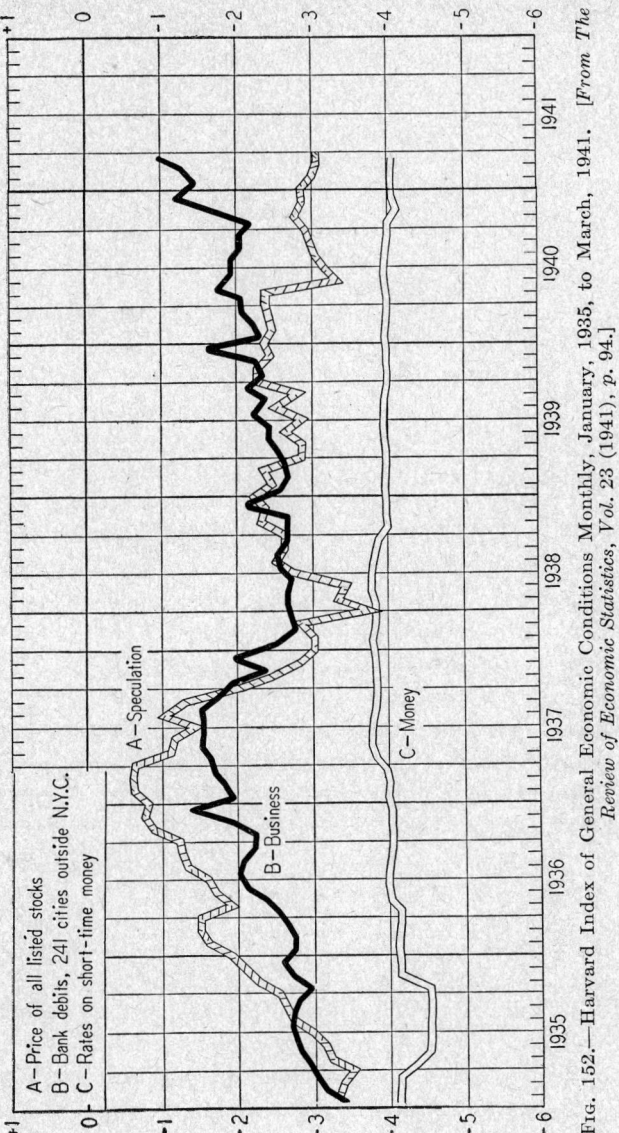

FIG. 152.— Harvard Index of General Economic Conditions Monthly, January, 1935, to March, 1941. [From The Review of Economic Statistics, Vol. 23 (1941). p. 94.]

A — Price of all listed stocks
B — Bank debits, 241 cities outside N.Y.C.
C — Rates on short-time money

A — Speculation

B — Business

C — Money

levels are reached, for example, (*i.e.*, when loans are high relative to deposits) strained credit conditions are in evidence and a crisis will be forecasted.

More elaborate analyses making use of the historical analogy for forecasting combine several economic series. A well-known example of such a combination is that prepared by the Harvard Economic Society and published in the *Review of Economic Statistics*. While the society itself makes no forecasts from its statistical series, they have been found useful for such purposes and it is generally understood that that is what they are published for. These are shown in Fig. 152.

The Harvard series consist of three curves, known as the *A*, *B*, and *C* curves. The *A* curve represents speculation, the *B* curve business, and the *C* curve money. The actual data upon which these curves have been based vary from time to time. In those shown in Fig. 152, the curves are constituted as follows:[1] The *A* curve, speculation, is based on the price of all securities listed on the New York Stock Exchange. The *B* curve, business, is based on bank debits in 241 cities outside of New York City. The *C* curve, money, is based on short-term money rates. In each of the constituent series the trend and seasonal variation were removed (when it was deemed appropriate) before the final indexes were computed.

The theory that underlies the use of the Harvard curves for forecasting is that changes in speculation will generally precede changes in general business and that the significance of these changes will be more clearly understood when the course of the money curve is noted. A sharp rise in speculation at a time when money rates are low and still falling would appear to forecast better business conditions. On the other hand, a fall in speculation at a time when money rates are rising would appear to forecast a decline in general business. If coupled with a detailed crosscut analysis of the current business situation, these curves are found very helpful in predicting general business conditions.

The Harvard curves are but one set of curves that have been employed in this attempt to forecast general business conditions. Various combinations of curves have been used. A number

[1] FRICKEY, EDWIN, "Revision of the Index of General Business Conditions," *Review of Economic Statistics*, Vol. 14 (1932), pp. 80–87.

make use of capital issue by private corporations and capital expenditures of the various government bodies. The idea behind the use of investment curves is that the volume of income, and hence business, is largely determined by the volume of investment.

As the result of a great amount of research work during the past twenty or twenty-five years, mostly under the auspices of the National Bureau of Economic Research or the National Industrial Conference Board, but also by scholars in the United States Department of Commerce, increasing attention has been given to methods of measuring business conditions based upon quantity and distribution of national income. Instead of indexes of production, employment, volume of trade, and the like, these new indexes attempt to measure national income and its distribution, consumer expenditures and producer expenditures, savings, capital formation, and the like. Figure 153 gives a picture of annual consumer spending, 1919–1942, showing indexes constructed by Kuznets (National Bureau of Economic Research) and by the United States Department of Commerce.[1] Figure 154 is another illustration of the use of national-income statistics and their derivatives to show the cycle in general business conditions. This figure reproduces an index of that part of the national income devoted to expenditures for new durable goods and indexes of gross capital formation, net capital formation, and offsets to savings. The United States Department of Commerce index of private gross capital expenditures is presumably equivalent to Kuznet's gross capital formation; to these are added indexes by Laughlin Currie reputed to measure income-producing Federal expenditures that offset savings and net government contribution to savings. The index of expenditures for new durable goods is constructed by the Board of Governors of the Federal Reserve System.

Time and experience will reveal whether or not the national-income type of indexes proves to be better than the barometer or over-all measure of business activity types. The national-income type has been made possible by the increasing amount of

[1] HOFFENBERG, MARVIN, and MABEL S. LEWIS, "Estimates of National Output, Distributed Income, Consumer Spending, Saving, and Capital Formation," *Review of Economic Statistics*, Vol. 25 (May, 1943), pp. 107–174, 124.

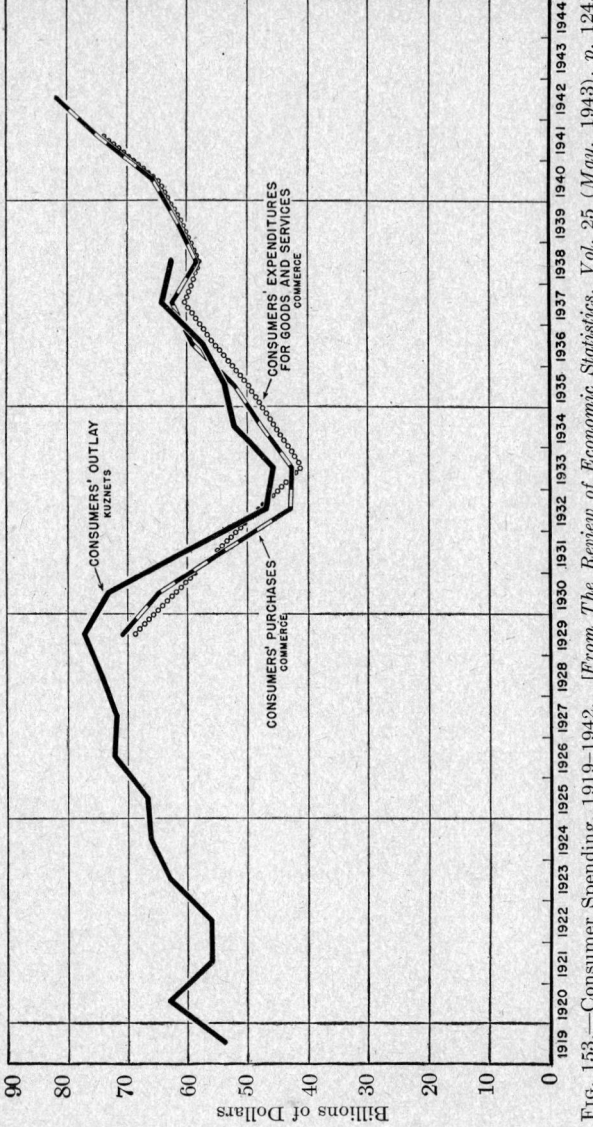

Fig. 153.—Consumer Spending, 1919–1942. [From *The Review of Economic Statistics, Vol. 25 (May,* 1943), *p.* 124.]

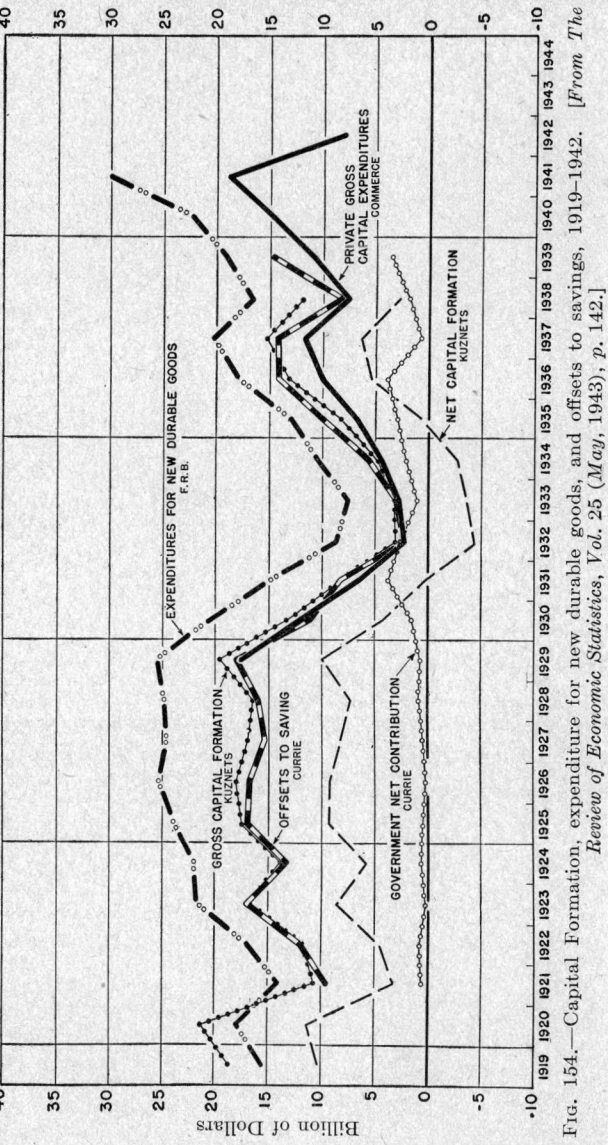

Fig. 154.—Capital Formation, expenditure for new durable goods, and offsets to savings, 1919–1942. [From The Review of Economic Statistics, Vol. 25 (May, 1943), p. 142.]

statistical data on income resulting from the administration of the Federal personal and corporate income taxes.

Perhaps the greatest difficulty with all forecasting series is that the amount of the lead or lag is likely to vary considerably from time to time, so that the timing of the forecasted change becomes difficult.[1] Another difficulty is to judge how great a change in the forecasting series must be before it is considered significant. The curve is almost bound to show minor ups and downs that are little related to general business. Presumably a movement either up or down must be great and persistent before any significant change is forecasted, but how great and how persistent is the question. The answer to this question is always easy to read ex post facto, but in following the forecaster from month to month this is more difficult. If a lead is short and data are not reported quickly, a given forecasting series, consistent and reliable as it may be, is unlikely to have much forecasting value since the change would be under way before it was manifested by the forecasting data.

These difficulties apply in differing degrees to the various kinds of forecasters. In the case of the barometer type, which is ordinarily dependent upon one presumably indicating series such as unfilled orders of the United States Steel Corporation, the data are usually promptly available; but the minor ups and downs and the varying degree of lead and lag in the barometer as compared with general business constitute ever-present difficulties in their use. The indexes of general business activity based upon combinations of several series are less affected by difficulties with respect to lead and lag and minor fluctuations, but it is often difficult to find a combination of series that are promptly reported. The national-income type of indexes suffer particularly from the fact that the data are not available currently, except for estimates that are being attempted, and these are dependent upon other types of data.

A unique type of forecasting by historical analogy is employed by Roger Babson. The forecasting instrument is the Babson index of the physical volume of production. This covers manufacturing production, mineral production, agricultural market-

---

[1] But see p. 674 for application of leads and lags to the forecasting of specific lines of business activity, in which it can be more successfully applied.

ings, building and construction, railway freight, electric power, and foreign trade. The long-run trend of this curve is taken as normal, and the cyclical fluctuations are forecasted on the mechanical principle that a given action has an equal and opposite reaction.[1] Thus the area of a given period of prosperity will indicate the area, but not the shape, of the coming depression. The slope of the depression area is forecasted to some extent with the help of other series and contemporary crosscut analysis of individual lines of activity.

Forecasting by Crosscut Analysis. Even if considerable reliance is placed upon certain forecasting series based upon the historical-analogy principle, it would seem desirable to supplement the analysis by a more detailed study of the current situation. This will help to time the forecast better. It will also assure the forecaster that the forecasting series continue to hold their theoretical significance in the ebb and flow of business. The great danger is that the business-cycle theory on which the forecasting series are based may become outmoded or may be too simple to be fully satisfactory as new conditions unfold. Crosscut analysis may possibly reveal these defects and help to remedy them.

Some believe that business cycles are unique and that the roles played by various economic developments shift from cycle to cycle. If this were true, crosscut analysis would be the only logical method of forecasting. Some general theory would necessarily have to underlie the forecast, even if it were the negative theory that all cycles are unique. Nevertheless, it is necessary to examine all the important sectors of the economy, to weigh their relative importance in the given situation, and to determine the net outcome. This requires comprehensive surveys and shrewd judgment based on wide experience.

Such agencies as the Brookmire Economic Service, Standard & Poor's Corporation, and Moody's Investor's Service generally follow the crosscut method. The Brookmire Economic Service watches carefully selected series, such as building construction, motorcar output and registration, exchange rates, and industrial employment. The importance attributed to the various series differs from time to time. Also, new ones are added and old ones discarded as the economic situation changes. In all cases where

[1] Seasonal variations in individual series are eliminated.

warranted, the Brookmire Economic Service distinguishes carefully between basic trends, seasonal variation, and business cycles in its appraisal of the business outlook. The Standard & Poor's Corporation also watches many lines of activity and forecasts development in each line. The forecast of general business is mainly a summary of these many individual forecasts. Moody's Investor's Service likewise bases its general forecast upon many individual analyses. In making its forecasts, however, Moody's appears to be especially influenced by businessmen's anticipations of profits, a factor that receives much emphasis in modern business-cycle theory.

Forecasting Particular Lines of Activity.   The same methods are used to forecast particular lines of activity as for general business conditions. Crude historical analogy, the use of leading series, and crosscut analysis all play their roles.

Crude Historical Analogy.   Figure 155 is an excellent example of the use of crude historical analogy in forecasting the course of agricultural prices and of wage rates during a long and extensive world war.   Here the course of agricultural prices and wages in the First World War is taken as the pattern for the expected course of agricultural prices and wages in the Second World War. From the proximity of the two series to each other until the beginning of 1943 it would seem that the forecasting power of the former series is relatively high.   This method is of greater value in forecasting particular lines of activity than it is when applied to general business conditions, although crosscut analysis might modify judgment of this forecast by pointing out that the efforts at price control and inflation control in the Second World War appear to be more courageous than they were in the First World War.

Lead-Lag Relationships.   Figure 156 illustrates the lead-lag relationship in forecasting hog production.   In raising hogs the principal cost is the corn on which the hogs are fed.   Furthermore, the ratio between the amount of corn fed to a hog and his weight is fairly constant.   Hence, the profitability of hog raising is essentially indicated by the so-called "corn-hog differential," which is the difference between the price of 100 pounds of hogs and the cost of enough corn to raise 100 pounds of hogs. As this differential increases, hog production becomes more profitable; as it decreases, hog production becomes less profitable.

The increase or decrease in profitability affects hog production with several months lag. Hence, changes in the corn-hog differential can be used to forecast changes in hog production, as shown in the figure.

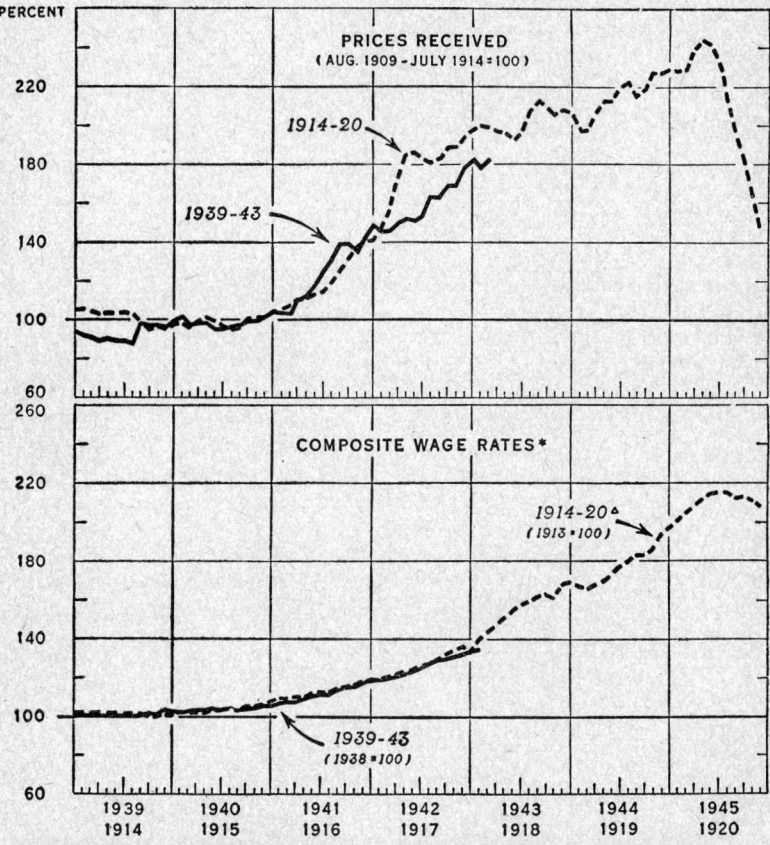

FIG. 155.—Prices received by farmers and composite wage rates. Index numbers, United States, 1914–1920, and 1939–1943. [*From The Agricultural Situation*, (*May*, 1943), *p.* 8, *published by the Bureau of Agricultural Economics, United States Department of Agriculture.*]

The Cycle Hypothesis. The lag of hog production behind the corn-hog differential not only permits forecasting of the former but also tends to cause periodic upswings and downswings in the two series. The reason for this is as follows: Suppose that the demand for pork increases and, owing to the inability to increase rapidly the production of hogs, the corn-hog differential rises. This makes hogs more profitable to produce, and their number is gradually increased. The lag in response, however, may cause the differential to go higher than it would otherwise, and this in turn might stimulate a greater increase in production than is required to meet the new demand that caused the original rise in the ratio. When this enlarged production comes on the market, prices fall and the corn-hog differential drops. Owing to

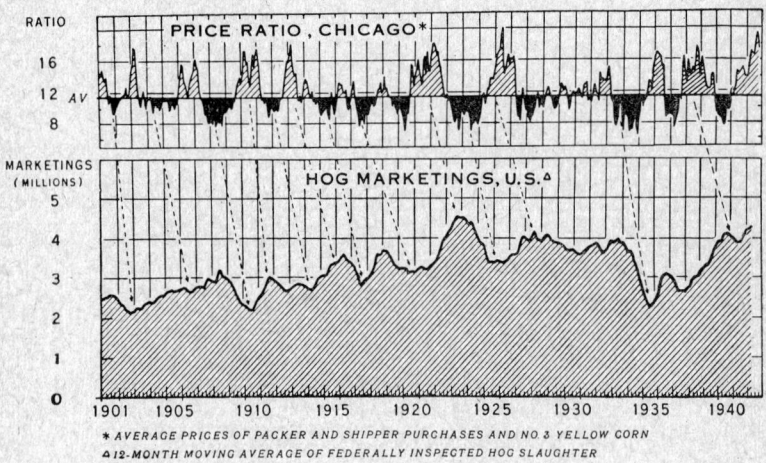

Fig. 156.—Hog-corn price ratio and hog marketings, 1901–1942. (*From Bureau of Agricultural Economics, United States Department of Agriculture.*)

the greatly increased supply, prices go lower than their natural level and hog production becomes less profitable for a while. The change in profitability causes hog production to drop off, and ultimately prices tend to rise again, completing the cycle.

This existence of a periodic movement in the corn-hog differential and in hog production permits forecasting for some distance into the future. If a great war does not interrupt the normal course of economic forces, the high and low periods in the corn-hog differential can be predicted with a fair degree of accuracy. Wise hog farmers gain considerably from this long-range forecasting. Similar periodic movements tend to appear in other lines of agriculture in which production lags behind price stimuli. For example, the cattle cycle runs about fifteen years, according to studies made by the United States Department of Agriculture.

Crosscut Analysis. The application of crosscut analysis to particular lines of activity is based in many instances on the analysis of supply and demand conditions. In agriculture, the carry-over and current crop prospects are important factors on the supply side. The economic condition of industries or of sections of the population using the given product, the prices of competing products, and the output of competing areas are important factors on the demand side. If the product has widespread uses, possibly prediction of changes in consumer incomes or in general industrial activity might be the best way of forecasting the future demand for it.

In manufacturing, principal attention is likely to be devoted to demand. When the demand is industrial, the forecasting takes primarily the form of predicting conditions in those lines of activity immediately supplied by the given line of manufacturing. Thus steel production might be forecasted from railroad construction and maintenance, automobile production, road construction, and building activity. When the product is one sold to the consuming public and not to other industries, the analysis of demand becomes largely a study of the flow of income to consuming areas. This will be dependent on the prosperity of important industries in these areas and on the net flow of incomes from outside sources. The prices of competing products will also be an important demand factor.

A statistical technique using multiple and partial correlation, mathematical and graphic methods, has been developed for making crosscut analyses such as those suggested in the two preceding paragraphs. This technique is widely used; in the case of many products the multiple- and partial-correlation technique makes it possible to derive demand curves that will forecast with considerable accuracy the amount of change in sales that would accompany a given contemplated change in price.[1]

FORECASTS WITH SEASONAL VARIATION

Forecasting with seasonal variation is probably the oldest of all types of modern forecasting and is so general as to be common-

---

[1] *Cf.* SCHULTZ, HENRY, *The Theory and Measurement of Demand* (1938).

place. It is applied to particular lines of activity more specifically than to general business conditions.

Historical Analogy. Use of historical analogy for forecasting with seasonal variation is simpler and more dependable than the use of historical analogy for cyclical or trend forecasts. The conditions underlying persistent seasonal variations are more readily analyzed than are the rational explanations of cycles and

DEATH RATES PER 1,000 · ANNUAL BASIS (*1943 figures are provisional*)

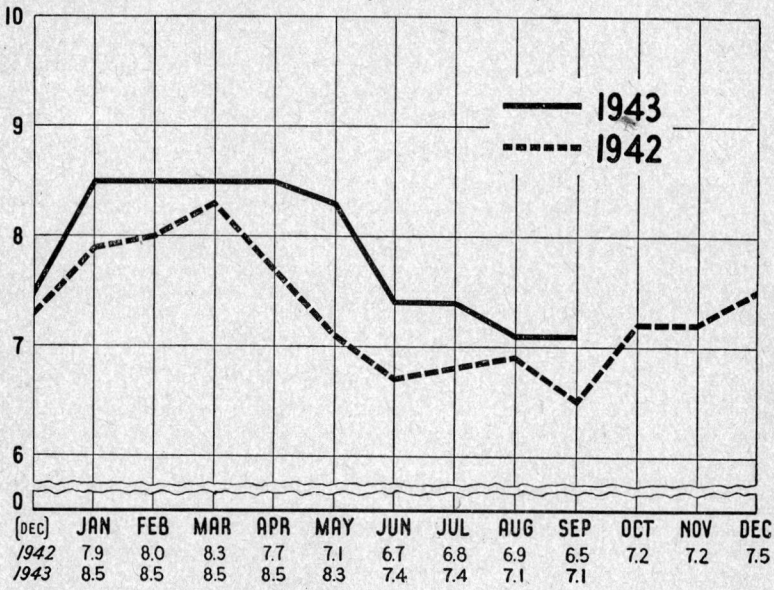

	[DEC]	JAN	FEB	MAR	APR	MAY	JUN	JUL	AUG	SEP	OCT	NOV	DEC
1942		7.9	8.0	8.3	7.7	7.1	6.7	6.8	6.9	6.5	7.2	7.2	7.5
1943		8.5	8.5	8.5	8.3	7.4	7.4	7.1	7.1				

Fig. 157.—Mortality from all causes. Metropolitan Life Insurance Company industrial department, weekly premium-paying business. [*From the Statistical Bulletin, Vol.* 24 (*July,* 1943), *p.* 12, *published by the Metropolitan Life Insurance Company.*]

trends. Moreover, the forecasting is for a shorter period into the future and can therefore depend upon conditions remaining approximately unchanged pending the outcome of the forecasted events. Statistical techniques have been developed for measuring the dependability of a given seasonal variation.[1]

Figure 157 illustrates the extrapolation of seasonal variation, which is the use of historical analogy for making a forecast with seasonal variation. From the figure it can be forecast, by

[1] See pp. 631–636.

assuming a continued agreement between 1942 and coming 1943 seasonal movement in mortality from all causes, that the September death rate per 1,000, annual basis, will be about 7.25, the October and November rate about 8.25, and the December rate about 8.50.

Figure 158 is an application of the use of forecasting seasonal variation by historical analogy to the field of agricultural economics. Extrapolation of the 1943 curve predicts that income from farm marketings in the South Central region of the United States will fluctuate around 200 million dollars monthly until

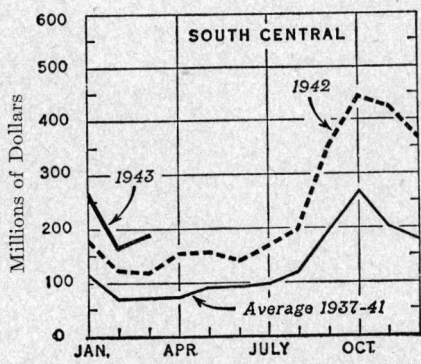

FIG. 158.—Cash income from farm marketings 1942–1943 compared with 1937–1941 average. [*From The Agricultural Situation, Vol. 27 (June, 1943), p. 8, published by the Bureau of Agricultural Economics, United States Department of Agriculture.*]

July or August; thereafter, monthly cash income from farm marketings in that region will rise sharply to a peak in October of perhaps 500 million dollars or higher, since the 1943 level appears to be a higher average than that of 1942. This figure shows the annual average seasonal movement, 1937–1941, which gives a somewhat more dependable seasonal indicator than a single year's figures.

Combining Seasonal with Cyclical Forecasting. Whenever it is desired to make forecasts on the basis of a period shorter than a year, it is necessary to apply a seasonal forecast along with cyclical forecasting. In the case of conventional forecasting by the use of business-cycle studies and the resulting barometers, general business indexes, and crosscut analysis, discussed in a preceding section of this chapter, short-period forecasts based upon known seasonal variations are used as well as the cyclical forecasts.

Many illustrations could be found of the application of this combination of seasonal with cyclical forecasting. Figure 159 is an illustration in the field of agricultural economics. Based upon statistical forecasting of the cycles in production of livestock, similar to the cycle analysis of hog production already outlined, the levels of livestock marketings for 1943 and 1944

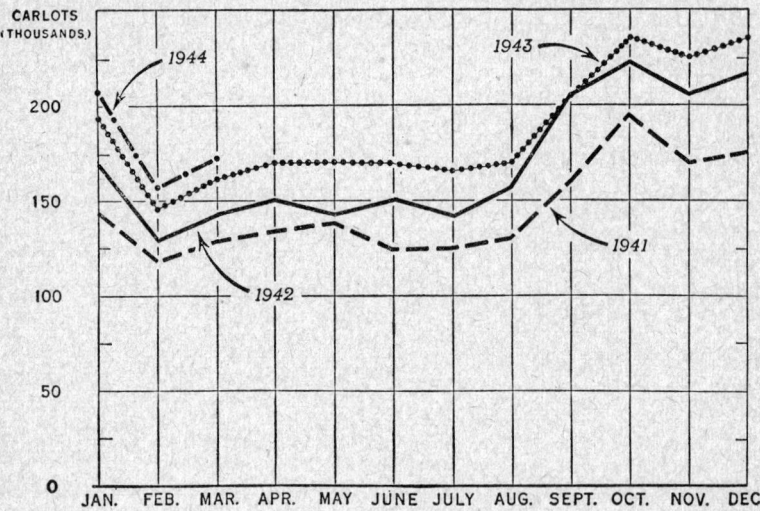

Fig. 159.—Transportation loads for livestock, estimated on basis of indicated marketings and shipments from public markets, United States, January, 1941– March, 1944. [*From The Agricultural Situation, Vol.* 27 (*February,* 1943), *p.* 8, *published by the Bureau of Agricultural Economics, United States Department of Agriculture.*]

are forecast. The annual amount is then distributed throughout the months of the year according to the predetermined index of seasonal variation. The figure presents the resulting forecast of monthly transportation loads for livestock, estimated from indicated marketings and shipments from public markets in the United States. On the same figure are shown the actual amounts monthly for the years 1941 and 1942, for purposes of comparison. Figures similar to this one for various lines of industrial and manufacturing activity appear frequently in such publications as the *Survey of Current Business* and in the publications of the various forecasting agencies.

THE QUALITY OF FORECASTING

The success of forecasting is hard to judge. First it is to be noted that if an agency declines to make forecasts in difficult situations and makes rather limited forecasts in general, it is likely to have less failures than one that boldly undertakes to forecast on all occasions and in considerable detail. The success of a forecasting agency should be judged according to what it attempts to do.

The success of forecasting should also be judged in the light of what might be accomplished by mere random guessing. In other words, an agency should be right at least 50 per cent of the time, or it is worse than useless. Judged on these bases, the various economic forecasting agencies have been fairly successful in forecasting general business conditions. Although not registering anything near a perfect score, they have at least been better than chance.

One of the chief problems of economic forecasting lies in the effect of the forecast itself. The effect of the forecast may conceivably be such, on the one hand, that the forecast actually causes the forecasted event to occur, or, on the other hand, that the forecast actually prevents the forecasted event from occurring. Whether or not such untoward results are produced depends largely on how widely the forecast circulates. On the one hand, suppose a forecasting agency predicts a general inflation of prices and enough people become convinced that the forecast is a true one; in such a case, the forecast may not only become true but be itself the cause of the thing that is forecasted. On the other hand, a subscriber to a forecast expects to profit from its use, in that his plans will anticipate probable future conditions of which a competitor is supposedly not so well informed. The fewer who have this information, the more likely it is that they will profit and that the forecast will be a true one. But the wider the acceptance of the forecast, the less chance the individual subscriber has to gain and the less likely is it that the forecast will prove to be true. Suppose, for example, that a forecasting agency advises its clients in a given productive activity that the price of its product is going to rise as a result of some foreseen increase in demand; if too many of the producers obtain the forecaster's service and follow its advice, overproduction will result and the price will decline rather than rise. This is an illustration of how a forecast might defeat itself.

In the final analysis, it may be said that the greatest value of modern forecasting work lies in the large amount of statistical economic analysis that it promotes. Research into the business cycle and continued improvements in the statistical approach to social and economic problems cannot fail to reveal closer and closer approximations to the truth and thereby improve general knowledge about economic and social conditions.

APPENDIX

TABLE I.—FOUR-PLACE COMMON LOGARITHMS OF NUMBERS[1]

	0	1	2	3	4	5	6	7	8	9	10	Tenths of the Tabular Difference 1 2 3 4 5
1.0	0.0000	0043	0086	0128	0170	0212	0253	0294	0334	0374	0414	
1.1	0414	0453	0492	0531	0569	0607	0645	0682	0719	0755	0792	
1.2	0792	0828	0864	0899	0934	0969	1004	1038	1072	1106	1139	
1.3	1139	1173	1206	1239	1271	1303	1335	1367	1399	1430	1461	
1.4	1461	1492	1523	1553	1584	1614	1644	1673	1703	1732	1761	
1.5	1761	1790	1818	1847	1875	1903	1931	1959	1987	2014	2041	
1.6	2041	2068	2095	2122	2148	2175	2201	2227	2253	2279	2304	
1.7	2304	2330	2355	2380	2405	2430	2455	2480	2504	2529	2553	
1.8	2553	2577	2601	2625	2648	2672	2695	2718	2742	2765	2788	
1.9	2788	2810	2833	2856	2878	2900	2923	2945	2967	2989	3010	
2.0	0.3010	3032	3054	3075	3096	3118	3139	3160	3181	3201	3222	2 4 6 8 11
2.1	3222	3243	3263	3284	3304	3324	3345	3365	3385	3404	3424	2 4 6 8 10
2.2	3424	3444	3464	3483	3502	3522	3541	3560	3579	3598	3617	2 4 6 8 10
2.3	3617	3636	3655	3674	3692	3711	3729	3747	3766	3784	3802	2 4 5 7 9
2.4	3802	3820	3838	3856	3874	3892	3909	3927	3945	3962	3979	2 4 5 7 9
2.5	3979	3997	4014	4031	4048	4065	4082	4099	4116	4133	4150	2 3 5 7 9
2.6	4150	4166	4183	4200	4216	4232	4249	4265	4281	4298	4314	2 3 5 7 8
2.7	4314	4330	4346	4362	4378	4393	4409	4425	4440	4456	4472	2 3 5 6 8
2.8	4472	4487	4502	4518	4533	4548	4564	4579	4594	4609	4624	2 3 5 6 8
2.9	4624	4639	4654	4669	4683	4698	4713	4728	4742	4757	4771	1 3 4 6 7
3.0	0.4771	4786	4800	4814	4829	4843	4857	4871	4886	4900	4914	1 3 4 6 7
3.1	4914	4928	4942	4955	4969	4983	4997	5011	5024	5038	5051	1 3 4 6 7
3.2	5051	5065	5079	5092	5105	5119	5132	5145	5159	5172	5185	1 3 4 5 7
3.3	5185	5198	5211	5224	5237	5250	5263	5276	5289	5302	5315	1 3 4 5 6
3.4	5315	5328	5340	5353	5366	5378	5391	5403	5416	5428	5441	1 3 4 5 6
3.5	5441	5453	5465	5478	5490	5502	5514	5527	5539	5551	5563	1 2 4 5 6
3.6	5563	5575	5587	5599	5611	5623	5635	5647	5658	5670	5682	1 2 4 5 6
3.7	5682	5694	5705	5717	5729	5740	5752	5763	5775	5786	5798	1 2 3 5 6
3.8	5798	5809	5821	5832	5843	5855	5866	5877	5888	5899	5911	1 2 3 5 6
3.9	5911	5922	5933	5944	5955	5966	5977	5988	5999	6010	6021	1 2 3 4 6
4.0	0.6021	6031	6042	6053	6064	6075	6085	6096	6107	6117	6128	1 2 3 4 5
4.1	6128	6138	6149	6160	6170	6180	6191	6201	6212	6222	6232	1 2 3 4 5
4.2	6232	6243	6253	6263	6274	6284	6294	6304	6314	6325	6335	1 2 3 4 5
4.3	6335	6345	6355	6365	6375	6385	6395	6405	6415	6425	6435	1 2 3 4 5
4.4	6435	6444	6454	6464	6474	6484	6493	6503	6513	6522	6532	1 2 3 4 5
4.5	6532	6542	6551	6561	6571	6580	6590	6599	6609	6618	6628	1 2 3 4 5
4.6	6628	6637	6646	6656	6665	6675	6684	6693	6702	6712	6721	1 2 3 4 5
4.7	6721	6730	6739	6749	6758	6767	6776	6785	6794	6803	6812	1 2 3 4 5
4.8	6812	6821	6830	6839	6848	6857	6866	6875	6884	6893	6902	1 2 3 4 4
4.9	6902	6911	6920	6928	6937	6946	6955	6964	6972	6981	6990	1 2 3 4 4
5.0	0.6990	6998	7007	7016	7024	7033	7042	7050	7059	7067	7076	1 2 3 3 4
5.1	7076	7084	7093	7101	7110	7118	7126	7135	7143	7152	7160	1 2 3 3 4
5.2	7160	7168	7177	7185	7193	7202	7210	7218	7226	7235	7243	1 2 2 3 4
5.3	7243	7251	7259	7267	7275	7284	7292	7300	7308	7316	7324	1 2 2 3 4
5.4	7324	7332	7340	7348	7356	7364	7372	7380	7388	7396	7404	1 2 2 3 4

[1] Taken, with permission, from E. V. Huntington's *Four Place Tables of Logarithms and Trigonometric Functions* (Harvard Cooperative Society, Inc., 1907).

TABLE I.—FOUR-PLACE COMMON LOGARITHMS OF NUMBERS.— (*Continued*)

	0	1	2	3	4	5	6	7	8	9	10	Tenths of the Tabular Difference 1 2 3 4 5
5.5	7404	7412	7419	7427	7435	7443	7451	7459	7466	7474	7482	1 2 2 3 4
5.6	7482	7490	7497	7505	7513	7520	7528	7536	7543	7551	7559	1 2 2 3 4
5.7	7559	7566	7574	7582	7589	7597	7604	7612	7619	7627	7634	1 2 2 3 4
5.8	7634	7642	7649	7657	7664	7672	7679	7686	7694	7701	7709	1 1 2 3 4
5.9	7709	7716	7723	7731	7738	7745	7752	7760	7767	7774	7782	1 1 2 3 4
6.0	0.7782	7789	7796	7803	7810	7818	7825	7832	7839	7846	7853	1 1 2 3 4
6.1	7853	7860	7868	7875	7882	7889	7896	7903	7910	7917	7924	1 1 2 3 4
6.2	7924	7931	7938	7945	7952	7959	7966	7973	7980	7987	7993	1 1 2 3 3
6.3	7993	8000	8007	8014	8021	8028	8035	8041	8048	8055	8062	1 1 2 3 3
6.4	8062	8069	8075	8082	8089	8096	8102	8109	8116	8122	8129	1 1 2 3 3
6.5	8129	8136	8142	8149	8156	8162	8169	8176	8182	8189	8195	1 1 2 3 3
6.6	8195	8202	8209	8215	8222	8228	8235	8241	8248	8254	8261	1 1 2 3 3
6.7	8261	8267	8274	8280	8287	8293	8299	8306	8312	8319	8325	1 1 2 3 3
6.8	8325	8331	8338	8344	8351	8357	8363	8370	8376	8382	8388	1 1 2 3 3
6.9	8388	8395	8401	8407	8414	8420	8426	8432	8439	8445	8451	1 1 2 3 3
7.0	0.8451	8457	8463	8470	8476	8482	8488	8494	8500	8506	8513	1 1 2 2 3
7.1	8513	8519	8525	8531	8537	8543	8549	8555	8561	8567	8573	1 1 2 2 3
7.2	8573	8579	8585	8591	8597	8603	8609	8615	8621	8627	8633	1 1 2 2 3
7.3	8633	8639	8645	8651	8657	8663	8669	8675	8681	8686	8692	1 1 2 2 3
7.4	8692	8698	8704	8710	8716	8722	8727	8733	8739	8745	8751	1 1 2 2 3
7.5	8751	8756	8762	8768	8774	8779	8785	8791	8797	8802	8808	1 1 2 2 3
7.6	8808	8814	8820	8825	8831	8837	8842	8848	8854	8859	8865	1 1 2 2 3
7.7	8865	8871	8876	8882	8887	8893	8899	8904	8910	8915	8921	1 1 2 2 3
7.8	8921	8927	8932	8938	8943	8949	8954	8960	8965	8971	8976	1 1 2 2 3
7.9	8976	8982	8987	8993	8998	9004	9009	9015	9020	9025	9031	1 1 2 2 3
8.0	0.9031	9036	9042	9047	9053	9058	9063	9069	9074	9079	9085	1 1 2 2 3
8.1	9085	9090	9096	9101	9106	9112	9117	9122	9128	9133	9138	1 1 2 2 3
8.2	9138	9143	9149	9154	9159	9165	9170	9175	9180	9186	9191	1 1 2 2 3
8.3	9191	9196	9201	9206	9212	9217	9222	9227	9232	9238	9243	1 1 2 2 3
8.4	9243	9248	9253	9258	9263	9269	9274	9279	9284	9289	9294	1 1 2 2 3
8.5	9294	9299	9304	9309	9315	9320	9325	9330	9335	9340	9345	1 1 2 2 3
8.6	9345	9350	9355	9360	9365	9370	9375	9380	9385	9390	9395	1 1 2 2 3
8.7	9395	9400	9405	9410	9415	9420	9425	9430	9435	9440	9445	0 1 1 2 2
8.8	9445	9450	9455	9460	9465	9469	9474	9479	9484	9489	9494	0 1 1 2 2
8.9	9494	9499	9504	9509	9513	9518	9523	9528	9533	9538	9542	0 1 1 2 2
9.0	0.9542	9547	9552	9557	9562	9566	9571	9576	9581	9586	9590	0 1 1 2 2
9.1	9590	9595	9600	9605	9609	9614	9619	9624	9628	9633	9638	0 1 1 2 2
9.2	9638	9643	9647	9652	9657	9661	9666	9671	9675	9680	9685	0 1 1 2 2
9.3	9685	9689	9694	9699	9703	9708	9713	9717	9722	9727	9731	0 1 1 2 2
9.4	9731	9736	9741	9745	9750	9754	9759	9763	9768	9773	9777	0 1 1 2 2
9.5	9777	9782	9786	9791	9795	9800	9805	9809	9814	9818	9823	0 1 1 2 2
9.6	9823	9827	9832	9836	9841	9845	9850	9854	9859	9863	9868	0 1 1 2 2
9.7	9868	9872	9877	9881	9886	9890	9894	9899	9903	9908	9912	0 1 1 2 2
9.8	9912	9917	9921	9926	9930	9934	9939	9943	9948	9952	9956	0 1 1 2 2
9.9	9956	9961	9965	9969	9974	9978	9983	9987	9991	9996		0 1 1 2 2

TABLE I.—FOUR-PLACE COMMON LOGARITHMS OF NUMBERS.— (*Continued*)

	0	1	2	3	4	5	6	7	8	9	10
1.00	0.0000	0004	0009	0013	0017	0022	0026	0030	0035	0039	0043
1.01	0043	0048	0052	0056	0060	0065	0069	0073	0077	0082	0086
1.02	0086	0090	0095	0099	0103	0107	0111	0116	0120	0124	0128
1.03	0128	0133	0137	0141	0145	0149	0154	0158	0162	0166	0170
1.04	0170	0175	0179	0183	0187	0191	0195	0199	0204	0208	0212
1.05	0212	0216	0220	0224	0228	0233	0237	0241	0245	0249	0253
1.06	0253	0257	0261	0265	0269	0273	0278	0282	0286	0290	0294
1.07	0294	0298	0302	0306	0310	0314	0318	0322	0326	0330	0334
1.08	0334	0338	0342	0346	0350	0354	0358	0362	0366	0370	0374
1.09	0374	0378	0382	0386	0390	0394	0398	0402	0406	0410	0414
1.10	0.0414	0418	0422	0426	0430	0434	0438	0441	0445	0449	0453
1.11	0453	0457	0461	0465	0469	0473	0477	0481	0484	0488	0492
1.12	0492	0496	0500	0504	0508	0512	0515	0519	0523	0527	0531
1.13	0531	0535	0538	0542	0546	0550	0554	0558	0561	0565	0569
1.14	0569	0573	0577	0580	0584	0588	0592	0596	0599	0603	0607
1.15	0607	0611	0615	0618	0622	0626	0630	0633	0637	0641	0645
1.16	0645	0648	0652	0656	0660	0663	0667	0671	0674	0678	0682
1.17	0682	0686	0689	0693	0697	0700	0704	0708	0711	0715	0719
1.18	0719	0722	0726	0730	0734	0737	0741	0745	0748	0752	0755
1.19	0755	0759	0763	0766	0770	0774	0777	0781	0785	0788	0792
1.20	0.0792	0795	0799	0803	0806	0810	0813	0817	0821	0824	0828
1.21	0828	0831	0835	0839	0842	0846	0849	0853	0856	0860	0864
1.22	0864	0867	0871	0874	0878	0881	0885	0888	0892	0896	0899
1.23	0899	0903	0906	0910	0913	0917	0920	0924	0927	0931	0934
1.24	0934	0938	0941	0945	0948	0952	0955	0959	0962	0966	0969
1.25	0969	0973	0976	0980	0983	0986	0990	0993	0997	1000	1004
1.26	1004	1007	1011	1014	1017	1021	1024	1028	1031	1035	1038
1.27	1038	1041	1045	1048	1052	1055	1059	1062	1065	1069	1072
1.28	1072	1075	1079	1082	1086	1089	1092	1096	1099	1103	1106
1.29	1106	1109	1113	1116	1119	1123	1126	1129	1133	1136	1139
1.30	0.1139	1143	1146	1149	1153	1156	1159	1163	1166	1169	1173
1.31	1173	1176	1179	1183	1186	1189	1193	1196	1199	1202	1206
1.32	1206	1209	1212	1216	1219	1222	1225	1229	1232	1235	1239
1.33	1239	1242	1245	1248	1252	1255	1258	1261	1265	1268	1271
1.34	1271	1274	1278	1281	1284	1287	1290	1294	1297	1300	1303
1.35	1303	1307	1310	1313	1316	1319	1323	1326	1329	1332	1335
1.36	1335	1339	1342	1345	1348	1351	1355	1358	1361	1364	1367
1.37	1367	1370	1374	1377	1380	1383	1386	1389	1392	1396	1399
1.38	1399	1402	1405	1408	1411	1414	1418	1421	1424	1427	1430
1.39	1430	1433	1436	1440	1443	1446	1449	1452	1455	1458	1461
1.40	0.1461	1464	1467	1471	1474	1477	1480	1483	1486	1489	1492
1.41	1492	1495	1498	1501	1504	1508	1511	1514	1517	1520	1523
1.42	1523	1526	1529	1532	1535	1538	1541	1544	1547	1550	1553
1.43	1553	1556	1559	1562	1565	1569	1572	1575	1578	1581	1584
1.44	1584	1587	1590	1593	1596	1599	1602	1605	1608	1611	1614
1.45	1614	1617	1620	1623	1626	1629	1632	1635	1638	1641	1644
1.46	1644	1647	1649	1652	1655	1658	1661	1664	1667	1670	1673
1.47	1673	1676	1679	1682	1685	1688	1691	1694	1697	1700	1703
1.48	1703	1706	1708	1711	1714	1746	1749	1720	1723	1726	1729	1732
1.49	1732	1735	1738	1741	1744	1746	1749	1752	1755	1758	1761

TABLE I.—FOUR-PLACE COMMON LOGARITHMS OF NUMBERS.—
(Continued)

	0	1	2	3	4	5	6	7	8	9	10
1.50	0.1761	1764	1767	1770	1772	1775	1778	1781	1784	1787	1790
1.51	1790	1793	1796	1798	1801	1804	1807	1810	1813	1816	1818
1.52	1818	1821	1824	1827	1830	1833	1836	1838	1841	1844	1847
1.53	1847	1850	1853	1855	1858	1861	1864	1867	1870	1872	1875
1.54	1875	1878	1881	1884	1886	1889	1892	1895	1898	1901	1903
1.55	1903	1906	1909	1912	1915	1917	1920	1923	1926	1928	1931
1.56	1931	1934	1937	1940	1942	1945	1948	1951	1953	1956	1959
1.57	1959	1962	1965	1967	1970	1973	1976	1978	1981	1984	1987
1.58	1987	1989	1992	1995	1998	2000	2003	2006	2009	2011	2014
1.59	2014	2017	2019	2022	2025	2028	2030	2033	2036	2038	2041
1.60	0.2041	2044	2047	2049	2052	2055	2057	2060	2063	2066	2068
1.61	2068	2071	2074	2076	2079	2082	2084	2087	2090	2092	2095
1.62	2095	2098	2101	2103	2106	2109	2111	2114	2117	2119	2122
1.63	2122	2125	2127	2130	2133	2135	2138	2140	2143	2146	2148
1.64	2148	2151	2154	2156	2159	2162	2164	2167	2170	2172	2175
1.65	2175	2177	2180	2183	2185	2188	2191	2193	2196	2198	2201
1.66	2201	2204	2206	2209	2212	2214	2217	2219	2222	2225	2227
1.67	2227	2230	2232	2235	2238	2240	2243	2245	2243	2251	2253
1.68	2253	2256	2258	2261	2263	2266	2269	2271	2274	2276	2279
1.69	2279	2281	2284	2287	2289	2292	2294	2297	2299	2302	2304
1.70	0.2304	2307	2310	2312	2315	2317	2320	2322	2325	2327	2330
1.71	2330	2333	2335	2338	2340	2343	2345	2348	2350	2353	2355
1.72	2355	2358	2360	2363	2365	2368	2370	2373	2375	2378	2380
1.73	2380	2383	2385	2388	2390	2393	2395	2398	2400	2403	2405
1.74	2405	2408	2410	2413	2415	2418	2420	2423	2425	2428	2430
1.75	2430	2433	2435	2438	2440	2443	2445	2448	2450	2453	2455
1.76	2455	2458	2460	2463	2465	2467	2470	2472	2475	2477	2480
1.77	2480	2482	2485	2487	2490	2492	2494	2497	2499	2502	2504
1.78	2504	2507	2509	2512	2514	2516	2519	2521	2524	2526	2529
1.79	2529	2531	2533	2536	2538	2541	2543	2545	2548	2550	2553
1.80	0.2553	2555	2558	2560	2562	2565	2567	2570	2572	2574	2577
1.81	2577	2579	2582	2584	2586	2589	2591	2594	2596	2598	2601
1.82	2601	2603	2605	2608	2610	2613	2615	2617	2620	2622	2625
1.83	2625	2627	2629	2632	2634	2636	2639	2641	2643	2646	2648
1.84	2648	2651	2653	2655	2658	2660	2662	2665	2667	2669	2672
1.85	2672	2674	2676	2679	2681	2683	2686	2688	2690	2693	2695
1.86	2695	2697	2700	2702	2704	2707	2709	2711	2714	2716	2718
1.87	2718	2721	2723	2725	2728	2730	2732	2735	2737	2739	2742
1.88	2742	2744	2746	2749	2751	2753	2755	2758	2760	2762	2765
1.89	2765	2767	2769	2772	2774	2776	2778	2781	2783	2785	2788
1.90	0.2788	2790	2792	2794	2797	2799	2801	2804	2806	2808	2810
1.91	2810	2813	2815	2817	2819	2822	2824	2826	2828	2831	2833
1.92	2833	2835	2838	2840	2842	2844	2847	2849	2851	2853	2856
1.93	2856	2858	2860	2862	2865	2867	2869	2871	2874	2876	2878
1.94	2878	2880	2882	2885	2887	2889	2891	2894	2896	2898	2900
1.95	2900	2903	2905	2907	2909	2911	2914	2916	2918	2920	2923
1.96	2923	2925	2927	2929	2931	2934	2936	2938	2940	2942	2945
1.97	2945	2947	2949	2951	2953	2956	2958	2960	2962	2964	2967
1.98	2967	2969	2971	2973	2975	2978	2980	2982	2984	2986	2989
1.99	2989	2991	2993	2995	2997	2999	3002	3004	3006	3008	3010

TABLE II.—SQUARES OF NUMBERS[1]

N	0	1	2	3	4	5	6	7	8	9
100	10000	10201	10404	10609	10816	11025	11236	11449	11664	11881
110	12100	12321	12544	12769	12996	13225	13456	13689	13924	14161
120	14400	14641	14884	15129	15376	15625	15876	16129	16384	16641
130	16900	17161	17424	17689	17956	18225	18496	18769	19044	19321
140	19600	19881	20164	20449	20736	21025	21316	21609	21904	22201
150	22500	22801	23104	23409	23716	24025	24336	24649	24964	25281
160	25600	25921	26244	26569	26896	27225	27556	27889	28224	28561
170	28900	29241	29584	29929	30276	30625	30976	31329	31684	32041
180	32400	32761	33124	33489	33856	34225	34596	34969	35344	35721
190	36100	36481	36864	37249	37636	38025	38416	38809	39204	39601
200	40000	40401	40804	41209	41616	42025	42436	42849	43264	43681
210	44100	44521	44944	45369	45796	46225	46656	47089	47524	47961
220	48400	48841	49284	49729	50176	50625	51076	51529	51984	52441
230	52900	53361	53824	54289	54756	55225	55696	56169	56644	57121
240	57600	58081	58564	59049	59536	60025	60516	61009	61504	62001
250	62500	63001	63504	64009	64516	65025	65536	66049	66564	67081
260	67600	68121	68644	69169	69696	70225	70756	71289	71824	72361
270	72900	73441	73984	74529	75076	75625	76176	76729	77284	77841
280	78400	78961	79524	80089	80656	81225	81796	82369	82944	83521
290	84100	84681	85262	85849	86436	87025	87616	88209	88804	89401
300	90000	90601	91204	91809	92416	93025	93636	94249	94864	95481
310	96100	96721	97344	97969	98596	99225	99856	100489	101124	101761
320	102400	103041	103684	104329	104976	105625	106276	106929	107584	108241
330	108900	109561	110224	110889	111556	112225	112896	113569	114244	114921
340	115600	116281	116964	117649	118336	119025	119716	120409	121104	121801
350	122500	123201	123904	124609	125316	126025	126736	127449	128164	128881
360	129600	130321	131044	131769	132496	133225	133956	134689	135424	136161
370	136900	137641	138384	139129	139876	140625	141376	142129	142884	143641
380	144400	145161	145924	146689	147456	148225	148996	149769	150544	151321
390	152100	152881	153664	154449	155236	156025	156816	157609	158404	159201
400	160000	160801	161604	162409	163216	164025	164836	165649	166464	167281
410	168100	168921	169744	170569	171396	172225	173056	173889	174724	175561
420	176400	177241	178084	178929	179776	180625	181476	182329	183184	184041
430	184900	185761	186624	187489	188356	189225	190096	190969	191844	192721
440	193600	194481	195364	196249	197136	198025	198916	199809	200704	201610
450	202500	203401	204304	205209	206116	207025	207936	208849	209764	210681
460	211600	212521	213444	214369	215296	216225	217156	218089	219024	219961
470	220900	221841	222784	223729	224676	225625	226576	227529	228484	229441
480	230400	231361	232324	233289	234256	235225	236196	237169	238144	239121
490	240100	241081	242064	243049	244036	245025	246016	247009	248004	249001
500	250000	251001	252004	253009	254016	255025	256036	257049	258064	259081
510	260100	261121	262144	263169	264196	265225	266256	267289	268324	269361
520	270400	271441	272484	273529	274576	275625	276676	277729	278784	279841
530	280900	281961	283024	284089	285156	286225	287296	288369	289444	290521
540	291600	292681	293764	294849	295936	297025	298116	299209	300304	301401

[1] Source: WAUGH, ALBERT E., *Laboratory Manual and Problems for Elements of Statistical Method* (McGraw-Hill Book Company, Inc., 1944).

TABLE II.—SQUARES OF NUMBERS.—(Continued)

N	0	1	2	3	4	5	6	7	8	9
550	302500	303601	304704	305809	306916	308025	309136	310249	311364	312481
560	313600	314721	315844	316969	318096	319225	320356	321489	322624	323761
570	324900	326041	327184	328329	329476	330625	331776	332929	334084	335241
580	336400	337561	338724	339889	341056	342225	343396	344569	345744	346921
590	348100	349281	350464	351649	352836	354025	355216	356409	357604	358801
600	360000	361201	362404	363609	364816	366025	367236	368449	369664	370881
610	372100	373321	374544	375769	376996	378225	379456	380689	381924	383161
620	384400	385641	386884	388129	389376	390625	391876	393129	394384	395641
630	396900	398161	399424	400689	401956	403225	404496	405769	407044	408321
640	409600	410881	412164	413449	414736	416025	417316	418609	419904	421201
650	422500	423801	425104	426409	427716	429025	430336	431649	432964	434281
660	435600	436921	438244	439569	440896	442225	443556	444889	446224	447561
670	448900	450241	451584	452929	454276	455625	456976	458329	459684	461041
680	462400	463761	465124	466489	467856	469225	470596	471969	473344	474721
690	476100	477481	478864	480249	481636	483025	484416	485809	487204	488601
700	490000	491401	492804	494209	495616	497025	498436	498849	501264	502681
710	504100	505521	506944	508369	509796	511225	512656	514089	515524	516961
720	518400	519841	521284	522729	524176	525625	527076	528529	529984	531441
730	532900	534361	535824	537289	538756	540225	541696	543169	544644	546121
740	547600	549081	550564	552049	553536	555025	556516	558009	559504	561001
750	562500	564001	565504	567009	568516	570025	571536	573049	574564	576081
760	577600	579121	580644	582169	583696	585225	586756	588289	589824	591361
770	592900	594441	595984	597529	599076	600625	602176	603729	605284	606841
780	608400	609961	611524	613089	614656	616225	617796	619369	620944	622521
790	624100	625681	627264	628849	630436	632025	633616	635209	636804	638401
800	640000	641601	643204	644809	646416	648025	649636	651249	652864	654481
810	656100	657721	659344	660969	662596	664225	665856	667489	669124	670761
820	672400	674041	675684	677329	678976	680625	682276	683929	685584	687241
830	688900	690561	692224	693889	695556	697225	698896	700569	702244	703921
840	705600	707281	708964	710649	712336	714025	715716	717409	719104	720801
850	722500	724201	725904	727609	729316	731025	732736	734449	736164	737881
860	739600	741321	743044	744769	746496	748225	749956	751689	753424	755161
870	756900	758641	760384	762129	763876	765625	767376	769129	770884	772641
880	774400	776161	777924	779689	781456	783225	784996	786769	788544	790321
890	792100	793881	795664	797449	799236	801025	802816	804609	806404	808201
900	810000	811801	813604	815409	817216	819025	820836	822649	824464	826281
910	828100	829921	831744	833569	835396	837225	839056	840889	842724	844561
920	846400	848241	850084	851929	853776	855625	857476	859329	861184	863041
930	864900	866761	868624	870489	872356	874225	876096	877969	879844	881721
940	883600	885481	887364	889249	891136	893025	894916	896809	898704	900601
950	902500	904401	906304	908209	910116	912025	913936	915849	917764	919681
960	921600	923521	925444	927369	929296	931225	933156	935089	937024	938961
970	940900	942841	944784	946729	948676	950625	952576	954529	956484	958441
980	960400	962361	964324	966289	968256	970225	972196	974169	976144	978121
990	980100	982081	984064	986049	988036	990025	992016	994009	996004	998001

TABLE III.—SQUARE ROOTS OF NUMBERS FROM 10 TO 100[1]

N	0.0	0.1	0.2	0.3	0.4	0.5	0.6	0.7	0.8	0.9
10	3.162	3.178	3.194	3.209	3.225	3.240	3.256	3.271	3.286	3.302
11	3.317	3.332	3.347	3.362	3.376	3.391	3.406	3.421	3.435	3.450
12	3.464	3.479	3.493	3.507	3.521	3.536	3.550	3.564	3.578	3.592
13	3.606	3.619	3.633	3.647	3.661	3.674	3.688	3.701	3.715	3.728
14	3.742	3.755	3.768	3.782	3.795	3.808	3.821	3.834	3.847	3.860
15	3.873	3.886	3.899	3.912	3.924	3.937	3.950	3.962	3.975	3.987
16	4.000	4.012	4.025	4.037	4.050	4.062	4.074	4.087	4.099	4.111
17	4.123	4.135	4.147	4.159	4.171	4.183	4.195	4.207	4.219	4.231
18	4.243	4.254	4.266	4.278	4.290	4.301	4.313	4.324	4.336	4.347
19	4.359	4.370	4.382	4.393	4.405	4.416	4.427	4.438	4.450	4.461
20	4.472	4.483	4.494	4.506	4.517	4.528	4.539	4.550	4.561	4.572
21	4.583	4.593	4.604	4.615	4.626	4.637	4.648	4.658	4.669	4.680
22	4.690	4.701	4.712	4.722	4.733	4.743	4.754	4.764	4.775	4.785
23	4.796	4.806	4.817	4.827	4.837	4.848	4.858	4.868	4.879	4.889
24	4.899	4.909	4.919	4.930	4.940	4.950	4.960	4.970	4.980	4.990
25	5.000	5.010	5.020	5.030	5.040	5.050	5.060	5.070	5.079	5.089
26	5.099	5.109	5.119	5.128	5.138	5.148	5.158	5.167	5.177	5.187
27	5.196	5.206	5.215	5.225	5.234	5.244	5.254	5.263	5.273	5.282
28	5.292	5.301	5.310	5.320	5.329	5.339	5.348	5.357	5.367	5.376
29	5.385	5.394	5.404	5.413	5.422	5.431	5.441	5.450	5.459	5.468
30	5.477	5.486	5.495	5.505	5.514	5.523	5.532	5.541	5.550	5.559
31	5.568	5.577	5.586	5.595	5.604	5.612	5.621	5.630	5.639	5.648
32	5.657	5.666	5.674	5.683	5.692	5.701	5.710	5.718	5.727	5.736
33	5.745	5.753	5.762	5.771	5.779	5.788	5.797	5.805	5.814	5.822
34	5.831	5.840	5.848	5.857	5.865	5.874	5.882	5.891	5.899	5.908
35	5.916	5.925	5.933	5.941	5.950	5.958	5.967	5.975	5.983	5.992
36	6.000	6.008	6.017	6.025	6.033	6.042	6.050	6.058	6.066	6.075
37	6.083	6.091	6.099	6.107	6.116	6.124	6.132	6.140	6.148	6.156
38	6.164	6.173	6.181	6.189	6.197	6.205	6.213	6.221	6.229	6.237
39	6.245	6.253	6.261	6.269	6.277	6.285	6.293	6.301	6.309	6.317
40	6.325	6.332	6.340	6.348	6.356	6.364	6.372	6.380	6.387	6.395
41	6.403	6.411	6.419	6.427	6.434	6.442	6.450	6.458	6.465	6.473
42	6.481	6.488	6.496	6.504	6.512	6.519	6.527	6.535	6.542	6.550
43	6.557	6.565	6.573	6.580	6.588	6.595	6.603	6.611	6.618	6.626
44	6.633	6.641	6.648	6.656	6.663	6.671	6.678	6.686	6.693	6.701
45	6.708	6.716	6.723	6.731	6.738	6.745	6.753	6.760	6.768	6.775
46	6.782	6.790	6.797	6.804	6.812	6.819	6.826	6.834	6.841	6.848
47	6.856	6.863	6.870	6.878	6.885	6.892	6.899	6.907	6.914	6.921
48	6.928	6.935	6.943	6.950	6.957	6.964	6.971	6.979	6.986	6.993
49	7.000	7.007	7.014	7.021	7.029	7.036	7.043	7.050	7.057	7.064
50	7.071	7.078	7.085	7.092	7.099	7.106	7.113	7.120	7.127	7.134
51	7.141	7.148	7.155	7.162	7.169	7.176	7.183	7.190	7.197	7.204
52	7.211	7.218	7.225	7.232	7.239	7.246	7.253	7.259	7.266	7.273
53	7.280	7.287	7.294	7.301	7.308	7.314	7.321	7.328	7.335	7.342
54	7.348	7.355	7.362	7.369	7.376	7.382	7.389	7.396	7.403	7.409

[1] Source: WAUGH, ALBERT E., *Laboratory Manual and Problems for Elements of Statistical Method* (McGraw-Hill Book Company, Inc., 1944).

TABLE III.—SQUARE ROOTS OF NUMBERS FROM 10 TO 100.—(*Continued*)

N	0.0	0.1	0.2	0.3	0.4	0.5	0.6	0.7	0.8	0.9
55	7.416	7.423	7.430	7.436	7.443	7.450	7.457	7.463	7.470	7.477
56	7.483	7.490	7.497	7.503	7.510	7.517	7.523	7.530	7.537	7.543
57	7.550	7.556	7.563	7.570	7.576	7.582	7.589	7.596	7.603	7.609
58	7.616	7.622	7.629	7.635	7.642	7.649	7.655	7.662	7.668	7.675
59	7.681	7.688	7.694	7.701	7.707	7.714	7.720	7.727	7.733	7.740
60	7.746	7.752	7.759	7.765	7.772	7.778	7.785	7.791	7.797	7.804
61	7.810	7.817	7.823	7.829	7.836	7.842	7.849	7.855	7.861	7.868
62	7.874	7.880	7.887	7.893	7.899	7.906	7.912	7.918	7.925	7.931
63	7.937	7.944	7.950	7.956	7.962	7.969	7.975	7.981	7.987	7.994
64	8.000	8.006	8.012	8.019	8.025	8.031	8.037	8.044	8.050	8.056
65	8.062	8.068	8.075	8.081	8.087	8.093	8.099	8.106	8.112	8.118
66	8.124	8.130	8.136	8.142	8.149	8.155	8.161	8.167	8.173	8.179
67	8.185	8.191	8.198	8.204	8.210	8.216	8.222	8.228	8.234	8.240
68	8.246	8.252	8.258	8.264	8.270	8.276	8.283	8.289	8.295	8.301
69	8.307	8.313	8.319	8.325	8.331	8.337	8.343	8.349	8.355	8.361
70	8.367	8.373	8.379	8.385	8.390	8.396	8.402	8.408	8.414	8.420
71	8.426	8.432	8.438	8.444	8.450	8.456	8.462	8.468	8.473	8.479
72	8.485	8.491	8.497	8.503	8.509	8.515	8.521	8.526	8.532	8.538
73	8.544	8.550	8.556	8.562	8.567	8.573	8.579	8.585	8.591	8.597
74	8.602	8.608	8.614	8.620	8.626	8.631	8.637	8.643	8.649	8.654
75	8.660	8.666	8.672	8.678	8.683	8.689	8.695	8.701	8.706	8.712
76	8.718	8.724	8.730	8.735	8.741	8.746	8.752	8.758	8.764	8.769
77	8.775	8.781	8.786	8.792	8.798	8.803	8.809	8.815	8.820	8.826
78	8.832	8.837	8.843	8.849	8.854	8.860	8.866	8.871	8.877	8.883
79	8.888	8.894	8.899	8.905	8.911	8.916	8.922	8.927	8.933	8.939
80	8.944	8.950	8.955	8.961	8.967	8.972	8.978	8.983	8.989	8.994
81	9.000	9.006	9.011	9.017	9.022	9.028	9.033	9.039	9.044	9.050
82	9.055	9.061	9.066	9.072	9.077	9.083	9.088	9.094	9.099	9.105
83	9.110	9.116	9.121	9.127	9.132	9.138	9.143	9.149	9.154	9.160
84	9.165	9.171	9.176	9.182	9.187	9.192	9.198	9.203	9.209	9.214
85	9.220	9.225	9.230	9.236	9.241	9.247	9.252	9.257	9.263	9.268
86	9.274	9.279	9.284	9.290	9.295	9.301	9.306	9.311	9.317	9.322
87	9.327	9.333	9.338	9.343	9.349	9.354	9.359	9.365	9.370	9.376
88	9.381	9.386	9.391	9.397	9.402	9.407	9.413	9.418	9.423	9.429
89	9.434	9.439	9.445	9.450	9.455	9.460	9.466	9.471	9.463	9.482
90	9.487	9.492	9.497	9.503	9.508	9.513	9.518	9.524	9.529	9.534
91	9.539	9.545	9.550	9.555	9.560	9.566	9.571	9.576	9.581	9.586
92	9.592	9.597	9.602	9.607	9.612	9.618	9.623	9.628	9.633	9.638
93	9.644	9.649	9.654	9.659	9.664	9.670	9.675	9.680	9.685	9.690
94	9.695	9.701	9.706	9.711	9.716	9.721	9.726	9.731	9.737	9.742
95	9.747	9.752	9.757	9.762	9.767	9.772	9.778	9.783	9.788	9.793
96	9.798	9.803	9.808	9.813	9.818	9.823	9.829	9.834	9.839	9.844
97	9.849	9.854	9.859	9.864	9.869	9.874	9.879	9.884	9.889	9.894
98	9.899	9.905	9.910	9.915	9.920	9.925	9.930	9.935	9.940	9.945
99	9.950	9.955	9.960	9.965	9.970	9.975	9.980	9.985	9.990	9.995

APPENDIX 689

TABLE IV.—SQUARE ROOTS OF NUMBERS FROM 100 TO 1000[1]

N	0	1	2	3	4	5	6	7	8	9
100	10.00	10.05	10.10	10.15	10.20	10.25	10.30	10.34	10.39	10.44
110	10.49	10.54	10.58	10.63	10.68	10.72	10.77	10.82	10.86	10.91
120	10.95	11.00	11.05	11.09	11.14	11.18	11.22	11.27	11.31	11.36
130	11.40	11.45	11.49	11.53	11.58	11.62	11.66	11.70	11.75	11.79
140	11.83	11.87	11.92	11.96	12.00	12.04	12.08	12.12	12.17	12.21
150	12.25	12.29	12.33	12.37	12.41	12.45	12.49	12.53	12.57	12.61
160	12.65	12.69	12.73	12.77	12.81	12.85	12.88	12.92	12.96	13.00
170	13.04	13.08	13.11	13.15	13.19	13.23	13.27	13.30	13.34	13.38
180	13.42	13.45	13.49	13.53	13.56	13.60	13.64	13.67	13.71	13.75
190	13.78	13.82	13.86	13.89	13.93	13.96	14.00	14.04	14.07	14.11
200	14.14	14.18	14.21	14.25	14.28	14.32	14.35	14.39	14.42	14.46
210	14.49	14.53	14.56	14.59	14.63	14.66	14.70	14.73	14.76	14.80
220	14.83	14.87	14.90	14.93	14.97	15.00	15.03	15.07	15.10	15.13
230	15.17	15.20	15.23	15.26	15.30	15.33	15.36	15.39	15.43	15.46
240	15.49	15.52	15.56	15.59	15.62	15.65	15.68	15.72	15.75	15.78
250	15.81	15.84	15.87	15.91	15.94	15.97	16.00	16.03	16.06	16.09
260	16.12	16.16	16.19	16.22	16.25	16.28	16.31	16.34	16.37	16.40
270	16.43	16.46	16.49	16.52	16.55	16.58	16.61	16.64	16.67	16.70
280	16.73	16.76	16.79	16.82	16.85	16.88	16.91	16.94	16.97	17.00
290	17.03	17.06	17.09	17.12	17.15	17.18	17.20	17.23	17.26	17.29
300	17.32	17.35	17.38	17.41	17.44	17.46	17.49	17.52	17.55	17.58
310	17.61	17.64	17.66	17.69	17.72	17.75	17.78	17.80	17.83	17.86
320	17.89	17.92	17.94	17.97	18.00	18.03	18.06	18.08	18.11	18.14
330	18.17	18.19	18.22	18.25	18.28	18.30	18.33	18.36	18.38	18.41
340	18.44	18.47	18.49	18.52	18.55	18.57	18.60	18.63	18.65	18.68
350	18.71	18.74	18.76	18.79	18.81	18.84	18.87	18.89	18.92	18.95
360	18.97	19.00	19.03	19.05	19.08	19.10	19.13	19.16	19.18	19.21
370	19.24	19.26	19.29	19.31	19.34	19.36	19.39	19.42	19.44	19.47
380	19.49	19.52	19.54	19.57	19.60	19.62	19.65	19.67	19.70	19.72
390	19.75	19.77	19.80	19.82	19.85	19.87	19.90	19.92	19.95	19.98
400	20.00	20.02	20.05	20.07	20.10	20.12	20.15	20.17	20.20	20.22
410	20.25	20.27	20.30	20.32	20.35	20.37	20.40	20.42	20.44	20.47
420	20.49	20.52	20.54	20.57	20.59	20.62	20.64	20.66	20.69	20.71
430	20.74	20.76	20.78	20.81	20.83	20.86	20.88	20.90	20.93	20.95
440	20.98	21.00	21.02	21.05	21.07	21.10	21.12	21.14	21.17	21.19
450	21.21	21.24	21.26	21.28	21.31	21.33	21.35	21.38	21.40	21.42
460	21.45	21.47	21.49	21.52	21.54	21.56	21.59	21.61	21.63	21.66
470	21.68	21.70	21.73	21.75	21.77	21.79	21.82	21.84	21.86	21.89
480	21.91	21.93	21.95	21.98	22.00	22.02	22.05	22.07	22.09	22.11
490	22.14	22.16	22.18	22.20	22.23	22.25	22.27	22.29	22.32	22.34
500	22.36	22.38	22.41	22.43	22.45	22.47	22.49	22.52	22.54	22.56
510	22.58	22.61	22.63	22.65	22.67	22.69	22.72	22.74	22.76	22.78
520	22.80	22.83	22.85	22.87	22.89	22.91	22.93	22.96	22.98	23.00
530	23.02	23.04	23.07	23.09	23.11	23.13	23.15	23.17	23.19	23.22
540	23.24	23.26	23.28	23.30	23.32	23.35	23.37	23.39	23.41	23.43
550	23.45	23.47	23.49	23.52	23.54	23.56	23.58	23.60	23.62	23.64

[1] Source: WAUGH, ALBERT E., *Laboratory Manual and Problems for Elements of Statistical Method* (McGraw-Hill Book Company, Inc., 1944).

TABLE IV.—SQUARE ROOTS OF NUMBERS FROM 100 TO 1000.—(*Continued*)

N	0	1	2	3	4	5	6	7	8	9
550	23.45	23.47	23.49	23.52	23.54	23.56	23.58	23.60	23.62	23.64
560	23.66	23.69	23.71	23.73	23.75	23.77	23.79	23.81	23.83	23.85
570	23.87	23.90	23.92	23.94	23.96	23.98	24.00	24.02	24.04	24.06
580	24.08	24.10	24.12	24.15	24.17	24.19	24.21	24.23	24.25	24.27
590	24.29	24.31	24.33	24.35	24.37	24.39	24.41	24.43	24.45	24.47
600	24.49	24.52	24.54	24.56	24.58	24.60	24.62	24.64	24.66	24.68
610	24.70	24.72	24.74	24.76	24.78	24.80	24.82	24.84	24.86	24.88
620	24.90	24.92	24.94	24.96	24.98	25.00	25.02	25.04	25.06	25.08
630	25.10	25.12	25.14	25.16	25.18	25.20	25.22	25.24	25.26	25.28
640	25.30	25.32	25.34	25.36	25.38	25.40	25.42	25.44	25.46	25.48
650	25.50	25.51	25.53	25.55	25.57	25.59	25.61	25.63	25.65	25.67
660	25.69	25.71	25.73	25.75	25.77	25.79	25.81	25.83	25.85	25.86
670	25.88	25.90	25.92	25.94	25.96	25.98	26.00	26.02	26.04	26.06
680	26.08	26.10	26.12	26.13	26.15	26.17	26.19	26.21	26.23	26.25
690	26.27	26.29	26.31	26.32	26.34	26.36	26.38	26.40	26.42	26.44
700	26.46	26.48	26.50	26.51	26.53	26.55	26.57	26.59	26.61	26.63
710	26.65	26.66	26.68	26.70	26.72	26.74	26.76	26.78	26.80	26.81
720	26.83	26.85	26.87	26.89	26.91	26.93	26.94	26.96	26.98	27.00
730	27.02	27.04	27.06	27.07	27.09	27.11	27.13	27.15	27.17	27.18
740	27.20	27.22	27.24	27.26	27.28	27.29	27.31	27.33	27.35	27.37
750	27.39	27.40	27.42	27.44	27.46	27.48	27.50	27.51	27.53	27.55
760	27.57	27.59	27.60	27.62	27.64	27.66	27.68	27.69	27.71	27.73
770	27.75	27.77	27.78	27.80	27.82	27.84	27.86	27.87	27.89	27.91
780	27.93	27.95	27.96	27.98	28.00	28.02	28.04	28.05	28.07	28.09
790	28.11	28.12	28.14	28.16	28.18	28.20	28.21	28.23	28.25	28.27
800	28.28	28.30	28.32	28.34	28.35	28.37	28.39	28.41	28.43	28.44
810	28.46	28.48	28.50	28.51	28.53	28.55	28.57	28.58	28.60	28.62
820	28.64	28.65	28.67	28.69	28.71	28.72	28.74	28.76	28.78	28.79
830	28.81	28.83	28.84	28.86	28.88	28.90	28.91	28.93	28.95	28.97
840	28.98	29.00	29.02	29.03	29.05	29.07	29.09	29.10	29.12	29.14
850	29.15	29.17	29.19	29.21	29.22	29.24	29.26	29.27	29.29	29.31
860	29.33	29.34	29.36	29.38	29.39	29.41	29.43	29.44	29.46	29.48
870	29.50	29.51	29.53	29.55	29.56	29.58	29.60	29.61	29.63	29.65
880	29.66	29.68	29.70	29.72	29.73	29.75	29.77	29.78	29.80	29.82
890	29.83	29.85	29.87	29.88	29.90	29.92	29.93	29.95	29.97	29.98
900	30.00	30.02	30.03	30.05	30.07	30.08	30.10	30.12	30.13	30.15
910	30.17	30.18	30.20	30.22	30.23	30.25	30.27	30.28	30.30	30.32
920	30.33	30.35	30.36	30.38	30.40	30.41	30.43	30.45	30.46	30.48
930	30.50	30.51	30.53	30.54	30.56	30.58	30.59	30.61	30.63	30.64
940	30.66	30.68	30.69	30.71	30.72	30.74	30.76	30.77	30.79	30.81
950	30.82	30.84	30.85	30.87	30.89	30.90	30.92	30.94	30.95	30.97
960	30.98	31.00	31.02	31.03	31.05	31.06	31.08	31.10	31.11	31.13
970	31.14	31.16	31.18	31.19	31.21	31.22	31.24	31.26	31.27	31.29
980	31.30	31.32	31.34	31.35	31.37	31.38	31.40	31.42	31.43	31.45
990	31.46	31.48	31.50	31.51	31.53	31.54	31.56	31.58	31.59	31.61

TABLE V.—RECIPROCALS OF NUMBERS[1]

N	.00	.01	.02	.03	.04	.05	.06	.07	.08	.09
1.00	1.0000	.9901	.9804	.9709	.9615	.9524	.9434	.9346	.9259	.9174
1.10	.9091	.9009	.8929	.8850	.8772	.8696	.8621	.8547	.8475	.8403
1.20	.8333	.8264	.8197	.8130	.8065	.8000	.7937	.7874	.7812	.7752
1.30	.7692	.7634	.7576	.7519	.7463	.7407	.7353	.7299	.7246	.7194
1.40	.7143	.7092	.7042	.6993	.6944	.6897	.6849	.6803	.6757	.6711
1.50	.6667	.6623	.6579	.6536	.6494	.6452	.6410	.6369	.6329	.6289
1.60	.6250	.6211	.6173	.6135	.6098	.6061	.6024	.5988	.5952	.5917
1.70	.5882	.5848	.5814	.5780	.5747	.5714	.5682	.5650	.5618	.5587
1.80	.5556	.5525	.5495	.5464	.5435	.5405	.5376	.5348	.5319	.5291
1.90	.5263	.5236	.5208	.5181	.5155	.5128	.5102	.5076	.5051	.5025
2.00	.5000	.4975	.4950	.4926	.4902	.4878	.4854	.4831	.4808	.4785
2.10	.4762	.4739	.4717	.4694	.4673	.4651	.4630	.4608	.4587	.4566
2.20	.4545	.4525	.4504	.4484	.4464	.4444	.4425	.4405	.4386	.4367
2.30	.4348	.4329	.4310	.4292	.4274	.4255	.4237	.4219	.4202	.4184
2.40	.4167	.4149	.4132	.4115	.4098	.4082	.4065	.4049	.4032	.4016
2.50	.4000	.3984	.3968	.3953	.3937	.3922	.3906	.3891	.3876	.3861
2.60	.3846	.3831	.3817	.3802	.3788	.3774	.3759	.3745	.3731	.3717
2.70	.3704	.3690	.3676	.3663	.3650	.3636	.3623	.3610	.3597	.3584
2.80	.3571	.3559	.3546	.3534	.3521	.3509	.3496	.3484	.3472	.3460
2.90	.3448	.3436	.3425	.3413	.3401	.3390	.3378	.3367	.3356	.3344
3.00	.3333	.3322	.3311	.3300	.3289	.3279	.3268	.3257	.3247	.3236
3.10	.3226	.3215	.3205	.3195	.3185	.3175	.3165	.3155	.3145	.3135
3.20	.3125	.3115	.3106	.3096	.3086	.3077	.3067	.3058	.3049	.3040
3.30	.3030	.3021	.3012	.3003	.2994	.2985	.2976	.2967	.2959	.2950
3.40	.2941	.2933	.2924	.2915	.2907	.2899	.2890	.2882	.2874	.2865
3.50	.2857	.2849	.2841	.2833	.2825	.2817	.2809	.2801	.2793	.2786
3.60	.2778	.2770	.2762	.2755	.2747	.2740	.2732	.2725	.2717	.2710
3.70	.2703	.2695	.2688	.2681	.2674	.2667	.2660	.2653	.2646	.2639
3.80	.2632	.2625	.2618	.2611	.2604	.2597	.2591	.2584	.2577	.2571
3.90	.2564	.2558	.2551	.2545	.2538	.2532	.2525	.2519	.2513	.2506
4.00	.2500	.2494	.2488	.2481	.2475	.2469	.2463	.2457	.2451	.2445
4.10	.2439	.2433	.2427	.2421	.2415	.2410	.2404	.2398	.2392	.2387
4.20	.2381	.2375	.2370	.2364	.2358	.2353	.2347	.2342	.2336	.2331
4.30	.2326	.2320	.2315	.2309	.2304	.2299	.2294	.2288	.2283	.2278
4.40	.2273	.2268	.2262	.2257	.2252	.2247	.2242	.2237	.2232	.2227
4.50	.2222	.2217	.2212	.2208	.2203	.2198	.2193	.2188	.2183	.2179
4.60	.2174	.2169	.2164	.2160	.2155	.2151	.2146	.2141	.2137	.2132
4.70	.2128	.2123	.2119	.2114	.2110	.2105	.2101	.2096	.2092	.2088
4.80	.2083	.2079	.2075	.2070	.2066	.2062	.2058	.2053	.2049	.2045
4.90	.2041	.2037	.2033	.2028	.2024	.2020	.2016	.2012	.2008	.2004
5.00	.2000	.1996	.1992	.1988	.1984	.1980	.1976	.1972	.1968	.1965
5.10	.1961	.1957	.1953	.1949	.1946	.1942	.1938	.1934	.1930	.1927
5.20	.1923	.1919	.1916	.1912	.1908	.1905	.1901	.1898	.1894	.1890
5.30	.1887	.1883	.1880	.1876	.1873	.1869	.1866	.1862	.1859	.1855
5.40	.1852	.1848	.1845	.1842	.1838	.1835	.1832	.1828	.1825	.1821

[1] Source: WAUGH, ALBERT E., *Laboratory Manual and Problems for Elements of Statistical Method* (McGraw-Hill Book Company, Inc., 1944).

TABLE V.—RECIPROCALS OF NUMBERS.—(*Continued*)

N	.00	.01	.02	.03	.04	.05	.06	.07	.08	.09
5.50	.1818	.1815	.1812	.1808	.1805	.1802	.1799	.1795	.1792	.1789
5.60	.1786	.1783	.1779	.1776	.1773	.1770	.1767	.1764	.1761	.1757
5.70	.1754	.1751	.1748	.1745	.1742	.1739	.1736	.1733	.1730	.1727
5.80	.1724	.1721	.1718	.1715	.1712	.1709	.1706	.1704	.1701	.1698
5.90	.1695	.1692	.1689	.1686	.1684	.1681	.1678	.1675	.1672	.1669
6.00	.1667	.1664	.1661	.1658	.1656	.1653	.1650	.1647	.1645	.1642
6.10	.1639	.1637	.1634	.1631	.1629	.1626	.1623	.1621	.1618	.1616
6.20	.1613	.1610	.1608	.1605	.1603	.1600	.1597	.1595	.1592	.1590
6.30	.1587	.1585	.1582	.1580	.1577	.1575	.1572	.1570	.1567	.1565
6.40	.1562	.1560	.1558	.1555	.1553	.1550	.1548	.1546	.1543	.1541
6.50	.1538	.1536	.1534	.1531	.1529	.1527	.1524	.1522	.1520	.1517
6.60	.1515	.1513	.1511	.1508	.1506	.1504	.1502	.1499	.1497	.1495
6.70	.1493	.1490	.1488	.1486	.1484	.1481	.1479	.1477	.1475	.1473
6.80	.1471	.1468	.1466	.1464	.1462	.1460	.1458	.1456	.1453	.1451
6.90	.1449	.1447	.1445	.1443	.1441	.1439	.1437	.1435	.1433	.1431
7.00	.1429	.1427	.1424	.1422	.1420	.1418	.1416	.1414	.1412	.1410
7.10	.1408	.1406	.1404	.1403	.1401	.1399	.1397	.1395	.1393	.1391
7.20	.1389	.1387	.1385	.1383	.1381	.1379	.1377	.1376	.1374	.1372
7.30	.1370	.1368	.1366	.1364	.1362	.1361	.1359	.1357	.1355	.1353
7.40	.1351	.1350	.1348	.1346	.1344	.1342	.1340	.1339	.1337	.1335
7.50	.1333	.1332	.1330	.1328	.1326	.1324	.1323	.1321	.1319	.1318
7.60	.1316	.1314	.1312	.1311	.1309	.1307	.1305	.1304	.1302	.1300
7.70	.1299	.1297	.1295	.1294	.1292	.1290	.1289	.1287	.1285	.1284
7.80	.1282	.1280	.1279	.1277	.1276	.1274	.1272	.1271	.1269	.1267
7.90	.1266	.1264	.1263	.1261	.1259	.1258	.1256	.1255	.1253	.1252
8.00	.1250	.1248	.1247	.1245	.1244	.1242	.1241	.1239	.1238	.1236
8.10	.1235	.1233	.1232	.1230	.1228	.1227	.1225	.1224	.1222	.1221
8.20	.1220	.1218	.1217	.1215	.1214	.1212	.1211	.1209	.1208	.1206
8.30	.1205	.1203	.1202	.1200	.1199	.1198	.1196	.1195	.1193	.1192
8.40	.1190	.1189	.1188	.1186	.1185	.1183	.1182	.1181	.1179	.1178
8.50	.1176	.1175	.1174	.1172	.1171	.1170	.1168	.1167	.1166	.1164
8.60	.1163	.1161	.1160	.1159	.1157	.1156	.1155	.1153	.1152	.1151
8.70	.1149	.1148	.1147	.1145	.1144	.1143	.1142	.1140	.1139	.1138
8.80	.1136	.1135	.1134	.1132	.1131	.1130	.1129	.1127	.1126	.1125
8.90	.1124	.1122	.1121	.1120	.1119	.1117	.1116	.1115	.1114	.1112
9.00	.1111	.1110	.1109	.1107	.1106	.1105	.1104	.1103	.1101	.1100
9.10	.1099	.1098	.1096	.1095	.1094	.1093	.1092	.1091	.1089	.1088
9.20	.1087	.1086	.1085	.1083	.1082	.1081	.1080	.1079	.1078	.1076
9.30	.1075	.1074	.1073	.1072	.1071	.1070	.1068	.1067	.1066	.1065
9.40	.1064	.1063	.1062	.1060	.1059	.1058	.1057	.1056	.1055	.1054
9.50	.1053	.1052	.1050	.1049	.1048	.1047	.1046	.1045	.1044	.1043
9.60	.1042	.1041	.1040	.1038	.1037	.1036	.1035	.1034	.1033	.1032
9.70	.1031	.1030	.1029	.1028	.1027	.1026	.1025	.1024	.1022	.1021
9.80	.1020	.1019	.1018	.1017	.1016	.1015	.1014	.1013	.1012	.1011
9.90	.1010	.1009	.1008	.1007	.1006	.1005	.1004	.1003	.1002	.1001

TABLE VI.—AREAS UNDER THE NORMAL CURVE

Fractional parts of the total area (1.000) under the normal curve between the mean and a perpendicular erected at various numbers of standard deviations (x/σ) from the mean.[1] To illustrate the use of the table, 39.065 per cent of the total area under the curve will lie between the mean and a perpendicular erected at a distance of 1.23σ from the mean.

Each figure in the body of the table is preceded by a decimal point.

x/σ	.00	.01	.02	.03	.04	.05	.06	.07	.08	.09
0.0	00000	00399	00798	01197	01595	01994	02392	02790	03188	03586
0.1	03983	04380	04776	05172	05567	05962	06356	06749	07142	07535
0.2	07926	08317	08706	09095	09483	09871	10257	10642	11026	11409
0.3	11791	12172	12552	12930	13307	13683	14058	14431	14803	15173
0.4	15554	15910	16276	16640	17003	17364	17724	18082	18439	18793
0.5	19146	19497	19847	20194	20450	20884	21226	21566	21904	22240
0.6	22575	22907	23237	23565	23891	24215	24537	24857	25175	25490
0.7	25804	26115	26424	26730	27035	27337	27637	27935	28230	28524
0.8	28814	29103	29389	29673	29955	30234	30511	30785	31057	31327
0.9	31594	31859	32121	32381	32639	32894	33147	33398	33646	33891
1.0	34134	34375	34614	34850	35083	35313	35543	35769	35993	36214
1.1	36433	36650	36864	37076	37286	37493	37698	37900	38100	38298
1.2	38493	38686	38877	39065	39251	39435	39617	39796	39973	40147
1.3	40320	40490	40658	40824	40988	41149	41308	41466	41621	41774
1.4	41924	42073	42220	42364	42507	42647	42786	42922	43056	43189
1.5	43319	43448	43574	43699	43822	43943	44062	44179	44295	44408
1.6	44520	44630	44738	44845	44950	45053	45154	45254	45352	45449
1.7	45543	45637	45728	45818	45907	45994	46080	46164	46246	46327
1.8	46407	46485	46562	46638	46712	46784	46856	46926	46995	47062
1.9	47128	47193	47257	47320	47381	47441	47500	47558	47615	47670
2.0	47725	47778	47831	47882	47932	47982	48030	48077	48124	48169
2.1	48214	48257	48300	48341	48382	48422	48461	48500	48537	48574
2.2	48610	48645	48679	48713	48745	48778	48809	48840	48870	48899
2.3	48928	48956	48983	49010	49036	49061	49086	49111	49134	49158
2.4	49180	49202	49224	49245	49266	49286	49305	49324	49343	49361
2.5	49379	49396	49413	49430	49446	49461	49477	49492	49506	49520
2.6	49534	49547	49560	49573	49585	49598	49609	49621	49632	49643
2.7	49653	49664	49674	49683	49693	49702	49711	49720	49728	49736
2.8	49744	49752	49760	49767	49774	49781	49788	49795	49801	49807
2.9	49813	49819	49825	49831	49836	49841	49846	49851	49856	49861
3.0	49865									
3.5	4997674									
4.0	4999683									
4.5	4999966									
5.0	4999997133									

[1] This table has been adapted, by permission, from F. C. Kent, "Elements of Statistics" (McGraw-Hill Book Company, Inc., 1924).

TABLE VII.—ORDINATES OF THE NORMAL CURVE

Ordinates (heights) of the standard normal curve.[1] The height (y) at any distance (x) from the mean is

$$y = 0.39894e^{-\frac{x^2}{2}}$$

To make the curve fit a histogram in which the abscissa scale is measured in original x units instead of standard-deviation (x/σ) units, multiply these ordinates by Ni/σ where N is the number of cases, i the class interval, and σ the standard deviation.

Each figure in the body of the table is preceded by a decimal point.

x/σ	.00	.01	.02	.03	.04	.05	.06	.07	.08	.09
0.0	39894	39892	39886	39876	39862	39844	39822	39797	39767	39733
0.1	39695	39654	39608	39559	39505	39448	39387	39322	39253	39181
0.2	39104	39024	38940	38853	38762	38667	38568	38466	38361	38251
0.3	38139	38023	37903	37780	37654	37524	37391	37255	37115	36973
0.4	36827	36678	36526	36371	36213	36053	35889	35723	35553	35381
0.5	35207	35029	34849	34667	34482	34294	34105	33912	33718	33521
0.6	33322	33121	32918	32713	32506	32297	32086	31874	31659	31443
0.7	31225	31006	30785	30563	30339	30114	29887	29658	29430	29200
0.8	28969	28737	28504	28269	28034	27798	27562	27324	27086	26848
0.9	26609	26369	26129	25888	25647	25406	25164	24923	24681	24439
1.0	24197	23955	23713	23471	23230	22988	22747	22506	22265	22025
1.1	21785	21546	21307	21069	20831	20594	20357	20121	19886	19652
1.2	19419	19186	18954	18724	18494	18265	18037	17810	17585	17360
1.3	17137	16915	16694	16474	16256	16038	15822	15608	15395	15183
1.4	14973	14764	14556	14350	14146	13943	13742	13542	13344	13147
1.5	12952	12758	12566	12376	12188	12001	11816	11632	11450	11270
1.6	11092	10915	10741	10567	10396	10226	10059	09893	09728	09566
1.7	09405	09246	09089	08933	08780	08628	08478	08329	08183	08038
1.8	07895	07754	07614	07477	07341	07206	07074	06943	06814	06687
1.9	06562	06438	06316	06195	06077	05959	05844	05730	05618	05508
2.0	05399	05292	05186	05082	04980	04879	04780	04682	04586	04491
2.1	04398	04307	04217	04128	04041	03955	03871	03788	03706	03626
2.2	03547	03470	03394	03319	03246	03174	03103	03034	02965	02898
2.3	02833	02768	02705	02643	02582	02522	02463	02406	02349	02294
2.4	02239	02186	02134	02083	02033	01984	01936	01888	01842	01797
2.5	01753	01709	01667	01625	01585	01545	01506	01468	01431	01394
2.6	01358	01323	01289	01256	01223	01191	01160	01130	01100	01071
2.7	01042	01014	00987	00961	00935	00909	00885	00861	00837	00814
2.8	00792	00770	00748	00727	00707	00687	00668	00649	00631	00613
2.9	00595	00578	00562	00545	00530	00514	00499	00485	00470	00457
3.0	00443									
3.5	0008727									
4.0	0001338									
4.5	0000160									
5.0	000001487									

[1] This table adapted, by permission, from Kent, "Elements of Statistics."

Ordinates may also be computed from the equation $\log y = 9.600910 - 10 - 0.217147\,x^2$ and for ordinates beyond 3σ it would be necessary to use $\log y = 9.6009100658 - 10 - 0.2171472910x^2$.

TABLE VIII.—HYPERBOLIC TANGENTS[1]

z	$r = \tanh z$	z	$r = \tanh z$	z	$r = \tanh z$
0.00	0.00000	0.55	0.50052	1.10	0.80050
0.10	.01000	0.56	.50798	1.11	.80406
0.02	.02000	0.57	.51536	1.12	.80757
0.03	.02999	0.58	.52267	1.13	.81102
0.04	.03998	0.59	.52990	1.14	.81441
0.05	0.04996	0.60	0.53705	1.15	0.81775
0.06	.05993	0.61	.54413	1.16	.82104
0.07	.06989	0.62	.55113	1.17	.82427
0.08	.07983	0.63	.55805	1.18	.82745
0.09	.08976	0.64	.56490	1.19	.83058
0.10	0.09967	0.65	0.57167	1.20	0.83365
0.11	.10956	0.66	.57836	1.21	.83668
0.12	.11943	0.67	.58498	1.22	.83965
0.13	.12927	0.68	.59152	1.23	.84258
0.14	.13909	0.69	.59798	1.24	.84546
0.15	0.14889	0.70	0.60437	1.25	0.84828
0.16	.15865	0.71	.61068	1.26	.85106
0.17	.16838	0.72	.61691	1.27	.85380
0.18	.17808	0.73	.62307	1.28	.85648
0.19	.18775	0.74	.62915	1.29	.85913
0.20	0.19738	0.75	0.63515	1.30	0.86172
0.21	.20697	0.76	.64108	1.31	.86428
0.22	.21652	0.77	.64693	1.32	.86678
0.23	.22603	0.78	.65271	1.33	.86925
0.24	.23550	0.79	.65841	1.34	.87167
0.25	0.24492	0.80	0.66404	1.35	0.87405
0.26	.25430	0.81	.66959	1.36	.87639
0.27	.26362	0.82	.67507	1.37	.87869
0.28	.27291	0.83	.68048	1.38	.88095
0.29	.28213	0.84	.68581	1.39	.88317
0.30	0.29131	0.85	0.69107	1.40	0.88535
0.31	.30044	0.86	.69626	1.41	.88749
0.32	.30951	0.87	.70137	1.42	.88960
0.33	.31852	0.88	.70642	1.43	.89167
0.34	.32748	0.89	.71139	1.44	.89370
0.35	0.33638	0.90	0.71630	1.45	0.89569
0.36	.34521	0.91	.72113	1.46	.89765
0.37	.35399	0.92	.72590	1.47	.89958
0.38	.36271	0.93	.73059	1.48	.90147
0.39	.37136	0.94	.73522	1.49	.90332
0.40	0.37995	0.95	0.73978	1.50	0.90515
0.41	.38847	0.96	.74428	1.51	.90694
0.42	.39693	0.97	.74870	1.52	.90870
0.43	.40532	0.98	.75307	1.53	.91042
0.44	.41364	0.99	.75736	1.54	.91212
0.45	0.42190	1.00	0.76159	1.55	0.91379
0.46	.43008	1.01	.76576	1.56	.91542
0.47	.43820	1.02	.76987	1.57	.91703
0.48	.44624	1.03	.77391	1.58	.91860
0.49	.45422	1.04	.77789	1.59	.92015
0.50	0.46212	1.05	0.78181	1.60	0.92167
0.51	.46995	1.06	.78566	1.61	.92316
0.52	.47770	1.07	.78946	1.62	.92462
0.53	.48538	1.08	.79320	1.63	.92606
0.54	.49299	1.09	.79688	1.64	.92747

[1] Source: HODGMAN, CHARLES C., *Mathematical Tables from Handbook of Chemistry and Physics* (1941).

TABLE VIII.—HYPERBOLIC TANGENTS.—(Continued)

z	$r = \tanh z$	z	$r = \tanh z$	z	$r = \tanh z$
1.65	0.92886	2.20	0.97574	2.75	0.99186
1.66	.93022	2.21	.97622	2.76	.99202
1.67	.93155	2.22	.97668	2.77	.99218
1.68	.93286	2.23	.97714	2.78	.99233
1.69	.93415	2.24	.97759	2.79	.99248
1.70	0.93541	2.25	0.97803	2.80	0.99263
1.71	.93665	2.26	.97846	2.81	.99278
1.72	.93786	2.27	.97888	2.82	.99292
1.73	.93906	2.28	.97929	2.83	.99306
1.74	.94023	2.29	.97970	2.84	.99320
1.75	0.94138	2.30	0.98010	2.85	0.99333
1.76	.94250	2.31	.98049	2.86	.99346
1.77	.94361	2.32	.98087	2.87	.99359
1.78	.94470	2.33	.98124	2.88	.99372
1.79	.94576	2.34	.98161	2.89	.99384
1.80	0.94681	2.35	0.98197	2.90	0.99396
1.81	.94783	2.36	.98233	2.91	.99408
1.82	.94884	2.37	.98267	2.92	.99420
1.83	.94983	2.38	.98301	2.93	.99431
1.84	.95080	2.39	.98335	2.94	.99443
1.85	0.95175	2.40	0.98367	2.95	0.99454
1.86	.95268	2.41	.98400	2.96	.99464
1.87	.95359	2.42	.99431	2.97	.99475
1.88	.95449	2.43	.98462	2.98	.99485
1.89	.95537	2.44	.98492	2.99	.99496
1.90	0.95624	2.45	0.98522	3.0	0.99505
1.91	.95709	2.46	.98551	3.1	.99595
1.92	.95792	2.47	.98579	3.2	.99668
1.93	.95873	2.48	.98607	3.3	.99728
1.94	.95953	2.49	.98635	3.4	.99777
1.95	0.96032	2.50	0.98661	3.5	0.99818
1.96	.96109	2.51	.98688	3.6	.99851
1.97	.96185	2.52	.98714	3.7	.99878
1.98	.96259	2.53	.98739	3.8	.99900
1.99	.96331	2.54	.98764	3.9	.99918
2.00	0.96403	2.55	0.98788	4.0	0.99933
2.01	.96473	2.56	.98812	4.1	.99945
2.02	.96541	2.57	.98835	4.2	.99955
2.03	.96609	2.58	.98858	4.3	.99963
2.04	.96675	2.59	.98881	4.4	.99970
2.05	0.96740	2.60	0.98903	4.5	0.99975
2.06	.96803	2.61	.98924	4.6	.99980
2.07	.96865	2.62	.98946	4.7	.99983
2.08	.96926	2.63	.98966	4.8	.99986
2.09	.96986	2.64	.98987	4.9	.99989
2.10	0.97045	2.65	0.99007	5.0	0.99991
2.11	.97103	2.66	.99026		
2.12	.97159	2.67	.99045		
2.13	.97215	2.68	.99064		
2.14	.97269	2.69	.99083		
2.15	0.97323	2.70	0.99101		
2.16	.97375	2.71	.99118		
2.17	.97426	2.72	.99136		
2.18	.97477	2.73	.99153		
2.19	.97526	2.74	.99170		

AUTHOR INDEX

A

Agnew, H. E., 9
Anderson, O. N., 57

B

Barker, P. W., 77
Barlow, P., 209
Barrows, H. K., 17
Baumann, A. O., 624
Beckhart, B. H., 518, 575, 617–618
Bergen, H. B., 16
Berridge, W. A., 619
Binder, Rudolph, 11
Blume, Johannes, 249
Bowditch, H. P., 322
Bowley, Arthur L., 191, 552
Boyd, Anne Morris, 65
Bratt, Elmer C., 662, 663
Brigham, Carl C., 10
Brown, William A., 617
Brunt, David, 294, 561
Bryan, W. L., 322

C

Campbell, F. L., 15
Campbell, Leon, 13
Carmichael, F. L., 524, 562
Carver, H. C., 196
Chaddock, R. E., 174
Cheyney, Edward P., 25
Chugerman, Samuel, 11
Clare, George, 617
Conklin, Maxwell R., 531–532
Cook, H. B., 17
Copeland, A. H., 250
Cowden, D. J., 174, 578, 633
Cox, G. V., 662
Cramer, H., 236

Creager, W. P., 17
Crowder, W. F., 176
Croxton, F. E., 104, 174, 578
Crum, W. L., 561
Cummings, John, 71–72
Czuber, Emanuel, 297

D

D'Abro, A., 21
Daly, Patricia, 658
Davenport, D. H., 63
Davies, G. R., 176
Davis, Michael M., 16
Day, E. E., 663
De Broglie, Louis, 19
Dewey, Edward Russell, 653
Dewey, John, 22
Dieulefait, Carlos E., 563
Director, Aaron, 619
Douglas, Paul H., 619, 658
Dublin, Louis I., 551
Duffendack, O. S., 19
Duncan, A. J., 165, 193, 242, 283, 287, 294–297, 300, 302, 304, 307–310, 315–319, 331, 492, 653
Dygert, W. B., 9

E

Eddington, Sir Arthur, 5, 18–19, 21–22
Ehrenberg, R., 651
Elderton, W. Palin, 196
Eldridge, J. A., 19–21
Ezekiel, M., 12

F

Fairchild, Henry Pratt, 27
Falkner, Helen D., 623

697

SUBJECT INDEX

A

Accuracy, in calculating statistics, 230–231

Agricultural Situation, 80

Agricultural Statistics, 80

  U.S. Department of Agriculture, 80

    Bureau of Agricultural Economics, 80–81

      Agricultural Situation, 80

      Agricultural Yearbook, 80

      Crops and Markets, 80

American Bankers Association, 51

Analysis of variance, in mutliple correlation, 422–429

  in nonlinear correlation, correlation index, 395–396

    correlation ratio, 373–376

  in simple correlation, 352–353

Annalist, 534

Arithmetic charts, 129–131

Array, 139–140

Asymmetry (*see* Skewness)

Attributes, variable, 157

Averages (*see* Frequency distributions, averages)

Avogadro's law, 57

B

Banking statistics, sources of, 79–86

  Federal Reserve, Board of Governors, 82

    Federal Reserve Bulletin, 82

    Member Bank Call Report, 82

  National Monetary Commission, 83

  Statesman's Yearbook, 86

Banking statistics, U.S. Treasury Department, 79

  Abstract of Condition of National Banks, 79

Bar charts, 104–105

Bayes, T., 242

Bernoulli, Daniel, 242

Bernoulli, Jacques, 242

Beta coefficient, 192–193

Beta cross-product term, 425

Biennial Census of Manufactures, 537

Binomial distribution, symmetrical (*see* Symmetrical binomial distribution)

Bivariate frequency distribution, 325–353

  first-order standard deviation, relation to r, 351–353

  illustration of, 325–327

    table, 326

  joint variation illustrated (bivariate scatter diagrams), 339, 343, 345

  methods of summarization and comparison, 327–353

  Pearsonian coefficient of correlation, 338–349

    analysis of variance, 352–353

    calculation of, 347, 349

  progressions of means, 328–329

    illustrated (graphs), 328–329

Bivariate frequency surface, 471–486

  bivariate histogram, 469–471

    illustrated (three-dimensional diagram), 470

  independent variables, 471

  lines of regression, 486–488

    mathematical representation, 487–488

    nonnormal, 491–492

D